D1020740

Elementary Mechanics of Deformable Bodies

Elementary Mechanics of Deformable Bodies

J. O. Smith
UNIVERSITY OF ILLINOIS

O. M. Sidebottom
UNIVERSITY OF ILLINOIS

THE MACMILLAN COMPANY
COLLIER-MACMILLAN LIMITED, LONDON

Third Printing, 1972

Library of Congress catalog card number: 69–10363

THE MACMILLAN COMPANY
866 Third Avenue, New York, New York 10022
COLLIER-MACMILLAN CANADA, LTD., Toronto, Ontario

Preface

Development of the Subject

The subject of mechanics of deformable bodies is highly important in the practice of certain phases of the profession of engineering; it deals with actual engineering conditions. Therefore, this book has continued the tradition we began in our earlier books in still further development of a rational theory that is readily applicable to these conditions.

The underlying philosophy of this rational theory is the prediction of the actual behavior of an element or member of a machine or structure throughout the complete history of its loading, and especially including the phases of loading history that might be associated with the failure of the member to perform its load-carrying function in the machine or structure. The loads cause the member to deform and create internal forces (stresses) in the member. The deformation may be either elastic, plastic, or visco-elastic, or a combination of these. Either the deformation or the internal force (stress) in the member may become sufficiently large to cause the member to cease functioning satisfactorily in resisting the load (i.e., to fail).

The problem, therefore, consists of three main parts: (1) to derive relationships between the loads and the deformation; (2) to derive relationships between the loads and the stresses; and in addition (3) to use these relationships, in conjunction with the predicted behavior of the member and the properties of the material, to introduce a rational method for determining the appropriate dimensions of the member (i.e., for the design of the member).

The problem is developed with the help of stress-strain relations or stress-strain time relations, force or stress equilibrium relationships, and the consideration of geometrical requirements of strain compatibility with constraints on displacements in the analysis of the various problems that are treated.

Plan of the Book

We have used the example of the relatively simple problem of the axially loaded straight bar to illustrate completely the combined role of force or stress equilibrium equations, stress-strain relations, and the geometrical requirements of strain compatibility with constraints on displacements in the solution of problems in mechanics of deformable bodies. To further emphasize the role of strain compatibility with constraints on displacements, the problem of static indeterminacy is also introduced in Chapter 1. Furthermore, the principle of virtual work is introduced in Chapter 1 to give still further emphasis to the role of force-displacement and stress-strain relationships. In addition, the relation between material properties and failure of tension members is emphasized. Material properties are presented for the following material behaviors: elastic, plastic, linear viscoelastic, and fatigue.

The emphasis upon equilibrium, stress-strain relations, and strain compatibility should be extended into two- and three-dimensional cases, and Chapter 1 gives the reader the proper motivation for engaging in such preparation in Chapters 2, 3, and 4. Furthermore, it must be recognized that for engineering reasons there are limiting conditions, expressed by theories of failure, that must be considered in relating the equilibrium equations, stress-strain relations, and compatibility conditions. Such limiting conditions are discussed under the title of theories of failure. This topic is emphasized in Chapter 1 and is extended to two- and three-dimensional problems in Chapter 4. The discussion of internal pressure vessels (Chapter 5) is placed immediately following Chapter 4 in order to provide several good examples to illustrate the role of theories of failure in solving problems involving three-dimensional stresses.

The basic role of statics in the subject of mechanics of deformable bodies is developed in Chapter 6 where methods are given for transforming a complicated load system on a bar into axial, bending, and torsional components. The main reason for this transformation is to solve the problem for each separate component (axial, bending, and torsion) and then to obtain the complete solution by the superposition of the separate solutions. Chapters 7 and 8 take up the problem of bending of members, Chapter 9 that of torsion of members, and Chapter 10 (combined loads) deals with the question of superposing the separate solutions obtained in Chapter 1 (axial loads), Chapters 7 and 8 (bending), and Chapter 9 (torsion).

There is one theory of failure that, by its nature, must be discussed in a separate fashion. It occurs in a member (or structure) when its resistance to loads becomes unstable and failure consists of sudden collapse that is usually associated with compressive forces; it is referred to as failure by buckling. Chapter 11 treats the problem of computing buckling loads of columns and eccentrically loaded columns. Special topics in this chapter include a discussion of the effect upon the buckling load of a column of various degrees of restraint of the freedom of rotation of the ends of the column.

Of special interest is the chapter on dynamic loads. The response of a member of a machine or structure to dynamic loads is usually somewhat different from that associated with static loads. Chapter 12 gives a special treatment of dynamic loads.

While the first 12 chapters of the book deal with members of a machine or structure, most structures and machines consist of an assemblage of members. Thus, the members of an assemblage must somehow be connected. Chapter 13 treats the subject of the strength of connections by rivets or welds. Most books deal only with static strength of joints, but ours also deals with the strength of joints that are subjected to repeated loads.

Most of the newer books on deformable bodies (resistance of materials) have little or no material in them on properties of areas. We have found that it is necessary to supplement such texts with additional printed material on properties of areas. Therefore, our book has an adequate treatment in Appendix A.

J. O. S.
O. M. S.

Contents

CHAPTER **2**
Stresses at a Point
page **96**

Part 1. Basic Concepts

Part 2. Analysis of Plane Stress

Part 3. Analysis of Three-Dimensional Stress

CHAPTER **3**
Strains at a Point
page **134**

Part 1. Basic Concepts

Part 2. Analysis of the Plane Problem of Strain

CHAPTER **9**
Torsion of Cylindrical Members
page **393**

CHAPTER **10**
Combined Loading
page **448**

APPENDIX **A**

Second Moment or Moment of Inertia of an Area
page **588**

APPENDIX **B**

Properties of Rolled-Steel Sections
page **610**

Index
page **615**

Elementary Mechanics of
Deformable Bodies

Relations Among Loads, Stresses, and Deformations

1

1.1. Introduction

Engineering machines or structures, such as automobiles, airplanes, rockets, bridges, buildings, electric generators, steam turbines, and so forth, are usually constructed by connecting or assembling various bodies, called parts or members, so that the structure, assemblage, or machine performs a given function. In most machines and structures the main function of a member is to resist the external forces (called loads) that are applied to it. Such members are called load-carrying members, for although they may have other purposes in the structure or machine, the main requirement that they satisfy is to resist the loads without causing the structure or machine to fail.

Mechanics of deformable bodies cuts across all branches of the profession of engineering with a remarkably large variety of applications. Some engineers specialize in designing members of structures and machines. Other engineers are sometimes called upon to design load-carrying members even if this is not their area of specialization. The problem in each design is to develop a member that will not fail during service. In practice or in the laboratory we determine when a member ceases to function satisfactorily or, to state it differently, when it fails, by observing the response of the member when the loads that act on it are increased in magnitude. In general, failure is found to result from one of the following types of behavior that occur when the member is loaded beyond its capacity; (1) fracture, (2) general yielding, (3) excessive deformation, or (4) instability. The first three of these types or modes of failure are discussed in Section 4.5; instability is considered in Chapter 11.

1

The failure of a member, especially if by fracture, suggests that something happens internally to cause the failure. Most members transmit loads from one point in a structure or machine to another point in the structure or machine where reactions are developed between the member and other parts of the structure or machine. From the point where loads are applied to a member to the point where the reaction occurs, the forces are carried internally within the member. One of the main objectives of this book is to determine how these forces are transmitted internally through the member.

Method of Sections—Internal Forces. The first step in determining how the forces are transmitted internally through the member is to imagine that the member is severed at a section, usually a plane, somewhere along the path of the internal forces between the location in the member where loads are applied and the location in the member where the reactions are developed. The internal forces acting on this section hold the member in equilibrium, and hence, a free body diagram can be drawn for that part of the member to one side of the severed section, provided the internal forces on the section are shown as external forces.

Let the member shown in Figure 1.1a be in equilibrium under the action of the loads F_y and F_z shown acting in the yz-plane at the left end and the reactions at the rigid wall to which the member is securely fastened at the right end. Let the axes x and y lie in a plane that is perpendicular to the longitudinal axis z of the member. Pass a plane section H normal to the z-axis to sever the portion of the member in Figure 1.1b. The internal resisting forces N_z and V_y and the internal resisting moment M_x act on cross section H. In Figure 1.1b the loads F_y and F_z, the internal resisting forces N_z and V_y, and the internal resisting moment M_x hold the severed part of the body in equilibrium. The internal resisting forces and resisting moment at cross section H in Figure 1.1a have become external in Figure 1.1b. Thus, Figure 1.1b is a free-body diagram. Application of the equations of equilibrium confirm the existence of the quantities N_z, V_y, and M_x. The internal resisting force N_z is an axial centric force normal to the cross section H, and V_y is a transverse force that lies in cross section H; both N_z and V_y lie in the yz-plane. The internal resisting moment M_x represents a couple that lies in a plane perpendicular to the x axis—that is, M_x lies in the yz-plane or in a plane parallel to it.

Stresses. In Figure 1.1b the forces N_z and V_y have been shown as concentrated forces acting through the centroid O of cross section H, and the moment M_x is described as a couple lying in a plane perpendicular to the x-axis. The fact is, however, that N_z, V_y, and M_x are resultants of internal forces that are distributed over the entire cross section H. As already noted, part of the distributed force system lies in the cross section H and part is normal (perpendicular) to the cross section H.

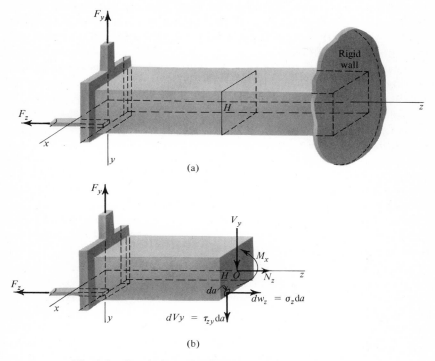

Fig. 1.1. Loaded member having constant cross section.

Let a small part of the area of cross section H be chosen and designated da as shown in Figure 1.1b. Because the normal force N_z and the moment M_x produce a distribution of internal normal forces over the cross section H, let dw_z be the part of this normal force acting on area da. Let dV_y be the part of the shearing force V_y acting on area da. Choose a point in area da. The normal stress σ_z at that point is defined as the limiting value of the ratio dw_z/da as da approaches zero at that point. The shearing stress τ_{zy} at that point is defined as the limiting value of the ratio dV_y/da as da approaches zero at that point. Thus,

$$\sigma_z = \lim_{da \to 0} \frac{dw_z}{da} \qquad \tau_{zy} = \lim_{da \to 0} \frac{dV_y}{da}.$$

Stress has units of force per unit area. In further considerations, da is considered to be an infinitesimal area and the stress components σ_z and τ_{zy} are assumed to be uniformly distributed over the area da.

In Figure 1.1b, $\sigma_z\,da$ is the normal force acting on the infinitesimal area da and $\tau_{zy}da$ is the shearing force acting in the plane of the infinitesimal area da. Thus, the distribution of the normal forces on cross section H is known when the distribution of normal stress σ_z is known, and the distribution of the shearing forces on cross section H is known when the distribution of the shearing stress τ_{zy} is known. One of the important problems in this book will be to derive load-stress relations by which the distributions of σ_z and τ_{zy} can be determined when the loads F_y and F_z are specified and when the dimensions of the member in Figure 1.1 are given.

Strains.   When loads are applied to a member it deforms, that is, it changes its volume and its shape. These geometrical changes or deformations are expressed in terms of normal and shearing strains that correspond to the normal and shearing stresses, respectively. The deformations of most load-carrying members are so small that they cannot be observed by the naked eye; therefore, we exaggerate the deformations in order to picture them as illustrated by the deformed plate indicated by the dashed lines and the undeformed plate indicated by the solid lines in Figure 1.2.

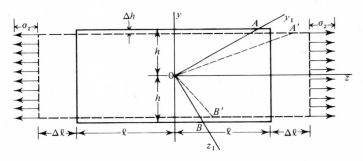

Fig. 1.2.   Undeformed and deformed plate subjected to axial centric tensile load.

The plate in Figure 1.2 lies in the yz-plane and has a constant small thickness t, a length 2ℓ, and a width $2h$. The origin O of the y and z coordinate axes is at the center of the plate and is assumed to be at the same location for the undeformed and deformed plate. The loads on the plate produce only a uniform distribution of normal stress σ_z on the two faces of the plate normal to the z axis. In Section 1.4 we find that a uniform, normal stress distribution will be produced by an axial centric tension load $P = 2ht\sigma_z$ whose line of action passes through the centroid of each cross section of the plate. The deformations indicated by the difference between the dashed lines of the deformed plate and the solid lines of the undeformed plate are assumed to be homogeneous; that is, if a square grid was scribed on the undeformed plate, each square would deform into the same size rectangle. Note that the member elongates a distance $\Delta\ell$ over the half-length ℓ in the z-direction where the normal stress is σ_z and contracts a distance $-\Delta h$ over the half-width h in the y-direction where the normal stress $\sigma_y = 0$.

Normal Strain. The normal strain in any direction is defined to be the change in length per unit length of a line segment in the given direction; it will be denoted by ϵ and is dimensionless. By making use of this definition, the normal strain ϵ_z in the z-direction and the normal strain ϵ_y in the y-direction are given by the following relations:

$$\epsilon_z = \frac{\Delta\ell}{\ell} \quad \text{and} \quad \epsilon_y = -\frac{\Delta h.}{h}. \tag{1-1}$$

Equations (1–1) actually define the average normal strains over the gage length ℓ and h; they also define the normal strains at each point in the gage lengths if the deformations are homogeneous over the gage lengths ℓ and h. Note that the normal strain ϵ_z is positive and that the normal strain ϵ_y is negative. Since the geometries of the deformed and undeformed plate are known in Figure 1.2, the normal strain along any other axis such as the z_1-axis or the y_1-axis can be determined. Straight line OB deforms into straight line OB' if the deformations of the plate are homogeneous. The normal strain ϵ_{z_1} is equal to the difference between lengths OB' and OB divided by length OB. It is noted that the magnitude of ϵ_{z_1} lies between the magnitudes of ϵ_z and ϵ_y. Thus, the value of the normal strain in the plate in Figure 1.2 depends on the direction of the axis along which the normal strain is determined.

Poisson's Ratio. Note that in Figure 1.2 the stress σ_z is directly associated with the strain ϵ_z in the same direction. But the strain ϵ_y in the y-direction is not accompanied by a stress in the y-direction; that is, $\sigma_y = 0$. Under the condition that the plate is loaded in one direction only, the ratio of the lateral strain ϵ_y to the longitudinal strain ϵ_z (in the direction of loading) is designated by the symbol v; that is, $v = -\epsilon_y/\epsilon_z$. The ratio v is called Poisson's ratio.

Shearing Strain. In Figure 1.2 let Oy_1 and Oz_1 be any rectangular axes through the point O other than Oy and Oz. These axes intersect the boundary of the plate at points A and B. After the plate is loaded, these points take positions A' and B'. Straight lines OA and OB remain straight lines (dashed lines OA' and OB') after deformation since the deformations of the plate are homogeneous. It will be noted that the dashed lines OA' and OB' no longer are perpendicular to each other. The change in the angle between any two axes, such as Oy_1 and Oz_1, that were originally perpendicular to each other gives evidence of shearing strain. The change in the angle is $\pi/2 -$ angle

$A'OB'$ and the shearing strain, designated $\gamma_{z_1 y_1}$, is defined as the tangent of this angle; that is,

$$\gamma_{z_1 y_1} = \tan(\pi/2 - \text{angle } A'OB').$$ (1–2)

In Figure 1.2 the shearing strain $\gamma_{z_1 y_1}$ is positive. The shearing strain is positive when the angle between the positive ends of the Oz_1 and Oy_1 axes decreases in magnitude. It should be noted that there is no change in the angle between Oz and Oy axes, and hence the shearing strain $\gamma_{zy} = 0$. Hence, the shearing strain is a function of the direction of the axes Oz_1 and Oy_1.

1.2.   Load-Deformation and Stress-Strain Relationships

In Section 1.1 the definitions of stress and strain have been given along with the idea that deformations of a member can be observed and measured when loads are applied to it (see Fig. 1.2). Because stress is characterized by its internal location within a member, it can not be measured. Instead, the deformations are measured, the distributions of normal strains and shearing strains in the member are determined from the measured deformations, and the distributions of normal and shearing stresses are predicted from the strain distributions. Consequently, a direct relationship between stress and strain for the material in a member is an important step to be used in determining the stress distributions in the member when the strain distributions are known.

The relation between stress and strain may be different for each of the thousands of different materials used in design. These relations are usually obtained by making a tension test of a specimen of the material and recording successive values of force and deformation for the specimen. In some materials (most metals at room temperature for instance), the shape of the load-deformation diagram for the tension specimen is found to be practically independent of the time required to make the test except for extremely short (impact) applications of the tensile loads. The load-deformation diagram and the stress-strain relationships obtained from the load-deformation diagram are said to be time-independent. Other materials such as lead, plastics, and concrete at room temperature and metals at elevated temperatures exhibit time-dependent deformations even under constant loads. The deformations of members made of such materials as wood, plastics, and concrete are also influenced by the relative humidity of the surrounding atmosphere. The relation between stress, strain, time, temperature, and relative humidity may be extremely complex for a given material and for a given member. When these relations are known, they are called the constitutive relations for the material and the member; the constitutive relations may be different for different members made of the same material. The further discussions in this section assume that the material behavior is time-independent. Time-dependent material behavior is considered in Sections 1.11 and 1.12.

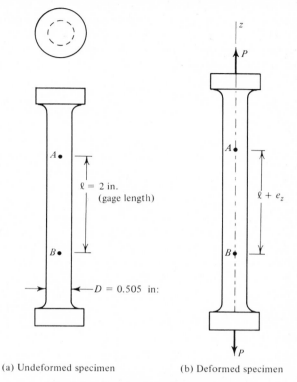

(a) Undeformed specimen   (b) Deformed specimen

Fig. 1.3. Standard tension specimen

Time-Independent Deformation of Tension Specimen Subjected to Axial Centric Loading. A standard tension specimen is shown in Figure 1.3; the specimen has a diameter $D = 0.505$ in., a gage length $\ell = 2$ in., and although the length of the specimen is not standardized, the specimen has sufficient length so that points A and B are located at least a distance equal to the diameter D away from the enlarged ends. The reason for standardization is that some material properties are influenced by the dimensions D and ℓ; however, many important material properties are not influenced by either the cross-sectional shape of the specimen or the relative dimensions of D and ℓ for specimens having circular cross section.

Let Figure 1.3 represent a tension specimen machined from a bar of alloy steel. The specimen is mounted in a testing machine that loads it axially so that the load P_z acts along the longitudinal z-axis of the cylinder. Furthermore, a device called an extensometer is attached at points A and B that are 2 in. apart to measure values of the elongation e_z of the specimen between these two points. As the load is increased, values of the elongation e_z and

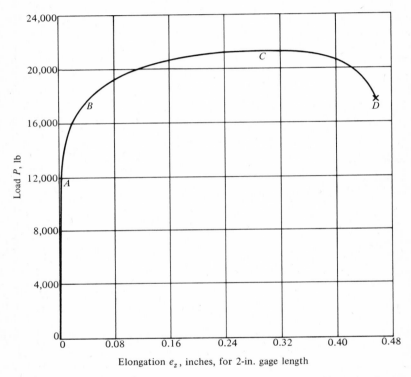

Fig. 1.4. Load-elongation curve for a tension specimen of alloy steel.

of the load P_z are taken simultaneously. Figure 1.4 is a graph in which ordinates represent the load P_z and abscissas the elongation e_z. In Figure 1.4 the smooth curve $OABCD$ has been drawn through the plotted points that represent pairs of values of P_z and e_z taken simultaneously.

The curve $OABCD$ in Figure 1.4 has three important characteristics. It is a straight line from O to A, which indicates a linear relationship between P_z and e_z up to a load of about $P_z = 12,000$ lb and an elongation $e_z = 0.0040$ in. The metal is a polycrystalline material the crystals of which have crystallographic planes that are randomly oriented. From O to A these crystals will remain nearly undamaged and the material on unloading is assumed to be the same as before loading. For loads greater than that at point A, the metal yields plastically as the result of slip along preferred planes of slip of the individual crystals. Perfect crystals have an ordered arrangement of atoms. Real crystals are not perfect but contain a large number of imperfections called dislocations. Slip occurs as the result of the movement of these dislocations within the crystals. At a given stress the movement of a given dislocation is stopped either by other imperfections in the crystal or by the boundary of the crystal. An increase in stress causes some of the blocked dislocations to move, as well as others to start to move. The process by which greater loads are required to cause increasing deformations of the specimen after yielding starts is called strain hardening or work hardening of the material.

The plastic deformation is permanent since the specimen is found to have a permanent elongation when it is unloaded. It should be noted that some material properties (the yield strength, for instance) for the material are continually changing during the plastic deformation. As indicated in Figure 1.2 for a plate subjected to axial centric loading, the cross-sectional area of the tension specimen in Figure 1.3 decreases in magnitude as e_z increases. From O to A the decrease in cross-sectional area is so small that it can be neglected. From A to C the material in the tension specimen strengthens, as the result of strain hardening, more rapidly than the specimen is weakened by the decrease in cross-sectional area. At C the load reaches its maximum value of $P_z = 21,300$ lb at an elongation of $e_z = 0.280$ in. From C to D the material in the specimen continues to strain harden but the ability of the material to be strengthened by the strain hardening is less than the weakening of the specimen by the decrease in cross-sectional area, the load falls off, and the specimen finally fractures as indicated at point D in Figure 1.4.

Stress-Strain Relationship. In the axially centric loaded tensile specimen of Figure 1.3 it is assumed that the normal stress σ_z is uniformly distributed over the cross-sectional area, which is $A = \pi D^2/4 = \pi(0.505)^2/4 = 0.200$ in^2. Thus, $\sigma_z = P_z/0.200$. Furthermore, the normal strain ϵ_z is assumed to be uniform over the 2-in. gage length between the points A and B, and hence $\epsilon_z = e_z/2$. Values of σ_z and ϵ_z have been computed from the load deformation data of Figure 1.4 and the pairs of corresponding values of σ_z and ϵ_z have been plotted in Figure 1.5, where ordinates represent values of σ_z and abscissas represent values of ϵ_z. Note that the smooth curve $OABCD$ drawn through the experimental data in Figure 1.5 appears to be exactly similar to that of Figure 1.4. This similarity arises from the fact that

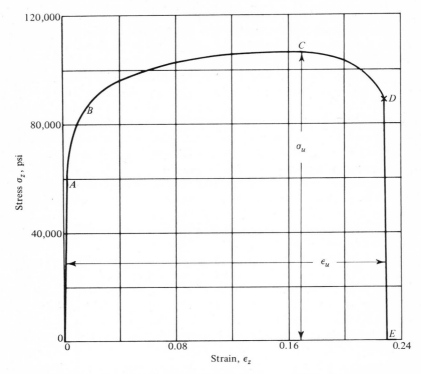

Fig. 1.5. Stress-strain diagram for the tension specimen of alloy steel of Fig. 1.4.

the area A of the original cross section (before loading) is used to compute the stress, and the original 2-in. gage length is used to compute the strain. The effect of the change in the area A on the actual normal stress (true stress) and of the change in the gage length ℓ on the actual normal strain (true strain) will be discussed in Section 1.10. Although the stress-strain diagram in Figure 1.5 is similar to the load-elongation diagram in Figure 1.4, the portion of the stress-strain diagram from O to C is generally assumed to be independent of specimen size and shape and independent of gage length. The shape of the stress-strain diagram from C to D in Figure 1.5 may be influenced by either shape or size of specimen or gage length used to measure e_z.

Stress-Strain Diagram. The curve $OABCD$ of Figure 1.5 is called the tensile stress-strain diagram for the alloy steel. A stress-strain diagram is an important aid to an engineer in making the selection of a material to be used in the design of a load-carrying member. Furthermore, certain quantities, called properties of the material, which can be determined from the stress-strain diagram, are used by engineers in determining the dimensions of a load-carrying member.

1.3. Material Properties

A material property, as defined here, is a mechanical property that is assumed to have a constant value for a given material when its value is determined from data taken from a standard test that is interpreted in accordance with the prescribed definition of the property.

Figure 1.5 is the tensile stress-strain diagram that has been drawn from test data taken from a standard test of a specimen of alloy steel (see Fig. 1.3 and Section 1.2). The results of this test will be used to give the definitions of certain material properties and these definitions will be used to determine these properties for the alloy steel.

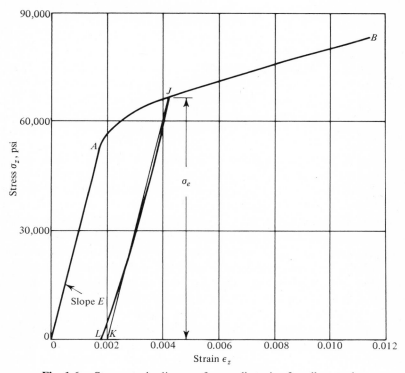

Fig. 1.6. Stress-strain diagram for small strains for alloy steel.

Ultimate Tensile Strength. The ultimate tensile strength, σ_u, is the maximum stress the material will resist in the tension test. It is the ordinate to point C in Figure 1.5 and is equal to the maximum load on the specimen divided by the original cross-sectional area of the specimen. For this alloy, steel $\sigma_u = 106{,}000$ psi.

Per Cent Elongation. The per cent elongation is the ultimate value of the elongation divided by the original gage length and multiplied by 100 to give a percentage. In Figure 1.5 the per cent elongation is the abscissa of point D multiplied by 100. Its value is 23 per cent for this alloy steel. The per cent elongation is often used as a measure of *ductility* of a material, where ductility is defined as the capacity of a material to undergo large strains while resisting a load.

Many of the material properties require that the portion OAB of the stress-strain diagram in Figure 1.5 be replotted as in Figure 1.6 where the ordinate scale is unchanged but the abscissa scale is changed to give more detail of the curve in the portion near point A where the stress-strain diagram ceases to be a straight line as from O to A. In the linear portion of the stress-strain diagram the material is said to be linearly elastic. Beyond point A the stress-strain diagram is nonlinear and the material is said to be plastic (inelastic).

Modulus of Elasticity. Because the stress-strain diagram is a straight line from O to A in Figures 1.5 and 1.6, it is concluded that stress is directly proportional to strain from O to A. The constant of proportionality, E, of the strain to the stress is called the modulus of elasticity; that is,

$$\sigma_z = E\epsilon_z. \tag{1-3}$$

Equation (1–3) is the constitutive equation for linearly elastic behavior of a material in a member subjected to axial centric loading. In Figure 1.6 the value of the modulus of elasticity E for the alloy steel is 30,000,000 psi.

Proportional Limit. The proportional limit is the greatest stress that can be developed in the material without causing a deviation from the law of proportionality of stress to strain. For the alloy steel the value of the proportional limit is about 52,000 psi as shown by the ordinate to point A in Figure 1.6. However, the proportional limit as determined from the stress-strain diagram of Figure 1.5 is about 60,000 psi. The value for the proportional limit is influenced not only by the abscissa scale chosen to plot the stress-strain diagram but by the fact that the change from the linear to the nonlinear portion of the stress-strain diagram may be very gradual. For this reason the proportional limit is one material property that is seldom determined and little used.

Yield Strength. The yield strength of a material is defined to be the maximum stress that can be developed in a test specimen of a material without causing more than a specified permanent strain. In Figure 1.6 let the line KJ be drawn parallel to the line OA. The ordinate to the point J is the yield strength, σ_e, corresponding to a permanent strain as represented by the abscissa of point K. The assumption has been made that if the test specimen is loaded to the stress at point J and is then unloaded the stress-strain relationship during the unloading will be represented by the straight line JK. The actual stress-strain relationship during the unloading is represented by the curved line JL. In other words, the actual permanent strain is OL instead of OK. For the reason that OK is not the actual permanent strain, it is usually called an "offset." In Figure 1.6 the offset OK is 0.002 or 0.2 per cent strain and the yield strength based on 0.2 per cent offset is the ordinate to J, which is $\sigma_e = 66,000$ psi for the alloy steel.

Elastic Limit. The elastic limit of a material is defined to be the maximum stress that can be developed in a tension specimen without causing permanent strain. The stress must be applied and released before the actual permanent strain can be determined. The elastic limit is seldom determined and is approximately equal to the proportional limit for the materials considered in this book.

Yield Point. One of the most common structural materials is low carbon steel which is commonly called either structural steel or mild steel. The stress-strain diagram for a tension specimen of structural steel is shown in Figure 1.7a. The portion OAB of the stress-strain diagram is expanded in Figure 1.7b. Structural steel usually exhibits an upper yield point σ_{YU} in that the stress required to initiate yielding is greater than the lower yield point $\sigma_{YL} = \sigma_e$ required to cause yielding to spread along the tension specimen. The stress-strain diagram is flat topped for strains as great as $10\epsilon_e$ to $40\epsilon_e$ ($\epsilon_e = \sigma_e/E$). The upper yield point is usually disregarded and the stress-strain diagram for small strains is approximated as indicated in Figure 1.7c. Note in Figure 1.7c that the yield point, the yield strength, the proportional limit, and the elastic limit have the same magnitude for this material.

Energy Absorption Properties—Modulus of Resilience. Some members are subjected to impact or shock loads, which are usually thought of as energy loads that have dimensions of either foot-pounds (ft-lb) or inch-pounds (in.-lb). As an energy load is applied to a member, internal forces are developed within the member, and these internal forces move because of deformations of the member. The work done by the internal forces is defined as the strain energy U for the member. The amount of strain energy absorbed per unit volume is defined as the strain energy density U_0 and, for the tension

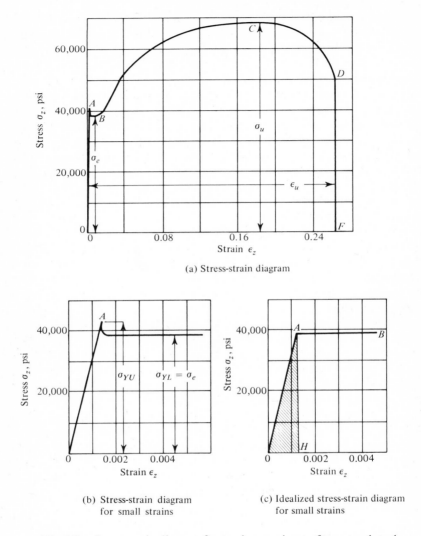

(a) Stress-strain diagram

(b) Stress-strain diagram
for small strains

(c) Idealized stress-strain diagram
for small strains

Fig. 1.7. Stress-strain diagram for tension specimen of structural steel.

specimen, is given by the area under the stress-strain diagram. The maximum strain energy density that a material can absorb without becoming permanently strained is called the modulus of resilience U_{0e}. In the case of the stress-strain diagram for structural grade steel in Figure 1.7c, the modulus of resilience is equal to the cross-hatched area OAH; the area is $\frac{1}{2}(AH)(OH) =$

$\frac{1}{2}\sigma_e\epsilon_e$. But $\epsilon_e = \sigma_e/E$; therefore, for the tension specimen

$$U_{0e} = \text{modulus of resilience} = \tfrac{1}{2}\frac{\sigma_e^2}{E}, \qquad (1\text{--}4)$$

which has units of inch-pound per inch cubed.

Toughness. The toughness of a material in a tensile specimen is defined as the maximum strain energy density that the material can absorb without fracture occurring. Hence the toughness is considered to be equal to the strain energy density U_{0f} absorbed in stressing the material to the ultimate strength. The energy absorbed by a unit volume at fracture is obtained by measuring or computing the area $OABCDF$ in Figure 1.7a (or Fig. 1.5) under the complete stress-strain diagram up to fracture of the tensile specimen. A good approximation of the area $OABCDF$ is given by the following relation:

$$U_{0f} = \frac{\sigma_e + \sigma_u}{2}\,\epsilon_u. \qquad (1\text{--}5)$$

Statistical Characteristics of Tension Test Data. Of the material properties discussed in this section and Poisson's ratio discussed in Section 1.2, those that are commonly used in design are listed in Table 1.1. Only a limited number of the thousands of different materials are listed in Table 1.1. Note that material properties for compression test data and pure shear data (pure shear data are discussed and used in Chapters 4 and 9) are also listed in Table 1.1. Each material property listed in Table 1.1 is a statistical average of data from several specimens. If several tension specimens are machined from the same bar of material, some of the material properties may vary by ± 5 per cent or more. If the same material is ordered from several different manufacturers, the variability of many of the properties may be ± 10 per cent or more. The least variable of the properties are the elastic properties, E and v (also G as discussed in Chapters 4 and 9), associated with the linear portion of the stress-strain diagram (see OA in Figs. 1.6 and 1.7). The modulus of elasticity E and Poisson's ratio v are little influenced either by small variations of chemical composition or by heat treatment.

The most variable of the material properties are those associated with the transition from elastic to plastic behavior and those associated with the plastic portion of the stress-strain diagram. These material properties are the yield stress, σ_e, the ultimate strength, σ_u, and the per cent elongation. Note that, whereas Poisson's ratio for a given material is a constant for linearly elastic conditions, plastic deformation causes Poisson's ratio to increase in magnitude from the value listed in Table 1.1 and approaches a value of 0.50 for large plastic strains. A value of $v = 0.50$ means that the

Table 1.1

Values of Strength, Stiffness, and Ductility of Various Structural Materials

These are *average* values; test results for a specimen of a given material may deviate considerably from the values in the table.

Material	TENSILE STRENGTH, PSI Yield Strength σ_e	TENSILE STRENGTH, PSI Ultimate Strength σ_u	COMPRESSIVE STRENGTH, PSI Yield Strength σ_e	COMPRESSIVE STRENGTH, PSI Ultimate Strength σ_u	SHEARING STRENGTH, PSI Yield Strength τ_e	SHEARING STRENGTH, PSI Ultimate Strength τ_u	MODULUS OF ELASTICITY, PSI Tensile and Compressive E	MODULUS OF ELASTICITY, PSI Shearing G	Poisson's Ratio ν	ELONGATION IN 2 IN., PER CENT
Structural steel (about 0.30% carbon), hot rolled	35,000	65,000	35,000	(a)	21,000	45,000	30,000,000	11,600,000	0.29	30
Steel (about 0.60% carbon), hot rolled	60,000	110,000	60,000	(a)	36,000	85,000	30,000,000	11,600,000	0.29	15
Structural nickel steel (3.5% nickel), hot rolled	55,000	110,000	55,000	(a)	30,000	65,000	30,000,000	11,600,000	0.29	25
Chrome–nickel (SAE 3245) steel, heat-treated (carbon 0.40–0.50%, Ni 1.50–2.00%, Cr 0.90–1.25%)	110,000	130,000	110,000	(a)	65,000	95,000	30,000,000	11,600,000	0.29	25
Gray (cast) iron	—	20,000	—	75,000	—	30,000	15,000,000	6,250,000	0.20	1
Alloy (cast) iron*	—	45,000	—	90,000	24,000	55,000	20,000,000	8,000,000	—	1
Bronze,* rolled (copper 95%, tin 5%)	40,000	65,000	35,000	(a)	24,000	—	14,000,000	6,000,000	—	30
Brass,* rolled (copper 60%, zinc 40%)	40,000	60,000	35,000	(a)	24,000	—	12,000,000	4,450,000	0.35	30
Aluminum alloy,* rolled, tempered (aluminum 96%, copper 4%)	35,000	58,000	35,000	(a)	22,000	36,000	10,000,000	3,860,000	0.33	{20, 15}
Magnesium alloy,* high strength, extruded (magnesium 93%, aluminum 6.0%, zinc 0.7%)	30,000	42,000	28,000	(a)	16,000	20,000	6,500,000	2,410,000	0.35	16
Monel metal,* hot rolled (nickel 67%, copper 28%)	45,000	85,000	40,000	(a)	25,000	50,000	25,000,000	9,500,000	—	40
Plastic laminate,* glass fabric base, cross laminated	45,000	58,000	—	—	—	—	3,000,000	—	—	1
Concrete (1 cement : 2 sand : 3.5 crushed stone)	—	—	—	3,500	—	—	2,500,000	—	—	—
Timber { Yellow pine, small clear dry specimen	—	—	5,000 (Parallel to grain)	7,000	—	1,300	1,800,000	—	—	—
Timber { White oak, small clear dry specimens	—	—	4,300	7,000	—	1,800	1,600,000	—	—	—

* There are many materials in this classification with different compositions and made under different conditions that have a wide range of values (see, for example, *Metals Handbook* of the American Society for Metals.

(a) The yield strength is considered to be the maximum static compressive strength of ductile metals.

volume of the member remains constant as the member deforms. Large deformations of most materials occurs under the conditions of constancy of volume (constant density).

1.4. Members Subjected to Axial Centric Loading

In Figure 1.8b is shown a straight prismatic member with general cross section subjected to a tensile load P at each end. The condition of equilibrium requires that the action lines of the two loads P be collinear. Assume that the line of action of the two loads P is parallel to the z-axis that passes through

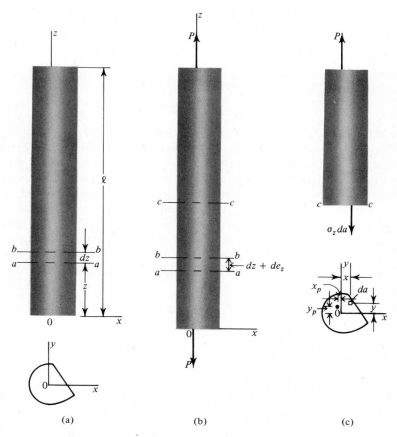

(a)   (b)   (c)

Fig. 1.8.   Tension member subjected to axial centric loading.

the centroid O of each cross section. Later it will be shown that the line of action of P must coincide with the z-axis in order that the member be subjected to axial centric loading.

Stress. The problem is to determine the stress σ_z at any point on a cross section of the member. To do this a cross section such as c–c is chosen as shown in Figure 1.8b. The part of the member above section c–c is chosen as a free-body diagram (Fig. 1.8c) and the forces $\sigma_z\,da$ that act on every element of area da of the cross section are shown as external forces. The location of an element of area da is determined by the coordinates x and y as shown in the cross section in Figure 1.8c. Also, let x_P and y_P denote the coordinates in the cross section through which the action line of the load P passes.

The force system that acts on the free body of Figure 1.8c is a parallel non-coplanar system for which three equations of equilibrium are written as follows:

$$\sum F_z = 0 = P - \int \sigma_z\,da,$$
$$\sum M_x = 0 = Py_P - \int \sigma_z y\,da, \tag{1-6}$$
$$\sum M_y = 0 = Px_P - \int \sigma_z x\,da.$$

In each of these equations the integral represents the sum of the quantities over the cross-sectional area. Before the integrals in Equations (1–6) can be evaluated, the distribution of the stress σ_z over the cross section must be determined. But the stresses σ_z are really internal and thus cannot be measured directly. However, the strains on the outer surface can be measured, as was illustrated in Figure 1.2, where it was found that when the load is an axially centric load the strains are uniformly distributed on the surface of the member. Since for elastic behavior the stress is proportional to the strain, it is now assumed that the material is homogeneous and that the stresses are also uniformly distributed over the cross section. By assuming that σ_z is constant, Equations (1–6) are rewritten as follows:

$$P = \sigma_z \int da = \sigma_z A, \tag{1-7}$$

$$\frac{Py_P}{\sigma_z} = \int y\,da = \bar{y}A, \tag{1-8}$$

$$-\frac{Px_P}{\sigma_z} = \int x\,da = \bar{x}A. \tag{1-9}$$

But the x- and y-axes intersect at the centroid O of the cross section, and hence the integrals on the right side of Equations (1–8) and (1–9) are each equal to zero because $\bar{x} = \bar{y} = 0$. On the left side of Equations (1–8) and

(1–9) the quantities P and σ_z are not zero and therefore $x_P = y_P = 0$. Because these coordinates are zero, the action line of the load P must be along the z-axis, and thus P is an axial centric load when σ_z is uniformly distributed. Equation (1–7) can be rewritten as

$$\sigma_z = \frac{P}{A}. \qquad (1\text{--}10)$$

Equation (1–10) is the load-stress relation for members of homogeneous material subjected to axial centric loads.

Elongation. The undeformed member in Figure 1.8a has a length ℓ. Consider two sections of the member, section a–a located at a distance z from the origin and section b–b located at a distance $z + dz$ from the origin. The axial centric load P in Figure 1.8b causes the member to elongate and the distance between the two sections a–a and b–b elongates by an amount de_z. The elongation de_z for the length dz is given by the relation (see Eq. 1–1) $de_z = \epsilon_z \, dz$, in which the longitudinal strain ϵ_z is assumed to be constant for the infinitesimal length dz but in some problems may vary along the finite length ℓ. The total elongation e_z of the length ℓ is then

$$e_z = \int_0^\ell \epsilon_z \, dz. \qquad (1\text{--}11)$$

For the elastic bar of Figure 1.8b the modulus of elasticity $E = \sigma_z/\epsilon_z$. But $\sigma_z = P/A$ as given by Equation (1–10). Therefore, $\epsilon_z = P/AE$ and, if this expression is substituted into Equation (1–11), it becomes

$$e_z = \int_0^\ell \frac{P \, dz}{AE}. \qquad (1\text{--}12)$$

Equation (1–12) is the load-elongation relation for members made of homogeneous material subjected to axial centric loads. In many members, P, A, and E are constant as for the member in Figure 1.8 and Equation (1–12) simplifies to

$$e_z = \frac{P\ell}{AE}. \qquad (1\text{--}13)$$

Stiffness Constant for Axially Centric Loaded Members. For an elastically loaded tension member subjected to an axial centric load P that is constant over its length ℓ, the constant, k, that must be multiplied by the elongation e_z to give the load P is called the *stiffness constant* for the member. Hence, by this definition

$$P = ke_z. \qquad (1\text{--}14)$$

For the special case in which the tension member has a uniform cross section over its length ℓ, Equation (1–13) gives

$$P = \frac{AE}{\ell} e_z, \tag{1–15}$$

and hence by comparing Equations (1–14) and (1–15) it is seen that the stiffness constant is

$$k = \frac{AE}{\ell}. \tag{1–16}$$

Elongation of Member Because of Temperature Change. Let α be the coefficient of thermal expansion (or contraction) of the material in the member. The quantity α is defined as the strain that occurs in the material when the temperature changes $1°F$. If the bar in Figure 1.8a has its temperature raised $\Delta T°F$, the strain ϵ_z is then $\alpha \Delta T$ before the load P is applied. The axial elongation e_z, due to the increase in temperature, is given by the substitution $\alpha \Delta T$ for e_z in Equation (1–11), which gives the relation

$$e_z = \int_0^\ell \alpha \Delta T \, dz. \tag{1–17}$$

where α is the coefficient of thermal expansion having dimensions of inch per inch per degree Fahrenheit and $\Delta T = T_2 - T_1$ is the temperature change when T_2 and T_1 are within a moderate temperature range in which the material does not change its structural properties.

Average values of α for several structural materials for use with temperature changes expressed by the Fahrenheit temperature scale are given in Table 1.2.

Table 1.2

MATERIAL	α
Brick	0.000 0050
Concrete	0.000 0062
Cast iron	0.000 0062
Steel	0.000 0065
Brass	0.000 0092
Aluminum	0.000 0130

For the general case in which the member is subjected to both an axial centric load and to a temperature change, the axial elongation of the member is given by the sum of Equations (1–12) and (1–17).

$$e_z = \int_0^\ell \left(\frac{P}{AE} + \alpha \, \Delta T \right) dz \qquad (1\text{–}18)$$

Illustrative Problems

1.1. A $\frac{1}{4}$-in. diameter steel rod ($E = 30,000,000$ psi and $\sigma_e = 59,000$ psi) is used as a pump rod for a pump at the bottom of a 5,000-ft oil well. The rod weighs 0.167 lb/ft. Let Q be the load applied to the rod by the piston of the pump at the bottom of the well. Neglect buoyancy effect of the oil on the pump rod. Determine the magnitude of Q and the elongation of the rod necessary to initiate yielding in the rod. Assume that the yield strength σ_e of the material is equal to the proportional limit.

SOLUTION.   Yielding will initiate at the upper end of the rod. Using Equation (1–10)

$$P_{max} = \sigma_e A = Q + 5,000(0.167) = Q + 835 \quad \text{and} \quad A = \frac{\pi}{64} = 0.0491 \text{ in.}^2,$$

$$Q = 59,000(0.0491) - 835,$$

$$= 2,062 \text{ lb.}$$

The elongation of the rod can be obtained using Equation (1–12). It is necessary to express the axial force P_z at any length z, where z is measured in inches from the piston, as a function of z. Since the weight of length z of the rod is proportional to z,

$$P_z = 2,062 + \frac{835z}{5,000(12)},$$

$$e_z = \frac{1}{30,000,000(0.0491)} \int_0^{60,000} \left(2,062 + \frac{835z}{5,000(12)} \right) dz,$$

$$= 101.0 \text{ in.}$$

Although this elongation is large, it is only 0.17 per cent of the total length of the rod.

1.2. A $\frac{1}{2}$-in. diameter brass rod is fixed at one end and is used to carry a tensile load P. The undeformed length of the rod is 60.00 in. at 50°F. In addition to the load P, the rod is heated along its length and the temperature is found to vary linearly from 50°F at the fixed end to 150°F at the loaded end. Determine the magnitude of P if the allowable elongation of the rod including the temperature effect is 0.080 in. Is the rod elastically loaded? See Table 1.1 for elastic properties of the brass. See Table 1.2 for coefficient of thermal expansion for brass.

SOLUTION. Let the z-axis lie along the rod with the origin at the fixed end. The temperature change ΔT can be written as a function of z by the relation $\Delta T = 100z/60$. Substituting in Equation (1–18) gives

$$e_z = 0.080 = \int_0^{60} \left(\frac{P}{AE} + \alpha \frac{100}{60} z \right) dz,$$

$$0.080 = \frac{60P}{12,000,000A} + 0.0000092 \frac{10}{6} \frac{3,600}{2},$$

$$\frac{P}{A} = 10,480 \text{ psi (elastic)},$$

$$P = 10,480 \frac{\pi}{16} = 2,060 \text{ lb}.$$

Problems

In the following problems the proportional limit of each material is assumed to be equal to the yield strength σ_e.

1.3. A tension specimen of 2024-T4 aluminum alloy has a gage length of 8 in. and a diameter of 0.5050 in. A load of 9,580 lb was found to develop a stress in the specimen equal to the proportional limit of the material. At this load the specimen has a deformed length of 8.036 in. and a diameter of 0.5043 in. Determine the following material properties: modulus of elasticity E, proportional limit σ_e, and Poisson's ratio v. Note that accurate measurements cannot be made for changes in diameter because of the short length; therefore, Poisson's ratio cannot be accurately determined using this specimen.

1.4. A structural steel tension member has a length of 40 in., a width of 10.000 in., and a thickness of 1 in. The member is subjected to an axially centric tension load. When the member is loaded to the proportional limit, the width of the plate is found to be 9.9965 in. Using values of E and v from Table 1.1, determine the proportional limit of the material.

ans. $\sigma_e = 36,200$ psi.

1.5. The wall bracket in Figure P1.5 carries a load $P = 15,000$ lb. Compute the normal stress at any section of the straight portion in each of the two eyebars.

ans. $\sigma = 9,750$ psi.

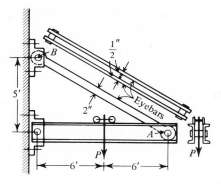

Fig. P 1.5.

1.6. In Figure P1.6, AB is made of an aluminum alloy for which $E = 10,000,000$ psi, and it has a rectangular cross section with dimensions 2 in. by $\frac{1}{4}$ in. It is specified (a) that the maximum normal stress in AB must not exceed 12,000 psi and (b) that the elastic elongation of AB must not exceed 0.20 in. Assume that the member deforms elastically. Determine whether or not each specification is satisfied.

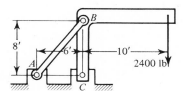

Fig. P 1.6.

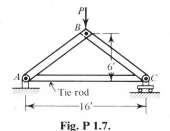

Fig. P 1.7.

1.7. In Figure P1.7 the load P acting on the pin-connected frame is 6,000 lb. The rod AC is made of structural steel and has a cross-sectional area of 0.25 in.² Will the tie rod AC act elastically? If so, calculate the stretch of the rod. See Table 1.1 for material properties.

1.8. A circular-section tension member has a length of 25 in. and is subjected to a tension load of 10,000 lb. The allowable elongation for the member is 0.0150 in. Using the material properties in Table 1.1, choose a metal and determine the diameter D of the member, subject to the condition that the ratio of the maximum normal stress to the yield strength is a maximum.

ans.   High-strength extruded magnesium alloy; $D = 1.81$ in.; $\sigma_e/\sigma_z = 7.69$

1.9. The tension member in Figure P1.9 has a $\frac{1}{4}$ in. by 1 in. rectangular cross section and is subjected to the loads shown. The member is made of a steel having a yield point $\sigma_e = 36,000$ psi and a modulus of elasticity of $E = 30,000,000$ psi. Determine the magnitude of Q for maximum elastic conditions and the elongation of the tension member when these loads are applied.

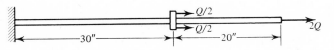

Figs. P 1.9 and P 1.10.

1.10. The tension member in Figure P1.10 is made of brass (see Tables 1.1 and 1.2 for material properties) and has a circular cross section 1 in. in diameter. Assuming linearly elastic conditions, determine the magnitude of Q if the temperature of the member is increased 80°F and the allowable elongation of the member is 0.068 in. Is the assumption that the material is linearly elastic justified?

ans. $Q = 2,260$ lb; $\sigma_{max} = 8,640$ psi (yes).

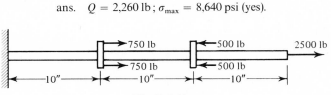

Fig. P 1.11.

1.11. The tension member in Figure P1.11 has a circular cross section with a diameter of $\frac{1}{2}$ in. and is made of an aluminum alloy (see Table 1.1 for material properties). Assuming linearly elastic conditions, determine the maximum normal stress in the tension member and the elongation of the tension member. Is the assumption that the material is linearly elastic justified?

1.12. In Figure P1.12 when the load Q is equal to 200 lb, arm AB is horizontal, and BC is vertical. If an increment $\Delta Q = 800$ lb is added to Q, the deflection of point A is $\Delta = 0.125$ in. What is the diameter D of the steel rod CD? The rod is made of high-strength steel having a tensile proportional limit of 65,000 psi. Assume that CD is

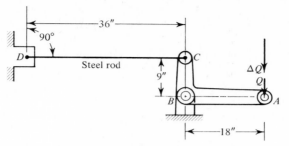

Fig. P 1.12.

strained elastically and that *ABC* is a rigid body; the deflection of *A*, therefore, is caused solely by rotation of *ABC* about *B* due to the elongation of *DC*. Assume that $E = 30,000,000$ psi for steel. After determining the value of *D*, calculate the tensile stress in *CD* to determine whether or not the assumption that *CD* acts elastically is justified.

ans. $D = 0.198$ in.

1.13.   In Figure P1.13 bar *AC* can be considered rigid. Tension member *BD*, which has a cross sectional area of 0.20 in.^{2}, is made of an aluminum alloy ($E = 10,800,000$ psi

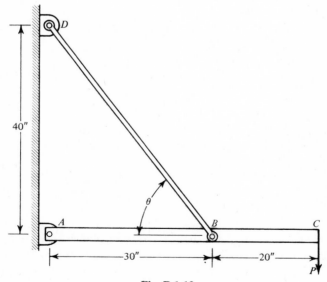

Fig. P 1.13.

and $\sigma_e = 48{,}000$ psi). If $P = 3{,}000$ lb, determine the stress in BD and the vertical move-ment of point C. *Hint*: the change in magnitude of angle θ is an infinitesimal.

1.14. A 1-in. steel cable is used by a mine to lift an elevator in removing ore from a mine that is 2,000 ft deep. The cable weighs 1.5 lb/ft. The load-elongation curve for the cable is found to be linear up to a load of 50,000 lb. The normal axial strain for the cable is given by the relation $\epsilon = 3 \times 10^{-7} P$, where P is the axial load assumed to be less than 50,000 lb. Determine the elongation of the cable if the loaded elevator weighs 15,000 lb and is located near the bottom of the mine.

ans. $e = 118.8$ in.

1.15. A tension member of length ℓ of constant cross-sectional area A and of total weight W is supported at its upper end. The modulus of elasticity of the material is E. Derive the relation for the elongation of the tension member due to its own weight in terms of W, ℓ, A, and E.

1.16. In Figure P1.16 let it be assumed that the known quantities are P, R_1, R_2, ℓ, and the tensile modulus of elasticity is E. Assuming that Equations (1–10) and (1–12) are valid at every section of the member, derive a relation for the elastic elongation e in terms of the known quantities.

ans. $e = \dfrac{Pb\ell}{\pi R_1^2 E}\left[\dfrac{1}{\ell + b}\right].$

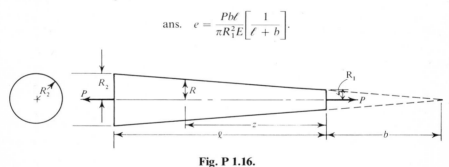

Fig. P 1.16.

1.17. A slab of concrete is 25-ft long in winter when at a uniform temperature of 30°F. (1) How much longer will it be on a day in summer when its temperature is 120°F if it is free to expand? (2) If the slab is partially restrained from expanding by abutments at its ends so that only one-third of the free expansion is permitted, what will be the compressive elastic stress developed in the concrete? (For concrete, $E = 2{,}000{,}000$ psi.)

ans.   (1) 0.014 ft;   (2) 744 psi.

1.18. A 20-ft steel tie rod containing a turnbuckle has its ends attached to walls and is tightened by the turnbuckle in summer when the temperature is 90°F to give a normal stress of 1,000 psi. How much do the walls move if the stress in the rod increases to 16,000 psi as the temperature of the rod is decreased to -20°F?

1.19. A distance between two points is exactly 100 ft. This distance is indicated correctly on a surveyor's tape when used at a temperature of 70°F and subjected to a pull of 10 lb. If in measuring a certain distance the tape indicates the distance to be 100 ft when the tape is subjected to a temperature of 100°F and a pull of 20 lb, what is the correct distance being measured? The tape is $\frac{1}{32}$ in. thick and $\frac{3}{8}$ in. wide.

ans.   100.022 ft.

1.20. An elastically deformed tension member is subjected to a load P which produces a normal stress $\sigma_z = P/A$. Derive an expression for the decrease in temperature ΔT of the tension member if the elongation of the member remains zero. If $\sigma_z = 10{,}000$ psi, determine ΔT for the condition that the tension member is made of either steel or aluminum.

1.21. The tension member in Problem 1.12 has a diameter of $\frac{3}{4}$ in. and is made of an aluminum alloy for which $\sigma_e = 45{,}000$ psi and $E = 10{,}000{,}000$ psi. The allowable elongation for the member is 0.120 in. Determine the magnitude of Q if in addition to the load the temperature is increased 100°F. Is the assumption that the material remains linearly elastic justified?

ans. $Q = 4{,}500$ lb; $\sigma_z = 20{,}300$ psi (yes).

1.22. When the steel cable is wound on the drum to lift the elevator to the ground surface in Problem 1.14, the elevator remains at the surface long enough for the cable to be cooled to the atmospheric temperature of 50°F. The elevator is then quickly lowered and is allowed to stand at the bottom of the mine where the temperature is 80°F. As the cable heats, its temperature is found to vary linearly from 50°F at the top of the shaft to 80°F at the bottom. Determine the change in length of the cable caused by the change in temperature. Use value of α for steel.

1.23. High-strength steel wires BC and CD in Figure P1.23 have a yield stress of $\sigma_e = 150{,}000$ psi and are used to carry a weight W of 1,000 lb as shown. The wires

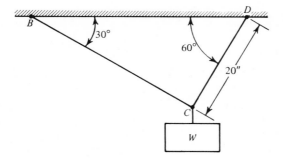

Fig. P 1.23.

have a diameter of $\frac{1}{8}$ in. Determine the maximum normal stress in the wires and the vertical movement Δ of point C due to the elongation of the wires.

ans. $\sigma_{max} = 70,600$ psi; $\Delta = 0.0643$ in.

1.24.   A rigid beam BC in Figure P1.24 is supported by a steel wire DF ($A = 0.010$ in.^{2} and $E = 30,000,000$ psi) and an aluminum wire GH ($A = 0.030$ in.^{2} and $E = 10,000,000$ psi). Determine the magnitude of P necessary to cause an axial strain in steel wire DF equal to $\epsilon = 0.00080$. Assume linearly elastic conditions.

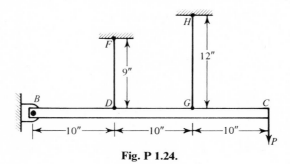

Fig. P 1.24.

1.25.   If the proportional limit of the steel wire and aluminum wire in Problem 1.24 are equal to 50,000 psi, determine the magnitude of P required to initiate plastic deformation in one of the wires.

1.5.   Statically Indeterminate Members Subjected to Axial Centric Loading

When members subjected to axial centric loading are put together to form a structure, it may be statically determinate as indicated by the pin-connected structure in Figure 1.9a or statically indeterminate as indicated by the pin-connected structure in Figure 1.10a. The free-body diagram in Figure 1.9b indicates that the reactions in the two members can be obtained from equations of equilibrium alone. Note that the three unknown reactions in Figure 1.10b cannot be obtained from equations of equilibrium alone since there are only two independent equations of equilibrium valid for this free-body diagram. The structure in Figure 1.10 is said to be statically indeterminate because one member such as DC can be removed and the structure would still be in equilibrium. This member is called a *redundant member*, and the axial force it exerts is called the *redundant reaction*.

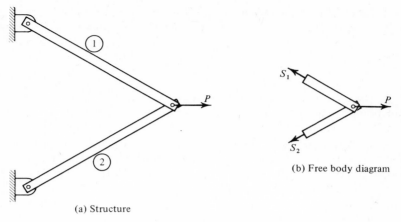

(a) Structure

(b) Free body diagram

Fig. 1.9. Statically determinate structure.

The number of redundant reactions for a given structure is easily determined. Draw a free-body diagram for the structure and write the equations of equilibrium. The difference between the number of unknown reactions and the number of independent equations of equilibrium will be equal to the number of redundant reactions. One additional relation among the loads is needed for each redundant reaction if the load carried by each member of the structure is to be determined. The conditions to be satisfied and the procedure to be followed in obtaining each additional relation among the loads will now be considered.

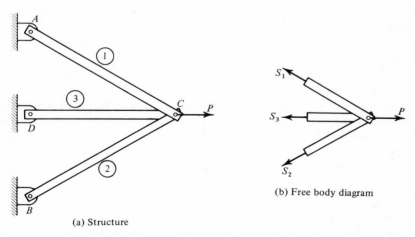

(a) Structure

(b) Free body diagram

Fig. 1.10. Statically indeterminate structure.

Conditions to be Satisfied. Both in the derivation of load-stress and load-deformation relations for members, and in the use of these relations to solve statically indeterminate problems, there are three conditions that have to be satisfied.

1. For conditions of rest, equations of equilibrium must be satisfied for each member or any part of each member or for an assemblage of members. If members are in motion, equations of motion must be satisfied.

2. The geometry of deformation for each volume element of each member must satisfy the conditions that the deformed volume elements must fit together perfectly with adjacent volume elements. Similarly the geometry of deformation of several members of a structure or machine must satisfy the condition that the deformed members must fit together (i.e., each member must satisfy the boundary condition of rotation, elongation, and deflection imposed by other members on the given member).

3. For a given member, the stresses at a given point, which satisfy equations of equilibrium, and the strains at that point, which satisfy the geometry of deformation, must also satisfy stress-strain relations for the material of which the member is made. For an assemblage of members, the role of the stress-strain relation is taken over by the load-deformation relation or relations for the member since the stress-strain relation at each point of the member was assumed to be satisfied in the derivation of the load-deformation relations.

Since condition 1 of equilibrium is satisfied for the statically indeterminate structure in Figure 1.10a, conditions 2 and 3 will be used in obtaining the additional relation among the loads needed to solve the problem. The geometry of deformation in Figure 1.10a must be such that point C of all three tension members will be located at the same point for the deformed structure. Thus there is a geometrical relation between the elongation of member DC and the elongations of members AC and BC. The geometrical equation relating the elongations when used with Equation (1–13) or Equation (1–18) gives the additional relations among the loads for linearly elastic material behavior. The solution of statically indeterminate problems when one or more of the members become plastic are considered in the next section.

Method of Solution. The recommended procedure for determining the redundant reactions of statically indeterminate structures may be outlined in five steps as follows:

Step 1. Draw a free-body diagram showing all loads and reactions.

Step 2. Determine the number of redundant reactions for the statically indeterminate structure.

Step 3. By considering the geometry of deformation, obtain the same number of independent relations among the elongations as there are redundant reactions.

Step 4. Write the equations of equilibrium for the free-body diagram. There will be more unknown reactions in these equations than there are equations of equilibrium. In fact the number of unknown reactions will exceed the number of equations of equilibrium by the number of redundant reactions.

Step 5. Using Equation (1–13) or Equation (1–18) to substitute for the elongations in the equations of Step 3, these equations are additional relations among the loads that are added to the equations of equilibrium to give a set of simultaneous equations with the number of unknown reactions equal to the number of equations. Solve the simultaneous equations for the unknown reactions.

The most difficult step in the solution of statically indeterminate problems is step 3. The deformations of most structures are so small that they are not observable by the naked eye; hence, the reader may find it difficult to picture the geometry of deformation of a given structure. Draw a picture of the structure before and after deformation with the deformations greatly exaggerated.

The five steps in the solution of statically indeterminate structures can best be demonstrated by solving illustrative problems.

Illustrative Problems

1.26. In Figure Pl.26*a* the steel member K has such great stiffness that it can be considered rigid. Also consider member K to be weightless. For the condition that $P = 0$, the three tension members are stress-free. Member AB is made of steel ($E = 30,000,000$ psi) and has a cross-sectional area of 0.10 in.^{2} Member CD is made of brass ($E = 15,000,000$ psi) and has a cross-sectional area of 0.20 in.^{2} Member FH is made of aluminum ($E = 10,000,000$ psi) and has a cross-sectional area at 0.30 in.^{2} If $P = 15,000$ lb, determine the load carried by each of the tension members and the elongation of each member. Note that the connection of dissimilar metals without insulation is not good engineering practice because contact between them may cause corrosion.

SOLUTION. Step 1 is satisfied by the free-body diagram of member K as shown in Figure P1.26*b*. For the parallel coplanar-force system there are three unknown reactions P_1, P_2, and P_3 and the known force P, and there are two equations of equilibrium; therefore, there is one redundant reaction (step 2). One boundary condition among the elongations of the

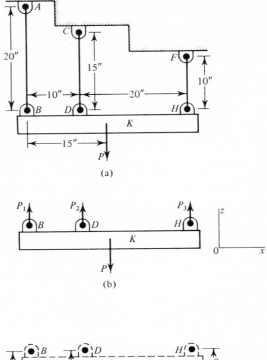

Fig. P 1.26.

three tension members for step 3 can be obtained by considering the position of member K before and after deformation as indicated in Figure P1.26c. It is not known whether the elongation of AB or FH will be greater. In Figure P1.26c the elongation of AB is assumed greater than that of FH. Fortunately, it does not matter which is assumed to be greater as long as member K is not assumed to be horizontal in the deformed configuration. The undeformed position of member K is indicated by dashed lines in Figure P1.26c; the elongations $e_1 = BB'$, $e_2 = DD'$, and $e_3 = HH'$ are greatly exaggerated in order to be observable. Let θ be the small angle between the horizontal line BH and the inclined line $B'H'$. Because $\sin \theta = \tan \theta = \theta$,

$$e_1 = e_2 + 10\theta,$$

$$e_1 = e_3 + 30\theta.$$

By eliminating θ between these two equations we obtain the desired boundary condition:

or
$$3e_1 - e_1 = 3e_2 - e_3$$
$$2e_1 = 3e_2 - e_3. \tag{a}$$

In step 4 the equations of equilibrium give

$$\sum F_z = 0, \qquad P_1 + P_2 + P_3 - 15{,}000 = 0, \tag{b}$$

$$\sum M_B = 0. \qquad 10P_2 + 30P_3 - 15{,}000(15) = 0. \tag{c}$$

The third equation among the three unknown reactions is obtained in step 5 by using Equation (1–13) and Equation (a).

$$\frac{2P_1 \ell_1}{A_1 E_1} = \frac{3P_2 \ell_2}{A_2 E_2} - \frac{P_3 \ell_3}{A_3 E_3}.$$

When the various quantities are substituted into the latter equation it becomes

$$\frac{2P_1(20)}{0.10(30{,}000{,}000)} = \frac{3P_2(15)}{0.20(15{,}000{,}000)} - \frac{P_3(10)}{0.30(10{,}000{,}000)}$$

or

$$8P_1 = 9P_2 - 2P_3. \tag{d}$$

Step 5 can now be completed. Equations (b), (c), and (d) are three equations in the three unknown reactions. Eliminate P_1 between Equations (b) and (d):

$$17P_2 + 6P_3 = 120{,}000.' \tag{e}$$

Eliminate P_3 between Equations (e) and (c), which gives

$$P_2 = 5{,}000 \text{ lb}.$$

Then, from Equation (e),

$$P_3 = 5{,}833 \text{ lb},$$

and, from Equation (b),

$$P_1 = 4{,}167 \text{ lb}.$$

The elongation of each of the three tension members can be obtained using Equation (1–13).

$$e_1 = \frac{4{,}167(20)}{0.10(30{,}000{,}000)} = 0.02778 \text{ in.}$$

$$e_2 = \frac{5{,}000(15)}{0.20(15{,}000{,}000)} = 0.02500 \text{ in.}$$

$$e_3 = \frac{5{,}833(10)}{0.30(10{,}000{,}000)} = 0.01944 \text{ in.}$$

1.27. The circular cross-section tension members AB and BC in Figure P1.27a have a diameter of 2 in., are connected at B, and are mounted in rigid walls at A and C when the temperature is 100°F. At this temperature the members are stress-free. As the temperature is lowered, the tension members tend to contract. We assume that the rigid walls do not move when the temperature is changed; therefore, tensile stresses are developed in the

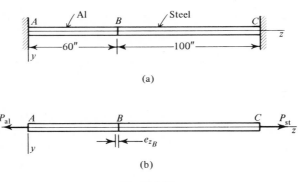

(a)

(b)

Fig. P 1.27.

tension members when the temperature is lowered. Determine the tensile force developed in the tension members and the movement of B when the temperature is lowered to 50°F. Member AB is made of an aluminum alloy ($E_{al} = 10{,}000{,}000$ psi and $\alpha_{al} = 0.0000130$ in./in.°F), and member BC is made of steel ($E_{st} = 30{,}000{,}000$ psi and $\alpha_{st} = 0.0000065$ in./in.°F.) (See note of caution concerning connecting dissimilar metals in Problem 1.26.)

SOLUTION. Step 1 is satisfied by the free-body diagram in Figure P1.27b that shows the unknown forces P_{al} and P_{st}. In step 2 we note that there is one equation of equilibrium and hence there is one redundant reaction.

The one boundary condition among the elongations needed for step 3 is given by the fact that the elongation of the member ABC is zero because the walls are rigidly fixed.

For step 4 the equilibrium force equation in the z-direction gives

$$\sum F_z = 0 = P_{st} - P_{al},$$

$$P_{st} = P_{al} = P. \tag{a}$$

The magnitude of P is obtained in step 5 by using Equation (1–18):

$$e_z = \int_0^{60} \left[\frac{P}{AE_{al}} + \alpha_{al}(\Delta t) \right] dz + \int_{60}^{160} \left[\frac{P}{AE_{st}} + \alpha_{st}(\Delta t) \right] dz = 0,$$

or

$$0 = \frac{60P}{10,000,000\pi} + 0.0000130(60)(-50)$$

$$+ \frac{100P}{30,000,000\pi} + 0.0000065(100)(-50). \tag{b}$$

From Equation (b),

$$P = 24,100 \text{ lb.}$$

The movement of B, e_{z_B} is given by Equation (1–18):

$$e_{z_B} = \int_0^{60} \left[\frac{P}{AE_{al}} + \alpha_{al}(\Delta t) \right] dz$$

$$= \frac{24,100(60)}{10,000,000\pi} + 0.0000130(-50)(60) = 0.0070 \text{ in.}$$

Thus, B moves to the right a distance of 0.0070 in.

Problems

1.28. The three tension members in Figure P1.28 are uniformly spaced along the 120,000-lb rigid slab. The two tension members B and D are made of steel ($\sigma_e = 45,000$ psi and $E = 30,000,000$ psi), have an initial length of 20 in., and a cross-sectional area of 1.0 in.^{2} Tension member C is made of an aluminum alloy ($\sigma_e = 50,000$ psi and $E = 10,000,000$ psi), has an initial length of 10 in., and a cross-sectional area of 2.0 in.^{2} (See note of caution in Problem 1.26 concerning connection between dissimilar metals.) (1) Determine the load carried by each of the three tension members. (2) What is the magnitude of an additional load P applied at the center of the slab to initiate yielding in any of the tension members?

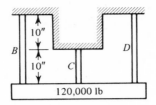

Fig. P 1.28.

1.29. The steel bar ($A = 1.0$ in.^{2} and $E = 30,000,000$ psi) in Figure P1.29 is welded to the ceiling and is subjected to an axial load P at its midlength. When $P = 0$, the bar has a clearance of 0.002 in. at the floor. Determine the stress at section a–a when $P = 10,000$ lb if it is assumed that the ceiling is rigid.

ans. $\sigma = -2,000$ psi.

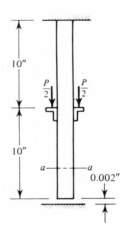

Fig. P 1.29.

1.30. A rigid slab weighing 10,000 lb is supported as shown in Figure P1.30 by three pin-ended steel tension members each 100-in. long. The figure shows that the final equilibrium position of the slab (elongations greatly exaggerated) is not necessarily horizontal. Find the tension load in each of the tension members. $E = 30 \times 10^6$ psi.

1.31. Three pin-ended tension members are arranged as shown in Figure P1.31. Members A and C are made of steel ($E = 30,000,000$ psi) and have the same cross-sectional area of 0.40 in.^{2} Member B is made of aluminum ($E = 10,000,000$ psi) and has a cross-sectional area of 0.30 in. (See note of caution in Problem 1.26 concerning

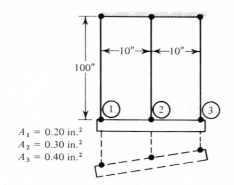

Fig. P 1.30.

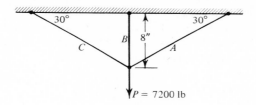

Fig. P 1.31.

connections between dissimilar metals.) Determine the stress in each member when $P = 7,200$ lb.

ans. $\sigma_{st} = 9,000$ psi; $\sigma_{al} = 12,000$ psi.

1.32. In Figure P1.32 a $\frac{1}{2}$-in. diameter steel bolt ($\alpha = 0.0000065$ in./in.°F and $E = 30,000,000$ psi) extends through an aluminum alloy ($\alpha = 0.0000130$ in./in.°F and $E = 10,000,000$ psi) circular cylinder with inside diameter of 0.60 in. and outside diameter of 0.80 in. (See note of caution in Problem 1.26 concerning connections between dissimilar metals). The cylinder has a length of 20 in. at 0°F. At 0°F the nut on the bolt is adjusted until the bolt will not move with respect to the cylinder but the members are stress-free. What is the stress in each member when both members are heated to 100°F? What is the final length of the cylinder?

ans. $\sigma_{st} = 5,310$ psi; $\sigma_{al} = 4,730$ psi;   final length = 20.01654 in.

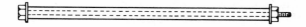

Fig. P 1.32.

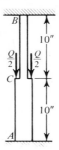

Fig. P 1.33.

1.33. The steel member in Figure P1.33 has a cross-sectional area of 4.00 in.^{2} from A to C and a cross-sectional area of 2.00 in.^{2} from C to B. The member is held by two rigid supports at A and B. When $Q = 0$, the member is stress-free. (1) If $Q = 24,000$ lb, determine the load carried by length AC and length CB. (2) What is the increase in temperature necessary for AC to carry all of the load?

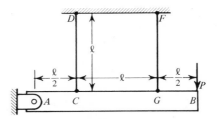

Fig. P 1.34.

1.34. In Figure P1.34 AB is a rigid bar that is supported at A by a frictionless pin and by wires CD and GF; each wire has a cross-sectional area of 0.10 in.^{2} and a length ℓ. Wire CD is made of steel, and GF is made of an aluminum alloy. (See Table 1.1 for properties.) If the maximum allowable elastic stress in either wire is 20,000 psi, determine the maximum allowable value of P.

ans. $P = 2,000$ lb.

1.35. A rigid beam BC in Figure P1.35 is supported by a steel wire DF ($E = 30,000,000$ psi and area of 0.010 in.^{2}) and an aluminum wire GH ($E = 10,000,000$ psi and area of 0.030 in.^{2}). If $P = 400$ lb, determine the stress in each wire.

ans. $\sigma_{DF} = 30,000$ psi and $\sigma_{GH} = 15,000$ psi.

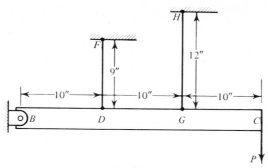

Fig. P 1.35.

1.36. Solve Problem 1.35 for the condition that when $P = 0$ wire DF was too long by 0.0030 in.

1.37. Solve Problem 1.35 for the condition that in addition to $P = 400$ lb the temperature is decreased by 50°F.

ans. $\sigma_{st} = 27,600$ psi and $\sigma_{al} = 15,400$ psi.

1.38. Let $P = 1,000$ lb be the load acting at the free end of the rigid bar in Problem 1.34. Determine the temperature change such that the aluminum wire carries all of the load.

1.39. Solve Problem 1.31 for the condition that the holes in member B were made oversize and the initial clearance is 0.0030 in.

ans. $\sigma_{st} = 10,400$ psi and $\sigma_{al} = 10,100$ psi.

1.40. Solve Problem 1.31 for the condition that the temperature is increased 50°F.

1.6. Elastic-Plastic and Fully Plastic Loads for Statically Indeterminate Structures

Once yielding starts in a given member of a statically indeterminate structure, Equation (1–18) is no longer the load-elongation relation for that member. For the alloy steel in Figure 1.4, the load-elongation relation for small plastic strains is given by curve AB for plastic conditions. Because this curve may have a different shape for each material, it is convenient to consider only those materials for which curve AB is horizontal at the fully plastic load, P_{fp}, given by the relation

$$P_{fp} = \sigma_e A. \tag{1–19}$$

where σ_e is the yield point (see Fig. 1.7c) and A is the cross-sectional area of the centrally loaded member. Note that the load given by Equation (1–19) for a given member is independent of the elongation of that member.

If the members of a statically indeterminate structure are made of materials for which Equation (1–19) is valid, the solution of the plastic problem is simpler than the elastic solution once yielding starts in one or more of the members. The simplification is introduced by the fact that the load in a member that has yielded is given by Equation (1–19), and this load is independent of further deformations of the structure. Because the load-elongation relation for a plastically deformed member is different for loading than for unloading, it is assumed that the loads on the structure are not decreased once yielding starts in one or more of the members.

Note that the number of unknown reactions decreases by one for each member that yields. When the number of yielded members equals the number of redundant reactions, the problem can be solved by using equations of equilibrium alone. An elastic-plastic solution is obtained when one or more of the centrally loaded members remains elastic. A fully plastic solution is obtained when all of the members have either yielded or yielding is impending. These solutions are indicated in the illustrative problem that follows.

Illustrative Problem

1.41. Let a rigid bar AB be supported by the three pin-connected members CD, NF, and GH as shown in Figure P1.41a. Members CD and NF are made of the same material with yield point σ_{e1} and modulus of elasticity E_1, have the same length ℓ_1, and the same cross-sectional area A_1. Member GH has a cross-sectional area A_2, length ℓ_2, and is made of a material with yield point σ_{e2} and modulus of elasticity E_2. Determine the ratio of the fully plastic load P_{fp} to maximum elastic load P_e. (1) What is the magnitude of this ratio when $\ell_1 = \ell_2$, $A_1 = A_2$, $\sigma_{e1} = \sigma_{e2}$, and $E_1 = E_2 = E$? (2) Determine the magnitude of the ratio and plot the load displacement curve for bar AB when $\ell_2 = 3\ell_1 = 60$ in., $A_2 = 2A_1 = 2$ in.^{2}, $\sigma_{e2} = 2\sigma_{e1} = 60{,}000$ psi, and $E_1 = E_2 = 30{,}000{,}000$ psi.

SOLUTION. The elastic solution is obtained using the method of Section 1.5. The free-body diagram in Figure P1.41b indicates that there are three unknowns. Because there are two equations of equilibrium, the order of redundancy is one. The boundary condition needed to determine the redundant reaction is specified by the condition that all three tension members elongate the same amount because of symmetry; that is,

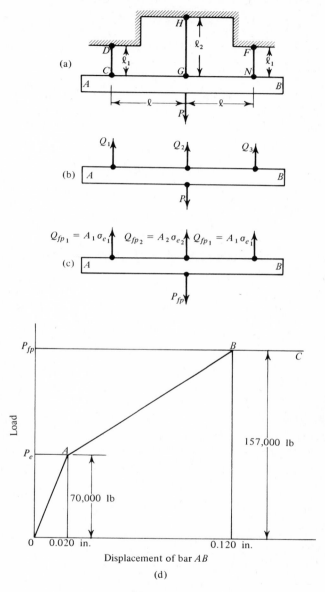

Fig. P 1.41.

$e_1 = e_2 = e_3$. Equations of equilibrium give

$$\sum F_z = 0 = P - Q_1 - Q_2 - Q_3,$$

$$\sum M_G = 0 = Q_3 \ell - Q_1 \ell,$$

which reduce to

$$Q_2 = P - 2Q_1. \tag{a}$$

The additional relation among the unknowns is obtained from the boundary condition $e_1 = e_2$ and Equation (1–13), which gives

$$\frac{Q_1 \ell_1}{A_1 E_1} = \frac{Q_2 \ell_2}{A_2 E_2},$$

or, solving for Q_2, we obtain

$$Q_2 = Q_1 \frac{\ell_1}{\ell_2} \frac{A_2}{A_1} \frac{E_2}{E_1}. \tag{b}$$

The magnitude of the redundant reaction Q_1 is given by eliminating Q_2 from Equations (a) and (b).

$$Q_1 = \frac{P}{2 + (\ell_1/\ell_2)(A_2/A_1)(E_2/E_1)}. \tag{c}$$

The substitution of this value of Q_1 in Equation (b) gives

$$Q_2 = \frac{\ell_1}{\ell_2} \frac{A_2}{A_1} \frac{E_2}{E_1} \left[\frac{P}{2 + (\ell_1/\ell_2)(A_2/A_1)(E_2/E_1)} \right] \tag{d}$$

Elastic-Limit Load P_e. The elastic-limit load is the load that will initiate yielding in one of the tension members. The condition specified in parts (1) and (2) of this problem that $E_1 = E_2$ dictates that yielding will initiate in members CD and NF. Since $Q_1 = \sigma_{e1} A_1$ when $P = P_e$, the magnitude of P_e is given by Equation (c) as follows:

$$P_e = \sigma_{e1} A_1 \left[2 + \frac{\ell_1}{\ell_2} \frac{A_2}{A_1} \frac{E_2}{E_1} \right]. \tag{e}$$

Fully Plastic Load P_{fp}. The fully plastic load is the load for which all three tension members are yielding. When the maximum elastic load P_e is applied, the load given by Equation d for tension member GH is less than or equal to the yield load $\sigma_{e2} A_2$ for that member. As the load P is increased, the load carried by members CD and NF each remain equal to $\sigma_{e1} A_1$ while member GH takes the additional load until the load in GH is equal to $\sigma_{e2} A_2$.

The load $P = P_{fp}$ required to initiate yielding in member GH is the fully plastic load for the structure. At the fully plastic load the stress in each of the three tension members is at the yield point. Since the strain in each tension member is indeterminate at the yield point, the displacement of bar AB is indeterminate at the fully plastic load. The loads in the three tension members at the fully plastic load are shown in Figure P1.41c. The equilibrium force equation gives

$$\sum F_z = 0 = P_{fp} - 2\sigma_{e1}A_1 - \sigma_{e2}A_2,$$

$$P_{fp} = 2\sigma_{e1}A_1 + \sigma_{e2}A_2 = \sigma_{e1}A_1[2 + (\sigma_{e2}/\sigma_{e1})(A_2/A_1)]. \tag{f}$$

Ratio of P_{fp} to P_e. The ratio of the fully plastic load to maximum elastic load can be obtained using Equations (e) and (f).

$$\frac{P_{fp}}{P_e} = \frac{2 + (\sigma_{e2}/\sigma_{e1})(A_2/A_1)}{2 + (\ell_1/\ell_2)(A_2/A_1)(E_2/E_1)} \tag{g}$$

Solution to Part (1). In part (1) all of the three tension members are identical in length and cross-sectional area. Thus,

$$\frac{P_{fp}}{P_e} = 1,$$

and the fully plastic load is equal to the maximum elastic load.

Solution to Part (2). The substitution of the data in part (1) in Equation (g) gives

$$\frac{P_{fp}}{P_c} = \frac{2 + (2)(2)}{2 + (1/3)(2)(1)} = 2.25.$$

which indicates that for part (2) of the problem the fully plastic load is 2.25 times greater than the maximum elastic load. Also, for part (2) of the problem the load-displacement curve for the movement of the bar AB can now be constructed. The maximum elastic load is given by Equation (e):

$$P_e = (30,000)(1)\left[2 + \frac{(20)(2)E}{(60)(2)(1)E}\right] = 70,000 \text{ lb.}$$

The displacement of bar AB when P_e is applied is equal to the maximum elastic elongation of tension member CD

$$e_{e1} = \epsilon_{e1}\ell_1 = \frac{\sigma_{e1}\ell_1}{E} = \frac{(30,000)(20)}{30,000,000} = 0.020 \text{ in.}$$

The minimum displacement of bar AB at the fully plastic load is the maximum elastic elongation of tension member GH:

$$e_{e2} = \epsilon_{e2}\ell_2 = \frac{\sigma_{e2}\ell_2}{E} = \frac{(60,000)(60)}{30,000,000} = 0.120 \text{ in.}$$

The load-displacement curve for bar AB for part (2) is shown in Figure P1.41d. Note that the load-displacement curve is made up of three straight lines. Line OA represents the elastic solution, line AB represents the elastic-plastic solution, line BC represents the fully-plastic solution.

Problems

It is convenient in the following problems to assume that each material exhibits a yield point so that Equation (1–19) is valid. Although many structural metals strain harden, the assumption that the stress-strain diagram is flat topped at the yield strength does not introduce a serious error and the solution is conservative.

1.42. A load of 50,000 lb in addition to the 120,000-lb slab must be carried by the three tension members of the structure described in Problem 1.28. (1) Determine the load in each of the three tension members. (2) What is the displacement of the slab when these loads are applied?

ans.   (1) $F_B = F_D = 45,000$ lb and $F_C = 80,000$ lb;   (2) Displacement = 0.040 in.

1.43.   What is the fully plastic load for the structure described in Problem 1.28?

1.44.   The member loaded as indicated in Problem 1.29 is made of structural steel, which has a yield point $\sigma_e = 36,000$ psi. Determine the magnitude of P to initiate yielding in the member and the fully plastic value of the load.

ans. $P = 66,000$ lb and $P_{fp} = 72,000$ lb.

1.45. Let the steel tension members in Problem 1.31 have a yield point $\sigma_e = 36,000$ psi, and let the aluminum alloy have a yield strength of $\sigma_e = 75,000$ psi. Determine the load in each of the tension members when $P = 32,000$ lb.

1.46.   Using the material properties in Problem 1.45 for the structure in Problem 1.31, determine the fully plastic load.

ans. $P_{fp} = 36,900$ lb.

1.47. Let the steel wire in Problem 1.35 have a yield stress of $\sigma_e = 150,000$ psi and the aluminum wire have a yield strength of $\sigma_e = 75,000$ psi. Determine the fully plastic load P_{fp}.

1.7. Axially Centrically Loaded Members with Abrupt Changes in Cross Section

Load-carrying members having constant cross section are the exception rather than the rule. There are many reasons why most members have abrupt changes in cross section. Often the shape of the member has to be altered in order to apply loads, to attach other members to the given member, or to locate other members with respect to the given member. These shapes are

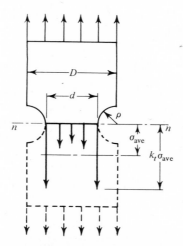

Fig. 1.11. Stress distribution at abrupt change in cross section.

illustrated in Figures 1.11, 1.12, and 1.13 for members subjected to axial centric loading and consisting of flat bars containing semicircular grooves, fillets, and circular hole, respectively. In order to demonstrate the strain distribution at the abrupt change in section, a rubber model was made of the flat bar with semicircular grooves. A square grid was marked on the surface

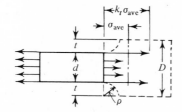

Fig. 1.12. Stress distribution at fillet.

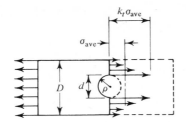

Fig. 1.13. Stress distribution at hole.

before loading. The deformed grid after loading is shown in Figure 1.14 where it is indicated that the strain distribution is not uniform and that the maximum strain occurs at the root of the grooves.

For linearly elastic conditions the stress distribution is not uniform at an abrupt change in section since the stress is directly proportional to the strain. The stress distributions are shown in Figures 1.11, 1.12, and 1.13 for the three types of abrupt changes in section for elastic tension members subjected to axial centric loading. In each case the stress $\sigma_{ave} = P/A$ is the stress given by Equation (1–10) for the assumption that the stress distribution is uniform; the area A is the net area equal to bd (where b is the thickness of the bar) in Figures 1.11 and 1.12 and equal to $b(D - d)$ in Figure 1.13. The ratio of the maximum stress at each change in section to σ_{ave} is called the

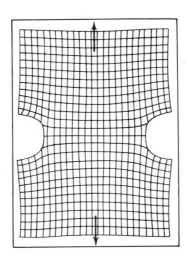

Fig. 1.14.   Effect of abrupt change in cross section on elastic strain distribution at the change in section.

theoretical or elastic stress-concentration factor and is denoted by k_t. Thus,

$$\sigma_{\max} = k_t \frac{P}{A}. \qquad (1\text{--}20)$$

The magnitude of the theoretical stress-concentration factor k_t depends on the geometry of the member, that is, on the relative values of the dimensions of the member in the neighborhood of the stress concentration. Values of k_t for the types of abrupt change of section indicated in Figures 1.11, 1.12, and 1.13 are given as ordinates to the curves in Figure 1.15; the abscissas for

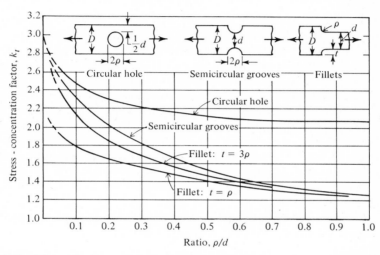

Fig. 1.15.   Theoretical stress-concentration factors for three types of abrupt changes in cross section.

the curves are values of the ratio ρ/d, which takes account of the geometry or shape and indicates the rate of the change in section. In a limited number of cases, exact load-stress relations can be derived for the member containing the stress concentration, and values of k_t can be calculated. In most cases, however, values of k_t are determined using one of several different experimental techniques, such as photoelasticity or strain measurements. In later chapters when other types of loading, such as bending or torsion are considered, the magnitude of k_t will be given for such members. The values of k_t for a given member of a given shape will be different for each type of loading.

An important fact should be noted regarding the two curves in Figure 1.15 for tension members having fillets. If the radius ρ at the change in section is relatively large ($\rho/d > 0.5$), the value of k_t is relatively small. On the other hand, when the radius ρ is relatively small, the value of k_t is relatively large. This fact means that, whenever possible, a fillet in a member should have as large a radius as practicable, so that the abrupt change in section is made as gradual as feasible. Likewise, any other change in cross section should be made as gradual as possible so that k_t will be small.

    Saint-Venant's Principle. It will be noted that, while the stress distributions in Figures 1.11, 1.12, and 1.13 are nonuniform at the abrupt change in section, the stress distributions at short distances from the abrupt changes in section are shown as uniform. The following question arises. How far along the member does each abrupt change in section influence the stress distributions? In 1853 Barre de Saint-Venant stated a principle that the effect of local disturbances, such as at abrupt changes in section, disappears rapidly at sections in the member only a short distance from the disturbance. This principle is easily verified experimentally as illustrated by Figure 1.14, which shows that the strain distribution near the upper and lower ends of the rubber member are nearly uniform. A safe distance is a distance equal to the largest cross-sectional dimension. For instance, in Figure 1.12 the stress distribution would be approximately uniform at a distance d to the left of the abrupt change in section or at a distance D to the right of the abrupt change in section.

1.8. Fatigue Strength for Repeated Cycles of Complete Reversals of Tensile-Compressive Stresses

    If an axially centrically loaded specimen is subjected to repeated cycles of alternately applied tensile load and compressive load of equal value, it may fail by fracture without visual evidence of plastic deformation even though the specimen is made of a ductile material. Fracture of a load-carrying member by repeated cycles of loads is commonly referred to as fatigue failure. Failure by fatigue starts by the initiation of one or more small cracks usually at a point of maximum stress in the member. The maximum stress could be caused by an abrupt change in cross section of the member or by an abrupt change in the structure of the material such as at an inclusion of foreign material or at a void in the material. Continued applications of the loads cause the crack or cracks to grow until that section of the member is no longer able to carry the applied load. At that instance the member ruptures. The mechanism of the initiation and growth of fatigue cracks is complex and not completely understood. The discussion that follows will not be concerned with the mechanism of fatigue failure but with the problem of determining the material property used in the design of members subjected to fatigue loading.

The material property needed to design members subjected to fatigue loading is the fatigue strength of the material, that is, the maximum stress the material can resist for a given number of cycles of the repeated stress. This property cannot be obtained from the stress–strain diagram considered in Section 1.2. Usually special fatigue-testing machines are used to subject specimens to fatigue loading; however, some types of testing machines that are used to obtain data for the stress–strain diagram may also be used to create the alternately applied push-pull load for fatigue strength tests.

Several specimens are required to determine the fatigue strength of a given material for completely reversed loading. Each specimen is subjected to equal tensile and compressive stresses, which are applied alternately a large number of times. The testing machine is set so that the maximum value of the stress is constant throughout the test. A typical specimen is shown in Figure 1.16.

Fig. 1.16. Typical tension-compression fatigue specimen.

It has been found that the number of cycles to cause fracture depends on the magnitude of the maximum stress, but when several specimens are tested at the same stress, there may be a wide difference in the number of cycles to failure. A specimen stressed nearly to the static ultimate strength of the material in each cycle will fracture in a small number of cycles. By lowering the load, and therefore the stress, on successive specimens, the number of cycles to produce fracture increases with a decrease in stress.

The results of fatigue tests are usually plotted in a graph with logarithmic scale in which ordinates represent stress and abscissas represent the number of cycles to fracture the specimen. Such a graph is called a σ–N diagram.

Figure 1.17 shows that 13 specimens* of 18 per cent chromium and 9 per cent nickel stainless steel were tested. One specimen was tested at each of the following stresses: 100,000 psi, 90,000 psi, 65,000 psi, and 50,000 psi; two specimens were tested at 110,000 psi, 51,000 psi, and 49,000 psi; and three specimens were tested at 58,000 psi. When more than one specimen is tested at a given stress, there is a difference in the number of cycles N to cause failure. This difference in the values of N is sometimes called "scatter" in the data and serves to illustrate the statistical nature of the properties of materials. However, there were not enough specimens of stainless steel tested to show how much statistical effect really exists.

In order to further illustrate the statistical effect on the number of cycles N to cause failure, there were 101 specimens† of the aluminum alloy 2024–T4 extruded rod tested; the results are shown in Figure 1.17. Ten specimens were tested at each of the following stresses: 50,000 psi, 40,000 psi, 27,000 psi, 22,000 psi, and 19,000 psi; eleven specimens were tested at 20,000 psi; and twenty specimens were tested at 30,000 psi and at 25,000 psi, respectively. Note that the more specimens tested at a given stress, the more scatter there is in the number of cycles N to cause failure. The ratio of the greatest value of N to the least value of N when several specimens are tested at a given stress is of interest here. At 50,000 psi with 10 specimens the ratio is 1.87; at 40,000 psi with 10 specimens it is 1.92; at 30,000 psi with 20 specimens it is 12.0; at 27,000 psi with 10 specimens it is 1.90; at 25,000 psi with 20 specimens it is 7.70; at 22,000 psi with 10 specimens it is 4.15; at 20,000 psi with 11 specimens it is 16.7; and at 19,000 psi with 10 specimens it is 11.0.

The preceding detailed examination of the data plotted in Figure 1.17 shows that there is no exact relationship between the stress and the number of cycles N to cause failure of a specimen. The points representing the test data all lie within a band across the graph as shown by the shaded lines that are drawn above and below the data points for each of the two materials tested.

* W. J. Bell and P. P. Benham, ASTM Special Technical Publication no. 338, 1962.
† H. F. Hardrath and E. C. Utley, Jr., NACA Technical Note 2798, October 1952.

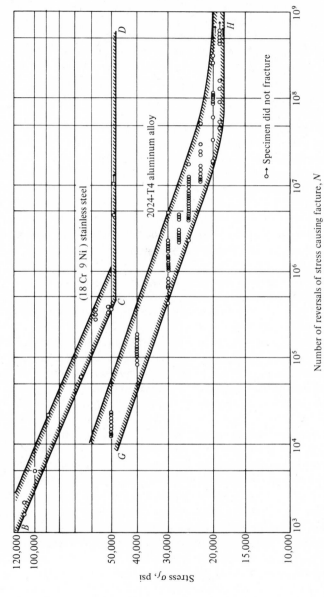

Fig. 1.17. σ-N diagram for (18 cr 9 ni) stainless steel and 2024-T4 aluminum alloy for completely reversed loading.

The fatigue strength σ_f of a material is defined as the magnitude of the stress that can be completely reversed without causing fracture of a tension-compression specimen for any number of cycles less than N. Although this quantity is not well defined, the curve representing the relation between σ_f and N is assumed to be given by the lower shaded curve BCD for the 18 Cr 9 Ni. stainless steel and by the lower shaded curve GH for the aluminum alloy 2024–T4 in Figure 1.17. For example, for $N = 100,000$ cycles of stress in Figure 1.17, the fatigue strength is $\sigma_f = 60,000$ psi for the stainless steel and $\sigma_f = 35,000$ psi for the aluminum alloy.

Some materials, steels for instance, have a limiting fatigue strength called the fatigue limit, or endurance limit σ_r below which the specimen can be stressed an indefinitely large number of times without fracture. For these materials the σ–N diagram becomes horizontal at the fatigue limit. The fatigue limit for the stainless steel in Figure 1.17 is $\sigma_r = 47,000$ psi.

1.9. Fatigue Strength for Repeated Cycles of Unequal Tensile and Compressive Stresses

Most structural and machine members are subjected to loads that are not completely reversed; that is, the stresses at a given point on a given plane in the member are cycled from a tensile stress to a lower stress not equal in magnitude to the tensile stress.

For the purpose of discussing cycles of unequal stresses, let Figure 1.18a represent a stress-time graph of a completely reversed cycle of stress where $\sigma_{min} = -\sigma_{max}$, where σ_{min} is the value of the maximum compressive stress and σ_{max} is the maximum tensile stress; the ratio of σ_{min} to σ_{max} is defined as r and, in Figure 1.18a, $r = \sigma_{min}/\sigma_{max} = -1$. Let Figure 1.18b represent a cycle of stress in which $\sigma_{min} = -\sigma_{max}/2$ or $r = -\frac{1}{2}$. Again, let Figure 1.18c represent a cycle of stress in which both σ_{max} and σ_{min} are tensile stresses where $\sigma_{min} = \sigma_{max}/2$ or $r = \frac{1}{2}$.

The problem posed here is how to determine the value of the fatigue strength, σ_{max} for a given value of N and a given value of the ratio r. Fortunately, the value of σ_{max} can be found from the fatigue strength σ_f for complete reversals of stress for the specified N (see Fig. 1.17) and the ultimate tensile strength of the material as obtained from the stress-strain diagram (see Section 1.3). The values of σ_f and σ_u are used to construct what is called a Goodman diagram as shown in Figure 1.18d.

Goodman Diagram. This diagram is constructed by taking the perpendicular axes OI and OE in Figure 1.18d and drawing a straight line AOC bisecting the angle between OI and OE. The point C on OAC is selected so

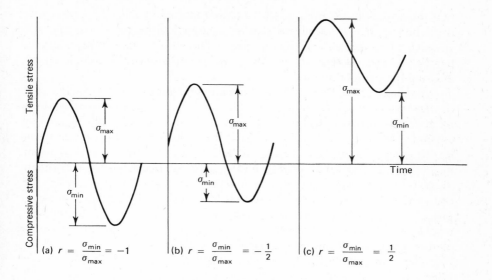

(a) $r = \dfrac{\sigma_{min}}{\sigma_{max}} = -1$ (b) $r = \dfrac{\sigma_{min}}{\sigma_{max}} = -\dfrac{1}{2}$ (c) $r = \dfrac{\sigma_{min}}{\sigma_{max}} = \dfrac{1}{2}$

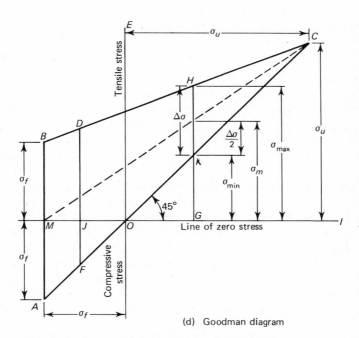

(d) Goodman diagram

Fig. 1.18. Range of stress for specimens without notch.

that the ordinate to C is equal to the tensile ultimate strength σ_u. The point A on the line AOC is selected so that its ordinate is equal to $-\sigma_f$, the fatigue strength for complete reversals of stress. The straight line AMB is drawn parallel to OE so that $AM = MB = \sigma_f$. The diagram is completed by drawing the straight line BC.

To make use of the diagram, draw any line parallel to OE, such as DF or HG, intersecting the lines AOC and BC. The ordinates to the points of intersection with AOC and BC give the values of σ_{max} and σ_{min}. For example, $JD = \sigma_{max}$ and $FJ = \sigma_{min}$ for the ratio $r = -\frac{1}{2}$ or, that is, when $\sigma_{min} = -\sigma_{max}/2$; and $GH = \sigma_{max}$ and $KG = \sigma_{min}$ for the ratio $r = \frac{1}{2}$ when $\sigma_{min} = \sigma_{max}/2$. The values of σ_{max} and σ_{min} determined from the Goodman diagram correspond to the same number of cycles to failure N as σ_f for completely reversed stresses. Note that the Goodman diagram is an empirical means of obtaining σ_{max} for a specified r when σ_f for completely reversed stress and σ_u are known for the material. The reliability of the Goodman diagram for this purpose is widely recognized.

The data usually available for a given problem are the values of the ratio r, the fatigue strength σ_f, and the ultimate strength σ_u. By making use of similar triangles in Figure 1.18d an expression for computing σ_{max} in terms of r, σ_f, and σ_u has been derived and is given by the equation:

$$\sigma_{max} = \frac{2\sigma_f}{1 - r + (\sigma_f/\sigma_u)(1 + r)} = \frac{\sigma_{min}}{r}. \tag{1–21}$$

The validity of the Goodman diagram and Equation 1–21 have been confirmed by many experimental investigations.*

The difference $\sigma_{max} - \sigma_{min} = \Delta\sigma$ is called the range of stress. One half of the range of stress $\Delta\sigma/2$ is called the alternating stress, and $\sigma_m = (\sigma_{max} + \sigma_{min})/2$ is called the mean stress. These quantities are shown in Figure 1.18d.

Effect of Stress Concentration. The effect of a fillet (Fig. 1.12), a hole (Figure 1.13), or some other abrupt change in cross section is to reduce the fatigue strength of a member. Let k_f represent the effect of such a notch on reducing the strength of a member that is subjected to repeated loads. The factor k_f is called a *strength reduction factor*; the strength of the material is not considered to be reduced by the stress raiser, but the strength (load-carrying capacity) of the member is reduced. For materials that are extremely sensitive to stress concentrations, such as ideal elastic materials, the factor k_f is equal to the theoretical stress concentration factor k_t, as discussed in

* James O Smith, "The Effect of Range of Stress on the Fatigue Strength of Metals," Bulletin no. 334, Engineering Experiment Station, University of Illinois, 1942.

Section 1.7. But for most engineering materials, the factor k_f may be some-what less than the theoretical stress concentration factor k_t as discussed in *Advanced Mechanics of Materials.*[*]

A peculiarity of fatigue test results for notched members subjected to a range of stress is that the strength reduction factor k_f is applied only to the alternating component of the load and not to the mean load. Thus, the mean stress is calculated by disregarding the effect of the notch, that is, by assuming that $k_f = 1.00$. Stresses calculated to assume that $k_f = 1.00$ are called nominal stresses. It is convenient to have all stress calculations as nominal stresses when working with notched members. This is done by adjusting the Goodman diagram to include the effect of k_f in the diagram as explained in the paragraph that follows.

Let unnotched specimens made of a given material be subjected to completely reversed cycles of stress to determine the fatigue strength $MB = \sigma_f$ and $MA = -\sigma_f$ as shown in Figure 1.19. Straight lines BC and

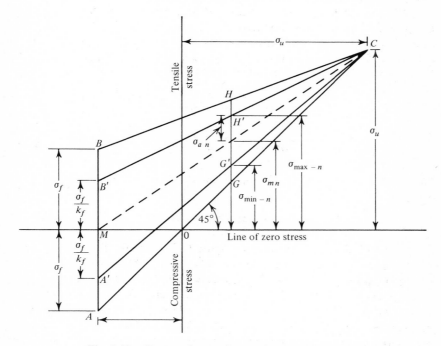

Fig. 1.19. Range of stress for specimens with notch.

[*] F. B. Seely and J. O. Smith, *Advanced Mechanics of Materials*, John Wiley & Sons, New York, 1952.

AC represent the Goodman diagram for the material in the unnotched specimens. Notched specimens of the same material are subjected to completely reversed cycles of stress to determine the nominal fatigue strength represented by MB' and MA' in Figure 1.19. The ratio of MB to MB' is defined as the strength reduction factor k_f; therefore, $MB' = \sigma_f/k_f$ and $MA' = -\sigma_f/k_f$. Straight lines $B'C$ and $A'C$ represent the adjusted Goodman diagram, which includes the effect of the strength-reduction factor k_f. For any vertical line, such as GH' in Figure 1.19, the ordinates representing nominal values of maximum normal stress, σ_{max-n}, and nominal values of minimum normal stress, σ_{min-n}, for the notched specimens are represented as shown by the ordinates to H' (σ_{max-n}) and K' (σ_{min-n}). An equation similar to Equation (1–21) can be derived:

$$\sigma_{max-n} = \frac{(2\sigma_f/k_f)}{1 - r + (\sigma_f/k_f\sigma_u)(1 + r)} = \frac{\sigma_{min-n}}{r}. \qquad (1\text{–}22)$$

It is desirable that actual values of σ_{max} and σ_{min} be determined. The derivation of these quantities requires that the nominal value of the mean normal stress σ_{mn} and the nominal value of the alternating stress σ_{an} be defined as follows: $\sigma_{mn} = (\sigma_{max-n} + \sigma_{min-n})/2$ and $\sigma_{an} = (\sigma_{max-n} - \sigma_{min-n})/2$. Values of σ_{max} and σ_{min} are given by the following relations:

$$\sigma_{max} = \sigma_{mn} + k_f\sigma_{an} = \frac{k_f + 1}{2}\sigma_{max-n} - \frac{k_f - 1}{2}\sigma_{min-n} \qquad (1\text{–}23)$$

$$\sigma_{min} = \sigma_{mn} - k_f\sigma_{an} = -\frac{k_f - 1}{2}\sigma_{max-n} + \frac{k_f + 1}{2}\sigma_{min-n}. \qquad (1\text{–}24)$$

Note that $\sigma_{min-n} = r\sigma_{max-n}$ in Equations (1–23) and (1–24).

Illustrative Problem

1.48. The tension member in Figure 1.12 is made of 2024–T4 aluminum alloy, which has an ultimate strength of $\sigma_u = 68,000$ psi and whose fatigue properties are given in Figure 1.17 for complete reversals of stress. The thickness of the member is $\frac{1}{4}$ in. The other dimensions of the member are $D = 2.36$ in., $d = 2.00$ in., and $t = \rho = 0.18$ in. The tension member is subjected to a range in tension load from $P_{min} = 4,000$ lb to P_{max}. Determine P_{max} required to produce fracture of the tension member in 1,000,000 cycles of load. Also determine σ_{max} and σ_{min}. Assume that $k_f = k_t$ for the fillet.

SOLUTION. The theoretical stress-concentration factor k_t for the fillet can be obtained from the curve, fillet $t = \rho$, in Figure 1.15. The magnitude of

ρ/d is 0.09. As read from the curve,

$$k_t = 1.80,$$

but

$$k_f = k_t = 1.80.$$

The fatigue strength of 2024–T4 aluminum alloy for 1,000,000 completely reversed cycles of stress can be read from Figure 1.17; $\sigma_f = 27,000$ psi. The stress corresponding to point G' in Figure 1.19 is given by Equation 1–10 when $P = 4000$ lb:

$$\sigma_{min-n} = \frac{P_{min}}{A} = \frac{4000}{0.25(2)} = 8,000 \text{ psi},$$

The magnitude of σ_{max-n} can be determined once r is determined since $\sigma_{max-n} = \sigma_{min-n}/r$. Substituting this value for σ_{max-n} and values for σ_f, σ_u, and k_f in Equation (1–22) gives

$$\frac{8,000}{r} = \frac{2(27,000)/1.8}{1 - r + [27,000/1.8(68,000)](1 + r)},$$

$$r = 0.269.$$

The magnitude of σ_{max-n} is given by the relation

$$\sigma_{max-n} = \frac{\sigma_{min-n}}{r} = \frac{8,000}{0.269} = 29,740 \text{ psi}.$$

The magnitude of P_{max} is given by the relation

$$P_{max} = \sigma_{max-n}A = 29,740(0.25)(2) = 14,870 \text{ lb}.$$

The magnitudes of σ_{max} and σ_{min} are given by Equations (1–23) and (1–24).

$$\sigma_{max} = \frac{1.8 + 1}{2}(29,740) - \frac{1.8 - 1}{2}(8,000) = 38,400 \text{ psi},$$

$$\sigma_{min} = -\frac{1.8 - 1}{2}(29,740) + \frac{1.8 + 1}{2}(8,000) = -700 \text{ psi}.$$

Problems

In the problems that follow, the strength-reduction factor k_f is assumed to be equal to the theoretical stress-concentration factor k_t.

1.49. A tension member is subjected to completely reversed loads. It has a thickness of 1 in. and contains semicircular grooves (see Fig. 1.11). The other dimensions of the member are $D = 5$ in., $d = 4$ in., and $\rho = \frac{1}{2}$ in. The member is made of the stainless steel, which has a fatigue limit $\sigma_r = 47,000$ psi shown in Figure 1.17 and an ultimate strength of $\sigma_u = 150{,}000$ psi. Determine the maximum load that can be completely reversed completely reversed an indefinite number of cycles.

1.50.   Let the load on the member in Problem 1.49 vary between the limits from zero to P. Determine the maximum value of P if the load cycle is repeated 10^7 cycles without fracture. Also determine σ_{max} and σ_{min}.

ans. $k_f = k_t = 2.24$; $r = 0$; $P_{max} = 147{,}200$ lb; $\sigma_{max} = 59{,}600$ psi; $\sigma_{min} = -22{,}800$ psi.

1.51.   The member in Figure P1.51 is subjected to completely reversed, repeated load P. The material in the member has the following properties: $\sigma_e = 55{,}000$ psi,

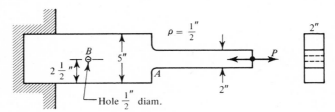

Fig. P 1.51.

$\sigma_u = 85{,}000$ psi, $\sigma_r = 42{,}000$ psi. Determine the maximum value of P that can be completely reversed completely reversed an indefinite number of cycles.

1.52.   Solve Problem 1.51 if the member is subjected to loading such that $r = \frac{1}{2}$.
1.53.   Solve Problem 1.51 if the member is subjected to loading such that $r = -\frac{1}{2}$.
1.54.   In Problem 1.1 let the ultimate strength of the steel in the pump rod be $\sigma_u = 100{,}000$ psi, and let the fatigue limit from completely reversed direct tension-compression fatigue tests be $\sigma_r = 50{,}000$ psi. Determine the maximum value of the load Q on the piston at the bottom of the oil well, based on the assumption that failure will occur by fatigue fracture of the rod at a section away from the joints in the rod. Assume that on the return stroke (i.e., as the rod is going downward) the load in the rod is the weight of the rod.
1.55.   Solve Problem 1.54 if there is a stress concentration at the upper end of the rod and $k_t = 1.85$.

ans. $Q = 1{,}735$ lb.

1.10.   True Stress and True Strain

In Section 1.1 normal stress at a given point on a given area in a member is defined as the internal force per unit area acting at the point perpendicular to the area. Also, normal strain is defined as the increase (or decrease) in length per unit length in a given direction in a body as it is deformed.

True Stress. When the foregoing definition of stress was used in Section 1.2 to compute the stress for a tension specimen, the stress was computed using $\sigma_z = P/A$, in which P is the load and $A = 0.20$ in.^{2} is the area of the cross section that had a diameter of $D = 0.505$ in. at the start of the test. The original area of 0.20 in.^{2} was used for all stress calculations. However, as the load P increased, the true diameter D_t decreased because of Poisson's ratio. Hence, the cross-sectional area A_t, which corresponds to the load P, continuously decreases with the increase in the load P. The true stress σ_{zt} in a tension specimen is defined as

$$\sigma_{zt} = \frac{P}{A_t}. \tag{1-25}$$

From the definition of true stress it can be seen that the true diameter D_t of the specimen must be measured when the value of the load P is measured. Thus, in Equation (1–25) the load P and the diameter D_t used in computing $A_t = \pi D_t^2/4$ must be measured simultaneously. In the tension test the load is increased by increments and after each increase the diameter D_t is measured.

True Strain. Like the definition for true stress, the definition of true strain is based on measured values of the elongation e_z of the original gage length ℓ. The true gage length ℓ_t is defined as

$$\ell_t = \ell + e_z. \tag{1-26}$$

Hence ℓ_t, like A_t does not remain constant during the tension test. In the tension test the load is increased by small increments and after each small increase the increment de_z of increase in gage length is measured. But de_z is the change in length $d\ell_t$ of the true gage length. Thus, one increment $d\epsilon_{zt}$ of the true strain is defined as

$$d\epsilon_{zt} = \frac{d\ell_t}{\ell_t}. \tag{1-27}$$

The true strain is defined as the sum of the increments of true strain, that is,

$$\epsilon_{zt} = \sum d\epsilon_{zt}. \tag{1-28}$$

If the increments are taken over very small changes, $d\ell_t$, Equation (1–28) is written as

$$\epsilon_{zt} = \int_\ell^{\ell_t} d\epsilon_{zt} = \int_\ell^{\ell_t} \frac{d\ell_t}{\ell_t} = \log_e \frac{\ell_t}{\ell} = \log_e\left(1 + \frac{e_z}{\ell}\right) = \log_e(1 + \epsilon_z). \tag{1-29}$$

Necking Down of Cross Section of Ductile Metal Tension Specimen. When the ultimate or maximum load is reached in testing a tension specimen of ductile metal, the specimen begins to neck down somewhere along its length as illustrated in Figure 1.20*a*. The gage length ℓ usually extends from points such as E and J near the ends of the specimen and the necked-down portion usually occurs somewhere near the midlength of the specimen. Before the test begins, let the specimen be marked by points H, G, F, A, B, C, and D that divide the original gage length ℓ between E and J into equal segments. After necking down begins two marks, such as A and B near the necking down, will be stretched much farther apart than the other pairs of marks. Thus, after necking down begins, the strain distribution along the length of the specimen, as defined by the change in length of each of the several gage lengths (8 in Figure 1.20*a*) divided by the original gage length, would be nonuniform as shown in Figure 1.20*b*. The necking down has somewhat the same effect on the distribution of true strain ϵ_{zt} along the specimen length as that shown in Figure 1.20*b* for the strain ϵ_z.

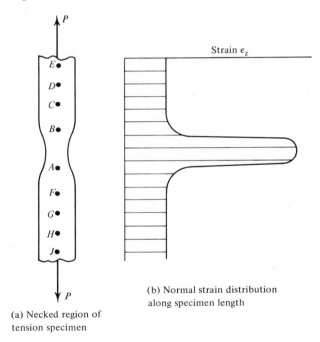

(a) Necked region of tension specimen

(b) Normal strain distribution along specimen length

Fig. 1.20. Necking of tension specimen and its effect on distribution of normal strains.

There is a way to avoid the difficulty caused by the necking down in measuring the strain and the true strain. This method makes use of the fact that when the strain or true strain becomes large, that is, after considerable plastic strain has occurred, the volume of the material remains virtually constant. Based on this assumption the following equation is written:

$$A\ell = A_t(\ell + e_z),$$ (1–30)

where A and ℓ are the original cross-sectional area and gage length, respectively, A_t is the true area at any value of load or strain, and e_z is the elongation of the original gage length ℓ based on the assumption that A_t is constant over the length $\ell + e_z$. Dividing Equation (1–30) by $A\ell$ and noting that $\epsilon_z = e_z/\ell$, the resulting equation can be solved for the strain ϵ_z as follows:

$$\epsilon_z = \frac{A}{A_t} - 1 = \frac{D^2}{D_t^2} - 1.$$ (1–31)

The substitution of Equation (1–31) into Equation (1–29) gives the true strain ϵ_{zt}. as shown in the following equation:

$$\epsilon_{zt} = \log_e \frac{A}{A_t} = \log_e \frac{D^2}{D_t^2} = 2 \log_e \frac{D}{D_t}.$$ (1–32)

Note that Equations (1–31) and (1–32) should be used in computing strains and true strains, respectively, commencing when the ultimate or maximum load is reached and necking down is starting. Of course, the measurement of the true diameter D_t is taken at the minimum diameter where the necking down is occurring.

True-Stress True-Strain Diagram. The values of the true stress versus the true strain obtained from data taken from a tension test and from a compression test of specimens of a structural steel are shown by the plotted points denoted by solid circles and solid triangles, respectively, in Figure 1.21. The values of the stress versus the strain from the same tests are shown by the plotted points denoted by the open circles and open triangles, respectively. Note that a single curve could be drawn to represent the true-stress true-strain data for both the tension and compression test data, whereas this could not be done for the stress-strain data for the tension and compression tests. This fact makes the true-stress true-strain diagram very useful when relatively large deformations are encountered—such as in the forming of steel rods into bent shapes for reinforcing concrete, in the forming of flat metal sheets into automobile bodies, in the deep forming of metal into cartridge shells, and so forth.

Small Strains. When strains are very small as they are for elastic conditions, the true-stress true-strain diagram can be assumed to coincide with the stress-strain diagram for small strains, and therefore that $\epsilon_{zt} = \epsilon_z$.

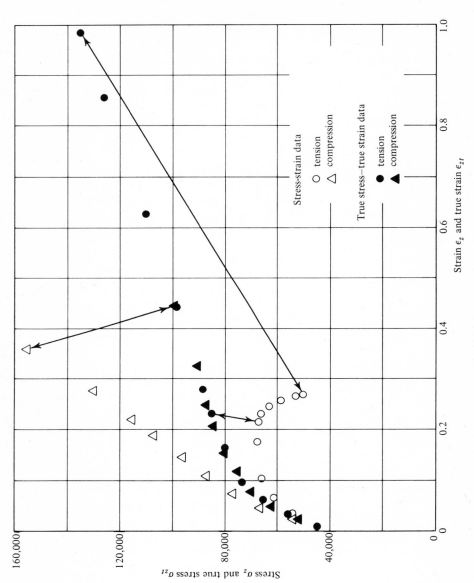

Fig. 1.21.   Comparison of stress-strain and true stress-true strain diagrams for structural steel.

1.11. Time Dependent Material Behavior—Viscoelastic Behavior

As discussed in Section 1.2, the stress-strain relation for many materials (most metals at room temperature, for instance) can be considered independent of time. A load-carrying member made of one of these materials will not deform further without a change in magnitude of one or more of the loads that are applied to the member. Metals whose material behavior can be considered time independent at room temperature become time dependent when the temperature of the metal is increased to sufficiently high magnitudes. Other materials, such as lead, plastics, and concrete exhibit time-dependent behavior even at room temperature. A member loaded under conditions in which the stress-strain behavior is time dependent will continue to deform even when the loads remain constant. When the material behavior is time dependent, the time-dependent material properties are usually exhibited in the form of creep and relaxation curves for the material.

Creep.   Let a tension specimen be subjected to a constant load. A plot of the axial strain ϵ_z versus time t is called a creep curve; a typical creep curve is shown in Figure 1.22. The creep curve is usually divided into three ranges

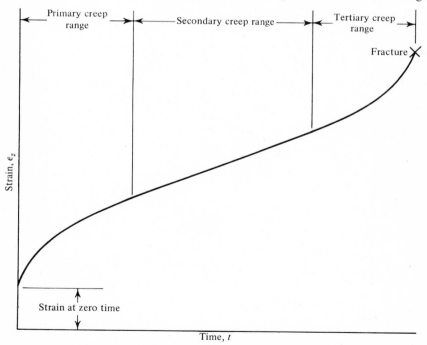

Fig. 1.22.   Typical constant load tension creep curve.

with respect to time. The primary creep range is the range in which the creep rate $d\epsilon_z/dt$ is decreasing in magnitude. In the secondary creep range, the creep rate remains approximately constant and is called the range of steady-state creep. In general the magnitudes of ϵ_z associated with the primary and secondary creep ranges is so small that the change in cross-sectional area is small enough to be neglected and the stress in the specimen is assumed to remain constant as long as the load remains constant. As the strains become large, the cross-sectional area decreases, the stress in the specimen increases, and the strain rate increases producing the tertiary creep range, which terminates in fracture. In this book the strains in load-carrying members are limited to small values; therefore, the tertiary creep range will not be of interest.

When creep curves are used to represent time-dependent material

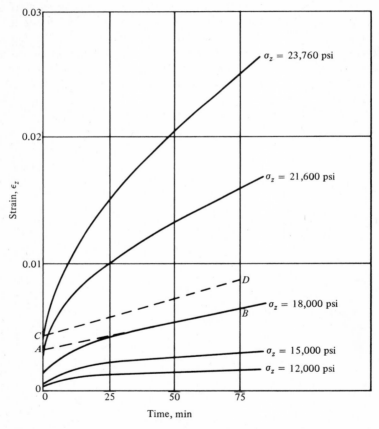

Fig. 1.23. Constant stress tension creep curves for annealed SAE 1035 steel at 975° F.

properties, the creep data are presented as a family of constant-stress creep curves, as indicated in Figure 1.23 by the curves for annealed SAE 1035 steel 975°F. Note that only a small part of the time-dependent material properties for this material is represented by this family of creep curves because only one temperature has been used and also the tests have been limited to 75 minutes. Furthermore, in each of these five tests, both the stress and temperature were kept constant once the load was applied. In Figure 1.24

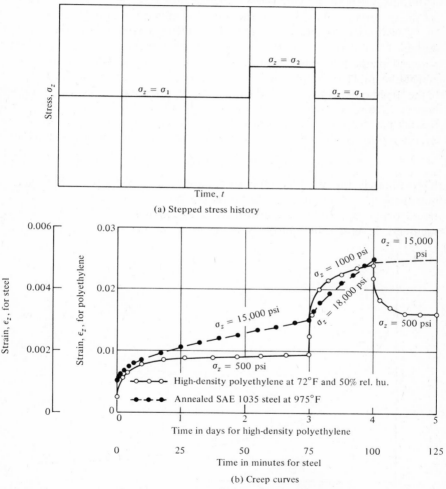

(a) Stepped stress history

(b) Creep curves

Fig. 1.24. Creep curves for tension specimens of a plastic at room temperature and a metal at elevated temperature subjected to a stepped stress history.

test data show the effect on the strain ϵ_z for changes in the loading of a tension specimen of high density polyethylene at 72°F and 50 per cent relative humidity and of annealed SAE 1035 steel at 975°F.

Relaxation.   Let a tension specimen be subjected to a rapidly increasing load to produce a specified strain ϵ_z in the specimen, and let this strain be held constant. If the specimen is made of a material whose deformation is time-dependent, the load and hence the stress in the specimen will decrease with time. A plot of the axial stress σ_z versus time is called a relaxation curve for the material. A typical relaxation curve is shown in Figure 1.25.

Constitutive Equation for Time-Dependent Material Behavior.   The design of load-carrying members made of a material with time-dependent material properties requires that a constitutive equation for the material and the member be determined. The variables that influence the magnitude of the strain ϵ_z are the stress σ_z, the time t, the temperature T, the temperature history T_H, and the stress history σ_H; the latter give the influence of changing the temperature and stress during the loading period. The constitutive equation for a given material and member is given by the following relation:

$$\epsilon_z = f(\sigma_z, t, T, T_H, \sigma_H). \tag{1–33}$$

Unfortunately Equation (1–33) is so complex that it has never been determined for any real material. Therefore, creep design of a given member is based on an approximate constitutive equation for the material and the member. Several different types of approximations have been made in

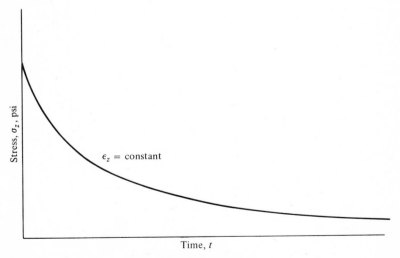

Fig. 1.25.   Relaxation curve.

obtaining a workable constitutive equation. Only one of these is considered in this book and it is based on the assumption that the material behavior can be approximated by combinations of elastic and viscous models. Such a material is said to be viscoelastic and it is described in the next section.

1.12. Linear Viscoelastic Constitutive Relations for Members Subjected to Axial Centric Loading

The viscoelastic behavior of the material can be visualized by representing the material behavior by elastic and viscous models consisting of a linearly elastic spring and a linear dashpot. The linear spring in Figure 1.26

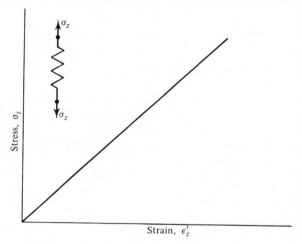

Fig. 1.26. Stress-strain diagram for linear spring.

represents the elastic response of the material. The linear dashpot in Figure 1.27 represents the viscous response of the material. Because behavior of a real material is being idealized, the force applied to the model corresponds to stress in the specimen of the real material and the movement of one end of the model with respect to the other end corresponds to strain in the specimen of the real material.

It is seen in Figure 1.26 that the linear spring represents the linearly elastic behavior of the material whose stress-strain relation is given by the relation

$$\epsilon_z' = \frac{\sigma_z}{E} \quad \text{or} \quad \sigma_z = E\epsilon_z'. \tag{1-34}$$

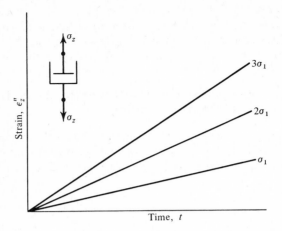

Fig. 1.27. Constant-stress creep curves for dashpot.

In Equation (1–34) E is the modulus of elasticity for the material and the single prime on the strain designates it as the elastic component of the strain. Equation (1–34) (see Eq. (1–3)) is the constitutive equation for linearly elastic behavior of a material in a member subjected to axial centric loading.

Several constant-stress creep curves are shown in Figure 1.27 for the linear dashpot. The linear dashpot represents the linear viscous behavior of the material whose stress-strain time relation (constitutive relation for members subjected to axial centric loading and made of a linear viscous material) is given by the relation

$$\frac{d\epsilon_z''}{dt} = \frac{\sigma_z}{\mu} \qquad \text{or} \qquad \sigma_z = \mu \frac{d\epsilon_z''}{dt}. \tag{1–35}$$

In Equation (1–35) μ is a viscosity coefficient (with dimensions of stress and time) that is assumed to be a constant for the material, and the double prime on the strain designates it as the viscous or inelastic component of strain. It is seen from Equation (1–35) that the strain rate $d\epsilon_z''/dt$ is a constant when the stress σ_z is a constant; hence constant-stress creep curves for the linear dashpot are straight lines.

When the time-dependent material behavior of real materials can be approximated by linear viscoelastic models, these models can be built up using the linear spring and linear dashpot as components. One of the simplest models to represent viscoelastic material behavior is the Maxwell model shown in Figure 1.28a, in which the spring and dashpot are in series. Other

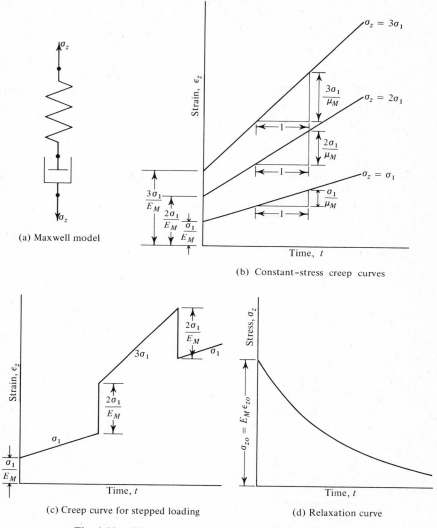

(a) Maxwell model

(b) Constant-stress creep curves

(c) Creep curve for stepped loading

(d) Relaxation curve

Fig. 1.28. Time-dependent behavior of Maxwell model.

simple linear viscoelastic models to approximate time-dependent material behavior are shown in Figure 1.29.

Maxwell Model. For the Maxwell model shown in Figure 1.28a, the stress σ_z is the same for the spring and the dashpot, and the strain ϵ_z is equal to the sum of the elastic component ϵ'_z given by Equation (1–34) and the

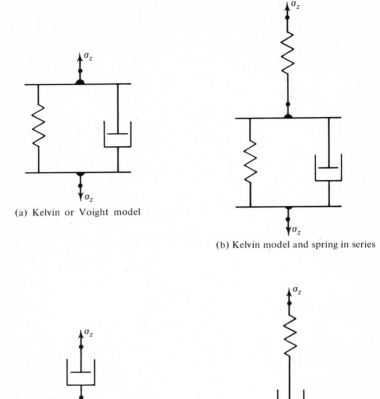

(a) Kelvin or Voight model

(b) Kelvin model and spring in series

(c) Kelvin model and dashpot in series

(d) Maxwell model and
Kelvin model in series

Fig. 1.29. Other simple linear viscoelastic models.

inelastic component ϵ_z'' given by Equation (1–35). Thus,

$$\epsilon_z = \epsilon_z' + \epsilon_z''.$$

Taking the derivative of this relation with respect to time, and using Equations (1–34) and (1–35) with $E = E_M$ and $\mu = \mu_M$, gives the differential equation

$$\frac{d\epsilon_z}{dt} = \frac{1}{E_M}\frac{d\sigma_z}{dt} + \frac{\sigma_z}{\mu_M}, \tag{1–36}$$

which is the stress-strain time relation for the Maxwell model. Equation (1–36) is the constitutive relation for a Maxwell model subjected to constant temperature. Note that the material constants E_M and μ_M are functions of temperature. In this book the temperature is assumed to remain constant in the discussions of time-dependent material behavior.

Equation (1–36) can be integrated to determine the relation for constant-stress creep curves or to determine the relation for constant-strain relaxation curves for the Maxwell model. If the stress σ_z is a constant equal to σ_1, $d\sigma_z$ is equal to zero, then Equation (1–36) can be integrated to give

$$\epsilon_z = \frac{\sigma_1 t}{\mu_M} + C_1,$$

where C_1 is the constant of integration. If σ_1 is applied so rapidly (almost instantaneously) that the dashpot does not have time to react, C_1 will be equal to the initial elastic strain (i.e., $C_1 = \sigma_1/E_M$). Constant-stress creep curves for the Maxwell model for this condition of loading are given by the relation

$$\epsilon_z = \frac{\sigma_1 t}{\mu_M} + \frac{\sigma_1}{E_M}. \tag{1–37}$$

By making use of Equation (1–37), a family of constant-stress creep curves has been constructed for the Maxwell model for $\sigma_z = \sigma_1$, $\sigma_z = 2\sigma_1$, and $\sigma_z = 3\sigma_1$ and are shown in Figure 1.28b.

A creep curve for a Maxwell model subjected to stepped loading from σ_1 to $3\sigma_1$ and back to σ_1 has been constructed by making use of Figure 1.28b and is shown in Figure 1.28c for the condition that the changes in strain (almost instantaneous) accompanying each change in stress are elastic.

The relaxation curve for the Maxwell model is obtained by setting $d\epsilon_z = 0$ in Equation (1–36). For the condition that the axial stress at zero time, σ_{z0}, is equal to $E_M \epsilon_{z0}$ (the material is assumed to behave elastically during the very short interval of time that σ_{z0} is being applied), and expressing the integrals of both sides the resulting equation becomes

$$\int_{E_M \epsilon_{z0}}^{\sigma_z} \frac{d\sigma_z}{\sigma_z} = -\frac{E_M}{\mu_M} \int_0^t dt,$$

which can be integrated to give

$$\sigma_z = E_M \epsilon_{z0} \, e^{-(E_M/\mu_M)t}, \tag{1–38}$$

in which e is the base of natural logarithms. Equation (1–38) is the relaxation equation for the Maxwell model for the condition that $\sigma_{z0} = E_M \epsilon_{z0}$ as previously indicated. A relaxation curve for this condition of loading of the Maxwell model has been constructed by using Equation (1–38) and is shown in Figure 1.28d.

A comparison of the constant-stress creep curves in Figure 1.28b, the creep curve for stepped loading in Figure 1.28c, and the relaxation curve in Figure 1.28d for the Maxwell model with corresponding curves shown in Figures 1.23, 1.24, and 1.25 for real materials indicates that the Maxwell model exhibits many of the time-dependent material behavior characteristics of real materials. Because of its simplicity and because the Maxwell model exhibits many of the characteristics of real materials, only the Maxwell model will be considered when analyzing time-dependent behavior of the load-carrying members considered in later chapters. The Maxwell model does have limitations and these limitations are worthy of note.

Limitations of the Maxwell Model. If the Maxwell model is to approximate the behavior of a given material, the magnitudes of the two material constants E_M and μ_M for the given material have to be determined. These are empirical constants for the material and can be determined by fitting one constant-stress creep curve for the Maxwell model (Eq. (1–37)), to the steady state (second stage of creep) portion of a given creep curve for the given material. Consider the tension creep curve for $\sigma_z = 18,000$ psi for the SAE 1035 steel at 975°F in Figure 1.23. The straight line AB coincides with the actual creep curve in the secondary creep range; this straight line is to be approximated by Equation (1–37). The strain ϵ_z at zero time is represented by $OA = 0.00321 = \sigma_z/E_M$. Since $\sigma_z = 18,000$ psi, $E_M = 5,610,000$ psi. From the slope of line AB, it is found that $\mu_M = 405,000,000$ lb min/in.^{2}

One limitation of the Maxwell model is readily apparent; it cannot represent primary creep. This is not a limitation in the design of members subjected to constant loads if the material behavior can be accurately approximated by a linear viscoelastic model, and if the times involved are in the secondary creep range. The Maxwell model predicts results as accurately as any other linear viscoelastic model for these conditions of loading. Loading in the primary creep range or variable loading requires a more complex linear viscoelastic model (see Fig. 1.29d, for instance).

The major limitation of the Maxwell model is noted when the material constants $E_M = 5,610,000$ psi and $\mu_M = 405,000,000$ lb min/in.^{2} are substituted into Equation (1–37) to approximate another creep curve in Figure 1.23. For instance when $\sigma_z = 23,760$ psi, Equation (1–37) gives the straight line CD in Figure 1.23. The reason the Maxwell model does such a poor job of approximating other creep curves for the annealed SAE 1035 steel at 975°F is that the material behavior is extremely nonlinear. It is impossible for any linear viscoelastic model to accurately approximate the material behavior of this material. This behavior can be accurately approximated by nonlinear viscoelastic models built up of nonlinear springs and nonlinear dashpots. These models are extremely complex to work with and are beyond the scope of this book.

All materials that creep are nonlinear, however, the nonlinearity may be so small for some materials (some plastics, for instance) under certain loading conditions that the time-dependent material behavior can be accurately approximated by linear viscoelastic models. In these cases the Maxwell model can be used for the conditions that the loads on the member are held constant for sufficiently long times that steady state conditions are developed.

Nonlinear Viscoelastic Constitutive Relation. One of the simplest non-linear viscoelastic models is obtained by replacing the linear dashpot in the Maxwell model (see Fig. 1.28a) by a nonlinear dashpot. The response of the dashpot is usually assumed to be approximated by a single power term as follows:

$$\frac{d\epsilon_z''}{dt} = B\left(\frac{\sigma_z}{\sigma'}\right)^n, \tag{1–39}$$

in which B is a dimensional constant for the material, σ' has a magnitude of unity with dimensions of stress, and n is a dimensionless material constant whose value is greater than 1. The relation, $\epsilon_z = \epsilon_z' + \epsilon_z''$ is valid for the model; taking the derivative of this relation with respect to time and using Equations (1–34) and (1–39) gives the differential equation

$$\frac{d\epsilon_z}{dt} = \frac{1}{E}\frac{d\sigma_z}{dt} + B\left(\frac{\sigma_z}{\sigma'}\right)^n, \tag{1–40}$$

which is the stress-strain time relation for the model having a linear spring and nonlinear dashpot in series. Equation (1–40) is the constitutive relation for members made of a material whose material properties can be accurately approximated by this model for the conditions that the temperature of the member remains constant and that the member is subjected to axial centric loading.* Note that Equation (1–40) reduces to Equation (1–36) when $n = 1$ with $\mu_M = \sigma'/B$ and $E_M = E$.

It is easy to show that constant-stress creep curves for this model are straight lines as was the case for the Maxwell model (see Fig. 1.28b); however, the stress dependence of the creep rate is much greater than for the Maxwell model where the creep rate was directly proportional to stress. This model may accurately predict the time-dependent behavior of a load-carrying member made of a time-dependent material if the member is subjected to constant loads for long periods of time and if the stresses in the member are small enough so that the strains in the member remain small. Because the model does not exhibit primary creep, it cannot be used without correction, either for members subjected to loads for short periods of time or for members subjected to loads that vary with time.

Illustrative Problems

1.56. Member OE in Fig. P1.56 can be considered to be a weightless rigid member. Before applying the load P, the distance between the stop and member OE is $\Delta_E = 0.40$ in. Tension member BC has a cross-sectional area of $A = 3.20$ in.^{2} and is made of a material that can be accurately approximated by a Maxwell model with $E_M = 10,000,000$ psi and $\mu_M = 500,000,000$ lb min/in.^{2} (1) Determine the time, measured from the instant $P = 10,000$ lb is applied, required for member OE to hit the stop. (2) What is the load carried by member BC 50 min after member OE hits the stop?

SOLUTION.—PART (1).   The equilibrium moment equation for a free-body diagram of member OE in Figure P1.56 gives

$$\sum M_O = 16(10,000) - 10P_{BC} = 0,$$

$$P_{BC} = 16,000 \text{ lb.}$$

The stress σ_1 in member BC is

$$\sigma_1 = \frac{P_{BC}}{A} = \frac{16,000}{3.20} = 5,000 \text{ psi.}$$

From the geometry of deformation, member BC has elongated an amount

---

* It can be shown that Equation (1–40) is valid for other members having uniaxial state of stress.

$e_z = 0.20$ in. when member OE hits the stop. Using Equation (1–37)

$$e_z = 80\epsilon_z = \frac{5,000(80)t}{500,000,000} + \frac{5,000(80)}{10,000,000} = 0.20,$$

$$t = 200 \text{ min.}$$

PART (2).   The stress in member BC is 5,000 psi when member OE hits the stop. Equation (1–38) is valid for member BC if zero time is specified

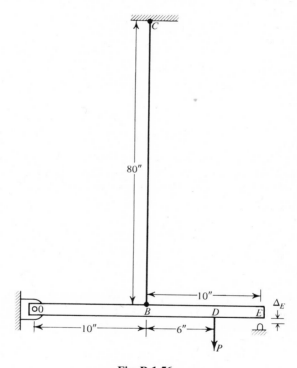

80"

—10"—

Δ_E

O O   B   D   E

—10"—   —6"—

P

Fig. P 1.56.

as the time that member OE hits the stop and if $E_M \epsilon_{z0}$ is set equal to the stress in member BC at zero time (i.e., the time when member OE hits the stop).

$$\sigma_z = E_M \epsilon_{z0} e^{-(E_M/\mu_M)t} = 5,000 e^{-\frac{10,000,000(50)}{500,000,000}} = \frac{5,000}{e} = \frac{5,000}{2.72} = 1,840 \text{ psi.}$$

$$P_{BC} = A\sigma_z = 3.20(1,840) = 5,890 \text{ lb.}$$

Problems

1.57. The tension member in Problem 1.9 is made of the high-density polyethylene whose creep curve for $\sigma_z = 500$ psi is shown in Figure 1.24. Show that, by fitting the Maxwell model to this creep curve, the material constants are $E_M = 59,500$ psi and $\mu_M = 1,315,000$ lb day/in.^{2} The tension member is loaded in a room maintained at 72°F and 50 per cent relative humidity. If $Q = 45$ lb, determine the creep rate in inches per day and the elongation of the tension member in 50 hours.

ans. $de_z/dt = 0.0178$ in./day; $e_z = 0.4306$ in. in 50 hr.

1.58. The tension member in Problem 1.11 is made of the high-density polyethylene whose material constants are given in Problem 1.57. Determine the minimum diameter for the member if the maximum stress is 500 psi. If the tension member is loaded in a room maintained at 72°F and 50 per cent relative humidity, determine the total elongation of the member in one week and the elongation rate in inches per hour at the free end.

ans. $D = 2.76$ in; $e_z = 0.258$ in.; $de_z/dt = 0.000370$ in./hr.

1.59. The steel rod DC in Problem 1.12 is replaced by a tension member made of a material whose time-dependent properties can be accurately approximated by a Maxwell model. The material constants for this material are $E_M = 100,000$ psi and $\mu_M = 50,000,000$ lb hr/in.^{2} Load Q is held constant at 100 lb for 100 hr. Determine the cross-sectional area of the tension member if the total movement of A is 0.30 in. in the 100 hr.

1.60. Let the tension member DC in Problem 1.59 have a cross-sectional area of 0.60 in.^{2} The material constants for the tension member are given in Problem 1.59. A load Q is applied at point A in such a short time that the tension member behaves linearly elastically while point A moves downward to a value $\Delta_A = 0.20$ in. Let time be measured from the instant $\Delta_A = 0.20$ in. If Δ_A is maintained at 0.20 in., determine the magnitude of Q for $t = 0$ and for $t = 1,000$ hr.

ans. $Q = 334$ lb for $t = 0$; $Q = 45.1$ lb for $t = 1,000$ hr.

1.61. The tension member BD in Problem 1.13 has a cross-sectional area of $\frac{1}{2}$ in.^{2} and is made of canvas laminate. A constant-stress creep curve for a tension specimen of this material at 75°F and 50 per cent relative humidity indicated that $\epsilon_z = 0.0060$ at 1,000 hr and $\epsilon_z = 0.0050$ at 200 hr for a stress $\sigma_z = 4,400$ psi. Assuming that this material can be approximated by a Maxwell model, determine E_M and μ_M. Determine the deflection rate for point C at the load if $P = 1,200$ lb. Also determine the total deflection of point C at 800 hr.

ans. $E_M = 9.27 \times 10^5$ psi; $\mu_M = 3.52 \times 10^9$ lb hr/in.^{2}; $d\Delta_C/dt = 0.000148$ in./hr

$\Delta_C = 0.680$ in. in 800 hr.

1.62. Point C of member ABC in Problem 1.61 is suddenly displaced downward a distance of $\frac{1}{2}$ in. against a stop not shown and held firmly in that position. Assume that the canvas laminate behaves linearly elastically during the initial displacement. The time at the completion of the displacement is zero time. Determine P when $t = 0$ and when $t = 4000$ hr.

1.63. The material constants for the Kelvin or Voigt model in Figure 1.29a are E_K and μ_K. Derive the expression for a constant-stress creep curve for this model with $\sigma_z = \sigma_1$. Note that all of the stress σ_1 is carried by the spring when time approaches infinity so that $\epsilon_{z(max)} = \sigma_1/E_K$.

$$\text{ans.} \quad \epsilon_z = \frac{\sigma_1}{E_K}(1 - e^{-(E_K/\mu_K)t})$$

1.64. The viscoelastic model in Figure 1.29d is made up by putting a Maxwell model and a Kelvin model in series. The material constants are $E_M = 10{,}000{,}000$ psi, $\mu_M = 500{,}000{,}000$ lb hr/in.^{2}, $E_K = 5{,}000{,}000$ psi, and $\mu_K = 250{,}000{,}000$ lb hr/in.^{2} Using Equation (1–37) and the answer to Problem 1.63, construct the constant-stress creep curve for the model for the first 500 hr if $\sigma_1 = 10{,}000$ psi.

1.13. Internal Energy in a Unit Volume of a Deformable Body

In Section 1.3 it was found that the strain energy density U_0 of a unit of volume of a member that is subjected to a uniaxial state of stress σ_z with a corresponding strain ϵ_z in the direction of σ_z is equal to the area OAB under the stress-strain curve as shown in Figure 1.30a. The area OAC above the stress-strain diagram shown in Figure 1.30b is called the complementary energy density, Φ_0; it has the units of energy per unit volume although physically it is not energy per unit volume. The complementary energy density Φ_0 and the strain energy density U_0 in a deformable body are both very useful quantities that can be used in the analysis of deformations when the body is subjected to external loads or to nonuniform temperature distributions.

Virtual Changes in Internal Energy of Unit Volume. In Figure 1.30c let a small but arbitrary change in strain $\delta\epsilon_z$ occur. The notation $\delta\epsilon_z$ is used instead of $d\epsilon_z$ to indicate that the increment of strain is a virtual strain increment. The virtual strain $\delta\epsilon_z$ will be accompanied by a virtual strain energy density δU_0 as shown by the area of the cross-hatched strip, which requires the following equation to be valid.

$$\delta U_0 = \sigma_z\,\delta\epsilon_z. \tag{1–41}$$

Similarly let a small but arbitrary change in stress $\delta\sigma_z$ occur as shown in

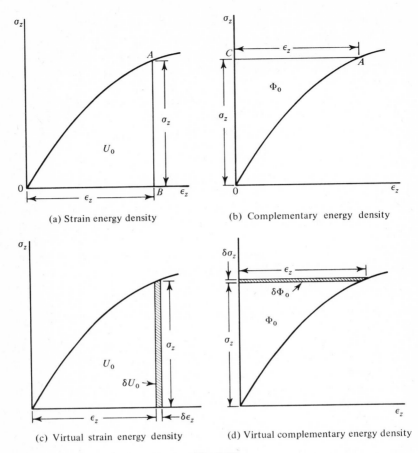

(a) Strain energy density

(b) Complementary energy density

(c) Virtual strain energy density

(d) Virtual complementary energy density

Fig. 1.30.

Figure 1.30d. The virtual stress $\delta\sigma_z$ will be accompanied by a virtual complementary energy density $\delta\Phi_0$ as shown by the area of the cross-hatched strip, which requires the following equation to be valid.

$$\delta\Phi_0 = \epsilon_z \, \delta\sigma_z. \tag{1–42}$$

1.14. External Work Done on a Deformable Body

Let Figure 1.31a represent a straight member of constant cross section that is subjected to an external axial-centric load P. The load P causes an

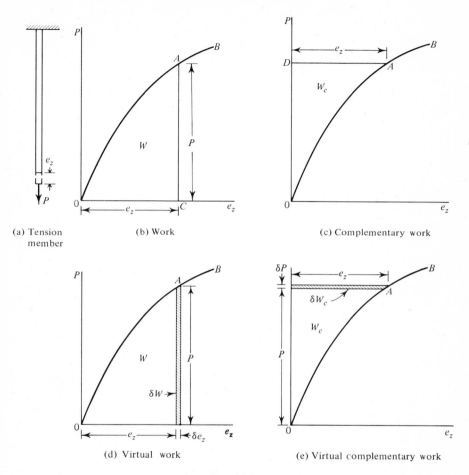

(a) Tension member

(b) Work

(c) Complementary work

(d) Virtual work

(e) Virtual complementary work

Fig. 1.31.

elongation e_z. The relationship between the load P and the elongation e_z, for various magnitudes of the load, is assumed to be represented by a curve such as OAB in Figure 1.31b. For a given pair of values of e_z and P the external work W done by the load P is represented by the area OAC in Figure 1.31b. In like manner the so-called complementary work W_c done by the load P is represented by the area OAD in Figure 1.31c.

Virtual Changes in External Work. In Figures 1.31d and e let small but arbitrary changes δe_z and δP, respectively, occur in the elongation e_z and the load P. The change δe_z is called a virtual displacement and the change δP is called a virtual load. Thus, as shown in Figure 1.31d, a virtual displacement δe_z is accompanied by a virtual work δW as shown by the area of the cross-hatched strip, which requires the following equation to be valid.

$$\delta W = P\,\delta e_z. \tag{1-43}$$

Also, as shown in Figure 1.31e, the virtual load δP is accompanied by a virtual complementary work δW_c, as shown by the area of the cross-hatched strip, which requires the following equation to be valid.

$$\delta W_c = e_z\,\delta P. \tag{1-44}$$

1.15. Principles of Virtual Work and Virtual Complementary Work

Of great usefulness is the fact that the virtual work of the external load is related to the virtual internal strain energy (or virtual internal work); and also that the virtual complementary work of the external load is related to the virtual internal complementary energy (or internal virtual complementary work). In this section these principles will be stated and their application to the problem of finding the deflection of a simple two-member truss will be illustrated.

Let Figure 1.32a represent a structure consisting of two straight members AB and BC fastened at A, B, and C by smooth pins. The structure is loaded at B by the forces P and T and is supported at A and C by rigid supports that do not permit displacement of the smooth pins at A and C. The pin at B is shown displaced from its original location at B', and the component q_P of this displacement of B in the direction of the load P is shown. The magnitude of q_P as shown in Figure 1.32a is exaggerated. In the analysis that follows the value of q_P must not be large enough to cause large changes in the lengths of AB and BC, or of the angle between them. All deformations are assumed to be small.

Suppose that the curve ODF in Figures 1.32b and c represents the corresponding values of the load P and the displacement q_P. Let δq_P represent a virtual displacement of the point B in the direction of the load P. The virtual work δW is (from Fig. 1.32b)

$$\delta W = P\,\delta q_P. \tag{1-45}$$

Also, let δP represent a virtual load (i.e., an arbitrarily small change in the load P). The virtual complementary work δW_c is (from Fig. 1.32c)

$$\delta W_c = q_P\,\delta P. \tag{1-46}$$

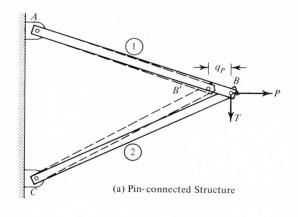

(a) Pin-connected Structure

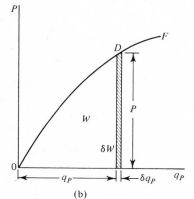

(b)

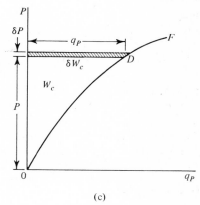

(c)

Fig. 1.32.

Principle of Virtual Work. Let δU be the virtual strain energy done by the internal forces in both members of the structure of Figure 1.32a simultaneously with the external virtual work δW produced by δq_P, as given by Equation (1–45). The principle of virtual work states that

$$\delta U = \delta W = P\,\delta q_P, \tag{1–47}$$

if the structure (Fig. 1.32a) is in equilibrium and if the virtual displacement δq_P is consistent with the geometrical constraints on the structure. (Note that if the supports at A and C are not rigid, the virtual work of the supports must also be included in δU.)

The virtual strain energy δU done by the internal forces of the structure can be expressed in terms of the partial derivative of the total strain energy U

with respect to the displacement q_P and the virtual displacement δq_P as follows*:

$$\delta U = \frac{\partial U}{\partial q_P} \delta q_P. \tag{1-48}$$

The substitution of Equation (1–48) into Equation (1–47) for δU gives

$$\frac{\partial U}{\partial q_P} \delta q_P = P \, \delta q_P, \tag{1-49}$$

which reduces to

$$\frac{\partial U}{\partial q_P} = P. \tag{1-50}$$

Principle of Virtual Complementary Work. Let $\delta\Phi$ be the virtual complementary energy done by the internal forces in both members of the structure of Figure 1.32a simultaneously with the external virtual complementary work δW_c produced by δP, as given by Equation (1–46). The principle of virtual complementary work states that

$$\delta\Phi = \delta W_c = q_P \, \delta P \tag{1-51}$$

if the structure (Fig. 1.32a) is in equilibrium, and if the structure remains in equilibrium after the virtual load δP is applied. (Note again the matter of constraints and that supports A and C are rigid.)

The virtual complementary energy $\delta\Phi$ done by the internal forces can be expressed in terms of the partial derivative of the total complementary energy Φ, with respect to the load P and the virtual load δP as follows†:

$$\delta\Phi = \frac{\partial\Phi}{\partial P} \delta P. \tag{1-52}$$

The substitution of Equation (1–52) into Equation (1–51) for $\delta\Phi$ gives

$$\frac{\partial\Phi}{\partial P} \delta P = q_P \, \delta P, \tag{1-53}$$

which reduces to

$$\frac{\partial\Phi}{\partial P} = q_P. \tag{1-54}$$

In the derivation of Equations (1–50) and (1–54) the material behavior has been assumed to be nonlinearly elastic. The theories that were used in

---

* Equation (1–48) also contains the additional term $(\partial U/\partial q_T)\delta q_T$, but $\delta q_T = 0$ because the only virtual displacement applied here is δq_P; that is, no change in the deflection in the direction of T is permitted while δq_P occurs.

† Equation (1–52) also contains the additional term $(\partial\Phi/\partial T)\delta T$, but $\delta T = 0$ because the only virtual load applied here is δP.

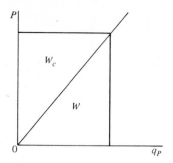

Fig. 1.33. Comparison of work and complementary work for linearly elastic behavior and small deformations.

the derivation do not distinguish between nonlinear elasticity and plasticity if the internal forces in the structure are monotonically increased and are never released.

Castigliano's Equation. Equation (1–54), which was derived by making use of the principle of virtual complementary work, is the general form for Castigliano's equation. For the special case in which the structure is made of linearly elastic materials, the relationship between the external work W and the complementary work W_c is, as shown by Figure 1.33, such that they are equal; that is,

$$W = W_c, \qquad (1–55)$$

and hence the internal strain energy U and the internal complementary energy Φ are also equal; that is,

$$U = \Phi. \qquad (1–56)$$

Therefore, for structures made of linearly elastic materials, U can replace Φ in Equation (1–54), which becomes

$$\frac{\partial U}{\partial P} = q_P. \qquad (1–57)$$

Equation (1–57) has been called Castigliano's equation ever since he derived it in 1873. In 1889, Engesser derived the more general form of Equation (1–54).

1.16. Application of Castigliano's Equation

Let S_1 and e_1 represent the internal axial centric force and elongation, respectively, for the member AB in Figure 1.32a. Likewise, let S_2 and e_2 similarly represent the member BC. The curve relating S_1 and e_1 is shown in

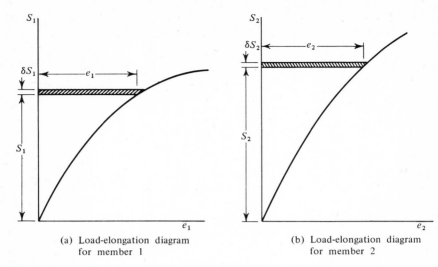

(a) Load-elongation diagram
for member 1

(b) Load-elongation diagram
for member 2

Fig. 1.34.

Figure 1.34a, and the curve relating S_2 and e_2 is shown in Figure 1.34b. The actual shape of these curves is determined by the material properties and the dimensions of the members.

The most convenient way to use Castigliano's equation is to begin with Equation (1–52). The virtual complementary energy $\delta\Phi$ (i.e., the left side of Equation (1–52)) is equal to the sum of the areas of the cross-hatched strips in Figures 1.34a and b; that is,

$$\delta\Phi = e_1\,\delta S_1 + e_2\,\delta S_2. \qquad (1\text{–}58)$$

But δS_1 and δS_2 can be represented as follows:

$$\delta S_1 = \frac{\partial S_1}{\partial P}\,\delta P \qquad \text{and} \qquad \delta S_2 = \frac{\partial S_2}{\partial P}\,\delta P.$$

These values are substituted into Equation (1–58) to give

$$\delta\Phi = e_1\frac{\partial S_1}{\partial P}\,\delta P + e_2\frac{\partial S_2}{\partial P}\,\delta P. \qquad (1\text{–}59)$$

In Equation (1–59) the value of $\delta\Phi$ is replaced by the right side of Equation (1–52), which gives

$$\frac{\partial\Phi}{\partial P}\,\delta P = e_1\frac{\partial S_1}{\partial P}\,\delta P + e_2\frac{\partial S_2}{\partial P}\,\delta P. \qquad (1\text{–}60)$$

In Equation (1–60) δP is a common factor that divides out. Then from Equations (1–60) and (1–54)

$$q_P = \frac{\partial \Phi}{\partial P} = e_1 \frac{\partial S_1}{\partial P} + e_2 \frac{\partial S_2}{\partial P} = \sum_{i=1}^{n} e_i \frac{\partial S_i}{\partial P}. \tag{1–61}$$

Note that Equation (1–61) is valid for nonlinear material behavior (subject to the conditions that deformations are small and that the load-elongation relations for each member is single valued); however, only linear elastic behavior is considered in the problems at the end of this section.

Physical Meaning of Terms in Equation (1–61). In Equation (1–61) it should be noted that the quantity e_i is the elongation of the ith member of a structure because of the actual external forces acting on the structure. The partial derivative $\partial S_i/\partial P$ is interpreted physically as the rate at which the axial force in the ith member changes when P changes in magnitude. This rate is always linear if the deflections and angle changes of the structure are small and hence it may be found as the change in S_i per unit change in P; that is, $\partial S_i/\partial P$ is the value of S_i caused by a value of P equal to unity. Thus, Castigliano's equation furnishes a method of finding the displacement (deflection) of any point in a structure, although it would appear that only the deflection of points at which the loads are applied could be found. However, the deflection of any point due to any system of loads may be found by introducing a fictitious load at the point in question in the direction the deflection is to be found, and then writing the expression for the derivative of the strain energy with respect to the fictitious load at this point. Such an expression will be valid for any magnitude of the fictitious load and the fictitious load can, therefore, be made equal to zero after the differentiation.

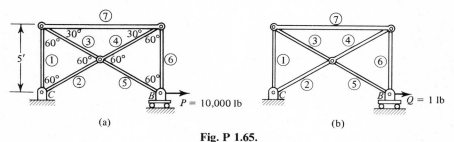

(a)   (b)

Fig. P 1.65.

Illustrative Problems

1.65. A pin-connected structure is pinned to a fixed support at C and loaded at B (Fig. P1.65) with a load $P = 10,000$ lb at B. There are seven members as numbered in the figure. The length ℓ and cross-sectional area A of each member is given in the table that accompanies the solution to the problem. Each of the members is made of a material whose modulus of elasticity is $E = 30,000,000$ psi. Determine the deflection q_P at the point of application of P in the direction of P.

SOLUTION.   Because the material is linearly elastic, the elongation e_i of each member is obtained by using Equation (1–13), which gives $e_i = S_i\ell_i/E_iA_i$. Because the modulus of elasticity E is the same for all members, Equation (1–61) can be written as:

$$q_P = \frac{1}{E}\sum_{i=1}^{7} \frac{S_i\ell_i}{A_i}\frac{\partial S_i}{\partial P}. \tag{a}$$

The axial force S_i in each of the members is found by applying the equations of equilibrium by either the method of joints or the method of sections. The results are tabulated in column 4 of the accompanying table. The negative sign indicates a compressive force.

MEMBER	LENGTH in.	AREA in^2	S_i lb	$\dfrac{\partial S_i}{\partial P}$	$\dfrac{S_i\ell_i}{A_i}\dfrac{\partial S_i}{\partial P}$
1	60.0	1.00	−5,775	−0.5775	200,000
2	60.0	1.00	11,550	1.1550	800,000
3	60.0	1.00	11,550	1.1550	800,000
4	60.0	1.00	11,550	1.1550	800,000
5	60.0	1.00	11,550	1.1550	800,000
6	60.0	1.00	−5,775	−0.5775	200,000
7	103.9	2.00	−10,000	−1.0000	519,000

$$\sum_{i=1}^{7}\frac{S_i\ell_i}{A_i}\frac{\partial S_i}{\partial P} = 4{,}119{,}000$$

Column 5 in the table gives the value of $\partial S_i/\partial P$ for each member of the structure. This value is obtained making use of the unit-load method. Figure P1.65b shows the structure with a 1-lb load applied at B (where P acts). The quantity $\partial S_i/\partial P$ for each member is the axial force in that member caused by the unit load at B. These forces are found by the same method that was used for determining the values of S_i (in this case, the same solution can be used as follows: divide each value of S_i by 10,000).

Column 6 in the table gives the product $S_i\ell_i/A_i(\partial S_i/\partial_P)$ for each of the members. The products in column 6 are added to give the following result:

$$\sum_{i=1}^{7}\frac{S_i\ell_i}{A_i}\frac{\partial S_i}{\partial P} = 4{,}119{,}000 \text{ lb/in.} \tag{b}$$

Hence, by putting the result from Equation (b) into Equation (a) and substituting the value of E, we have

$$q_P = \frac{4,119,000}{30,000,000} = 0.137 \text{ in.}$$

1.66. A pin-connected truss, in which all members have the same length $\ell = 10$ ft and modulus of elasticity $E = 30,000,000$ psi, is loaded as shown in Figure P1.66a. Find the deflection of the panel point D in the vertical direction. The cross-sectional area A of each member is given in the table accompanying the solution of the problem.

SOLUTION. Because ℓ and E are the same for all members, Equation (1–61) may be written as follows to obtain the vertical deflection:

$$q_Q = \frac{\ell}{E} \sum \frac{S_i}{A_i} \frac{\partial S_i}{\partial Q}, \tag{a}$$

where Q is a fictitious load at D in the vertical direction. The loads and reactions are shown in Figure P1.66a. The axial forces S_i in the members are found by applying the equations of equilibrium (by either the method of joints or the method of sections) and are tabulated in column 2 of the accompanying table, in which the computations are made for use in Equation (a). Note that the values of $\partial S_i/\partial Q$ are determined by differentiation of the quantities in column 2 of the table, respectively. However, the values of $\partial S_i/\partial Q$ can also be determined directly from the truss as loaded (and supported) in Figure P1.66b where a unit load $Q = 1$ lb is applied vertically at D. That is, the values of the forces S_i in the members of the truss in Figure P1.66b caused by the unit load $Q = 1$ lb are equal, respectively, to the value of $\partial S_i/\partial Q$ for each member.

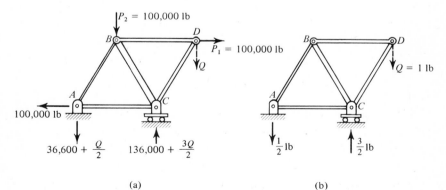

Fig. P 1.66.

MEMBER	AXIAL FORCE S_i IN EACH MEMBER DUE TO ALL LOADS, INCLUDING Q lb	$\dfrac{\partial S_i}{\partial Q}$	AREA in.^{2}	PRODUCT $\dfrac{S_i}{A_i}\dfrac{\partial S_i}{\partial Q}$ WHEN VALUE OF $Q = 0$ IS SUBSTITUTED
AB	$42{,}300 + \dfrac{Q}{\sqrt{3}}$	$\dfrac{1}{\sqrt{3}}$	2.5	9770
AC	$78{,}850 - \dfrac{Q}{2\sqrt{3}}$	$-\dfrac{1}{2\sqrt{3}}$	4.5	-5060
BC	$-157{,}700 - \dfrac{Q}{\sqrt{3}}$	$-\dfrac{1}{\sqrt{3}}$	12.0	7590
BD	$100{,}000 + \dfrac{Q}{\sqrt{3}}$	$\dfrac{1}{\sqrt{3}}$	6.0	9620
CD	$\dfrac{2Q}{\sqrt{3}}$	$\dfrac{2}{\sqrt{3}}$	6.0	0

The sum of terms in column 5 of the table gives

$$\sum \frac{S_i}{A_i}\frac{\partial S_i}{\partial Q} = 21{,}920 \text{ lb/in.}^2$$

Therefore the vertical deflection is obtained by the substitution of this latter value in Equation (a) as follows:

$$q_Q = \frac{\ell}{E}\sum \frac{S_i}{A_i}\frac{\partial S_i}{\partial Q} = \frac{120(21{,}920)}{30{,}000{,}000} = 0.0877 \text{ in.}$$

With the conventions used for signs, it is apparent that the plus sign for q_Q indicates that the deflection of point D in the direction of Q has the same sense as Q. A negative sign would mean that q_Q and Q would have opposite senses.

Problems

1.67. It is required that the horizontal deflection of the joint at D in the structure of Figure P1.66a in Problem 1.66 be determined. Note that the load Q as shown on the figure is zero.

ans. $q_{P_1} = 0.222$ in.

1.68. Determine the vertical deflection of the point D in the truss loaded as shown in Figure P1.68. The modulus of elasticity of the material in each of the members

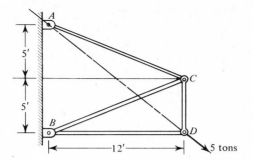

Fig. P 1.68.

of the truss is $E = 10,000,000$ psi. The cross-sectional areas are 1.00 in.² for members AC, CD, and BD and 2.00 in.² for member BC. The panel points A, B, C, and D are pin-connected and the supports at A and B are pin-connected and are assumed to be rigid.

1.69.   In Problem 1.68 determine the horizontal deflection of the point D.

1.70.   In Fig. P1.70 member AB is a steel cable whose cross-sectional area is 1.50 in.² and whose modulus of elasticity is 13,000,000 psi and member BC is an oak timber, which has a square cross section whose side is 12 in. and which has a modulus of elasticity of 1,500,000 psi. Determine the vertical deflection of the point B.

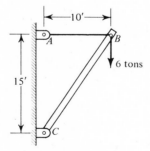

Fig. P 1.70.

1.17.   Principle of Least Complementary Work

The principle of least complementary work states that, for a statically indeterminate structure that is in equilibrium such as that shown in Figure 1.10a and b or in Figure 1.35a and b, the internal or resisting forces S_1, S_2, and S_3 take the set of values that give the minimum amount of internal

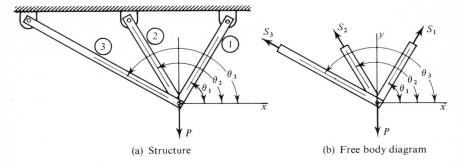

| (a) Structure | (b) Free body diagram |

Fig. 1.35.

complementary energy ($\Phi = W_c$). For the free-body diagram in Figure 1.35b this condition is expressed as follows: There are three internal forces and only two equations of equilibrium, namely,

$$\sum F_x = S_1 \cos \theta_1 + S_2 \cos \theta_2 + S_3 \cos \theta_3 = 0. \tag{1–62}$$

$$\sum F_y = S_1 \sin \theta_1 + S_2 \sin \theta_2 + S_3 \sin \theta_3 - P = 0. \tag{1–63}$$

Let S_2 represent the redundant force (see Section 1.5). Because the value of internal complementary energy Φ must be a minimum, this condition is represented by setting the partial derivative of Φ with respect to the redundant S_2 equal to zero; that is,

$$\frac{\partial \Phi}{\partial S_2} = 0. \tag{1–64}$$

Referring to Equation (1–61), it is possible to rewrite Equation (1–64) as follows:

$$e_1 \frac{\partial S_1}{\partial S_2} + e_2 \frac{\partial S_2}{\partial S_2} + e_3 \frac{\partial S_3}{\partial S_2} = \sum_{i=1}^{3} e_i \frac{\partial S_i}{\partial S_2} = 0. \tag{1–65}$$

Note in Equation (1–65) that $\partial S_2/\partial S_2 = 1$ and in order to obtain the partial derivatives $\partial S_1/\partial S_2$ and $\partial S_3/\partial S_2$ the values of S_1 and S_3, respectively, must be expressed in terms of S_2, P, and so forth, by making use of Equations (1–62) and (1–63).

Illustrative Problem

1.71. In Figure P1.71a the rigid bar K is loaded by the load $P = 15,000$ lb and is supported by four steel bars, AB, CD, EF, and GH, each having a length $\ell = 10$ in. and a cross-sectional area $A = 1.00$ in.[2]

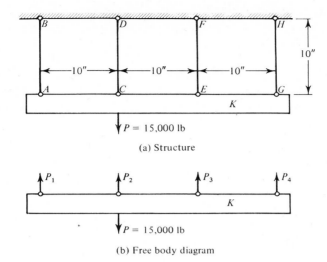

(a) Structure

(b) Free body diagram

Fig. P 1.71.

The modulus of elasticity of the steel is $E = 30,000,000$ psi. By making use of the principle of least complementary work, determine the values of the axial forces P_1, P_2, P_3, and P_4 in the steel bars. Assume that the elastic limit stress is not exceeded in any of the steel bars.

SOLUTION. By making use of the free-body diagram of Figure P1.71b two equations of equilibrium are written:

$$\sum F_y = P_1 + P_2 + P_3 + P_4 - 15,000 = 0. \tag{a}$$

$$\sum M_A = 10P_2 + 20P_3 + 30P_4 - 10(15,000) = 0. \tag{b}$$

Because there are four unknowns and only two equations of equilibrium, two of the unknowns, P_2 and P_3, are chosen as redundants. The two additional equations needed to solve for the four unknown forces are obtained by the principle of least complementary work. They are obtained by taking the derivative of the complementary energy Φ of the four steel bars with respect to P_2 and with respect to P_3 and setting each equal to zero (see Eqs. 1–64 and 1–65) as follows:

$$\frac{\partial \Phi}{\partial P_2} = e_1 \frac{\partial P_1}{\partial P_2} + e_2 \frac{\partial P_2}{\partial P_2} + e_3 \frac{\partial P_3}{\partial P_2} + e_4 \frac{\partial P_4}{\partial P_2} = 0. \tag{c}$$

$$\frac{\partial \Phi}{\partial P_3} = e_1 \frac{\partial P_1}{\partial P_3} + e_2 \frac{\partial P_2}{\partial P_3} + e_3 \frac{\partial P_3}{\partial P_3} + e_4 \frac{\partial P_4}{\partial P_3} = 0. \tag{d}$$

Four of the partial derivatives in Equations (c) and (d) are known as follows: $\partial P_2/\partial P_2 = 1$, $\partial P_3/\partial P_3 = 1$, $\partial P_2/\partial P_3 = 0$, and $\partial P_3/\partial P_2 = 0$. The latter two partial derivatives are zero because the two redundants P_2 and P_3 must be free to vary (i.e., they are independent of each other) in order to establish the minimum value of Φ. With these four values of the partial derivatives substituted into Equations (c) and (d) along with the values $e_1 = P_1\ell/AE$, $e_2 = P_2\ell/AE$, $e_3 = P_3\ell/AE$, and $e_4 = P_4\ell/AE$, Equations (c) and (d) reduce to the following:

$$P_1 \frac{\partial P_1}{\partial P_2} + P_2 + P_4 \frac{\partial P_4}{\partial P_2} = 0, \tag{e}$$

$$P_1 \frac{\partial P_1}{\partial P_3} + P_3 + P_4 \frac{\partial P_4}{\partial P_3} = 0. \tag{f}$$

To get the remaining partial derivatives in Equations (e) and (f) we differentiate the equations of equilibrium, Equations (a) and (b), partially with respect to the redundant P_2 with the result as shown in the two equations that follow:

$$\frac{\partial P_1}{\partial P_2} + 1 + \frac{\partial P_4}{\partial P_2} = 0, \tag{g}$$

$$1 + 3\frac{\partial P_4}{\partial P_2} = 0. \tag{h}$$

Solution of these two simultaneous equations gives

$$\frac{\partial P_1}{\partial P_2} = -\frac{2}{3} \quad \text{and} \quad \frac{\partial P_4}{\partial P_2} = -\frac{1}{3}. \tag{i}$$

Repeat the foregoing procedure by differentiating Equations (a) and (b) with respect to the second redundant P_3 with the following result:

$$\frac{\partial P_1}{\partial P_3} + 1 + \frac{\partial P_4}{\partial P_3} = 0, \tag{j}$$

$$2 + 3\frac{\partial P_4}{\partial P_3} = 0. \tag{k}$$

Solutions of these two simultaneous equations gives

$$\frac{\partial P_1}{\partial P_3} = -\frac{1}{3} \quad \text{and} \quad \frac{\partial P_4}{\partial P_3} = -\frac{2}{3}. \tag{l}$$

The partial derivatives from Equations (i) and (l) are substituted into

Equations (e) and (f), which give the following two equations:

$$-2P_1 + 3P_2 - P_4 = 0, \tag{m}$$

$$-P_1 + 3P_3 - 2P_4 = 0. \tag{n}$$

Equations (a), (b), (m) and (n) are four linear equations in the four unknowns P_1, P_2, P_3, and P_4 and are arranged as follows for solution by making use of determinants:

$$P_1 + P_2 + P_3 + P_4 = 15{,}000, \tag{a}$$

$$(0)P_1 + P_2 + 2P_3 + 3P_4 = 15{,}000, \tag{b}$$

$$-2P_1 + 3P_2 + (0)P_3 - P_4 = 0, \tag{m}$$

$$-P_1 + (0)P_2 + 3P_3 - 2P_4 = 0. \tag{n}$$

Setting up the solution by determinants, we have

$$P_1 = \frac{\begin{vmatrix} 15{,}000 & 1 & 1 & 1 \\ 15{,}000 & 1 & 2 & 3 \\ 0 & 3 & 0 & -1 \\ 0 & 0 & 3 & -2 \end{vmatrix}}{\begin{vmatrix} 1 & 1 & 1 & 1 \\ 0 & 1 & 2 & 3 \\ -2 & 3 & 0 & -1 \\ -1 & 0 & 3 & -2 \end{vmatrix}} = \frac{15{,}000\begin{vmatrix} 1 & 2 & 3 \\ 3 & 0 & -1 \\ 0 & 3 & -2 \end{vmatrix} - 15{,}000\begin{vmatrix} 1 & 1 & 1 \\ 3 & 0 & -1 \\ 0 & 3 & -2 \end{vmatrix}}{1\begin{vmatrix} 1 & 2 & 3 \\ 3 & 0 & -1 \\ 0 & 3 & -2 \end{vmatrix} - 2\begin{vmatrix} 1 & 1 & 1 \\ 1 & 2 & 3 \\ 0 & 3 & -2 \end{vmatrix} + 1\begin{vmatrix} 1 & 1 & 1 \\ 1 & 2 & 3 \\ 3 & 0 & -1 \end{vmatrix}}$$

$$P_1 = \frac{24(15{,}000)}{60} = 6{,}000 \text{ lb.}$$

In a similar manner the additional forces are found to be

$$P_2 = 4{,}500 \text{ lb}, \qquad P_3 = 3{,}000 \text{ lb}, \qquad P_4 = 1{,}500 \text{ lb.}$$

Problems

1.72. In the truss of Figure 1.35a let the dimensions of the members be as follows: $A_1 = 1.00$ in.^{2}, $A_2 = 2.00$ in.^{2}, $A_3 = 0.50$ in.^{2}, $\ell_1 = 7$ ft, $\ell_2 = 5$ ft, $\ell_3 = 10$ ft, $\theta_1 = 60°$, $\theta_2 = 120°$, and $\theta_3 = 150°$. Let the material in the members be linearly elastic with a modulus of elasticity of $E = 10{,}000{,}000$ psi. If the load $P = 30{,}000$ lb, determine the values of the internal forces S_1, S_2, and S_3 by making use of the principle of least complementary work. Assume that the elastic limit stress of the material is not exceeded in any member.

ans. $S_1 = 17{,}320$ lb; $S_2 = 18{,}700$ lb; $S_3 = -800$ lb.

1.73. By making use of the principle of least complementary work, solve Problem 1.26 for the internal forces in each of the members AB, CD, and FH as described in Figure P1.26 and in the statement of Problem 1.26.

1.74. In Figure P1.74 is shown a square truss consisting of members connected by smooth pins and loaded and supported as shown. All members, including the diagonals, have the same cross-sectional area A and all have the same modulus of elasticity E. By making use of the principle of least complementary work, determine the internal forces in the diagonals of the truss in terms of the load P. Assume that the members are all of a material that behaves linearly elastic. (*Hint*: The external reactions at A and B can be found in terms of the load P from equilibrium equations by making use of the free-body diagram of the truss; but the system of internal forces in the truss is statically indeterminate to the first degree.)

ans. $S_2 = 0.854P$; $S_4 = -0.560P$.

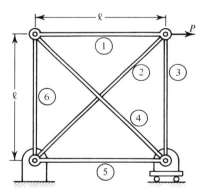

Fig. P 1.74.

1.75. In Figure P1.75 is shown a truss consisting of members connected by smooth pins that is loaded and supported as shown. All members have the same cross-sectional area A and all have the same modulus of elasticity E. Members 1, 2, 3, 4, and 5 all have the same length ℓ but the length of 6 is equal to $\sqrt{3}\ell$. By making use of the principle of least complementary work, determine the internal forces in the diagonals of the truss in terms of the load P. Assume that the members are all of a material that behaves linearly elastic. (*Hint*: The external reactions at A and B can be found in terms of the

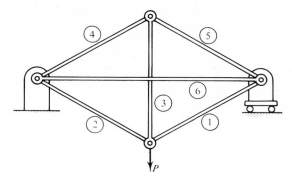

Fig. P 1.75.

load P from equilibrium equations by making use of the free body diagram of the truss; but the system of internal forces in the truss is statically indeterminate to the first degree.)

Stresses at a Point

PART ONE

Basic Concepts

2.1. Introduction

Stresses. In Chapter 1 it was shown that stress is an important quantity to be considered in the design of a load-carrying member because we relate stress to failure of the member if failure results from either fracture or yielding of the material in the member. Stress is a measure of the internal force per unit of area at a point in the member on a specified plane through that point. The load–stress formula derived in Chapter 1 for a tension member subjected to axial centric loading (Eq. 1–10) related the load applied to the tension member to the normal stress distribution acting on a plane perpendicular to the axis of the member. It is convenient, in considering the other members in subsequent chapters, to resolve the loading into components so that the load-stress formulas relate each component of load to either a normal stress distribution or a shearing stress distribution on the plane that is passed through the member. Many structural and machine members are subjected to loads that result in combinations of normal and shearing stresses acting at a point on the plane of the cross section. It will be shown in this chapter that the normal stress is not as large as the maximum normal stress and the shearing stress may not be as large as the maximum shearing stress acting on other planes through that point. Because failure of the member may be related to either the maximum normal stress or the

96

maximum shearing stress, it is necessary that we know how to determine these quantities and the location of the planes on which they act. The term "state of stress at a point" is sometimes used when the stresses on several planes passing through the point must be considered.

2.2. State of Stress

The method of defining the state of stress at a point in a given member consists first in considering that a small part or block of the member (including the point) is severed from the member by planes on which the stresses at the point are assumed to be given or known. If the member is in equilibrium, the block, usually in the form of a volume element, is also in equilibrium. It is convenient to choose a set of coordinate axes and to remove an infinitesimal volume element containing the point by passing planes through the member perpendicular to the coordinate axes as indicated in Figure 2.1. On the face perpendicular to the x axis, there are three components of stress, one of which is a normal stress σ_x and two shearing stresses τ_{xy} and τ_{xz}. The shearing stress τ_{xy} is in the plane perpendicular to the x axis, but the shearing stress is in the y-direction. In a similar manner, τ_{xz} is in the plane perpendicular to the x axis, but the shearing stress is in the z-direction. Note in Figure 2.1 that there are nine components of stress acting on the volume element. These nine components of stress define the state of stress

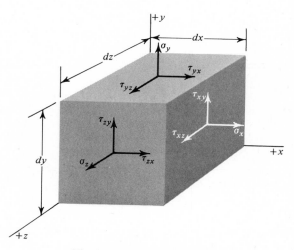

Fig. 2.1. Stresses at a point.

at a point. The sign convention of these stresses is discussed later in this section.

In Figure 2.1 the stress components are shown on only three of the six faces of the volume element. Here it is assumed that components of stress of equal magnitude but opposite sense occur on the other three faces. Actually, each stress component may and usually will change in magnitude in moving from one point to another in the member. For instance, the magnitude of σ_x will change by an infinitesimal amount over the infinitesimal distance between the two planes perpendicular to the x-axis in Figure 2.1.

The volume element of Figure 2.1 is converted into a free-body diagram by multiplying the components of stress by the area of the face they act upon. Let the edge of the volume element have dimensions dx, dy, and dz as indicated in Figure 2.1. There are nine forces acting on the three faces shown in Figure 2.1; there are also nine equal and opposite forces acting on the three faces not shown. The nine components of forces are known when the nine components of stress are known. Actually only six components of stress have to be known to determine the nine forces, because it can be proved that shearing stresses are equal in magnitude in pairs as follows:

$$\tau_{xy} = \tau_{yx}, \qquad \tau_{yz} = \tau_{zy}, \qquad \text{and} \qquad \tau_{zx} = \tau_{xz}.$$

PROOF: Let Figure 2.2a represent the forces acting on the volume element of Figure 2.1, which lies in the middle plane parallel to the xy-plane. For clarity the shearing forces $\tau_{zy}\,dx\,dy$ and $\tau_{zx}\,dx\,dy$ have not been shown because they appear as equal and opposite forces on the front and back faces.

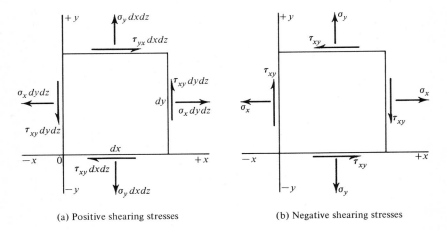

(a) Positive shearing stresses   (b) Negative shearing stresses

Fig. 2.2. Stresses in the xy plane.

By using one of the equations of equilibrium we obtain

$$\Sigma M_0 = \tau_{xy} \, dy \, dz \, (dx) - \tau_{yx} \, dx \, dz \, (dy),$$

$$\tau_{xy} = \tau_{yx}.$$

In the same way it can be proved that $\tau_{yz} = \tau_{zy}$ and $\tau_{zx} = \tau_{xz}$. As a result of this proof, the following theorem may be stated:

If a shearing stress τ occurs on a plane at a given point in a stressed body, there must exist a shearing stress of equal magnitude at that point on a second plane at right angles to the first plane. The vectors representing the two equal shearing stresses lie on a third plane, which is perpendicular to the other two planes.

This theorem shows that there are six independent components of stress instead of nine.

Sign Convention of Stresses. The positive directions of the components of stress are shown in Figure 2.1. The normal stresses σ_x, σ_y, and σ_z are positive when they are tension and negative when they are compression.

In Figure 2.1 all components of shearing stress are positive. The sign convention for the shearing stress is referred to the sign convention for the faces of the volume element; the faces of the volume element adjacent to the positive ends of the axes are the positive faces and the other (opposite) faces are negative faces of the volume element. A component of shearing stress on a positive face of the volume element is positive when its sense is in the positive direction of the axis to which it is parallel. The corresponding component of shearing stress on the opposite (negative) face has its sense in the negative direction of the axis. Thus, in Figure 2.2a the shearing stresses τ_{xy} are positive and the shearing stresses τ_{yx} are positive. In Figure 2.2b these shearing stresses are negative. Since in each case $\tau_{xy} = \tau_{yx}$, the shearing stress in Figure 2.2a is positive, and in Figure 2.2b the shearing stress is negative.

Principal Stresses. In Parts 2 and 3 of this chapter it will be shown that the directions of the x, y, and z axes of Figure 2.1 can always be chosen so that the shearing stresses τ_{xy}, τ_{yz}, and τ_{zx} are each equal to zero at any point in a body that is subjected to loads. The values of the normal stresses σ_x, σ_y, and σ_z whose vectors are parallel, respectively, to the directions of x-, y-, and z-axes that are chosen so that $\tau_{xy} = \tau_{yz} = \tau_{zx} = 0$ are called *principal normal stresses*. In this book the principal normal stresses are usually represented by the symbols σ_1, σ_2, and σ_3 as indicated in Figure 2.3. One of these three principal stresses is the maximum normal stress and another is the minimum normal stress at the point in the member; these

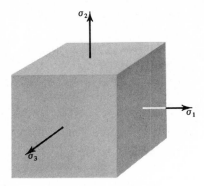

Fig. 2.3. Principal stresses.

values are of special interest to the engineer. Methods of determining the values of the principal stresses will be discussed in Sections 2.7 and 2.9 of this chapter.

2.3. Special Cases of State of Stress

Plane Stress. Let a thin rectangular plate be loaded at its boundary (edges) by forces parallel to the plane of the plate. Let the x- and y-axes be chosen in the plane of the plate at any point and the z-axis perpendicular to the plate. The stresses σ_z, τ_{zx}, and τ_{zy} will be zero on the faces of the plate perpendicular to the z-axis and, if the plate is thin, these three stresses may be assumed to be zero at all points within the plate (except at points near the loads). The stresses σ_x, σ_y, and τ_{xy} are the only remaining components of stress at any point in the plate. The vectors that represent these three stresses all lie in or are parallel to the xy-plane, as shown in Figure 2.2. When the state of stress at a point in a body is completely described by three components of stress all of whose vectors lie in a plane, it is called a state-of-plane stress. This special case of state-of-stress occurs frequently in problems concerned with machine and structural members that are subjected to loads. It will be discussed further in Part 2 of this chapter.

Pure Shear. A special case of plane stress of particular interest occurs when the maximum principal stress σ_1 (tension) is equal in magnitude to the minimum principal stress σ_2 (compression). The third principal stress σ_3 is zero since this is a state of plane stress. Such a state of stress is called *pure shear* and is illustrated in Figure 2.4a. The reason for calling this state-of-plane stress pure shear is explained by Figure 2.4b where the equilibrium

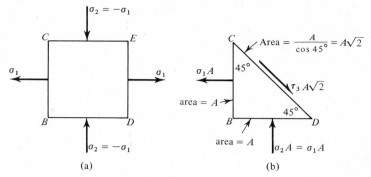

Fig. 2.4. Pure shear.

equations for a half of the volume element BCD will show that the maximum shearing stress τ_3 alone acts on the diagonal plane and that $\tau_3 = \sigma_1$. That is, since there is no normal stress on the plane CD (nor on BE if the volume element is cut along this diagonal), it is called pure shear.

Major Emphasis in This Book. The major emphasis in this book is concerned with members in which the state of stress is assumed to be plane stress. Transformation equations for plane stress can be derived without considering the general three-dimensional state of stress. If this approach is to be followed, continue with Part Two and omit Part Three. A better understanding of stresses at a point will be obtained by considering the three-dimensional state of stress and deriving transformation equations for the general case. The reader can continue from here to Part Three and then return to Part Two omitting Section 2.4.

PART TWO

Analysis of Plane Stress

2.4. Transformation Equations for Plane Stress

Consider a member loaded under conditions that produce a plane state of stress at every point in the member. Choose x, y, and z coordinate axes and, at a point in the member, consider an infinitesimal volume element surrounding the point whose sides are perpendicular to each of the coordinate axes. If the direction of the axes have been chosen correctly, the stress components σ_z, τ_{zx}, and τ_{zy} acting on the two faces of the volume element

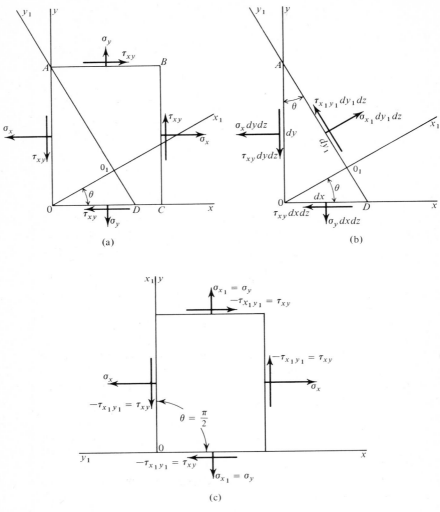

Fig. 2.5. Plane stress.

perpendicular to the z-axis will all be zero. The stress components σ_x, σ_y, and τ_{xy} are shown acting on the volume element in Figure 2.5a. In later chapters load-stress relations will be derived for the member to determine magnitudes for σ_x, σ_y, and τ_{xy}; not only are they assumed to be known quantities but they are assumed to be uniformly distributed over the infinitesimal areas of the volume element of Figure 2.5a.

The known stress components σ_x, σ_y, and τ_{xy} determine the plane state of stress at the specified point in the member. The problem posed here is to determine the magnitudes of the normal stress and shearing stress components on a plane through the volume element perpendicular to some axis x_1 as indicated by AD in Figure 2.5a. The x_1-axis lies in the xy-plane and is located counterclockwise through an angle θ from the x-axis as indicated in Figure 2.5a. Note that the sign convention for θ has been specified; θ is positive when the x_1-axis is located counterclockwise from the x-axis and is negative when the x_1-axis is located clockwise from the x-axis.

The part of the volume element severed by the plane perpendicular to the x_1-axis through points A and D is shown in Figure 2.5b. The unknown stress components σ_{x_1} and $\tau_{x_1y_1}$ are assumed to be positive. The triangular volume element AOD is converted into a free-body diagram by multiplying the stresses on each face by the area of the face. The magnitudes of σ_{x_1} and $\tau_{x_1y_1}$ are obtained in terms of the given values of σ_x, σ_y, τ_{xy}, and the cosine and sine of the angle θ by the following equations of equilibrium:

$$\sum F_{x_1} = 0 = \sigma_{x_1}\,dy_1\,dz - \sigma_x\,dy\,dz\cos\theta - \sigma_y\,dx\,dz\sin\theta - \tau_{xy}\,dy\,dz\sin\theta$$
$$- \tau_{xy}\,dx\,dz\cos\theta,$$

$$\sum F_{y_1} = 0 = \tau_{x_1y_1}\,dy_1\,dz + \sigma_x\,dy\,dz\sin\theta - \sigma_y\,dx\,dz\cos\theta - \tau_{xy}\,dy\,dz\cos\theta$$
$$+ \tau_{xy}\,dx\,dz\sin\theta.$$

When it is noted that $\sin\theta = dx/dy_1$ and $\cos\theta = dy/dy_1$, these relations simplify to

$$\sigma_{x_1} = \sigma_x\cos^2\theta + \sigma_y\sin^2\theta + 2\tau_{xy}\sin\theta\cos\theta, \qquad (2\text{--}1)$$

$$\tau_{x_1y_1} = (\sigma_y - \sigma_x)\sin\theta\cos\theta + \tau_{xy}(\cos^2\theta - \sin^2\theta). \qquad (2\text{--}2)$$

These are the transformation equations of stress for plane stress. Note that Equations (2–1) and (2–2) give the normal stress component σ_{x_1} and the shearing stress component $\tau_{x_1y_1}$ acting on a plane perpendicular to the x_1-axis and at the point in the member where σ_x, σ_y, and τ_{xy} have been determined.

2.5. Transformation Equations of Plane Stress as Functions of 2θ

The transformation equations of plane stress are usually expressed in terms of 2θ rather than in terms of θ. Using the trigometric identities $\sin^2\theta = (1 - \cos 2\theta)/2$, $\cos^2\theta = (1 + \cos 2\theta)/2$, and $2\sin\theta\cos\theta = \sin 2\theta$,

Equations (2–1) and (2–2) become

$$\sigma_{x_1} = \tfrac{1}{2}(\sigma_x + \sigma_y) + \tfrac{1}{2}(\sigma_x - \sigma_y)\cos 2\theta + \tau_{xy}\sin 2\theta, \qquad (2\text{–}3)$$

$$\tau_{x_1y_1} = -\tfrac{1}{2}(\sigma_x - \sigma_y)\sin 2\theta + \tau_{xy}\cos 2\theta. \qquad (2\text{–}4)$$

Confirming Equations (2–3) and (2–4). Equations (2–3) and (2–4) determine magnitudes and senses for the stress components σ_{x_1} and $\tau_{x_1y_1}$ which act on a plane perpendicular to the x_1-axis at the point in the member where σ_x, σ_y, and τ_{xy} are known. These equations are valid for all values of θ. When $\theta = 0$ in Figure 2.5a, the x- and x_1-axes coincide as do the y- and y_1-axes; therefore,

$$\sigma_{x_1} = \sigma_x \qquad \text{and} \qquad \tau_{x_1y_1} = \tau_{xy}$$

as is confirmed by Equations (2–3) and (2–4). When $\theta = \pi/2$ in Figure 2.5a, the x_1-axis coincides with the y-axis and the y_1-axis coincides with the $-x$-axis, as shown in Figure 2.5c (see also Figure 2.11d). From Equations (2–3) and (2–4), when $\theta = \pi/2$,

$$\sigma_{x_1} = \sigma_y \qquad \text{and} \qquad -\tau_{x_1y_1} = \tau_{xy}.$$

The fact that $\tau_{x_1y_1}$ is the negative of τ_{xy} is explained by the fact that the positive faces of the volume element are now the top and left faces, respectively, and on these positive faces $\tau_{x_1y_1}$ acts in the negative directions of the x_1- and y_1-axes, respectively.

Illustrative Problems

2.1.   A plane state of stress is given (Fig. P2.1a) in which $\sigma_x = 10{,}000$ psi, $\sigma_y = -4{,}000$ psi and $\tau_{xy} = 8{,}000$ psi. By making use of Equations (2–3) and

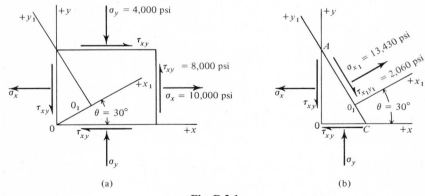

(a)   (b)

Fig. P 2.1.

(2–4) compute the values of the stresses σ_{x_1} and $\tau_{x_1y_1}$ when the x_1-axis is at a positive angle $\theta = 30°$ (counterclockwise) with the positive end of the x-axis.

SOLUTION.   Figure P2.1b shows the location of the plane AC on which the normal shearing stresses σ_{x_1} and $\tau_{x_1y_1}$ act. The normal stress is found by the substitution of the given values of $\sigma_x, \sigma_y, \tau_{xy}$, and θ into Equation (2–3), which gives

$$\sigma_{x_1} = \frac{10,000 - 4,000}{2} + \frac{10,000 + 4,000}{2}\cos 60° + 8,000 \sin 60°$$

$$= 13,430 \text{ psi}.$$

The substitution of these same quantities into Equation (2–4) gives

$$\tau_{x_1y_1} = -\frac{10,000 + 4,000}{2}\sin 60° + 8,000 \cos 60°$$

$$= -2,060 \text{ psi}.$$

The stress σ_{x_1} is positive and is shown in Figure P2.1b as a tensile stress on the plane AC, which is perpendicular to the x_1-axis, but the shearing stress $\tau_{x_1y_1}$ is negative and is shown on plane AC with the direction and sense toward the negative end of the y_1-axis. It should be recalled here that the sign of the shearing stress $\tau_{x_1y_1}$ depends on the choice of the positive directions of the x_1- and y_1-axes. This fact is further illustrated in the next problem.

2.2.   For the state of stress given in Problem 2.1 and Figure P2.1a determine the σ_{x_1} and $\tau_{x_1y_1}$ stresses when the positive (counterclockwise) angle $\theta = 120°$ with the positive end of the x-axis.

SOLUTION.   Figure P2.2a shows the location of the x_1 and y_1 axes as given in this problem. It is required that we compute the normal and shearing stresses σ_{x_1} and $\tau_{x_1y_1}$ on the plane AC' that is perpendicular to the x_1-axis. The substitution of the given quantities $\sigma_x = 10,000$ psi, $\sigma_y = -4,000$ psi, $\tau_{xy} = 8,000$ psi, and $\theta = 120°$ into Equation (2–3) gives

$$\sigma_{x_1} = \frac{10,000 - 4,000}{2} + \frac{10,000 + 4,000}{2}\cos 240° + 8,000 \sin 240°$$

$$= -7,430 \text{ psi}.$$

From a similar substitution into Equation (2–4) we get

$$\tau_{x_1y_1} = -\frac{10,000 + 4,000}{2}\sin 240° + 8,000 \cos 240°$$

$$= 2,060 \text{ psi}.$$

The normal stress σ_{x_1} is negative and is shown in Figure P2.2a as a compressive stress on plane AC'. The shearing stress $\tau_{x_1y_1}$ is positive and is shown on plane AC' in the positive direction of the y_1-axis.

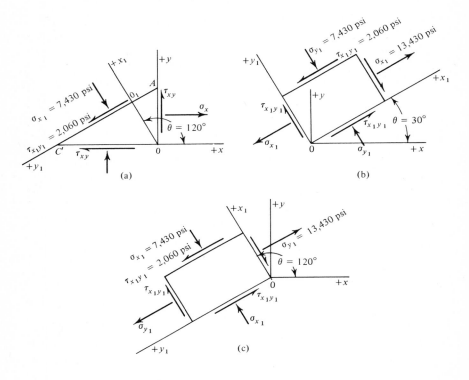

Fig. P 2.2.

Figures P2.2b and c further illustrate the fact that the sign of the shearing stress depends on the choice of the positive direction for the x_1- and y_1-axes. The state of stress is the same in both Figures P2.2b and c, but the shearing stress changes sense with the rotation of the x_1- and y_1-axes through $\theta = 90°$; that is from $\theta = 30°$ in Figure P2.2b to $\theta = 120°$ in Figure P2.2c.

Problems

2.3. In Figure 2.5a let $\sigma_x = 15,000$ psi, $\sigma_y = 2,000$ psi, $\tau_{xy} = 10,000$ psi, and $\theta = 60°$; determine the values of σ_{x_1} and $\tau_{x_1y_1}$.

2.4. In Figure 2.5a let $\sigma_x = -4,000$ psi, $\sigma_y = 10,000$ psi, $\tau_{xy} = 8,000$ psi, and $\theta = 30°$; determine the values of σ_{x_1} and $\tau_{x_1y_1}$.

ans. $\sigma_{x_1} = 5,430$ psi; $\tau_{x_1y_1} = 10,060$ psi.

2.5. In Figure 2.5a let $\sigma_x = -6,000$ psi, $\sigma_y = -12,000$ psi, $\tau_{xy} = -8,000$ psi, and $\theta = 45°$; determine the values of σ_{x_1} and $\tau_{x_1y_1}$.

2.6. Make use of Equations (2–3) and (2–4) to prove that in a state of pure shear as shown in Figure 2.4 the shearing stress on the plane making an angle of 45° with the principal normal stress directions is equal in magnitude to the principal normal stress. What is the magnitude of the normal stress on this face?

2.7. Make use of Equation (2–3) to prove that for a state of plane stress, the sum of the normal stresses on any two perpendicular planes that make angles θ and $\theta + 90°$ with the x axis is constant.

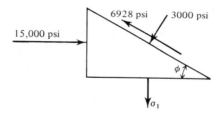

Fig. P 2.8.

2.8. The state of plane stress at a point in a member is as indicated in Figure P2.8. Determine the magnitudes of σ_1 and ϕ by using conditions of static equilibrium and show that Equations (2–3) and (2–4) are satisfied. Note that $\theta = \pi/2 - \phi$.

2.6. Mohr's Circle for Plane Stress

When a member is loaded under conditions that produce a plane state of stress, the state of stress at a point is specified by three known components σ_x, σ_y, and τ_{xy}; positive values of these stress components are shown on a volume element in Figure 2.5a. Transformation equations (Eqs. 2–3 and 2–4) were derived to determine the unknown stress components σ_{x_1} and $\tau_{x_1y_1}$ that act on a plane perpendicular to the x_1-axis in Figure 2.5 at the specified point. These unknown stress components can also be determined graphically using Mohr's circle of stress. The graphical procedure is developed in this section in order to better interpret the physical concepts involved. In Figure 2.6a the abscissas are values of the normal components of stress σ, and the

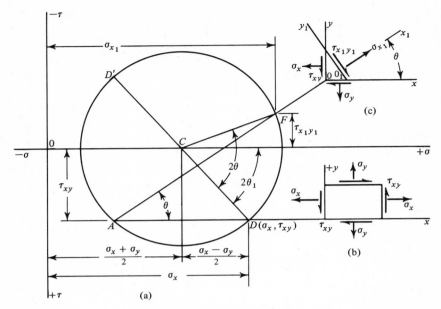

Fig. 2.6. Mohr's circle of stress.

ordinates are values of the shearing components of stress τ. Positive σ is to the right and positive τ is downward, so that the positive (counterclockwise rotation) sense of the angle θ between the x-axis and the x_1-axis is preserved in the graph, as will be shown later.

Equations (2–3) and (2–4), taken together, can be represented by a circle, called Mohr's circle of stress. To demonstrate this fact, the function of the angle 2θ is eliminated from Equations (2–3) and (2–4) by squaring both sides of both equations and adding them. Before Equation (2–3) is squared, the term $(\sigma_x + \sigma_y)/2$ is transposed to the left side. The equation resulting from squaring and adding is as follows:

$$[\sigma_{x_1} - \tfrac{1}{2}(\sigma_x + \sigma_y)]^2 + \tau_{x_1y_1}^2 = \tfrac{1}{4}(\sigma_x - \sigma_y)^2 + \tau_{xy}^2. \qquad (2\text{–}5)$$

In the graph of Figure 2.6a the circle $ADFD'$ represents Equation (2–5). The center of the circle is at C whose coordinates are as follows:

$$\sigma_{x_1} = \tfrac{1}{2}(\sigma_x + \sigma_y) \qquad \text{and} \qquad \tau_{x_1y_1} = 0.$$

Thus it is seen that the center of Mohr's circle of stress lies on the σ-axis at a distance OC from the origin O of the coordinate axes:

$$OC = \tfrac{1}{2}(\sigma_x + \sigma_y). \qquad (2\text{–}6)$$

The radius R of the circle is equal to the square root of the right side of Equation (2–5).

$$R = CA = CD = CF = CD' = \sqrt{\tfrac{1}{4}(\sigma_x - \sigma_y)^2 + \tau_{xy}^2}. \qquad (2\text{–}7)$$

With the center of Mohr's circle of stress located at a known distance OC from the origin and with the radius R of the circle known, the circle can be constructed. It is necessary now to interpret what the coordinates of each point of Mohr's circle of stress represents.

Points on Mohr's Circle of Stress. The coordinates of each point on Mohr's circle of stress should be interpreted as representing the stress components σ_{x_1} and $\tau_{x_1y_1}$ which act on a plane perpendicular to the x_1-axis. One point D on the circle is of particular importance because all other points on the circle will be interpreted in terms of its coordinates σ_x and τ_{xy}. The angle θ in Equations (2–3) and (2–4) is measured counterclockwise from the x-axis in Figure 2.6c and counterclockwise from the radius CD in Figure 2.6a. When $\theta = 0$, the x_1- and y_1-axes coincide with the x- and y-axes, respectively, and the stress components $\sigma = \sigma_{x_1} = \sigma_x$ and $\tau = \tau_{x_1y_1} = \tau_{xy}$ acting on a face perpendicular to the x_1-axis are known in magnitude and sense and are the coordinates of point D in Figure 2.6a.

Let point F be another point on Mohr's circle of stress in Figure 2.6a located at an angle 2θ counterclockwise from point D. The stress components σ_{x_1} and $\tau_{x_1y_1}$ are the coordinates of point F and act on a face perpendicular to the x_1-axis, which is located at an angle θ counterclockwise from the x-axis. This is easily proved as follows:

$$\sigma_{x_1} = OC + CF \cos(2\theta - 2\theta_1)$$

$$= \tfrac{1}{2}(\sigma_x + \sigma_y) + R \cos 2\theta \cos 2\theta_1 + R \sin 2\theta \sin 2\theta_1$$

$$\tau_{x_1y_1} = -CF \sin(2\theta - 2\theta_1)$$

$$= -R \sin 2\theta \cos 2\theta_1 + R \cos 2\theta \sin 2\theta_1.$$

The sign of $\tau_{x_1y_1}$ is negative because point F lies toward the negative end of the τ-axis. When it is noted that $R \cos 2\theta_1 = (\sigma_x - \sigma_y)/2$ and $R \sin 2\theta_1 = \tau_{xy}$, these relations agree exactly with Equations (2–3) and (2–4).

Each point on Mohr's circle of stress represents the normal and shearing components of stress acting on a face perpendicular to the x_1-axis. Consider any point F in Figure 2.6a. The direction of the x_1-axis corresponding to point F will now be determined. Draw a line through point D parallel to the σ-axis. This line is parallel to the line of action of σ_x and is labeled the x-axis as shown; the volume element with known stress components is shown in Figure 2.6b. The x-axis intersects Mohr's circle of stress at two points A and D. It will be shown that point A is the origin of both the x-axis and the x_1-axis. Construct chord AF. Angle DAF between AF and the x-axis is equal to θ since the arc length DF subtends angle $DCF = 2\theta$. But θ is the angle between the x-axis and the x_1-axis; therefore, the extension of chord AF is the x_1-axis and the stress components σ_{x_1} and $\tau_{x_1 y_1}$, which are the coordinates of point F, act on a face perpendicular to the x_1-axis as shown in Figure 2.6c. The positive y_1-axis is always located counterclockwise 90° from the positive x_1-axis. Because point F lies toward the negative end of the τ-axis, the shearing stress $\tau_{x_1 y_1}$ has a sense in the negative direction of the y_1-axis as shown in Figure 2.6c. Note that the infinitesimal volume element shown in Figure 2.6b and a portion of the same volume element shown in Figure 2.6c are located at the same point in the load-carrying member.

Illustrative Problems

2.9.   Solve Problem 2.1 by using Mohr's circle of stress.

SOLUTION.   The plane state of stress is $\sigma_x = 10{,}000$ psi, $\sigma_y = -4{,}000$ psi, and $\tau_{xy} = 8{,}000$ psi, and it is required to determine σ_{x_1} and $\tau_{x_1 y_1}$ for $\theta = 30°$.

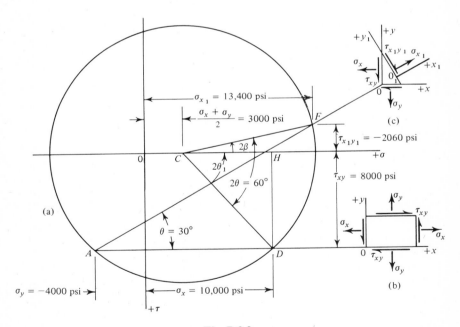

Fig. P 2.9.

Mohr's circle of stress is constructed by first choosing σ- and τ-axes as shown in Figure P2.9a with the origin at O. The center of Mohr's circle lies on the σ-axis at distance OC from the origin as given by Equation (2–6):

$$OC = \tfrac{1}{2}(\sigma_x + \sigma_y) = \frac{10{,}000 - 4{,}000}{2} = 3{,}000 \text{ psi.} \tag{a}$$

The radius of Mohr's circle is given by Equation (2–7):

$$R = \sqrt{\tfrac{1}{4}(\sigma_x - \sigma_y)^2 + \tau_{xy}^2} = \sqrt{(7{,}000)^2 + (8{,}000)^2} = 10{,}640 \text{ psi.} \tag{b}$$

Mohr's circle of stress can be drawn with center at C and radius $R = 10{,}640$ psi; however, the usual procedure is to locate point D whose coordinates on the circle are the known stress components $\sigma_x = 10{,}000$ psi and $\tau_{xy} = 8{,}000$ psi. Mohr's circle is drawn with C as center and CD as radius as shown in Figure P2.9a. The given state of stress is shown in Figure P2.9b where the x-axis is an extension of chord AD, which is parallel to the σ-axis.

If Mohr's circle of stress in Figure P2.9a is drawn to scale, the stress components σ_{x_1} and $\tau_{x_1 y_1}$ can be determined graphically as follows: Start with radius CD and rotate counterclockwise through the angle $2\theta = 60°$ to the radius CF. The coordinates of F are the stresses $\sigma_{x_1} = 13{,}400$ psi and $\tau_{x_1 y_1} = -2{,}060$ psi, as shown in Figure P2.9a. The direction of σ_{x_1} is along the x_1-axis, which is an extension of chord AF that makes the angle $\theta = 30°$ with chord AD (the x-axis). The sense of each of these stresses is as shown on the triangular block in Figure P2.9c.

Sometimes Mohr's circle of stress is not drawn to scale but is used in writing the geometrical equations relating known and unknown stress components. In Figure P2.9a note that

$$\sigma_{x_1} = OC + CF \cos 2\beta = OC + R \cos 2\beta, \tag{c}$$

$$\tau_{x_1 y_1} = -CF \sin 2\beta = -R \sin 2\beta. \tag{d}$$

Because $2\theta = 60°$ is known, the angle 2β can be obtained by determining the magnitude of $2\theta_1$. From the right triangle CHD,

$$\tan 2\theta_1 = \frac{HD}{CH} = \frac{\tau_{xy}}{(\sigma_x - \sigma_y)/2} = \frac{8{,}000}{7{,}000} = 1.143,$$

$$2\theta_1 = 48° \, 49'.$$

The magnitude of 2β is given by the relation

$$2\beta = 2\theta - 2\theta_1 = 60° - 48° \, 49' = 11° \, 11'.$$

Substituting this value of 2β into Equations (c) and (d) along with values of OC and $CF = R$ from Equations (a) and (b), gives

$$\sigma_{x_1} = OC + R \cos 11° 11' = 3,000 + 10,640(0.981) = 13,400 \text{ psi},$$

$$\tau_{x_1 y_1} = -R \sin 11° 11' = -10,640(0.194) = -2,060 \text{ psi}.$$

Problems

2.10. Given a plane state of stress where $\sigma_x = -6,000$ psi, $\sigma_y = 8,000$ psi, and $\tau_{xy} = -5,000$ psi. Determine the stresses σ_{x_1} and $\tau_{x_1 y_1}$ for an angle $\theta = -60°$ (the x_1-axis rotated clockwise from the x-axis) by using Equations (2–3) and (2–4) and check the results by making use of Mohr's circle of stress.

$$\text{ans.} \quad \sigma_{x_1} = 8,830 \text{ psi}; \ \tau_{x_1 y_1} = -3,560 \text{ psi}.$$

2.11. Solve Problem 2.3 by making use of Mohr's circle of stress.
2.12. Solve Problem 2.4 by making use of Mohr's circle of stress.
2.13. Solve Problem 2.5 by making use of Mohr's circle of stress.
2.14. Solve Problem 2.7 by making use of Mohr's circle of stress.
2.15. Solve Problem 2.8 by making use of Mohr's circle of stress.
2.16. The block in Figure P2.16 has a thickness of 1 in. and is subjected to the state of plane stress shown. Using equations of equilibrium alone, determine σ_{x_1} and $\tau_{x_1 y_1}$ and check the results using Mohr's circle of stress.

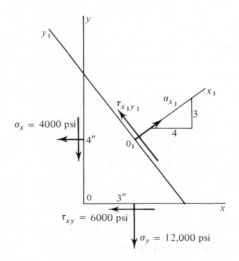

Fig. P 2.16.

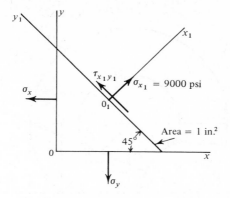

Fig. P 2.17.

2.17. At a point in a member a state of plane stress exists as indicated in Figure P2.17. Using equations of equilibrium alone, determine the magnitudes of the three unknown stress components for the condition that $\sigma_x = 2\sigma_y$, where σ_x and σ_y are principal stresses. Check your results using Mohr's circle of stress.

2.18. At a point in a member a state of plane stress exists as indicated in Figure P2.18. Determine the magnitudes of the two unknown stress components.

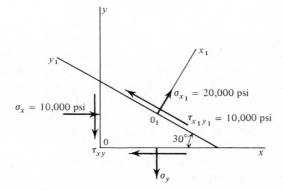

Fig. P 2.18.

2.7. Principal Stresses in a Plane State of Stress

In Sections 2.5 and 2.6 an analytical and a graphical method, respectively, have been given for determining the normal and shearing stresses on any

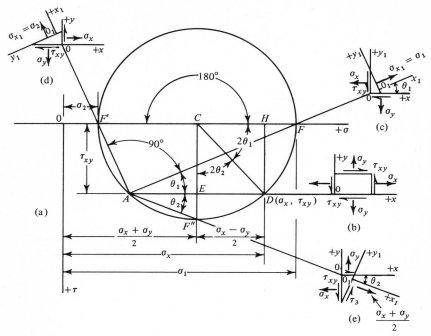

Fig. 2.7.

plane perpendicular to the x_1-axis, which is located with respect to the x-axis by the angle θ. Either of these methods may be used, by varying the angle θ, to determine the principal values of the normal and shearing stresses. The graphical method (Mohr's circle of stress) is used here.

Principal Values of Normal Stress. Let Figure 2.7a represent the Mohr's circle of stress for the given state of stress, σ_x, σ_y, and τ_{xy} as shown in Figure 2.7b (see Section 2.6 and Figure 2.6 for construction of Mohr's circle of stress).

The abscissas of the points F and F' give the values of σ_1 and σ_2, which are the maximum and minimum values of the normal stresses in the xy-plane. Figures 2.7c and d show the directions of σ_1 and σ_2. From Figure 2.7a we find the magnitude of σ_1 to be

$$\sigma_1 = OC + CF = OC + CD = OC + R.$$

The magnitudes of OC and R are given by Equations (2–6) and (2–7); therefore,

$$\sigma_1 = \tfrac{1}{2}(\sigma_x + \sigma_y) + \sqrt{\tfrac{1}{4}(\sigma_x - \sigma_y)^2 + \tau_{xy}^2} \qquad (2\text{–}8)$$

In a similar manner

$$\sigma_2 = OC - CF' = OC - R,$$

$$\sigma_2 = \tfrac{1}{2}(\sigma_x + \sigma_y) - \sqrt{\tfrac{1}{4}(\sigma_x - \sigma_y)^2 + \tau_{xy}^2}. \tag{2-9}$$

There are two values of θ, namely, θ_1 and $\theta_1 + \pi/2$ for which σ_{x_1} has principal values σ_1 and σ_2. From the geometry of Figure 2.7, it is seen that

$$\tan 2\theta_1 = \frac{DH}{CH} = \frac{\tau_{xy}}{\tfrac{1}{2}(\sigma_x - \sigma_y)}. \tag{2-10}$$

It should be pointed out that the third principal stress, $\sigma_3 = 0$, is perpendicular to the plane of the x- and y-axes. The stress σ_3 is the minimum principal stress if σ_1 and σ_2 in Equations (2–8) and (2–9) are both tensile stresses and is the maximum principal stress if σ_1 and σ_2 are both compressive stresses.

Principal Values of Shearing Stress. In Mohr's circle of stress of Figure 2.7a the ordinate of the point F'' represents a principal shearing stress τ_3, which is equal to the radius $CF'' = CD = R$. Thus from Equation (2–7)

$$\tau_3 = CD = R = \sqrt{\tfrac{1}{4}(\sigma_x - \sigma_y)^2 + \tau_{xy}^2}. \tag{2-11}$$

Note that Equation (2–11) is also obtained by taking one half the algebraic difference between Equations (2–8) and (2–9); that is

$$\tau_3 = \tfrac{1}{2}(\sigma_1 - \sigma_2). \tag{2-12}$$

Also,

$$\tan 2\theta_2 = \frac{DE}{CE} = -\frac{\tfrac{1}{2}(\sigma_x - \sigma_y)}{\tau_{xy}} \tag{2-13}$$

where the negative sign is due to the fact that $2\theta_2$ is measured clockwise from line CD. The extension of the chord AF'' represents the direction of O_1x_1-axis in Figure 2.7e and the stress τ_3 lies on the plane perpendicular to O_1x_1 with the positive sense as shown.

The other two principal shearing stresses, τ_1 and τ_2, are each found by taking one half the algebraic difference between two principal normal stresses; that is

$$\tau_1 = \tfrac{1}{2}(\sigma_2 - \sigma_3) \qquad \text{and} \qquad \tau_2 = \tfrac{1}{2}(\sigma_3 - \sigma_1). \tag{2-14}$$

Finally, the maximum shearing stress is found by taking one half the algebraic difference between the maximum and minimum principal normal stresses; that is

$$\tau_{max} = \tfrac{1}{2}(\sigma_{max} - \sigma_{min}). \tag{2-15}$$

Illustrative Problems

2.19. Given a plane state of stress $(\sigma_z = \tau_{zx} = \tau_{zy} = 0)$ where $\sigma_x = -10,000$ psi, $\sigma_y = -20,000$ psi, and $\tau_{xy} = -6,000$ psi. Determine the three principal normal stresses, the three principal shearing stresses, θ_1, and θ_2 using Equations (2–8) through (2–14). Check results for $\sigma_1, \sigma_2, \tau_3, \theta_1$, and θ_2 using Mohr's circle of stress.

SOLUTION. The required calculations for this problem are to be checked using Mohr's circle of stress. The advantage of working with Mohr's circle is that it gives a geometrical interpretation of Equations (2–8) through (2–14). It is convenient to construct Mohr's circle as shown in

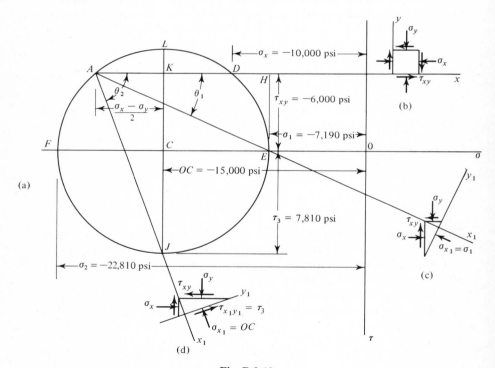

Fig. P 2.19.

Figure P2.19a and to interpret each equation used in terms of the geometry of the circle.

The center of Mohr's circle is located at distance OC from the origin O in Figure P2.19a as indicated by Equation (2–6):

$$OC = \tfrac{1}{2}(\sigma_x + \sigma_y) = \tfrac{1}{2}(-10,000 - 20,000) = -15,000 \text{ psi.}$$

The radius R of the circle is given by Equation (2–7).

$$R = \sqrt{\tfrac{1}{4}(\sigma_x - \sigma_y)^2 + \tau_{xy}^2} = \sqrt{(5,000)^2 + (-6,000)^2} = 7,810 \text{ psi.}$$

Mohr's circle of stress can be drawn with center C and radius R; however, the usual procedure is to locate point D whose coordinates on the circle are known stress components $\sigma_x = -10,000$ psi and $\tau_{xy} = -6,000$ psi. Mohr's circle is drawn with C as center and CD as radius as shown in Figure P2.19a. The given state of stress is shown in Figure P2.19b where the x-axis is an extension of chord AD, which is parallel to the σ-axis.

Two of the three principal normal stresses are given by the intersection of Mohr's circle with the σ-axis. Principal normal stress σ_1 is equal to $OE = OC + R$, which is the value given by Equation (2–8). Principal normal stress σ_2 is equal to $OF = OC - R$, which is the value given by Equation (2–9). The three principal normal stresses are

$$\sigma_1 = OC + R = -15,000 + 7,810 = -7,190 \text{ psi,}$$

$$\sigma_2 = OC - R = -15,000 - 7,810 = -22,810 \text{ psi,}$$

$$\sigma_3 = \sigma_z = 0.$$

Values of the angle θ_1 to determine the directions of the x_1-axes in the directions of principal normal stresses σ_1 and σ_2 are given by Equation (2–10).

$$\tan 2\theta_1 = \frac{2\tau_{xy}}{\sigma_x - \sigma_y} = \frac{2(-6,000)}{-10,000 + 20,000} = -1.2,$$

$$2\theta_1 = -50.2° \quad \text{or} \quad 129.8°,$$

$$\theta_1 = -25.1° \quad \text{or} \quad 64.9°.$$

These two values of θ_1 can be obtained from Mohr's circle of stress. The extension of chord AE gives the x_1-axis in the direction of the principal normal stress σ_1 corresponding to point E on Mohr's circle. The stress components $\sigma_{x_1} = \sigma_1$ and $\tau_{x_1y_1} = 0$, which are the coordinates of point E act on a face perpendicular to the x_1-axis as shown in Figure P2.19c. The angle between the x-axis and the x_1-axis is θ_1. Since the x_1-axis is located clockwise from the x-axis, θ_1 is negative. To determine the magnitude of θ_1, complete the right triangle AEH.

$$\tan \theta_1 = \frac{HE}{AH} \quad \text{where } HE = 6,000 \text{ psi and } AH = 5,000 + 7,810 = 12,810 \text{ psi}$$

$$= \frac{6,000}{12,810} = 0.4685,$$

$$\theta_1 = -25.1°,$$

which agrees with the previous calculation. The other value of θ_1 is the angle between the x-axis and the extension of chord AF.

The three principal shearing stresses are given by Equations (2–12) and (2–14).

$$\tau_1 = \tfrac{1}{2}(\sigma_3 - \sigma_1) = \tfrac{1}{2}(0 + 7,190) = 3,595 \text{ psi},$$

$$\tau_2 = \tfrac{1}{2}(\sigma_3 - \sigma_2) = \tfrac{1}{2}(0 + 22,810) = 11,405 \text{ psi},$$

$$\tau_3 = \tfrac{1}{2}(\sigma_1 - \sigma_2) = \tfrac{1}{2}(-7,190 + 22,810) = 7,810 \text{ psi}.$$

The maximum shearing stress for Mohr's circle of stress in Figure P2.19a is indicated by point J for which

$$\tau_3 = R = 7,810 \text{ psi}.$$

The values of θ_2 to determine the planes on which τ_3 act are given by Equation (2–13).

$$\tan 2\theta_2 = -\frac{\sigma_x - \sigma_y}{2\tau_{xy}} = -\frac{-10,000 + 20,000}{2(-6,000)} = 0.8333,$$

$$2\theta_2 = 39.8° \quad \text{or} \quad -140.2°,$$

$$\theta_2 = 19.9° \quad \text{or} \quad -70.1°.$$

These two values of θ_2 can be obtained from Mohr's circle of stress. The chord AJ gives the x_1-axis to determine the element in Figure P2.19d on which τ_3 acts. The stress components $\sigma_{x_1} = OC = -15,000$ psi and $\tau_{x_1 y_1} = \tau_{3.} = 7,810$ psi, which are the coordinates of point J, act on a face perpendicular to the x_1-axis. The angle between the x-axis and the x_1-axis is θ_2. Because the x_1-axis is located clockwise from the x-axis, θ_2 is negative. To determine the magnitude of θ_2, complete the right triangle AKJ.

$$\tan \theta_2 = \frac{KJ}{AK} \quad \text{where } KJ = 6,000 + 7,810 = 13,810 \text{ psi and } AK = 5,000 \text{ psi}$$

$$= \frac{13,810}{5,000} = 2.762,$$

$$\theta_2 = -70.1°$$

which agrees with the previous calculation. The other value of θ_2 is the angle between the x-axis and the extension of chord AL.

Problems

2.20 Through 2.23. In each of the following problems, the state of stress at the point is plane stress, that is, $\sigma_z = \tau_{zy} = \tau_{zx} = 0$. For each problem determine the three principal stresses, the three principal shearing stresses, θ_1 and θ_2 using Equations (2–8) through (2–15). Check results for σ_1, σ_2, τ_3, θ_1, and θ_2 using Mohr's circle of stress.

2.20. $\sigma_x = -24{,}000\,\text{psi}; \sigma_y = -12{,}000\,\text{psi}; \tau_{xy} = -8{,}000\,\text{psi}.$

ans. $\sigma_1 = -8{,}000\,\text{psi}; \sigma_2 = -28{,}000\,\text{psi}; \sigma_3 = 0; \tau_1 = 14{,}000\,\text{psi}; \tau_2 = 4{,}000\,\text{psi};$

$\tau_3 = 10{,}000\,\text{psi}; \theta_1 = -63.4°; \theta_2 = 71.6°.$

2.21. $\sigma_x = 0; \sigma_y = 20{,}000\,\text{psi}; \tau_{xy} = -10{,}000\,\text{psi}.$
2.22. $\sigma_x = 18{,}000\,\text{psi}; \sigma_y = 6{,}000\,\text{psi}; \tau_{xy} = 5{,}000\,\text{psi}.$

ans. $\sigma_1 = 19{,}800\,\text{psi}; \sigma_2 = 4{,}190\,\text{psi}; \sigma_3 = 0; \tau_1 = 2{,}095\,\text{psi}; \tau_2 = 9{,}905\,\text{psi};$

$\tau_3 = 7{,}810\,\text{psi}; \theta_1 = 19.9°; \theta_2 = -25.1°.$

2.23. $\sigma_x = -8{,}000\,\text{psi}; \sigma_y = 8{,}000\,\text{psi}; \tau_{xy} = -8{,}000\,\text{psi}.$

2.24 Through 2.29. In each of the following problems, the state of stress at a point is plane stress, i.e., $\sigma_z = \tau_{zy} = \tau_{zx} = 0$. For each problem determine the magnitude and sense of the principal stress whose absolute magnitude is a maximum. Determine the direction θ_1, measured from the x-axis, of the x_1-axis, which is in the direction of this principal stress. Also determine the maximum shearing stress.

2.24. $\sigma_x = 24{,}000\,\text{psi}; \sigma_y = 0; \tau_{xy} = 16{,}000\,\text{psi}.$
2.25. $\sigma_x = 0; \sigma_y = -18{,}000\,\text{psi}; \tau_{xy} = -10{,}000\,\text{psi}.$

ans. $\sigma_2 = -22{,}460\,\text{psi}; \theta_1 = 66.0°; \tau_{max} = 13{,}460\,\text{psi}.$

2.26. $\sigma_x = -6{,}000\,\text{psi}; \sigma_y = -26{,}000\,\text{psi}; \tau_{xy} = 10{,}000\,\text{psi}.$
2.27. $\sigma_x = 8{,}000\,\text{psi}; \sigma_y = 20{,}000\,\text{psi}; \tau_{xy} = -6{,}000\,\text{psi}.$

ans. $\sigma_1 = 22{,}480\,\text{psi}; \theta_1 = -67.5°; \tau_{max} = 11{,}200\,\text{psi}.$

2.28. $\sigma_x = -4{,}000\,\text{psi}; \sigma_y = 10{,}000\,\text{psi}; \tau_{xy} = 9{,}000\,\text{psi}.$
2.29. $\sigma_x = -8{,}000\,\text{psi}; \sigma_y = 16{,}000\,\text{psi}; \tau_{xy} = 9{,}000\,\text{psi}.$

2.30 Through 2.34. In each of the following problems, the state of stress at the point is plane stress, that is, $\sigma_z = \tau_{zy} = \tau_{zx} = 0$. For each problem determine the maximum shearing stress and if Part 3 of this chapter was covered determine the octahedral shearing stress.

2.30. $\sigma_x = 0; \sigma_y = 0; \tau_{xy} = -18{,}000\,\text{psi}.$

2.31. $\sigma_x = -18,000 \text{ psi}; \sigma_y = 0; \tau_{xy} = 5,000 \text{ psi}.$

ans. $\tau_{max} = 10,300 \text{ psi}; \tau_G = 9,420 \text{ psi}.$

2.32. $\sigma_x = -8,000 \text{ psi}; \sigma_y = -28,000 \text{ psi}; \text{ and } \tau_{xy} = 10,000 \text{ psi}.$

2.33. $\sigma_x = 5,000 \text{ psi}; \sigma_y = 17,000 \text{ psi}; \tau_{xy} = -8,000 \text{ psi}.$

ans. $\tau_{max} = 10,500 \text{ psi}; \tau_G = 9,670 \text{ psi}.$

2.34. $\sigma_x = 10,000 \text{ psi}; \sigma_y = 0; \tau_{xy} = -10,000 \text{ psi}.$

PART THREE

Analysis of Three Dimensional Stress

2.8.   Stresses at a Point on Oblique Plane Through the Point

In Section 2.2 a discussion is given of a three-dimensional state of stress that consists of six components of stress σ_x, σ_y, σ_z, τ_{xy}, τ_{yz}, and τ_{zx}, which act on the three coordinate planes shown in Figure 2.1. This state of stress given in terms of six components seldom gives any directly helpful information concerning the damaging effects, such as plastic behavior or fracture, that the stresses may cause in the material of which a machine or structural member is made. For the purpose of formulating a theory that can be used to predict the occurrence of plastic behavior or of fracture we need to know the values of the principal normal stresses (see Section 2.2) and of the principal shearing stresses. The principal normal stresses and the principal shearing stresses may act on oblique planes that make angles with the coordinate axes x, y, and z. In this section a method of determining the normal and shearing components of the stress on any oblique plane is developed.

Let the plane ABC in Figure 2.8 represent such an oblique plane. Let the direction cosines of the normal Ox_1 to the plane ABC be $\ell = \cos \alpha$, $m = \cos \beta$, and $n = \cos \gamma$, where α, β, and γ are the angles between Ox_1 and the x, y, and z axes, respectively. The dimensions of the volume element and the position of the plane through it can always be chosen so that the area ABC is equal to one unit. When ABC is so chosen, the areas of the projections OAB, OBC, and OCA on the coordinate planes are equal to the direction cosines ℓ, m, and n, respectively. Finally, let the normal component of stress on plane ABC be σ and the shearing component of stress be τ and, because the area $ABC = 1$, the forces on the plane are also σ and τ. Likewise, the

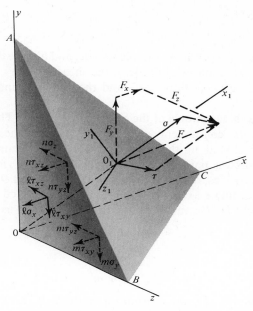

Fig. 2.8.   Stresses on oblique plane.

forces on each of the faces of the tetrahedral block in Figure 2.8 are as shown. For convenience in the analysis let F be the resultant of the normal and shearing forces σ and τ on the plane ABC and also let F_x, F_y, and F_z be the components of F in the x, y, and z directions, respectively. Therefore the following equations may be written:

$$F^2 = F_x^2 + F_y^2 + F_z^2,$$

$$\sigma = \ell F_x + m F_y + n F_z, \tag{2-16}$$

$$F^2 = \sigma^2 + \tau^2.$$

From the three equations of equilibrium for the free-body diagram of Figure 2.8 the following equations may be written:

$$\sum F_x = 0; \qquad \sigma_x \ell + \tau_{xy} m + \tau_{xz} n = F_x,$$

$$\sum F_y = 0; \qquad \tau_{xy} \ell + \sigma_y m + \tau_{yz} n = F_y, \tag{2-17}$$

$$\sum F_z = 0; \qquad \tau_{xz} \ell + \tau_{yz} m + \sigma_z n = F_z.$$

Magnitude of σ.   The expressions for F_x, F_y, and F_z from Equations (2–17) are substituted in the second of Equations (2–16), which gives the following equation:

$$\sigma = \ell^2\sigma_x + m^2\sigma_y + n^2\sigma_z + 2\ell m\tau_{xy} + 2mn\tau_{yz} + 2n\ell\tau_{xz}. \qquad (2\text{--}18)$$

The stress σ is perpendicular to plane ABC and has the direction cosines ℓ, m, n. The direction and magnitude of the shearing stress τ in plane ABC is found by finding two components and then determining their resultant as follows.

Directions and Magnitude of the Shearing Stress τ. The problem here is to determine the components $\tau_{x_1 y_1}$ and $\tau_{x_1 z_1}$ of the shearing stress τ in plane ABC (Fig. 2.8) along the $O_1 z_1$- and $O_1 y_1$-axes located in that plane where the $O_1 z_1$-axis is parallel to the xz-plane. Let ℓ', m', n', and ℓ'', m'', n'' be the direction cosines, respectively, of the axes $O_1 z_1$ and $O_1 y_1$ with respect to the x, y, z coordinate axes. The value of $\tau_{x_1 z_1}$ is obtained by summing up the components of F_x, F_y, and F_z in the direction of $O_1 z_1$ as follows:

$$\tau_{x_1 z_1} = F_x\ell' + F_y m' + F_z n',$$

and, similarly, $\qquad\qquad\qquad\qquad\qquad\qquad\qquad\qquad\qquad\qquad (2\text{--}19)$

$$\tau_{x_1 y_1} = F_x\ell'' + F_y m'' + F_z n''.$$

The substitution of F_x, F_y, and F_z from Equation (2–17) into Equation (2–19) gives

$$\begin{aligned}
\tau_{x_1 z_1} &= \sigma_x\ell\ell' + \sigma_y mm' + \sigma_z nn' + \tau_{xy}(\ell m' + \ell' m) \\
&\quad + \tau_{yz}(mn' + m'n) + \tau_{zx}(n\ell' + n'\ell), \\
\tau_{x_1 y_1} &= \sigma_x\ell\ell'' + \sigma_y mm'' + \sigma_z nn'' + \tau_{xy}(\ell m'' + \ell''m) \\
&\quad + \tau_{yz}(mn'' + m''n) + \tau_{zx}(n\ell'' + n''\ell).
\end{aligned} \qquad (2\text{--}20)$$

The magnitude of τ is

$$\tau = \sqrt{\tau_{x_1 y_1}^2 + \tau_{x_1 z_1}^2}$$

and the angle θ that τ makes with the $O_1 z_1$ axis is

$$\theta = \arctan\frac{\tau_{x_1 y_1}}{\tau_{x_1 z_1}}.$$

Direction Cosines of Axes $O_1 y_1$ and $O_1 z_1$. The choice of direction cosines ℓ', m', n' of $O_1 z_1$ and ℓ'', m'', n'' of $O_1 y_1$ must be restricted so that $O_1 x_1$, $O_1 y_1$, and $O_1 z_1$ (Fig. 2.8) are mutually perpendicular. A convenient choice of directions is to make $O_1 z_1$ parallel to BC and $O_1 y_1$ perpendicular to BC in Figure 2.8. When this choice is made the direction cosines take the following values :*

$$\ell' = \frac{-n}{\sqrt{\ell^2 + n^2}}, \qquad m' = 0, \qquad n' = \frac{\ell}{\sqrt{\ell^2 + n^2}}$$

$$\ell'' = \frac{-\ell m}{\sqrt{\ell^2 + n^2}}, \qquad m'' = \frac{\ell^2 + n^2}{\sqrt{\ell^2 + n^2}}, \qquad n'' = \frac{-mn}{\sqrt{\ell^2 + n^2}} \tag{2-21}$$

Illustrative Problem

2.35. Let the state of stress at a point be given by $\sigma_x = 1$, $\sigma_y = 2$, $\sigma_z = -1$, $\tau_{xy} = -2$, $\tau_{yz} = 1$, $\tau_{xz} = -3$ where all the values are in thousands of pounds per square inch. Determine the normal and shearing stresses on a plane that makes equal angles with the coordinate planes x, y, and z.

SOLUTION. Because $\ell^2 + m^2 + n^2 = 1$, the direction cosines of the line O_1x_1, making equal angles with the x, y, z axes which is perpendicular to the plane ABC (see Fig. 2.8), are $\ell = m = n = 1/\sqrt{3}$. From Equations (2–17) we find

$$F_x = (1)\frac{1}{\sqrt{3}} + (-2)\frac{1}{\sqrt{3}} + (-3)\frac{1}{\sqrt{3}} = -\frac{4}{\sqrt{3}},$$

$$F_y = (-2)\frac{1}{\sqrt{3}} + (+2)\frac{1}{\sqrt{3}} + (+1)\frac{1}{\sqrt{3}} = +\frac{1}{\sqrt{3}},$$

$$F_x = (-3)\frac{1}{\sqrt{3}} + (+1)\frac{1}{\sqrt{3}} + (-1)\frac{1}{\sqrt{3}} = -\frac{1}{\sqrt{3}}.$$

By the substitution of the foregoing values of F_x, F_y, and F_z into the first and second of Equations (2.16), respectively, we find

$$F^2 = \left(-\frac{4}{\sqrt{3}}\right)^2 + \left(\frac{1}{\sqrt{3}}\right)^2 + \left(-\frac{3}{\sqrt{3}}\right)^2 = \frac{26}{3},$$

$$\sigma = \left(\frac{1}{\sqrt{3}}\right)\left(-\frac{4}{\sqrt{3}}\right) + \left(\frac{1}{\sqrt{3}}\right)\left(\frac{1}{\sqrt{3}}\right) + \left(\frac{1}{\sqrt{3}}\right)\left(-\frac{1}{\sqrt{3}}\right) = -2.$$

These values of σ and F are now substituted into the third of Equations (2–16)

* In deriving Equations (2–21) use definitions $\ell^2 + m^2 + n^2 = (\ell')^2 + (m')^2 + (n')^2 = (\ell'')^2 + (m'')^2 + (n'')^2 = 1$ and the fact that the relations $\ell\ell' + mm' + nn' = \ell'\ell'' + m'm'' + n'n'' = \ell\ell'' + mm'' + nn'' = 0$ specify that O_1x_1, O_1y_1, and O_1z_1 are mutually perpendicular.

to find τ^2, which is found to be

$$\tau^2 = F^2 - \sigma^2 = \tfrac{26}{3} - (-2)^2 = \tfrac{14}{3}.$$

Therefore,

$$\tau = \sqrt{\tfrac{14}{3}} = 2.16.$$

The values of σ and τ are in thousands of pounds per square inch.

Problems

2.36. Let the state of stress at a point be given by $\sigma_1 = \sigma_2 = \sigma_3 = -30{,}000$ psi. Determine the normal and shearing stresses on a plane perpendicular to the x_1-axis with direction cosines ℓ, m, and n and show that they are independent of the magnitudes of ℓ, m, and n.

2.37. A tension member subjected to axial centric loading has a cross-sectional area A and is subjected to a tension load P parallel to the z-axis. (1) Determine the normal and shearing stresses on a plane perpendicular to the x_1-axis, which makes an angle θ with the z-axis. Note that $n = \cos\theta$ and the magnitudes of ℓ and m can have any value as long as the relation $\ell^2 + m^2 + n^2 = 1$ is satisfied. (2) Show that the maximum value of the shearing stress on the plane perpendicular to the x_1 axis is equal to $P/2A$ when $\theta = \pi/4$.

2.38. The only nonzero stress component in a given tension member subjected to axial centric loading is $\sigma_z = 10{,}000$ psi if the z-axis is parallel to the axis of the member. Let the x_1-axis make an angle of 30° with the z-axis. Determine the normal and shearing stresses on a plane perpendicular to the x_1-axis.

$$\text{ans.} \quad \sigma_{x_1} = 7{,}500 \text{ psi}; \tau = 4{,}330 \text{ psi}.$$

2.39. Consider a state of plane stress in which $\sigma_x = \sigma_y = \sigma_1 = \sigma_2 = 4{,}000$ psi and $\sigma_z = \sigma_3 = 0$. Let the angle between the x_1-axis and the z-axis be θ so that the direction cosine $n = \cos\theta$. The magnitudes of ℓ and m can have any values as long as the relation $\ell^2 + m^2 + n^2 = 1$ is satisfied. Determine the normal and shearing stresses on a plane perpendicular to the x_1-axis. What are the magnitudes of θ and τ when the shearing stress τ is maximum?

2.40. Consider a state of stress in which the nonzero stress components are σ_x, σ_y, σ_z, and τ_{xy}. This is a plane problem in stress since $\tau_{yz} = \tau_{zx} = 0$ but is not plane stress since $\sigma_z \neq 0$. Consider another set of coordinate axes x_1, y_1, and z_1 in which the z-axis and the z_1-axis coincide. Show that the normal and shearing stresses on a plane perpendicular to the x_1-axis, where the x_1-axis is located counterclockwise from the x-axis through angle θ, are independent of the magnitude of σ_z and are given by the relations

$$\sigma_{x_1} = \sigma_x \cos^2\theta + \sigma_y \sin^2\theta + 2\tau_{xy} \sin\theta \cos\theta,$$

$$\tau = (\sigma_y - \sigma_x) \sin\theta \cos\theta + \tau_{xy}(\cos^2\theta - \sin^2\theta).$$

Note that $\ell = \cos\theta$, $m = \cos(\pi/2 - \theta) = \sin\theta$, and $n = \cos \pi/2 = 0$.

2.41. Let the state of stress at a point be given by $\sigma_x = 10{,}000$ psi, $\sigma_y = -6{,}000$ psi, $\sigma_z = 4{,}000$ psi, $\tau_{xy} = 8{,}000$ psi, $\tau_{yz} = \tau_{zx} = 0$. Consider another set of coordinate axes x_1, y_1, and z_1 in which the z-axis and the z_1-axis coincide. Determine the normal and shearing stresses on a plane perpendicular to the x_1-axis where the x_1-axis is located counterclockwise from the x-axis through (1) $\theta = 30°$ and (2) $\theta = 22.5°$. Note that $\ell = \cos\theta$, $m = \cos(\pi/2 - \theta) = \sin\theta$, and $n = \cos\pi/2 = 0$.

ans. (2) $\sigma_{x_1} = 13{,}300$ psi; $\tau = 0$.

2.42. Let the state of stress at a point be given by $\sigma_x = -8{,}000$ psi, $\sigma_y = 12{,}000$ psi, $\sigma_z = -4{,}000$ psi, $\tau_{xy} = 4{,}000$ psi, $\tau_{yz} = -6{,}000$ psi, and $\tau_{zx} = 5{,}000$ psi. Determine the normal and shearing stresses on a plane perpendicular to the x_1 axis whose direction cosines are $\ell = \frac{1}{4}$, $m = \frac{1}{2}$, and n is given by the relation $\ell^2 + m^2 + n^2 = 1$.

2.9. Principal Stresses

The principal normal stresses as defined in Section 2.2., are the normal stresses on the three mutually perpendicular planes on which the shearing stresses are zero. In this section we will show that for any given state of stress $\sigma_x, \sigma_y, \sigma_z, \tau_{xy}, \tau_{yz}, \tau_{xz}$ a new set of axes x_1, y_1, z_1 can be chosen such that the shearing stresses $\tau_{x_1y_1}, \tau_{y_1z_1}, \tau_{z_1x_1}$ on this new set of coordinate planes will be zero; hence these axes are in the direction of the principal normal stresses, respectively. In order to do this start with Equation (2–18), which gives the normal stress σ on an oblique plane as shown in Figure 2.8. The direction cosines ℓ, m, and n are eliminated from Equation (2–18) as follows: choose an arbitrary length r along the normal Ox_1 from O in Figure 2.8 and let r be the diagonal of a rectangular parallelepiped with sides x, y, and z. The direction cosines can then be written as

$$\ell = \frac{x}{r}, \qquad m = \frac{y}{r}, \qquad \text{and} \qquad n = \frac{z}{r}. \qquad (2\text{–}22)$$

When these values of ℓ, m, and n are put into Equation (2–18) it becomes

$$\sigma r^2 = \sigma_x x^2 + \sigma_y y^2 + \sigma_z z^2 + 2\tau_{xy}xy + 2\tau_{yz}yz + 2\tau_{xz}xz. \qquad (2\text{–}23)$$

Because r is any arbitrary length, its length can be chosen such that the product σr^2 is equal to a constant c. When this constant c is substituted into Equation (2–23) it becomes

$$\sigma_x x^2 + \sigma_y y^2 + \sigma_z z^2 + 2\tau_{xy} xy + 2\tau_{yz} yz + 2\tau_{xz} xz - c = 0. \qquad (2–24)$$

Equation (2–24) is a second degree equation in x, y, and z. Hence, as the direction of the normal Ox_1 to the plane ABC is changed in Figure 2.8, the end of the vector $r = \sqrt{\sigma/c}$ always lies on the surface that is represented by Equation (2–24).

It is well known* that for a second-degree equation such as Equation (2–24) it is always possible to choose a new set of axes x_1, y_1, z_1 such that the coefficients of the terms containing the products $x_1 y_1$, $y_1 z_1$, and $z_1 x_1$ will vanish. When such a new set of axes is chosen, Equation (2–24) will be transformed into the following equation:

$$\sigma_{x_1} x_1^2 + \sigma_{y_1} y_1^2 + \sigma_{z_1} z_1^2 - c = 0. \qquad (2–25)$$

Note in Equation (2–25) that the coefficients $\sigma_{x_1} \equiv \sigma_1$, $\sigma_{y_1} \equiv \sigma_2$, and $\sigma_{z_1} \equiv \sigma_3$ are the principal stresses, and that the product terms containing $x_1 y_1$, $y_1 z_1$, and $x_1 z_1$ have vanished because of the fact that the coefficients $\tau_{x_1 y_1} = \tau_{y_1 z_1} = \tau_{x_1 z_1} = 0$; that is, the shearing stresses on the new coordinate planes x_1, y_1, and z_1 are all zero.

In Section 2.10 the method of determining the magnitude and direction of the principal stresses will be discussed.

2.10. Determination of Principal Stresses

It is the purpose of this section to determine the location of the oblique planes on which the three principal stresses act and to find the magnitude of each principal stress when the stresses $\sigma_x, \sigma_y, \sigma_z, \tau_{xy}, \tau_{yz}$, and τ_{zx} are given. Equations (2–17) are used to accomplish this purpose.

Let the three principal stresses be denoted by σ. There will be three values of σ, namely the principal stresses $\sigma_1, \sigma_2, \sigma_3$. Let the direction cosines for the direction in which a principal stress σ acts be denoted by ℓ, m, and n. There will be three sets of values of direction cosines, each set corresponding with a principal stress. For example, ℓ_1, m_1, and n_1 are the direction cosines for σ_1, and so forth. The problem, therefore, is to determine the values of $\sigma_1, \sigma_2, \sigma_3$ and the values of the three sets of direction cosines.

From the definition of principal stress (see Section 2.2) the shearing stress τ is zero on the plane upon which a principal stress σ acts. In Section 2.9

_____
* See, for example, Chapter 18 of *Coordinate Geometry*, H. B. Fine and H. D. Thompson, Macmillan, 1914.

it was shown that a set of axes can always be found such that the shearing stresses on the coordinate planes are zero. Let the plane ABC in Figure 2.8 be one of these coordinate planes. By referring to Figure 2.8 it can be seen that when $\tau = 0$ on the plane ABC the three components F_x, F_y, F_z are components of σ only and are given by the following equations, since $F = \sigma$:

$$F_x = \ell\sigma, \qquad F_y = m\sigma, \qquad \text{and} \qquad F_z = n\sigma. \tag{2-26}$$

Equations (2–26) are substituted into Equations (2–17) for F_x, F_y, and F_z. When this substitution is made and the terms are collected and placed on the left side, Equations (2–17) are as follows:

$$(\sigma_x - \sigma)\ell + \tau_{xy}m + \tau_{xz}n = 0,$$

$$\tau_{xy}\ell + (\sigma_y - \sigma)m + \tau_{yz}n = 0, \tag{2-27}$$

$$\tau_{xz}\ell + \tau_{yz}m + (\sigma_z - \sigma)n = 0.$$

Equations (2–27) are three homogeneous* linear equations in the three unknowns ℓ, m, and n that are the direction cosines for the principal stress σ, which is also unknown. Suppose that a value of σ is given (it is not, for it must be determined, too). In order that Equations (2–27) will have a solution for ℓ, m, and n (other than, $\ell = m = n = 0$) the determinant of the coefficients of ℓ, m, and n must be equal to zero; that is,

$$\begin{vmatrix} (\sigma_x - \sigma) & \tau_{xy} & \tau_{xz} \\ \tau_{xy} & (\sigma_y - \sigma) & \tau_{yz} \\ \tau_{xz} & \tau_{yz} & (\sigma_z - \sigma) \end{vmatrix} = 0. \tag{2-28}$$

When the determinant is expanded and the terms are collected, Equation (2–28) becomes

$$\sigma^3 - (\sigma_x + \sigma_y + \sigma_z)\sigma^2 + (\sigma_x\sigma_y + \sigma_y\sigma_z + \sigma_z\sigma_x - \tau_{xy}^2 - \tau_{yz}^2 - \tau_{xz}^2)\sigma$$

$$- (\sigma_x\sigma_y\sigma_z + 2\tau_{xy}\tau_{yz}\tau_{xz} - \sigma_x\tau_{yz}^2 - \sigma_y\tau_{xz}^2 - \sigma_z\tau_{xy}^2) = 0. \tag{2-29}$$

Equation (2–29) is a cubic equation in σ. There are always† three real roots of this equation. These roots are the values of the principal stresses σ_1, σ_2, and σ_3.

The use of Equations (2–27) and (2–29) to determine the value of the principal normal stresses and their direction cosines is illustrated in the following problem.

---

* For a discussion of homogeneous linear equations see pages 119–122 I. S. and E. S. Sokolnikoff, *Higher Mathematics for Engineers and Physicists*, 2nd ed., McGraw-Hill, 1941.

† For a proof by Cauchy that Equation (2–29) always has three real roots see pp. 272–273 of H. B. Fine and H. D. Thompson, *Coordinate Geometry*, Macmillan, 1914.

Illustrative Problem

2.43.   Determine the direction cosines and the magnitude and sense of each of the three principal stresses for the state of stress given in Problem 2.35.

SOLUTION.   The given stresses are substituted into Equation (2–29), which gives the following cubic equation:

$$\sigma^3 - 2\sigma^2 - 15\sigma + 5 = 0.$$

The three roots of this equation are found* to be $\sigma_1 = 4.87$, $\sigma_2 = 0.32$, and $\sigma_3 = -3.19$; all stresses are in thousands of pounds per square inch.

Two of Equations (2–27) and the condition that $\ell^2 + m^2 + n^2 = 1$ are used to determine the direction cosines ℓ, m, and n. To illustrate this procedure we take the value of σ_1 and substitute it and the given stresses into Equations (2–27) as follows:

$$(1 - 4.87)\ell_1 - 2m_1 - 3n_1 = 0,$$
$$-2\ell_1 + (2 - 4.87)m_1 + n_1 = 0, \tag{a}$$
$$-3\ell_1 + m_1 + (-1 - 4.87)n_1 = 0.$$

Now we have already made certain that the homogeneous linear Equations (a) have a solution. To obtain the solution we use an additional equation that relates ℓ_1, m_1, and n_1; namely

$$\ell_1^2 + m_1^2 + n_1^2 = 1, \tag{b}$$

which is a condition that all sets of direction cosines must satisfy. We take any two of Equations (a) and solve simultaneously with Equation (b) and the resulting values are

$$\ell_1 = 0.659, \qquad m_1 = -0.613, \qquad n_1 = -0.442.$$

In a similar manner we obtain the two additional sets of values of direction cosines for σ_3 and σ_2 to be $\ell_3 = 0.450$, $m_3 = 0.789$, $n_3 = -0.425$ and $\ell_2 = 0.603$, $m_2 = 0.0805$, $n_2 = 0.792$.

Problems

2.44.   Let the state of stress at a point be given by $\sigma_x = \sigma_1$, $\sigma_y = \sigma_2$, and $\sigma_z = \sigma_3$. Because these are principal stresses, show that they satisfy Equation (2–29). Determine the direction cosines for each of the three principal stresses.

---

* These roots were determined by guessing at the value of a root until three digits are correct. However, there are several methods such as Cardan's, Homer's, Newton's, and so forth, that are discussed in most books on algebra. See for example, p. 86, I. S. and E. S. Sokolnikoff, *Higher Mathematics for Engineers and Physicists*, 2nd ed., McGraw-Hill, 1941.

2.45. Determine the direction cosines and the magnitude and sense of each of the three principal stresses for the state of stress given in Problem 2.41.

ans. $\sigma_1 = 13,300$ psi; $\sigma_2 = -9,300$ psi; $\sigma_3 = 4,000$ psi;

$\ell_1 = 0.9239$ $m_1 = 0.3827$ $n_1 = 0$

$\ell_2 = 0.3827$ $m_2 = -0.9239$ $n_2 = 0$

$\ell_3 = 0$ $m_3 = 0$ $n_3 = 1.$

2.46. Let the state of stress at a point be given by $\sigma_x = \sigma_y = 0$, $\sigma_z = 10,000$ psi, $\tau_{xy} = -12,000$ psi, $\tau_{yz} = \tau_{zx} = 0$. Determine the direction cosines and the magnitude and sense of each of the three principal stresses for this state of stress.

2.47. Let the state of stress at a point be given by $\sigma_x = -2,000$ psi, $\sigma_y = 10,000$ psi, $\sigma_z = -5,000$ psi, $\tau_{xy} = -11,000$ psi, $\tau_{yz} = \tau_{zx} = 0$. Determine the direction cosines and the magnitude and sense of the three principal stresses for this state of stress.

2.48. Determine the magnitude and sense of each of the three principal stresses for the state of stress given in Problem 2.23.

2.49. Let the state of stress at a point be described by the following values of the stresses: $\sigma_x = 0$, $\sigma_y = 0$, $\sigma_z = 3$, $\tau_{xy} = -2$, $\tau_{yz} = 3$, $\tau_{yz} = 1$. Determine the direction cosines and the magnitude and sense of each of the three principal stresses for this state of stress. All stresses are in thousands of pounds per square inch.

ans. $\sigma_1 = 4.86$; $\sigma_3 = 1.48$; $\sigma_2 = -3.34$

$\ell_1 = 0.0489$; $m_1 = -0.539$; $n_1 = -0.841$

$\ell_3 = 0.830$; $m_3 = -0.448$; $n_3 = 0.332$

$\ell_2 = 0.554$; $m_2 = 0.715$; $n_2 = -0.425.$

2.50. Let $\sigma_x = 4$, $\sigma_y = 5$, $\sigma_z = -3$, $\tau_{xy} = 2$, $\tau_{yz} = 0$, and $\tau_{zx} = 0$. Determine the magnitude and direction of each of the three principal stresses.

2.11. Principal Shearing Stresses—Stresses on Octahedral Plane

In Section 2.7 it is shown (Eqs. 2–12 and 2–14) that each of the three principal shearing stresses is equal to one half of the algebraic difference between two principal normal stresses. For a three-dimensional state of stress, the maximum shearing stress is also equal to one half the algebraic difference between the maximum and minimum principal normal stresses (see Eq. 2–15). For example, in Figure 2.9a let the three principal normal stresses be σ_1, σ_2, and σ_3 and let $\sigma_1 > \sigma_3 > \sigma_2$. There are three principal

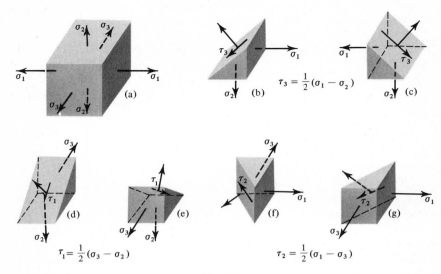

$$\tau_3 = \frac{1}{2}(\sigma_1 - \sigma_2)$$

$$\tau_1 = \frac{1}{2}(\sigma_3 - \sigma_2) \qquad \tau_2 = \frac{1}{2}(\sigma_1 - \sigma_3)$$

Fig. 2.9.

(maximum) shearing stresses, located as shown on diagonal planes of the cube in Figures 2.9b to g (for clarity the normal stress perpendicular to plane of interest is not designated); however, the largest of the three values is $\tau_3 = \tau_{max} = \frac{1}{2}(\sigma_1 - \sigma_2)$, as shown in Figures 2.9b and c.

Stresses on Octahedral Plane. In Section 2.8 a method of computing the normal and shearing stresses on any oblique plane is presented. Let it be required that the normal and shearing stresses be determined on a plane that makes equal angles with the directions of the three principal stresses. Let

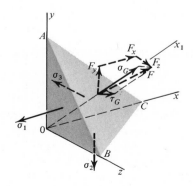

Fig. 2.10.

ABC in Figure 2.10 represent such a plane and let Ox_1 be a line perpendicular to the plane ABC. The direction cosines ℓ, m, and n of Ox_1 with respect to the principal axis directions OA, OB, and OC are each equal to $1/\sqrt{3}$. Following the method used in Illustrative Problem 2.35, we have from Figure 2.10 and Equations (2–17)

$$F_x = \sigma_1(1/\sqrt{3}); \qquad F_y = \sigma_2(1/\sqrt{3}); \qquad F_z = \sigma_3(1/\sqrt{3}).$$

The substitution of these values of F_x, F_y, and F_z in the first of Equations (2–16) gives the value of F^2 as follows:

$$F^2 = \tfrac{1}{3}(\sigma_1^2 + \sigma_2^2 + \sigma_3^2).$$

In addition, the substitution of these values of F_x, F_y, F_z, ℓ, m, and n in the second of Equations (2–16) gives the normal stress on the octahedral plane as follows:

$$\sigma_G = \ell F_x + m F_y + n F_z = \tfrac{1}{3}(\sigma_1 + \sigma_2 + \sigma_3). \tag{2–30}$$

The third of Equations (2–16) becomes

$$\tau_G^2 = F^2 - \sigma_G^2.$$

By substituting the foregoing values of F^2 and σ_G^2 into this equation and reducing the results to the simplest form, the following equation is obtained for the shearing stress on the octahedral plane:

$$\tau_G = \tfrac{1}{3}\sqrt{(\sigma_1 - \sigma_2)^2 + (\sigma_2 - \sigma_3)^2 + (\sigma_3 - \sigma_1)^2}. \tag{2–31}$$

2.12. Plane Stress as a Special Case of Three-Dimensional Stress

Let Figure 2.11a represent a plane state of stress; that is, $\sigma_z = \tau_{yz} = \tau_{zx} = 0$. Let the normal stress σ_{x_1} and the shearing stress $\tau_{x_1y_1}$ on plane AC be located as shown in perspective in Figure 2.11b. The problem here is to make use of the general Equations (2–18), (2–20), and (2–21) derived for the three-dimensional state of stress and determine the values of σ_{x_1} and $\tau_{x_1y_1}$. From Figure 2.11b the direction cosines of O_1x_1 are

$$\ell = \cos\theta, \qquad m = \sin\theta, \qquad \text{and} \qquad n = 0.$$

From Equations (2–21), with these values of ℓ, m, and n substituted, it is found that the direction cosines of O_1z_1 with respect to the x-, y-, and z-axes are

$$\ell' = 0, \qquad m' = 0, \qquad \text{and} \qquad n' = 1,$$

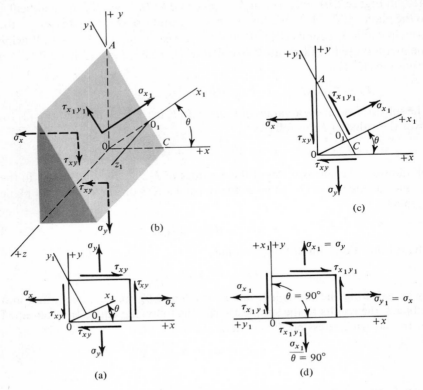

Fig. 2.11. Stresses on different planes through a point. Plane stress.

and, similarly,

$$\ell'' = -\sin\theta, \qquad m'' = \cos\theta, \qquad \text{and} \qquad n'' = 0$$

for the $O_1 y_1$-axis.

Normal Stress σ_{x_1}. The substitution into Equations (2–18) of $\ell = \cos\theta$, $m = \sin\theta$, $n = 0$, $\sigma_z = \tau_{yz} = \tau_{zx} = 0$ gives

$$\sigma_{x_1} = \sigma_x \cos^2\theta + \sigma_y \sin^2\theta + 2\tau_{xy} \sin\theta\cos\theta. \qquad (2\text{–}32)$$

Note that Equation (2–32) is the same as Equation (2–1).

Components of Shearing Stress. The substitution into Equations (2–20) of $\ell = \cos\theta$, $m = \sin\theta$, and $n = 0$; $\ell' = m' = 0$, and $n' = 1$; $\ell'' = -\sin\theta$, $m'' = \cos\theta$, and $n'' = 0$; $\sigma_z = \tau_{yz} = \tau_{zx} = 0$ gives the following values for the two components of shearing stress:

$$\tau_{x_1 z_1} = 0,$$

$$\tau_{x_1 y_1} = (\sigma_y - \sigma_x) \sin \theta \cos \theta + \tau_{xy}(\cos^2\theta - \sin^2\theta). \qquad (2\text{–}33)$$

Note that Equation (2–33) is the same as Equation (2–2). Figure 2.11c shows the location of the angle θ and the components σ_{x_1} and $\tau_{x_1 y_1}$ on the plane AC, which is perpendicular to the $O_1 x_1$-axis. The stresses σ_{x_1} and $\tau_{x_1 y_1}$ are shown with the positive sense and the angle θ is positive when measured counterclockwise from the positive end of the x-axis.

If the reader omitted Part 2 of this chapter, please continue with Section 2.5 in Part 2.

Strains at a Point

PART ONE

Basic Concepts

3.1. Introduction

One effect of applying loads to a given member is to develop within the member internal forces, the intensity of which at a specified point is given by the state of stress at that point. Another effect of applying loads to the given member is to cause deformations of the member—that is, to cause the member to change its volume and its shape. The main emphasis in this book is to derive load-stress and load-deflection relations for several different types of load-carrying members because these relations are required if these members are to be designed so that they will not fail during the intended life of the member. In addition to these relations, the design of a member requires that material properties be known (see Chapter 1) and that stress-strain relations be known (see Chapter 1 for uniaxial state of stress and Chapter 4 for multi-axial states of stress).

In Chapter 2 the state of stress at a point was investigated. A set of x, y, z coordinate axes was chosen. At a specified point in the member, an infinitesimal three-dimensional volume element whose sides were perpendicular to the coordinate axes was removed from the member. It was assumed that load-stress relations were available to determine the six stress components σ_x, σ_y, σ_z, τ_{xy}, τ_{yz}, and τ_{zx}, which define the state of stress at that point in the member. Transformation equations of stress were derived to determine the stress components that act on an oblique plane through the volume element; these were used to determine maximum values of normal stress and shearing stress at that point in the member. The transformation equations were derived using equations of equilibrium and did not require that the deformations of the member be considered.

This chapter will investigate the deformations of the same volume element at the specified point in the member as that used in Chapter 2 to study the state of stress at the point. The deformations of the volume element will be expressed in terms of the state of strain at the point defined by giving three normal strain components ϵ_x, ϵ_y, and ϵ_z, as defined in Section 3.3; and three shearing strain components γ_{xy}, γ_{yz}, and γ_{zx}, as defined in Section 3.4.

There are three reasons for the study of the state of strain at a point in a member. First, this knowledge is needed in the derivation of load-deflection relations for the member. Second, with very few exceptions, load-stress relations can not be derived without considering the strains in the member. Third, many members are so complex that load-stress relations cannot be derived; they are often designed using one of the experimental techniques considered in experimental stress analysis. This term is a misnomer because stresses cannot be measured experimentally. The deformations of the member are measured from which the state of strain at a point is determined; the stresses at the point are then obtained using stress-strain relations for the material in the member (see Chapters 1 and 4).

In addition to the known strain components ϵ_x, ϵ_y, ϵ_z, γ_{xy}, γ_{yz}, and γ_{zx}, which define the state of strain at the specified point in the member, it may be necessary to determine strain components at the same point corresponding to another set of coordinate axes x_1, y_1, z_1. Transformation equations of strain will be derived in this chapter to determine each of the unknown strain components ϵ_{x_1}, ϵ_{y_1}, ϵ_{z_1}, $\gamma_{x_1y_1}$, $\gamma_{y_1z_1}$, and $\gamma_{z_1x_1}$ in terms of the known strain components. These transformation equations do not depend on how the deformations are produced, but are based only on geometrical changes resulting from changes of size and shape of the member. These changes in size and shape of a member can best be expressed in terms of the displacements of the various points of the member.

The strain-displacement and strain-transformation equations derived in this chapter are based on the assumption that the member be continuous. This is another way of saying that the member is assumed to occupy all of the space within its boundaries. This would rule out consideration of a pile of sand, because there are voids between sand grains, but would not rule out members made of metal, wood, concrete, plastic, glass, putty, and so forth. The equations derived are valid whether the material behavior is elastic or plastic (inelastic).

3.2. Displacements

A body of arbitrary shape is shown in its initial (unloaded) and displaced positions in Figure 3.1. Every particle of the body occupies some point in space. The initial location of a given particle P can be located by giving its coordinates (x, y, z) with respect to the x, y, z coordinate axes. Particle P moves to a point P' with coordinates (x', y', z') in the displaced position. A vector from P to P' represents the displacement of point P. The x, y, and z components of this displacement are defined as u, v, and w, respectively.

In order to determine the deformation of a volume element at point P in the body, it is necessary to consider the displacement of other points in the neighborhood of P. Let Q and R be two other points joined to P by straight lines that intersect at angle θ. These particles take positions Q' and R' in the displaced position of the body. Two types of displacements are considered. First, the body may move as a rigid body from the initial to the displaced position without loads being applied to the body as the result of a constant linear velocity. The resulting displacements will be rigid body displacements for which the lines $P'Q'$ and $P'R'$ will remain straight, will have lengths identical with their initial values, and will intersect at angle θ' equal to θ. Rigid body displacements do not result in deformations of the body.

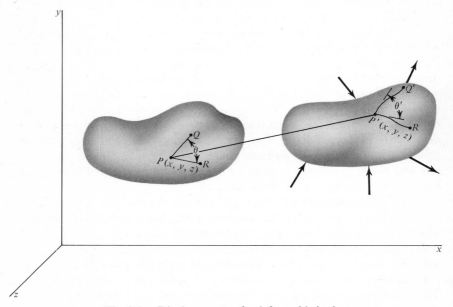

Fig. 3.1. Displacements of a deformable body.

Second, we consider the case in which the body in Figure 3.1 moves from its initial to its displaced positions as the result of having loads applied to the body. In the displaced position it will be found that, in general, the lines $P'Q'$ and $P'R'$ may be either lengthened or shortened, may be curved lines, and may intersect at an angle θ' not equal to θ. The deformations of bodies are determined by measuring changes in lengths of line segments in the body and by measuring changes in angles between intersecting line segments.

The deformations of a deformed body are obtained by subtracting the rigid body displacements from the actual displacements. For example, consider a tension member made of rubber and loaded as shown in Figure 3.2, fixed at end JK, and uniformly loaded at the free end MN. The member

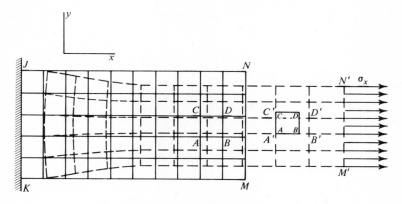

Fig. 3.2. Deformation of a tension member.

has a rectangular cross section with width MN large compared to the thickness. Before loading the tension member, solid horizontal and vertical lines were scribed on the member to form a square grid as shown. A tensile load P was applied to the member so that the stress σ_x is uniformly distributed over section $M'N'$. The dashed lines show the final locations of the original solid lines after loading. Note that the member elongates and every vertical dimension decreases in magnitude except at the fixed end JK. At a relatively short distance from section JK (distance about equal to JK) the restraining effects of the fixed end on the deformations disappear and all squares deform into rectangles. Consider the deformations of the original square $ABCD$ into the rectangle $A'B'C'D'$. The rigid body displacements of $A'B'C'D'$ can be subtracted by translating $ABCD$ in the x-direction until AC coincides with $A'C'$ and in the y-direction until AB coincides with $A'B'$, as shown in Figure 3.2. It is seen that the undeformed square $ABCD$ elongates in the x-direction by an amount $A'B' - AB$ and shortens in the y-direction by an amount $AC - A'C'$.

Special Cases. As the square $ABCD$ deforms into the rectangle $A'B'C'D'$ in Figure 3.2, the right angles made by the intersecting sides of the square remain at right angles in the deformed rectangle; deformation of this kind results in normal strains, as defined in Section 3.3.

There are members for which deformations can be determined by measuring only the change in magnitude of undeformed right angles. Consider the torsion member in Figure 3.3. Before applying the torque T, scribe

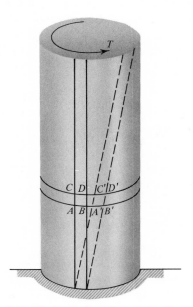

Fig. 3.3. Deformation of a torsion member.

solid axial and circumferential lines on the surface of the torsion member to form the square $ABCD$. After deformation, it is found that $A'B'$ equals AB and the axial spacing between the circumferential lines remains unchanged. The rigid body displacements of $A'B'C'D'$ can be subtracted by translating $ABCD$ until AB coincides with $A'B'$. The deformations of $A'B'C'D'$ are determined by subtracting angle $C'A'B'$ from the right angle CAB. Deformations of this kind result in shearing strains, as described in Section 3.4.

An illustration showing deformation which results in a combination of normal and shearing strains is seen in Figure 3.2, where the squares near the fixed end JK have the right angles as well as the length of sides changed.

General Case. In order to determine the deformations at a point in a body, the usual procedure is to choose three mutually perpendicular infinitesimal line segments intersecting at the specified point in the undeformed body. By subtracting rigid body displacements from the actual displacements, the changes in lengths of the three infinitesimal line segments are determined as well as the changes in magnitudes of the three right angles. These six quantities define the geometry of the deformation sufficiently so that the change in length of any other infinitesimal line segment through the point can be determined as well as the change in magnitude of the angle between any two infinitesimal line segments intersecting at the point. The engineer finds it convenient to define changes in lengths of line segments per unit length as normal strains and to define the tangents of the changes in magnitudes of original right angles for intersecting line segments as shearing strains.

3.3. Normal Strain

If the sides of square *ABCD* on the surface of the tension member in Figure 3.2 are chosen to be infinitesimal dimensions, they become the front face of the volume element *ABCDEFGH* shown in Figure 3.4. The only stress

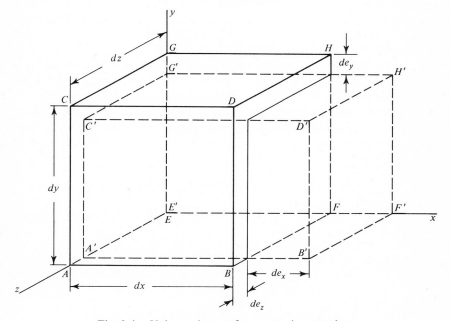

Fig. 3.4. Volume element from a tension member.

acting on the deformed volume element $A'B'C'D'E'F'G'H'$ is σ_x, which is uniformly distributed over face $B'F'D'H'$. In Figure 3.4 the undeformed volume element has been given rigid body displacements until lines EF, EA, and EG coincide with lines $E'F'$, $E'A'$, and $E'G'$, respectively. Note that side dx has increased in length by an amount de_x whereas sides dy and dz have decreased in lengths by amounts de_y and de_z, respectively.

The normal strain for a given line segment is defined as the change in length divided by the original length. The three normal strains for the volume element in Figure 3.4 are

$$\epsilon_x = \frac{de_x}{dx}, \qquad \epsilon_y = \frac{de_y}{dy}, \qquad \epsilon_z = \frac{de_z}{dz}, \qquad (3\text{-}1)$$

The normal strain is positive if the line segment elongates as is the case for ϵ_x in Figure 3.4, because de_x is positive and is negative if the line segment shortens, as is the case for ϵ_y and ϵ_z in Figure 3.4, because de_y and de_z are negative.

The definition of normal strain given by Equations (3–1) is the one commonly used by engineers if the strains are small compared to one. Other definitions may be used (see Section 1.10) when the strains become finite. In this chapter the strains are assumed to be infinitesimal. The exceptions are the strains in tension and compression specimens loaded to fracture to obtain stress-strain data.

An interesting observation can be made regarding the deformations of the tension member in Figure 3.2 and the volume element in Figure 3.4. The member is loaded so that the state of stress is uniaxial (i.e., only one non-zero principal stress σ_x exists); however, the state of strain is triaxial. Thus, it is not unusual to have a normal strain in a given direction at a given point in a deformed member without having a normal stress in the given direction.

Problems

3.1. A wire that has an undeformed length of 100 ft is stretched to a length of 100.05 ft. Determine the average normal longitudinal strain in the wire.

3.2. Let the wire in Problem 3.1 be suspended vertically from one end and thus extend along the y-axis from the fixed end at the origin. The normal strain is found to be given by the relation $\epsilon_y = \epsilon_{max} - cy$ subject to the condition that the normal strain is zero at the free end. If the elongation of the wire is 0.05 ft, determine the magnitudes of ϵ_{max} and c and the value of the normal strain at midlength.

ans. $\epsilon_{max} = 10^{-3}$; $c = 10^{-5}/\text{in.}$; $\epsilon_{y=50} = 5 \times 10^{-4}$.

3.3. A rubber band that will just slip over a 4-in. diameter cylinder when it is undeformed is stretched over a 5-in. diameter cylinder. Determine the average circumferential strain in the rubber band.

3.4. In stretching the rubber band over the 5-in. diameter cylinder in Problem 3.3, assume that the rubber band is not uniformly stretched. If the strain varies with θ, according to the law $\epsilon_\theta = K \sin^2\theta$, determine the maximum and minimum values of the circumferential strain in the rubber band.

3.5. The rigid bar AC in Figure P3.5 is horizontal when the wire DB is undeformed. Determine the average longitudinal strain in the wire when (1) point C moves downward $\frac{1}{4}$ in. and (2) when bar AC rotates clockwise with respect to A through an angle of 0.001 rad.

ans. (1) $\epsilon = 0.00125$; (2) $\epsilon = 0.00048$.

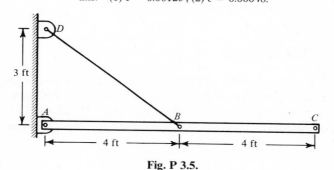

Fig. P 3.5.

3.6. Through 3.10. The undeformed positions of the three pin-connected members in Figure P3.6 are shown by the solid lines. The deformations of the three members are given by the displacements u and v. Determine the average longitudinal

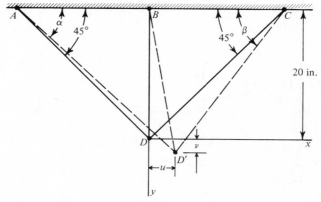

Fig. P 3.6.

strain in each of the three members for each of the following displacements. (*Hint*: for small deformations angles α and β can be assumed to be equal to 45°). All members remain straight after deformation.

   3.6. $u = 0$ and $v = 0.10$ in.
   3.7. $u = 0.10$ in. and $v = 0$.

$$\text{ans.} \quad \epsilon_{AD} = 0.0025; \epsilon_{BD} = 0; \epsilon_{CD} = -0.0025.$$

   3.8. $u = 0.10$ in. and $v = 0.10$ in.
   3.9. $u = 0.20$ in. and $v = 0.10$ in.

$$\text{ans.} \quad \epsilon_{AD} = 0.0075; \epsilon_{BD} = 0.0050; \epsilon_{CD} = -0.0025.$$

   3.10. $u = 0.10$ in. and $v = 0.20$ in.

3.4.   Shearing Strain

If the sides of the square *ABCD* on the surface of the torsion member in Figure 3.3 are chosen to have infinitesimal dimensions, they become the front face of the volume element *ABCDEFGH* shown in Figure 3.5. In Chapter 9 this volume element is found to have a state of stress called pure shear; that is,

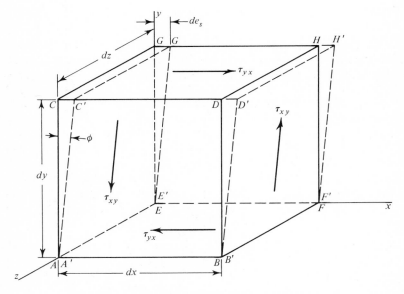

Fig. 3.5.   Volume element from torsion member.

the only nonzero stress is $\tau_{xy} = \tau_{yx}$. These stresses are shown acting on the deformed volume element $A'B'C'D'E'F'G'H'$ in Figure 3.5. As indicated in Figure 3.5, the undeformed volume element has been given rigid body displacements until face $ABEF$ coincides with face $A'B'E'F'$. Note that all cross sections parallel to $ABEF$ are displaced in the x-direction with no displacement in either the y- or z-directions. The shearing strain γ_{xy} is defined as the tangent of the change in the angle of an undeformed right angle, that is,

$$\gamma_{xy} = \tan \phi = \frac{de_s}{dy}. \tag{3–2}$$

The shearing strains γ_{yz} and γ_{zx} are defined in a similar manner. This definition has been proposed in the literature for both finite and infinitesimal shearing strains; however, there is still some question about its interpretation in the case of finite strains. Note that for finite shearing strains the stresses shown acting on the deformed element in Figure 3.5 would not be valid. Shearing stresses of equal magnitude occur on perpendicular planes, a condition which can be assumed to be valid for infinitesimal shearing strains. If the angle ϕ does not remain infinitesimal, the shearing stresses on the upper, lower, and inclined faces cannot have equal magnitudes, and normal stresses will have to be acting on these faces in addition to the shearing stresses.

In this book, only infinitesimal shearing strains will be considered. For infinitesimal shearing strains, the tangent of the angle is equal to the angle so that the shearing strain is equal to the change in magnitude of an undeformed right angle. The sign of the shearing strain is determined by the coordinate axes chosen, as was the case for the sign convention for shearing stress in Chapter 2. If the undeformed right angle is defined by the intersection of the positive directions of the x- and y-axes as indicated in Figure 3.5, a decrease in this right angle will be taken to mean that γ_{xy} is positive, whereas an increase in the right angle will be taken to mean that γ_{xy} is negative. With this sign convention the shearing strain will always have the same sign as the shearing stress, which has the sign convention given in Chapter 2. Although there are cases in which the normal strain in a given direction may be zero when the normal stress in that direction is not zero, and vice-versa, the shearing strain will be zero only if the shearing stress is zero.

Problems

3.11. Face $ABCD$ of a cubical body lies in the xy-plane as shown in Figure P3.11. After the body is deformed, $A'B'C'D'$ is a rectangle so that γ_{xy} is zero. The strains

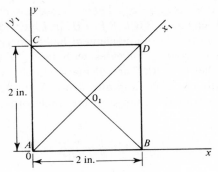

Fig. P 3.11.

are uniformly distributed through the body so that diagonals $A'D'$ and $C'B'$ remain straight lines. Let the axes O_1x_1 and O_1y_1 coincide with the diagonals AD and CB. Determine $\gamma_{x_1y_1}$ if the body is deformed so that (1) $\epsilon_x = 0.004$ and $\epsilon_y = 0$; (2) $\epsilon_x = 0$ and $\epsilon_y = 0.004$; (3) $\epsilon_x = 0.004$ and $\epsilon_y = 0.004$; (4) $\epsilon_x = 0.004$ and $\epsilon_y = -0.004$.

ans.   (4) $\gamma_{x_1y_1} = -0.0080$.

3.12. A torsional spring has an outer steel ring and an inner steel ring and has the space between the two rings filled with rubber as indicated in Figure P3.12. The

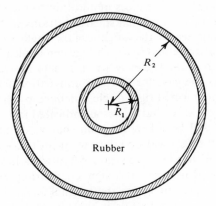

Fig. P 3.12.

inner radius of the rubber R_1 is equal to the 1 in., and the outer radius of the rubber R_2 is equal to 3 in. When a torsional load is applied to the rubber spring, the outer ring is found to rotate clockwise with respect to the inner ring through an angle of 0.020 rad. If radial lines in the undeformed rubber remain straight lines after deformation, determine the magnitude of the shearing strain $\gamma_{r\theta}$ in the rubber.

3.13. Let the shearing strain in the rubber in Problem 3.12 be inversely proportional to the square of the radius; that is, let $\gamma_{r\theta} = kR_1^2/R^2$. Determine the magnitude of $\gamma_{r\theta}$ at $R = R_1$ and $R = R_2$.

$$\text{and.}\quad \gamma_{r\theta(R = R_1)} = 0.090 \text{ and } \gamma_{r\theta(R = R_2)} = 0.010.$$

3.5. Strain-Displacement Relations

At a given point in a deformed body, the state of strain, for a volume element at that point with faces perpendicular to the x, y, z coordinate axes, is specified by the three components of normal strain ϵ_x, ϵ_y, ϵ_z and the three components of shearing strain γ_{xy}, γ_{yz}, γ_{zx}. Consider another volume element at another point in the neighborhood of the given point whose faces are also perpendicular to the x, y, z coordinate axes. Let the six components of strain for this volume element be ϵ_x', ϵ_y', ϵ_z', γ_{xy}', γ_{yz}', γ_{zx}'. In general these components of strain will not be the same as for the first volume element. Each of the two sets of six components of strain is a function of the x, y, z coordinates, but arbitrary functions of x, y, and z cannot be chosen for each of these six components of strain. Only three functions of x, y, and z are needed to relate the two states of strain at neighboring points because the state of strain at every point is determined by specifying the displacements u, v, and w as functions of the x, y, z coordinates. Thus, it is necessary to derive the strain–displacement relations.

The state of strain at a point in a deformed body will now be determined in terms of the displacements of the ends of three line segments, which meet at a point and which were perpendicular to each other in the undeformed body. Choose a set of Cartesian coordinate axes x, y, z. Specify the three line segments in the undeformed body as dx, dy, and dz parallel to the coordinate axes. Line segments AB and AC lie in the xy-plane as indicated in Figure 3.6. For convenience in sign convention, let all of the deformations be positive by specifying that each line segment increases in length and the three right angles formed by the three intersecting line segments decrease in magnitude in the deformed body. Furthermore, let the deformations of the body be small so that rigid body displacements as well as the deformations are small. For these conditions, the true lengths of the deformed line segments $A'B'$ and $A'C'$ and their projected lengths on the xy-plane will be the same, respectively.

The components of displacement of point A as it moves from A to A' are $u(x, y, z)$, $v(x, y, z)$, and $w(x, y, z)$ in the x-, y-, and z-directions, respectively. Only u and v are projected on the xy-plane as indicated in Figure 3.6. Because u is a function of x, y, and z, $\partial u/\partial x$ is the rate at which u is increasing in the

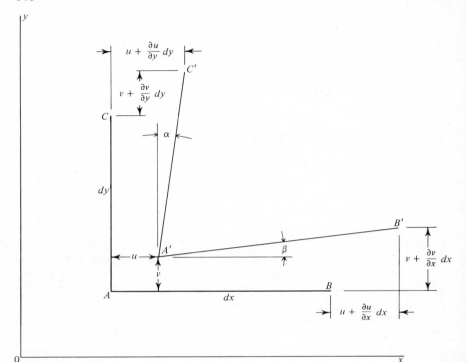

Fig. 3.6. Deformation of orthogonal line segments.

x-direction; the rate is assumed constant over the infinitesimal distance dx so that the x-component of the displacement of point B' is $u + (\partial u/\partial x)\,dx$. The other components of the displacements of B' and C' are as indicated in Figure 3.6. The two normal strains ϵ_x and ϵ_y can be obtained by dividing the change in length by the original length in each case:

$$\epsilon_x = \frac{[u + (\partial u/\partial x)\,dx] - u}{dx} = \frac{\partial u}{\partial x}, \tag{3-3}$$

$$\epsilon_y = \frac{[v + (\partial v/\partial y)\,dy] - v}{dy} = \frac{\partial v}{\partial y}. \tag{3-4}$$

The shearing strain is the tangent of the change in right angle CAB as it moves to the location $C'A'B'$. Because the change in the right angle is small, γ_{xy} is equal to the sum of the tangents of the two small angles α and β in Figure 3.6:

$$\gamma_{xy} = \frac{[u + (\partial u/\partial y)\,dy] - u}{dy} + \frac{[v + (\partial v/\partial x)\,dx] - v}{dx} = \frac{\partial u}{\partial y} + \frac{\partial v}{\partial x}. \tag{3-5}$$

Three of the six independent strain-displacement relationships at a point in the body are given by Equations (3–3), (3–4), and (3–5) and the remaining three are obtained by considering projections of the undeformed and deformed line segments on the xz- and yz-planes, respectively. The six strain-displacement relations are

$$\epsilon_x = \frac{\partial u}{\partial x} \qquad \gamma_{xy} = \frac{\partial u}{\partial y} + \frac{\partial v}{\partial x}$$

$$\epsilon_y = \frac{\partial v}{\partial y} \qquad \gamma_{yz} = \frac{\partial v}{\partial z} + \frac{\partial w}{\partial y} \qquad (3\text{–}6)$$

$$\epsilon_z = \frac{\partial w}{\partial z} \qquad \gamma_{zx} = \frac{\partial w}{\partial x} + \frac{\partial u}{\partial z}$$

The strain-displacement relations given by Equations (3–6) are valid only for Cartesian coordinates and for infinitesimal values.

Special Case of State of Strain. The major emphasis in this book is concerned with members that have a plane state of stress (see Section 2.3). The state of strain in these members is a plane problem of strain for which the nonzero strain components are ϵ_x, ϵ_y, ϵ_z, and γ_{xy}; the special case in which ϵ_z is also zero is defined as plane strain. Transformation equations for the plane problem of strain can be derived without considering the three-dimensional state of strain. If this approach is to be followed, we will continue with Part Two of this chapter and omit Part Three. In Part Two these equations are derived by considering only the geometry of the deformations.

A better understanding of the state of strain at a point will be obtained by considering the three-dimensional state of strain and deriving transformation equations for the general case presented in Part Three. These equations for the general case are based on purely mathematical definitions and do not require further geometrical considerations. This approach could have been used for the plane problem; however, the general problem is no more complex than the plane problem if the mathematical approach is followed. The reader can continue from here to Part Three and return to Part Two by omitting Section 3.6.

Illustrative Problem

3.14. The 20-in. square plate $ABCD$ in Figure P3.14 is deformed into the shape $A'B'C'D'$ indicated by the dashed lines. The state of strain at every point in the plate is identical. The deformations are greatly exaggerated. From the data given in the figure for the displacements of points B', C', and

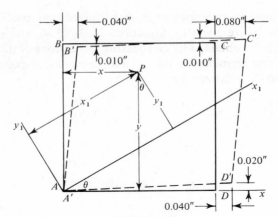

Fig. P 3.14.

D', (1) determine ϵ_x, ϵ_y, and γ_{xy}, (2) determine ϵ_{x_1}, ϵ_{y_1}, and $\gamma_{x_1y_1}$ when $\theta = 45°$, and (3) determine ϵ_{x_1}, ϵ_{y_1}, and $\gamma_{x_1y_1}$ when $\theta = 30°$.

SOLUTION. In order to use Equation (3–6), it is convenient to express the displacements u and v of any point in the square plate in terms of x and y and to express the displacements u_1 and v_1 in terms of x_1 and y_1. Let $u = ax + by$ and $v = cx + dy$. By substituting values of x and y for the coordinates of points B, C, and D, it is easy to determine the constants a, b, c, and d and show that

$$u = 0.0020x + 0.0020y,$$
$$v = 0.0010x - 0.0005y. \tag{a}$$

The displacement along the x_1-axis is u_1 and is equal to the sum of the components of u and v along the x_1-axis:

$u_1 = u \cos \theta + v \sin \theta,$

$\quad = x(0.0020 \cos \theta + 0.0010 \sin \theta) + y(0.0020 \cos \theta - 0.0005 \sin \theta). \tag{b}$

Similarly,

$v_1 = v \cos \theta - u \sin \theta,$

$\quad = x(0.0010 \cos \theta - 0.0020 \sin \theta) + y(-0.0005 \cos \theta - 0.0020 \sin \theta). \tag{c}$

The coordinates x and y can be expressed in terms of x_1 and y_1. Consider point P in Figure P3.14 with coordinates (x, y) or (x_1, y_1). From geometry it is seen that

$$x = x_1 \cos \theta - y_1 \sin \theta,$$
$$y = x_1 \sin \theta + y_1 \cos \theta.$$

Substituting these in Equations (b) and (c) gives

$$u_1 = x_1(0.0020 \cos^2\theta - 0.0005 \sin^2\theta + 0.0030 \sin\theta \cos\theta)$$
$$+ y_1(0.0020 \cos^2\theta - 0.0010 \sin^2\theta - 0.0025 \sin\theta \cos\theta)$$
$$v_1 = x_1(0.0010 \cos^2\theta - 0.0020 \sin^2\theta - 0.0025 \sin\theta \cos\theta) \tag{d}$$
$$+ y_1(-0.0005 \cos^2\theta + 0.0020 \sin^2\theta - 0.0015 \sin\theta \cos\theta)$$

The solutions of Parts (1), (2), and (3) are now obtained as follows:

(1) The strain components ϵ_x, ϵ_y, and γ_{xy} are obtained by taking the appropriate partial derivatives of u and v in Equations (a) and substituting in Equations (3–6), which gives the following results:

$$\epsilon_x = \frac{\partial u}{\partial x} = 0.0020,$$

$$\epsilon_y = \frac{\partial v}{\partial y} = -0.0005,$$

$$\gamma_{xy} = \frac{\partial u}{\partial y} + \frac{\partial v}{\partial x} = 0.0030.$$

(2) When $\theta = 45°$, $\cos^2\theta = \sin^2\theta = \sin\theta \cos\theta = 0.500$, and Equations (d) simplify to

$$u_1 = 0.00225x_1 - 0.00075y_1,$$
$$v_1 = -0.00175x_1 - 0.00075y_1. \tag{e}$$

The strain components ϵ_{x_1}, ϵ_{y_1}, and $\gamma_{x_1y_1}$ are obtained by taking the appropriate partial derivatives of u_1 and v_1 in Equations (e) and substituting in Equations (3–6), which give the following results:

$$\epsilon_{x_1} = \frac{\partial u_1}{\partial x_1} = 0.00225,$$

$$\epsilon_{y_1} = \frac{\partial v_1}{\partial y_1} = -0.00075,$$

$$\gamma_{x_1y_1} = \frac{\partial u_1}{\partial y_1} + \frac{\partial v_1}{\partial x_1} = -0.00250.$$

(3) When $\theta = 30°$, $\cos^2\theta = 0.750$, $\sin^2\theta = 0.250$, $\sin\theta \cos\theta = 0.433$, and Equations (d) simplify to

$$u_1 = 0.002674x_1 + 0.000168y_1,$$
$$v_1 = -0.000833x_1 - 0.001174y_1. \tag{f}$$

The strain components ϵ_{x_1}, ϵ_{y_1}, and $\gamma_{x_1y_1}$ are obtained by taking the appropriate partial derivatives of u_1 and v_1 in Equations (f) and substituting in Equations (3–6), which give the following results:

$$\epsilon_{x_1} = \frac{\partial u_1}{\partial x_1} = 0.002674,$$

$$\epsilon_{y_1} = \frac{\partial v_1}{\partial y_1} = -0.001174,$$

$$\gamma_{x_1y_1} = \frac{\partial u_1}{\partial y_1} + \frac{\partial v_1}{\partial x_1} = -0.000665.$$

Problems

3.15 Through 3.19. In each of the following problems, a 10-in. square plate $ABCD$ is deformed into the shape $A'B'C'D'$ indicated by the dashed lines. The state of strain in the plate is identical at every point. Determine ϵ_x, ϵ_y, γ_{xy}, ϵ_{x_1}, ϵ_{y_1}, and $\gamma_{x_1y_1}$. The deformations are greatly exaggerated in each case.

3.15.   The deformations are shown in Figure P3.15.

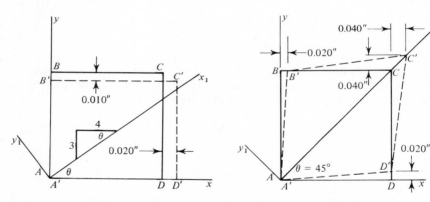

Fig. P 3.15.   Fig. P 3.16.

3.16.   The deformations are shown in Figure P3.16.
3.17.   The deformations are shown in Figure P3.17.

ans. $\epsilon_x = 0.0030$; $\epsilon_y = -0.0010$; $\gamma_{xy} = 0.0020$;

$\epsilon_{x_1} = 0.0020$; $\epsilon_{y_1} = 0$; $\gamma_{x_1y_1} = -0.0040.$

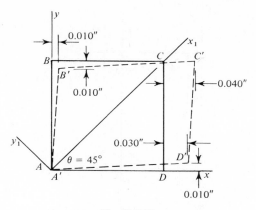

Fig. P 3.17.

3.18. The deformations are shown in Figure P3.18.
3.19. The deformations are shown in Figure P3.19.

ans. $\epsilon_x = -0.0020$; $\epsilon_y = 0.0030$; $\gamma_{xy} = -0.0020$;

$\epsilon_{x_1} = -0.0005$; $\epsilon_{y_1} = 0.0015$; $\gamma_{x_1y_1} = 0.0050$.

3.20. The 10-in. by 20-in. plate $ABCD$ in Figure P3.20 is deformed into the shape $A'B'C'D'$ indicated by the dashed lines. All straight lines parallel to either the x-axis or the y-axis before deformation remain straight lines after deformation. Show that the displacements are given by the relations $u = 0.00010xy$ and $v = -0.00015xy$. Determine

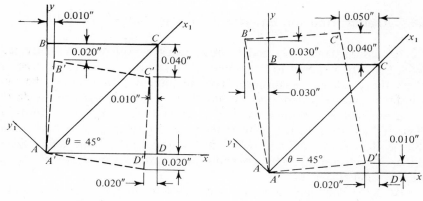

Fig. P 3.18.   **Fig. P 3.19.**

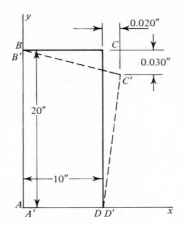

Fig. P 3.20.

ϵ_x, ϵ_y, and γ_{xy} at each of the following points whose coordinates before the deformation occurred were as follows: (1) (0, 0); (2) (10″, 0); (3) (0, 20″); (4) (10″, 10″); (5) (10″, 20″). The deformations in Figure P3.20 are greatly exaggerated.

PART TWO

Analysis of the Plane Problem of Strain

3.6. Transformation Equations for the Plane Problem

It is assumed that ϵ_x, ϵ_y, and γ_{xy} are known at a given point in a deformed body. Let it be required to determine ϵ_{x_1}, ϵ_{y_1}, and $\gamma_{x_1y_1}$ at the same point where the x_1- and y_1-coordinate axes are obtained by rotating the xy-coordinate axes counterclockwise about the z-axis through an angle θ. These two sets of coordinate axes, Ox, Oy and $O'x_1$, $O'y_1$, are shown in Figure 3.7 at the specified point O in the undeformed body. Choose two volume elements $OABC$ and $ODEF$ in the undeformed body whose faces in the xy-plane are the rectangles shown in Figure 3.7 with diagonals along the $O'x_1$- and $O'y_1$-axes.

After the body has been deformed, translate and rotate the body until points O', A', B', C', D', E', and F' lie in the xy-plane with O' at O, $O'F'$ and

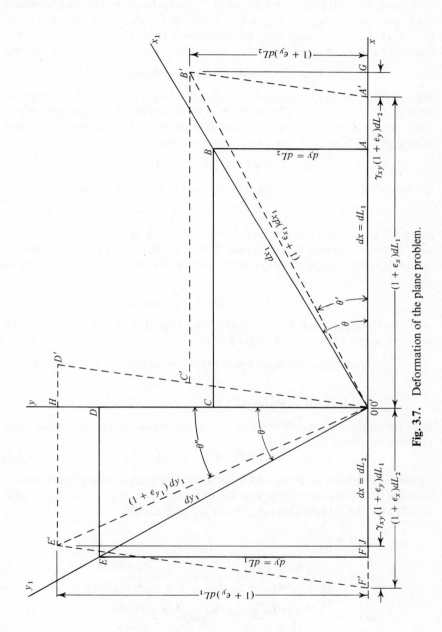

Fig. 3.7.   Deformation of the plane problem.

$O'A'$ on the Ox axis as shown in Figure 3.7. The rectangle $OABC$ has deformed into the parallelogram $O'A'B'C'$. Edge $OA = dL_1$ has elongated to $O'A' = (1 + \epsilon_x) dL_1$, edge OC has elongated to $O'C' = (1 + \epsilon_y) dL_2$, and angle $COA = \pi/2$ has decreased in magnitude to angle $C'O'A'$ indicating that

$$\gamma_{xy} = \tan(\pi/2 - \text{angle } C'O'A') = \tan(\text{angle } COC')$$

is positive. Note that the diagonal OB, parallel to the $O'x_1$-axis, has elongated to $O'B' = (1 + \epsilon_{x_1}) dx_1$. The problem is to determine the magnitude of ϵ_{x_1}. This can be done by drawing a line $B'G$ perpendicular to the x-axis and noting that $A'G = \gamma_{xy}(1 + \epsilon_y) dL_2$. For the right triangle $O'GB'$,

$$(1 + \epsilon_{x_1})^2 dx_1^2 = (1 + \epsilon_y)^2 dL_2^2 + [(1 + \epsilon_x) dL_1 + \gamma_{xy}(1 + \epsilon_y) dL_2]^2.$$

Because $dL_2/dx_1 = \sin\theta$ and $dL_1/dx_1 = \cos\theta$, the equation becomes

$$(1 + \epsilon_{x_1})^2 = (1 + \epsilon_y)^2 \sin^2\theta + [(1 + \epsilon_x)\cos\theta + \gamma_{xy}(1 + \epsilon_y)\sin\theta]^2.$$

Expanding the terms in the equation and noting that $\sin^2\theta + \cos^2\theta = 1$, each of the remaining terms include first, second, third, and fourth powers of the strains. The higher order terms can be discarded because the strains are infinitesimals, leaving

$$\epsilon_{x_1} = \epsilon_x \cos^2\theta + \epsilon_y \sin^2\theta + \gamma_{xy} \sin\theta \cos\theta. \tag{3-7}$$

The shearing strain $\gamma_{x_1 y_1}$ is equal to the tangent of the difference between the right angle EOB and the angle $E'O'B'$.

$$\gamma_{x_1 y_1} = \tan(\text{angle } EO'E' - \text{angle } BO'B') = \tan[(\theta - \theta'') - (\theta - \theta')]$$
$$= \frac{\tan(\theta - \theta'') - \tan(\theta - \theta')}{1 + \tan(\theta - \theta'')\tan(\theta - \theta')}.$$

Because $\tan(\theta - \theta'')\tan(\theta - \theta')$ is an infinitesimal of second order, this relation simplifies to

$$\gamma_{x_1 y_1} = \tan(\theta - \theta'') - \tan(\theta - \theta'). \tag{3-8}$$

Equation (3-8) can be evaluated by determining magnitudes of $\tan\theta$, $\tan\theta'$, and $\tan\theta''$. These quantities can be obtained from right triangles $O'AB$, $O'GB'$, and $O'E'J$ (note that $\epsilon_y \gamma_{xy}$ terms are neglected):

$$\tan\theta = \frac{dL_2}{dL_1},$$

$$\tan\theta' = \frac{(1 + \epsilon_y) dL_2}{(1 + \epsilon_x) dL_1 + \gamma_{xy} dL_2} = \frac{(1 + \epsilon_y)\tan\theta}{1 + \epsilon_x + \gamma_{xy}\tan\theta},$$

$$\tan\theta'' = \frac{(1 + \epsilon_x) dL_2 - \gamma_{xy} dL_1}{(1 + \epsilon_y) dL_1} = \frac{(1 + \epsilon_x)\tan\theta - \gamma_{xy}}{1 + \epsilon_y}.$$

The tangent of the difference between two angles is as follows:

$$\tan(\theta - \theta') = \frac{\tan \theta - \tan \theta'}{1 + \tan \theta \tan \theta'}.$$

The substitution of the value of $\tan \theta'$ from the preceding equation gives

$$\tan(\theta - \theta') = \frac{\tan \theta - [(1 + \epsilon_y) \tan \theta]/(1 + \epsilon_x + \gamma_{xy} \tan \theta)}{1 + [(1 + \epsilon_y) \tan^2\theta]/(1 + \epsilon_x + \gamma_{xy} \tan \theta)}$$

$$= \frac{\epsilon_x \tan \theta - \epsilon_y \tan \theta + \gamma_{xy} \tan^2\theta}{1 + \epsilon_x + \gamma_{xy} \tan \theta + \tan^2\theta + \epsilon_y \tan^2\theta}.$$

Because each of the terms $\epsilon_x, \gamma_{xy} \tan \theta$, and $\epsilon_y \tan^2\theta$ in the denominator are small when compared to $1 + \tan^2\theta$ (which is equal to $1/\cos^2\theta$),

$$\tan(\theta - \theta') = \frac{\epsilon_x \tan \theta - \epsilon_y \tan \theta + \gamma_{xy} \tan^2\theta}{1 + \tan^2\theta}$$

$$= (\epsilon_x - \epsilon_y) \sin \theta \cos \theta + \gamma_{xy} \sin^2\theta.$$

Similarly,

$$\tan(\theta - \theta'') = \frac{\epsilon_y \tan \theta - \epsilon_x \tan \theta + \gamma_{xy}}{1 + \tan^2\theta}$$

$$= (\epsilon_y - \epsilon_x) \sin \theta \cos \theta + \gamma_{xy} \cos^2\theta.$$

The substitution of these results into Equation (3–8) gives

$$\gamma_{x_1y_1} = 2(\epsilon_y - \epsilon_x) \sin \theta \cos \theta + \gamma_{xy}(\cos^2\theta - \sin^2\theta). \tag{3–9}$$

The transformation equations of strain for the plane problem are Equations (3–7) and (3–9). Given ϵ_x, ϵ_y, and γ_{xy}, these transformation equations determine ϵ_{x_1} and $\gamma_{x_1y_1}$ for coordinate axes $O'x_1$, $O'y_1$ in which the positive direction of the $O'x_1$-axis is rotated counterclockwise through an angle θ from the positive direction of the Ox-axis. In Chapter 2, transformation equations for plane stress were derived for stresses σ_{x_1} and $\tau_{x_1y_1}$ in terms of known stresses σ_x, σ_y, and τ_{xy} for the same coordinate axes. Note that the transformation equations for stress as given by Equations (2–1) and (2–2) (or Eqs. 2–32 and 2–33) are of the same form as the transformation equations for strain given by Equations (3–7) and (3–9).

3.7. Mohr's Circle for the Plane Problem of Strain

At a given point in a body, let a state of plane problem of strain be given by the strains ϵ_x, ϵ_y, and γ_{xy} as shown by Figure 3.8a; the strain ϵ_z is not zero

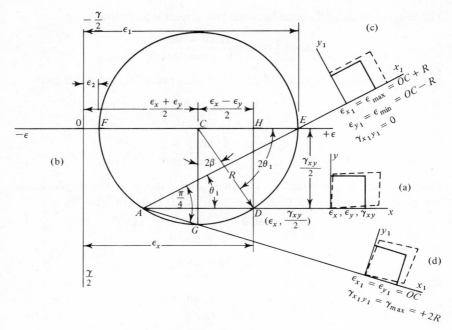

Fig. 3.8.   Mohr's circle of strain.

but cannot be observed in Figure 3.8a. It will be shown that the strains for
any arbitrarily chosen set of axes at the point can be constructed graphically
by using Mohr's circle of strain. The first step is to use the double-angle
trigometric identities to rewrite the strain transformation Equations (3–7)
and (3–9) as follows:

$$\epsilon_{x_1} = \tfrac{1}{2}(\epsilon_x + \epsilon_y) + \tfrac{1}{2}(\epsilon_x - \epsilon_y)\cos 2\theta + \tfrac{1}{2}\gamma_{xy}\sin 2\theta, \qquad (3\text{–}10)$$

$$\tfrac{1}{2}\gamma_{x_1y_1} = -\tfrac{1}{2}(\epsilon_x - \epsilon_y)\sin 2\theta + \tfrac{1}{2}\gamma_{xy}\cos 2\theta. \qquad (3\text{–}11)$$

These equations are identical in form with the stress transformation equations
(see Eqs. 2–3 and 2–4) except for the factor of $\tfrac{1}{2}$ for the shearing strains.
Note this factor of $\tfrac{1}{2}$ because the term $\gamma/2$ will be used as the ordinate in
constructing Mohr's circle of strain.

In Chapter 2 the stress transformation equations were expressed in
the form of an equation of a circle. Using the same procedure that was used
to combine Equations (2–3) and (2–4) to get (2–5), Equations (3–10) and (3–11)
when taken together can be shown to represent a circle in a plane where the
coordinates of a point on the circle are the normal strain (abscissa) and

one half the shearing strain (ordinate). This circle is called Mohr's circle of strain. The positive directions for the coordinates of the Mohr circle of strain are indicated in Figure 3.8b, where the positive direction of the normal strain ϵ-axis is to the right of the origin and the positive direction of the axis whose ordinates represent one half the shearing strain is downward.

By eliminating the functions of 2θ (see Section 2.6) from Equations 3–10 and 3–11 the equation for Mohr's circle of strain is obtained. The center of this circle is located (see Figure 3.8b) at C, where

$$OC = \frac{\epsilon_x + \epsilon_y}{2}. \tag{3-12}$$

The radius R of the circle is given by the relation

$$R = \sqrt{\left[\frac{\epsilon_x - \epsilon_y}{2}\right]^2 + \left[\frac{\gamma_{xy}}{2}\right]^2}. \tag{3-13}$$

Mohr's circle of strain in Figure 3.8b was constructed by using Equation (3–12) to locate the center C on the ϵ-axis and by using the coordinates ϵ_x and $\gamma_{xy}/2$ to locate the point D on the circle. Thus, with C as center and CD as radius, the circle is drawn. Equation (3–13) may be used to check the length of the radius R of the circle. Figure 3.8a has been drawn so that the x-axis is through D parallel to the ϵ-axis to intersect Mohr's circle at point A the origin of both the x-axis and the x_1-axis. An undeformed volume element at the specified point in the body with faces perpendicular to the x- and y-axes is shown in Figure 3.8a along with the deformed (dashed) volume element; although the deformations are assumed to be infinitesimal, they are shown as finite in order to be observable. The maximum and minimum normal strains for this circle are abscissas of points E and F, respectively. These are two of the principal strains ϵ_1 and ϵ_2. From Figure 3.8b we find the magnitude of $\epsilon_1 = \epsilon_{x_1}$ to be

$$\epsilon_1 = \epsilon_{x_1} = OC + CE = OC + R.$$

The magnitudes of OC and R are given by Equations (3–12) and (3–13); therefore,

$$\epsilon_1 = \epsilon_{x_1} = \tfrac{1}{2}(\epsilon_x + \epsilon_y) + \sqrt{\tfrac{1}{4}(\epsilon_x - \epsilon_y)^2 + \tfrac{1}{4}\gamma_{xy}^2}. \tag{3-14}$$

In a similar manner we find that

$$\epsilon_2 = OC - R$$

$$\epsilon_2 = \tfrac{1}{2}(\epsilon_x + \epsilon_y) - \sqrt{\tfrac{1}{4}(\epsilon_x - \epsilon_y)^2 + \tfrac{1}{4}\gamma_{xy}^2}. \tag{3-15}$$

The third principal strain is $\epsilon_3 = \epsilon_z$, which is unknown at present (theories required to determine ϵ_3 are presented in Chapter 4). There are two values of θ, θ_1 and $(\theta_1 + \pi/2)$, for which ϵ_{x_1} has principal values (ϵ_1 and ϵ_2). From geometry of Figure 3.8b it is seen that

$$\tan 2\theta_1 = \frac{DH}{CH} = \frac{\gamma_{xy}}{\epsilon_x - \epsilon_y}. \tag{3-16}$$

Once the three principal strains have been determined, the maximum shearing strain is given by the relation (see Eq. 2–15)

$$\gamma_{max} = \epsilon_{max} - \epsilon_{min}, \tag{3-17}$$

where ϵ_{max} and ϵ_{min} are the maximum and minimum values of the three principal strains ϵ_1, ϵ_2, and ϵ_3. For convenience in the further considerations of this chapter, we will assume that $\epsilon_3 = \epsilon_z$ is the intermediate principal strain and that ϵ_1 and ϵ_2 are the maximum and minimum values of the principal strains.

The direction of the maximum principal strain in Figure 3.8c is given by the x_1-axis drawn through points A and E. Note that the direction of the maximum principal strain is given by the positive angle $DAE = \theta_1$ measured counterclockwise from the x-axis. The magnitude of θ_1 can be obtained either by measuring the angle DAE or by computing the value of the tangent of the angle $DCE = 2\theta_1$ by using Equation (3–16). An undeformed volume element, solid-line rectangle, at the specified point in the body with faces perpendicular to the x_1- and y_1-axes is shown along with the deformed volume element, dashed-line rectangle, in Figure 3.8c.

Because $\epsilon_z = \epsilon_3$ is assumed to be the intermediate principal strain (in Fig. 3.8c it is not, for in this case, Poisson's ratio causes ϵ_z to be negative because both ϵ_1 and ϵ_2 are positive), the maximum shearing strain γ_{max} (see Eq. 3–17) at the specified point is given by the ordinate to point G on Mohr's circle of strain in Figure 3.8b. The two perpendicular line segments that intersect at the specified point in the undeformed body and that deform to give γ_{max} are parallel to the x_1- and y_1-axes is shown in Figure 3.8d along with the deformed volume element. Note that the location of the undeformed volume element where γ_{max} occurs is clockwise through an angle of $\pi/4$ from the undeformed volume element in Figure 3.8c where ϵ_{max} and ϵ_{min} occur. Remember that the three volume elements in Figures 3.8a, c, and d are all located at the same point in the body.

Illustrative Problem

3.21. Let the xy-plane lie in the free surface of a given member. The strains at a point on the surface have been found to be $\epsilon_x = -0.00160$,

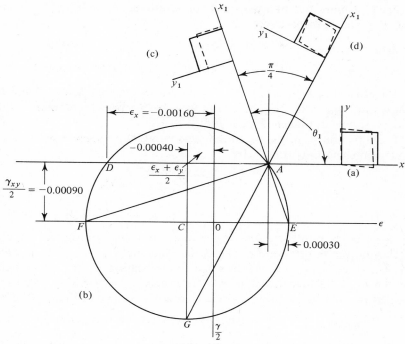

Fig. P 3.21.

$\epsilon_y = 0.00080$, and $\gamma_{xy} = -0.00180$. The principal strain $\epsilon_z = \epsilon_3$ is assumed to have an intermediate value between ϵ_x and ϵ_y. Determine $\epsilon_{max} = \epsilon_1$, $\epsilon_{min} = \epsilon_2$, γ_{max} and determine the location of the x_1 and y_1 coordinate axes to give the maximum principal strain and determine the location of the x_1- and y_1-axes to give the maximum shearing strain.

SOLUTION. The ϵ and $\gamma/2$ axes for Mohr's circle of strain are shown in Figure P3.21. The location of the center C of the circle is given by Equation (3–12):

$$OC = \frac{\epsilon_x + \epsilon_y}{2} = \frac{-0.00160 + 0.00080}{2} = -0.00040.$$

The radius R of the circle is given by Equation (3–13):

$$R = \sqrt{\tfrac{1}{4}(\epsilon_x - \epsilon_y)^2 + \tfrac{1}{4}\gamma_{xy}^2} = \sqrt{(-0.00120)^2 + (-0.00090)^2} = 0.00150.$$

The coordinates of point D are ϵ_x and $\gamma_{xy}/2$. With center C and radius $CD = R$, the circle is drawn as shown in Figure P3.21b. A line through point D parallel to the ϵ-axis locates point A the origin of the x-axis and the x_1-axis.

The maximum and minimum principal strains are given by the abscissas of points E and F, respectively:

$$\epsilon_{max} = \epsilon_E = \epsilon_1 = OC + R = -0.00040 + 0.00150 = 0.00110.$$

$$\epsilon_{min} = \epsilon_F = \epsilon_2 = OC - R = -0.00040 - 0.00150 = -0.00190.$$

The direction of ϵ_1 is given by the x_1-axis drawn through points A and E as shown in Figures P3.21b and c, and of ϵ_2 by the line AF parallel to the y_1-axis as shown in Figures P3.21b and c.

The direction θ_1 of the maximum and minimum principal strains can be obtained using Equation (3–16).

$$\tan 2\theta_1 = \frac{\gamma_{xy}}{\epsilon_x - \epsilon_y} = \frac{-0.00180}{-0.00240} = 0.75,$$

$$2\theta_1 = 216.87° \quad \text{or} \quad 216.87° + 180° \quad \text{and} \quad \theta_1 = 108.43° \quad \text{or} \quad 108.43° + 90°$$

The angle θ_1 is positive indicating counterclockwise rotation in Figure P3.21b from the positive end of the x-axis. The angle $\theta_1 = 108.43°$ locates line AE, the point on Mohr's circle indicating ϵ_{max}. The angle $\theta_1 = 108.43° + 90°$ locates line AF. The maximum shearing strain is indicated by point G on Mohr's circle of strain as shown in Figure P3.21b.

$$\gamma_{max} = \epsilon_{max} - \epsilon_{min} = 0.00110 - (-0.00190) = 0.00300.$$

The directions of the x_1- and y_1-axes (Fig. P3.21d) for γ_{max} are given by drawing the x_1-axis through points A and G. Note that the x_1-axis through points A and G bisects the right angle EAF.

In the statement of this problem it was pointed out that the third principal strain $\epsilon_z = \epsilon_3$ was an intermediate principal strain so that ϵ_{max}, ϵ_{min}, and γ_{max} would be given by Mohr's circle of strain shown in Figure P3.21b. Since $\sigma_z = 0$ at the free surface, the magnitude of ϵ_z cannot be determined until the stress-strain relations for the material are known as discussed in Chapter 4.

Problems

3.22. Solve Problem 3.11 by constructing Mohr's circle of strain.

3.23 Through 3.27. In each of Problems 3.15 through 3.19 the deformation of the plate is such that $\epsilon_z = \epsilon_3$ is a principal strain. In each case determine ϵ_x, ϵ_y, and γ_{xy} by using the given displacements. Using these values of ϵ_x, ϵ_y, and γ_{xy}, construct Mohr's circle of strain and determine ϵ_{x_1}, ϵ_{y_1}, and $\gamma_{x_1y_1}$ for $\theta = 45°$. Also determine the principal strains ϵ_1 and ϵ_2.

3.23. The deformations of the plate are described in Problem 3.15.
3.24. The deformations of the plate are described in Problem 3.16.
3.25. The deformations of the plate are described in Problem 3.17.

ans. $\epsilon_x = 0.0030$; $\epsilon_y = -0.0010$; $\gamma_{xy} = 0.0020$; $\epsilon_{x_1} = 0.0020$;

$\epsilon_{y_1} = 0$; $\gamma_{x_1y_1} = -0.0040$; $\epsilon_1 = 0.00324$; $\epsilon_2 = -0.00124$.

3.26. The deformations of the plate are described in Problem 3.18.
3.27. The deformations of the plate are described in Problem 3.19.

ans. $\epsilon_x = -0.0020$; $\epsilon_y = 0.0030$; $\gamma_{xy} = -0.0020$; $\epsilon_{x_1} = -0.0005$;

$\epsilon_{y_1} = 0.0015$; $\gamma_{x_1y_1} = 0.0050$; $\epsilon_1 = 0.00319$; $\epsilon_2 = -0.00219$.

3.28 Through 3.32. In each of the following problems, the principal strain $\epsilon_z = \epsilon_3$ is assumed to be an intermediate principal strain. By making use of the given values of ϵ_x, ϵ_y, and γ_{xy} construct Mohr's circle of strain and determine $\epsilon_{max} = \epsilon_1$, $\epsilon_{min} = \epsilon_2$, and γ_{max}. Also determine the direction of the x_1-axis where the x_1-axis is in the direction of ϵ_{max}.

3.28. $\epsilon_x = 0.00138$; $\epsilon_y = 0$; $\gamma_{xy} = 0.00138$.
3.29. $\epsilon_x = -0.00420$; $\epsilon_y = 0.00074$; $\gamma_{xy} = 0.00494$.

ans. $\epsilon_1 = 0.00176$; $\epsilon_2 = -0.00522$; $\gamma_{max} = 0.00698$; $\theta_1 = 67.5°$.

3.30. $\epsilon_x = 0.00068$; $\epsilon_y = -0.00112$; $\gamma_{xy} = -0.00240$.
3.31. $\epsilon_x = 0.00024$; $\epsilon_y = 0.00084$; $\gamma_{xy} = -0.00144$.

ans. $\epsilon_1 = 0.00132$; $\epsilon_2 = -0.00024$; $\gamma_{max} = 0.00156$; $\theta_1 = -33.7°$.

3.32. $\epsilon_x = 0$; $\epsilon_y = 0$; $\gamma_{xy} = 0.00068$.

3.33 Through 3.37. In each of the following problems, the principal strain $\epsilon_z = \epsilon_3$ is assumed to be an intermediate principal strain. By making use of the given values of ϵ_x, ϵ_y, and γ_{xy} construct Mohr's circle of strain and determine $\epsilon_{max} = \epsilon_1$, $\epsilon_{min} = \epsilon_2$, and γ_{max}. Also determine the direction of the x_1-axis where the x_1-axis is in the direction of the normal strain whose absolute magnitude is a maximum.

3.33. $\epsilon_x = 0$; $\epsilon_y = -0.00094$; $\gamma_{xy} = 0.00122$.

ans. $\epsilon_1 = 0.00030$; $\epsilon_2 = -0.00124$; $\gamma_{max} = 0.00154$; $\theta_1 = -63.81°$.

3.34. $\epsilon_x = -0.00222$; $\epsilon_y = -0.00022$; $\gamma_{xy} = -0.00200$.
3.35. $\epsilon_x = 0.00085$; $\epsilon_y = 0.00035$; $\gamma_{xy} = -0.00087$.

ans. $\epsilon_1 = 0.001102$; $\epsilon_2 = 0.000098$; $\gamma_{max} = 0.001004$; $\theta_1 = -30.06°$.

3.36. $\epsilon_x = -0.00042$; $\epsilon_y = -0.00042$; $\gamma_{xy} = -0.00132$.
3.37. $\epsilon_x = 0.00145$; $\epsilon_y = -0.00200$; $\gamma_{xy} = 0.00200$.

3.8. Experimental Strain Analysis, Rosette Analysis

In the design of members, engineers are called upon to determine relations between the loads that are applied to the member, the dimensions of the member, and either the state of stress or the state of strain, or both, for one or more points in the member where there is the greatest chance of damage to the member by the occurrence of plastic strain or fracture. The shape of many members is so complex that it is mathematically impractical or impossible to derive such relations. These relations have to be obtained by experimental means in such cases. It is physically impossible to measure either stresses or strains at a point in a given member. It is possible, however, to measure the change in length of a finite gage length near the point on the surface of a given member. The strain gages used in measuring the change in length over a finite gage length may be either mechanical, optical, or electrical. Electrical strain gages having a gage length as small as 0.0125 in. can be purchased on the market. By dividing the measured change in length by the gage length, we obtain the average value for the normal strain in the gage length. This value will represent the normal strain at any point in the gage length only if the normal strain remains constant at every point over the gage length.

The technique used for determining the state of strain at the free surface of a given member is to measure the normal strains along three lines intersecting at the point where it is desired to find the strains. Using the Mohr circle construction and the three measured normal strains, relations can be derived to give the two principal strains in the plane, their directions, and the maximum shearing strain.

A gage used in measuring average strains in three or more prescribed directions is called a *rosette strain gage*. In order to simplify the analysis, the prescribed axes for which the average strains are measured are arranged in a definite pattern. The three prescribed directions are either 0°, 60°, and 120° for the delta rosette or 0°, 45°, and 90° for the rectangular rosette. Electrical resistance delta rosettes can be purchased which cover an area as small as $\frac{3}{16}$ in. in diameter.

Delta Rosette. Let it be required that the Mohr's circle of strain be constructed from the three normal strains ϵ_d, ϵ_b, and ϵ_g obtained from measurements taken with a delta rosette strain gage. Let $\epsilon_d = \epsilon_x$ be the normal strain for $\theta = 0°$, let ϵ_b be the normal strain at $\theta = 60°$, and let ϵ_g be the normal strain at $\theta = 120°$, where these angles are all measured counterclockwise from the x-axis, which is parallel to the ϵ-axis in Figure 3.9. For convenience in sign convention, assume in this derivation that the three normal strains as well as γ_{xy} are positive as shown in Figure 3.9 and assume that ϵ_d is the maximum and ϵ_g is the minimum of the three normal strains. The relations that will be derived in the paragraphs that follow are valid for any measured values, whether positive or negative, for ϵ_d, ϵ_b, and ϵ_g. We cannot construct the actual Mohr's circle at this time in the analysis because there is no measured value of γ_{xy}. However, for the purpose of discussion of

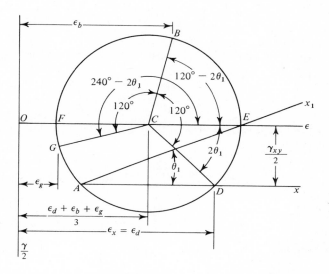

Fig. 3.9. Mohr's circle of strain for delta rosette.

the procedure for construction the correct Mohr's circle for the given data, let one possible Mohr's circle be constructed as shown in Figure 3.9. Let point D on the circle represent the point given by the coordinates $\epsilon_x = \epsilon_d$ and $\gamma/2 = \gamma_{xy}/2$ (where γ_{xy} is, as yet, unknown). Then the normal strain coordinate for point B at an angle of 120° counterclockwise from point D is ϵ_b whereas the normal strain coordinate for point G at an angle of 240° counterclockwise from point D is ϵ_g. From geometry

$$\epsilon_b = \epsilon_d - R \cos 2\theta_1 + R \cos(120° - 2\theta_1), \qquad \text{(a)}$$

$$\epsilon_g = \epsilon_d - R \cos 2\theta_1 + R \cos(240° - 2\theta_1), \qquad \text{(b)}$$

in which R is the radius of Mohr's circle and θ_1 is the angle measured counterclockwise from the positive direction of the x-axis to the direction of the maximum principal normal strain along the x_1-axis.

Because $\cos 240° = \cos 120° = -\cos 60° = -\frac{1}{2}$ and $\sin 240° =$ $-\sin 120° = -\sin 60° = -\dfrac{\sqrt{3}}{2}$, Equations (a) and (b) become

$$\epsilon_b - \epsilon_d = -R \cos 2\theta_1 + R \cos 120° \cos 2\theta_1 + R \sin 120° \sin 2\theta_1$$

$$= -\frac{3R}{2} \cos 2\theta_1 + \frac{\sqrt{3}R}{2} \sin 2\theta_1, \tag{c}$$

$$\epsilon_g - \epsilon_d = -R \cos 2\theta_1 + R \cos 240° \cos 2\theta_1 + R \sin 240° \sin 2\theta_1$$

$$= -\frac{3R}{2} \cos 2\theta_1 - \frac{\sqrt{3}R}{2} \sin 2\theta_1. \tag{d}$$

By adding Equations (c) and (d) and then taking the difference of Equations (c) and (d), we obtain

$$R \cos 2\theta_1 = \frac{2\epsilon_d - \epsilon_b - \epsilon_g}{3}, \tag{e}$$

$$R \sin 2\theta_1 = \frac{\epsilon_b - \epsilon_g}{\sqrt{3}}. \tag{f}$$

Dividing Equation (f) by Equation (e) gives

$$\tan 2\theta_1 = \frac{\sqrt{3}(\epsilon_b - \epsilon_g)}{2\epsilon_d - \epsilon_b - \epsilon_g}. \tag{3-18}$$

The location of the center of Mohr's circle of strain can be obtained combining Equation (e) and the relation $OC = \epsilon_d - R \cos 2\theta_1$, which simplifies to

$$OC = \frac{\epsilon_d + \epsilon_b + \epsilon_g}{3}. \tag{3-19}$$

The radius of the circle is given by Equation (e) as follows:

$$R = \frac{2\epsilon_d - \epsilon_b - \epsilon_g}{3 \cos 2\theta_1}. \tag{3-20}$$

From Figure 3.9 $\gamma_{xy}/2 = R \sin 2\theta_1$, and combining this result with Equation (f) we get

$$\gamma_{xy} = \frac{2}{\sqrt{3}}(\epsilon_b - \epsilon_g). \tag{3-21}$$

The coordinates $\epsilon_x = \epsilon_d$ and $\gamma_{xy}/2$(Eq. 3–21) locate point D on Mohr's circle of strain as indicated in Figure 3.9. A line drawn through point D parallel to the ϵ-axis locates point A, the origin of the x-axis and the x_1-axis. The direction of the maximum principal strain is the x_1-axis drawn through points A and E where E is the point on Mohr's circle of strain corresponding to ϵ_{max}.

Illustrative Problem

3.38.   A delta rosette on the free surface of a load carrying member gives the following strain data: 0.00136, -0.00131, -0.00245. Let $\epsilon_d = \epsilon_x = 0.00136$, $\epsilon_b = -0.00131$, and $\epsilon_g = -0.00245$, where ϵ_d is maximum, ϵ_b is intermediate, and ϵ_g is the minimum value. Let $\epsilon_z = \epsilon_3$ be the intermediate principal strain. Determine ϵ_{max}, ϵ_{min}, and γ_{max}. Determine the x_1 and y_1-axes to give ϵ_{max} and γ_{max}.

SOLUTION.   The center of Mohr's circle of strain is given by Equation (3–19).

$$OC = \frac{\epsilon_d + \epsilon_b + \epsilon_g}{3} = \frac{0.00136 - 0.00131 - 0.00245}{3} = -0.00080.$$

The magnitude of γ_{xy} is given by Equation (3–21).

$$\gamma_{xy} = \frac{2}{\sqrt{3}}(\epsilon_b - \epsilon_g) = 0.00132.$$

With the center of Mohr's circle of strain located at C and the coordinates of point D known ($\epsilon_x = 0.00136$, $\gamma_{xy}/2 = 0.00066$), the circle was drawn as shown in Figure P3.38. With ϵ_x, OC, and γ_{xy} known, the radius R of Mohr's circle of strain is given by the relation

$$R = \sqrt{(\epsilon_x - OC)^2 + (\gamma_{xy}/2)^2} = \sqrt{(0.00216)^2 + (0.00066)^2} = 0.00224.$$

The magnitudes of ϵ_{max}, ϵ_{min}, and γ_{max} are given by Equations (3–14), (3–15), and (3–17).

$$\epsilon_{max} = OC + R = 0.00144,$$

$$\epsilon_{min} = OC - R = -0.00304,$$

$$\gamma_{max} = 0.00448.$$

In Figure P3.38 a line through point D parallel to the ϵ-axis locates point A on Mohr's circle of strain. Point A is the origin of both the x-axis and the x_1-axis. A line through points A and E determines the x_1-axis, which is the

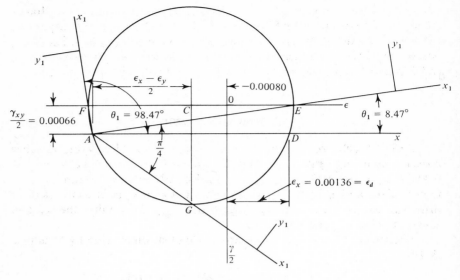

Fig. P 3.38.

direction of ϵ_{max}. The magnitude of θ_1 can be obtained using either Equation (3–16), Equation (3–18), or the geometry of Mohr's circle of strain (see Figure P3.38).

$$\tan 2\theta_1 = \frac{\sqrt{3}(\epsilon_b - \epsilon_g)}{2\epsilon_d - \epsilon_b - \epsilon_g} = \frac{\sqrt{3}(-0.00131 + 0.00245)}{2(0.00136) + 0.00131 + 0.00245} = 0.3047,$$

$$2\theta_1 = 16.94° \quad \text{or} \quad 196.94° \quad \text{and} \quad \theta_1 = 8.47° \quad \text{or} \quad 98.47°.$$

The x_1-axis is rotated counterclockwise from the x-axis through an angle of 8.47°. A line through points A and F determines the direction of ϵ_{min}; the line AF is rotated counterclockwise through an angle 98.47° from the x-axis.

The maximum shearing strain is indicated by point G on Mohr's circle of strain as shown in Figure P3.38. The directions of the x_1- and y_1-axes for γ_{max} are given by drawing the x_1-axis through points A and G. Note that the x_1-axis makes equal angles of $\pi/4$ with the lines AE and AF.

Problems

3.39 Through 3.43. In each of the problems a delta rosette was used to measure strains on a free surface of a member. The strains measured were $\epsilon_d = \epsilon_x$, ϵ_b measured on a line located 60° counterclockwise from the x-axis, and ϵ_g measured on a line located 120° counterclockwise from the x-axis. Let $\epsilon_z = \epsilon_3$ be the intermediate principal strain. Determine the distance OC to locate the center of Mohr's circle of strain, γ_{xy}, ϵ_1, ϵ_2, and γ_{max}. Also determine the direction of the x_1-axis where the x_1-axis is in the direction of $\epsilon_{max} = \epsilon_1$.

3.39. $\epsilon_d = 0.001224$; $\epsilon_b = 0.000442$; $\epsilon_g = -0.000066$.

3.40. $\epsilon_d = 0.000294$; $\epsilon_b = -0.000067$; $\epsilon_g = -0.000427$.

ans. $OC = -0.000067$; $\quad \gamma_{xy} = 0.000416$; $\quad \epsilon_1 = 0.000349$;

$\epsilon_2 = -0.000483$; $\quad \gamma_{max} = 0.000832$; $\quad \theta_1 = 15.0°$.

3.41. $\epsilon_d = 0.00163$; $\epsilon_b = -0.00010$; $\epsilon_g = -0.00222$.

3.42. $\epsilon_d = 0.001360$; $\epsilon_b = 0.000013$; $\epsilon_g = -0.001040$.

ans. $OC = 0.000111$; $\quad \gamma_{xy} = 0.001216$; $\quad \epsilon_1 = 0.001500$;

$\epsilon_2 = -0.001278$; $\quad \gamma_{max} = 0.002778$; $\quad \theta_1 = 13.0°$.

3.43. $\epsilon_d = 0.00136$; $\epsilon_b = 0$; $\epsilon_g = -0.00136$.

3.44. In the case of a rectangular rosette the strains measured are $\epsilon_d = \epsilon_x$, ϵ_b measured on a line located 45° counterclockwise from the x-axis, and $\epsilon_g = \epsilon_y$. Using Mohr's circle of strain, show that $\gamma_{xy} = 2\epsilon_b - \epsilon_d - \epsilon_g$.

PART THREE

Analysis of Three-Dimensional Strain

3.9. Transformation Equations of Strain

At a given point in a given load-carrying member, let it be assumed that the displacements $u(x, y, z)$, $v(x, y, z)$, and $w(x, y, z)$ are known functions of x, y, and z that are Cartesian coordinates. The six strain components given by Equations (3–6) are therefore known. Consider another set of Cartesian coordinates x_1, y_1, and z_1 such that the direction cosines of each of the three new coordinate axes with respect to the x, y, and z axes are known. Let ℓ, m, and n be the direction cosines for the x_1-axis, let ℓ'', m'', and n'' be the direction cosines for the y_1-axis, and let ℓ', m', and n' be the direction cosines for the z_1-axis.

The problem here is to derive transformation equations whereby the unknown strain components ϵ_{x_1}, ϵ_{y_1}, ϵ_{z_1}, $\gamma_{x_1y_1}$, $\gamma_{y_1z_1}$, and $\gamma_{z_1x_1}$ can be obtained in terms of the known strain components given by Equations (3–6). It will be necessary to derive the transformation equations for only one normal strain ϵ_{x_1} and one shearing strain $\gamma_{x_1y_1}$ because the other normal strain components and the other shearing strain components will have the same form. Because Equations (3–6) are valid for the x_1, y_1, and z_1 coordinate axes, it can be stated that

$$\epsilon_{x_1} = \frac{\partial u_1}{\partial x_1} \quad \text{and} \quad \gamma_{x_1y_1} = \frac{\partial u_1}{\partial y_1} + \frac{\partial v_1}{\partial x_1}. \tag{3–22}$$

The unknown displacements u_1 and v_1 can be obtained in terms of the known displacements u, v, and w by adding components of u, v, and w along each of x_1- and y_1-axes. Thus,

$$u_1 = \ell u + mv + nw,$$
$$v_1 = \ell''u + m''v + n''w. \tag{3–23}$$

Note that u_1 and v_1 are functions of x, y, and z. The partial derivatives that are needed in Equations (3–22) can be obtained by using the definition of a partial derivative and the definitions $\partial x/\partial x_1 = \ell$, $\partial x/\partial y_1 = \ell''$, $\partial y/\partial x_1 = m$, and so forth, as follows:

$$\frac{\partial u_1}{\partial x_1} = \frac{\partial u_1}{\partial x}\frac{\partial x}{\partial x_1} + \frac{\partial u_1}{\partial y}\frac{\partial y}{\partial x_1} + \frac{\partial u_1}{\partial z}\frac{\partial z}{\partial x_1} = \frac{\partial u_1}{\partial x}\ell + \frac{\partial u_1}{\partial y}m + \frac{\partial u_1}{\partial z}n,$$

$$\frac{\partial v_1}{\partial x_1} = \frac{\partial v_1}{\partial x}\frac{\partial x}{\partial x_1} + \frac{\partial v_1}{\partial y}\frac{\partial y}{\partial x_1} + \frac{\partial v_1}{\partial z}\frac{\partial z}{\partial x_1} = \frac{\partial v_1}{\partial y}\ell + \frac{\partial v_1}{\partial y}m + \frac{\partial v_1}{\partial z}n, \tag{3–24}$$

$$\frac{\partial u_1}{\partial y_1} = \frac{\partial u_1}{\partial x}\frac{\partial x}{\partial y_1} + \frac{\partial u_1}{\partial y}\frac{\partial y}{\partial y_1} + \frac{\partial u_1}{\partial z}\frac{\partial z}{\partial y_1} = \frac{\partial u_1}{\partial x}\ell'' + \frac{\partial u_1}{\partial y}m'' + \frac{\partial u_1}{\partial z}n''.$$

The substitution of the first of Equations (3–23) into the first of Equations (3–24) and into the first of Equations (3–22) gives

$$\epsilon_{x_1} = \ell\left[\frac{\partial u}{\partial x}\ell + \frac{\partial v}{\partial x}m + \frac{\partial w}{\partial x}n\right] + m\left[\frac{\partial u}{\partial y}\ell + \frac{\partial v}{\partial y}m + \frac{\partial w}{\partial y}n\right]$$

$$+ n\left[\frac{\partial u}{\partial z}\ell + \frac{\partial v}{\partial z}m + \frac{\partial w}{\partial z}n\right],$$

which simplifies by using Equations (3–6) to

$$\epsilon_{x_1} = \epsilon_x\ell^2 + \epsilon_y m^2 + \epsilon_z n^2 + \gamma_{xy}\ell m + \gamma_{yz}mn + \gamma_{zx}n\ell. \tag{3–25}$$

The substitution of Equations (3–23) into the last two of Equations (3–24) and into the second of Equations (3–22) gives

$$\gamma_{x_1 y_1} = \ell'' \left[\frac{\partial u}{\partial x} \ell + \frac{\partial v}{\partial x} m + \frac{\partial w}{\partial x} n \right] + m'' \left[\frac{\partial u}{\partial y} \ell + \frac{\partial v}{\partial y} m + \frac{\partial w}{\partial y} n \right]$$

$$+ n'' \left[\frac{\partial u}{\partial z} \ell + \frac{\partial v}{\partial z} m + \frac{\partial w}{\partial z} n \right] + \ell \left[\frac{\partial u}{\partial x} \ell'' + \frac{\partial v}{\partial x} m'' + \frac{\partial w}{\partial x} n'' \right]$$

$$+ m \left[\frac{\partial u}{\partial y} \ell'' + \frac{\partial v}{\partial y} m'' + \frac{\partial w}{\partial y} n'' \right] + n \left[\frac{\partial u}{\partial z} \ell'' + \frac{\partial v}{\partial z} m'' + \frac{\partial w}{\partial z} n'' \right],$$

which simplifies by using Equations (3–6) to

$$\gamma_{x_1 y_1} = 2\epsilon_x \ell \ell'' + 2\epsilon_y mm'' + 2\epsilon_z nn'' + \gamma_{xy}(\ell m'' + \ell'' m)$$

$$+ \gamma_{yz}(mn'' + m''n) + \gamma_{zx}(\ell n'' + \ell'' n) \qquad (3\text{–}26)$$

The similarity between Equation (2–18) and Equation (3–25) should be noted, as well as the similarity between the second of Equations (2–20) and Equation (3–26). It is seen that the transformation equations for strains can be obtained from the transformation equations for stress by replacing each normal stress by the corresponding normal strain and by replacing each shearing stress by one half the corresponding shearing strain.

3.10. Plane Problem as a Special Case

In deriving the transformation equations of strain for the plane problem, consider a point in the member where the state of strain is known and choose coordinate axes x, y, and z. Let the coordinate axes be oriented so that $\gamma_{xz} = \gamma_{yz} = 0$ and so that the strain components ϵ_x, ϵ_y, and γ_{xy} are known. Choose coordinate axes x_1, y_1, and z_1 subject to the conditions that the z-axis and the z_1-axis coincide and that the x_1- and y_1-axes are located by rotating the x- and y-axes counterclockwise through an angle θ as indicated in Figure 3.10. The problem here is to derive the transformation equations of strain to obtain ϵ_{x_1} and $\gamma_{x_1 y_1}$ in terms of the known strain components ϵ_x, ϵ_y, and γ_{xy} and the known angle θ. These equations are obtained from Equations (3–25) and (3–26) when the direction cosines in these equations are expressed in terms of θ. As discussed in Section 2.12, these direction cosines are

$$\ell = \cos \theta \qquad \ell' = 0 \qquad \ell'' = -\sin \theta$$

$$m = \sin \theta \qquad m' = 0 \qquad m'' = \cos \theta$$

$$n = 0 \qquad n' = 1 \qquad n'' = 0$$

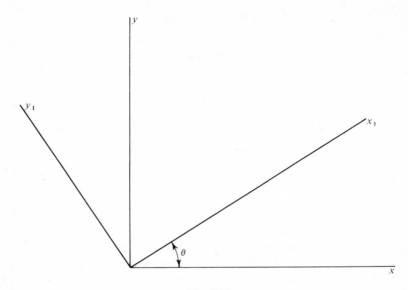

Fig. 3.10.

Substituting these values for the direction cosines in Equations (3–25) and (3–26) gives

$$\epsilon_{x_1} = \epsilon_x \cos^2\theta + \epsilon_y \sin^2\theta + \gamma_{xy} \sin\theta \cos\theta, \qquad (3\text{–}27)$$

$$\gamma_{x_1 y_1} = -2(\epsilon_x - \epsilon_y)\sin\theta\cos\theta + \gamma_{xy}(\cos^2\theta - \sin^2\theta). \qquad (3\text{–}28)$$

Note that the transformation equations for stress as given by Equations (2–32) and (2–33) are of the same form as the transformation equations of strain as given by Equations (3–27) and (3–28).

Equations (3–27) and (3–28) are identical with Equations (3–7) and (3–9), which are derived in Section 3.6. Continue with Section 3.7 in Part 2 of this chapter.

Stress-Strain Relations

4.1. Introduction

All machine and structural members have been designed by the engineer to transfer loads from one location of the machine or structure to another location. The effect of applying loads to a given member is to develop internal forces within the member and to develop deformations of the member. As discussed in Section 1.1, the term deformation is used to indicate the overall changes of shape and size of the member. Generally the engineer is interested in determining only one component of the deformation for each member. For instance the most important deformation of a tension member subjected to axial centric loading was found to be the elongation (see Section 1.4).

In Chapter 2 internal forces and their distribution in members were investigated. Six components of stress were required to specify the state of stress at a point. Equations of equilibrium for a volume element at that point were used to derive transformation equations of stress so that maximum values of normal and shearing stresses could be determined. These relationships did not require either that the deformations of the member be considered or that the material behavior be specified.

In Chapter 3 the deformations of a volume element of a member were investigated. Six components of strain were required to specify the state of strain at a point. Geometric relations for the volume element were used to derive transformation equations of strain so that maximum values of normal and shearing strains could be determined. These relationships did not require either that the stresses in the member be considered or that the material behavior be specified.

171

Transformation equations of stress for a volume element or transformation equations of strain for a volume element can be derived without considering how the state of stress and state of strain for the volume element are related. However, no member can be designed without knowing the relations between the components of stress and the components of strain. Stress-strain relations may be different for different materials, may be different for different load-carrying members made of the same material, and may be influenced by time, temperature, and relative humidity. Neither temperature nor relative humidity effects are considered in this book. The stress-strain time relations for a given material and given member are the constitutive relations for the material and member, are empirical relations, and must be obtained by mechanical tests. Most of this chapter and this book is concerned with members made of materials whose material properties can be considered to be independent of time. Time-dependent stress-strain relations are considered for a linear viscoelastic material in Section 4.8.

When the material behavior can be considered time independent, the only material properties usually obtained for a given material are represented by the stress-strain diagram for the material obtained from tension and compression specimens (see Sections 1.2 and 1.3). The stress-strain diagrams of a given material is a graphical representation of the constitutive relation for members (made of the material) having uniaxial state of stress.

An examination of the stress-strain diagrams in Section 1.3 indicates that below the proportional limit the stress-strain relation for the material is linear and the material behavior is said to be linearly elastic. In most of the problems considered in this book it is assumed that the material behavior is linearly elastic. In Section 4.2 the stress-strain relations (Hooke's laws) for all linearly elastic materials valid for all members (constitutive relations for all linear elastic materials and for all members) are presented.

Once linear elastic stress-strain relations are determined, we can derive for a given member relations among the following variables: the loads acting on the member, the dimensions of the member, and either the maximum stress or maximum deformation or both for the member. Much of this book is devoted to the task of deriving and using these relations for several of the simpler members made of linearly elastic materials.

The design of a given member is appreciably more complex than being able to calculate the maximum stresses and maximum deformations for the member for a given set of loads. In every design the engineer has to be concerned with the problem of safety. Every member will fail if the loads are increased to sufficient magnitudes; therefore, the engineer must know how to calculate failure loads for a given member if he is to know the factor of safety for the design or working loads. Theories of failure are discussed in Section 4.6.

The range of loading during the life of most members is such that the material behavior in these members can be considered to be linearly elastic. However, an increasingly larger number of members must be designed to make use of increased load-carrying capacity by allowing the material in the member to become plastic. An inelastic or plastic design requires that stress-strain relations for plastic behavior of materials be determined. The stress-strain relations for plastic behavior of materials are considered in Section 4.7.

Be aware that the design of a large number of members require material properties other than those obtained from stress-strain diagrams. As discussed in Sections 1.8 and 1.9 and in Section 4.5, the failure loads for members subjected to fatigue loading requires properties other than those given by the stress-strain diagram.

In this book it is assumed that the material properties are known. The problem at hand is to determine how these properties can be used in the design of members. The important study of materials on the atomic and microscopic levels to determine why materials exhibit certain properties and the variables that influence these properties is left to courses emphasizing material properties.

4.2. Linearly Elastic Stress-Strain Relations (Hooke's Law)

Before it is possible to design a given member made of a given material, it is necessary that we know the stress-strain relations for the material. At present it is assumed that these stress-strain relations are linear. Throughout this book we make use of two assumptions: the material is homogeneous and the material is isotropic.

A material is considered to be homogeneous if it has the same material properties at every location in a given member or in other members made of the same material. In general, it is assumed that a large number of members made of a given metal will have the same properties if all of the metal has the same chemical analysis and if all the members were given the same heat treatment. The most nearly homogeneous of all the material properties are the linearly elastic properties—those associated with the linear portion of the stress-strain diagram. In fact the linearly elastic properties of a given metal are assumed to be independent of type of heat treatment or small variations in chemical analysis. The most variable properties are those associated with the nonlinear plastic portion of the stress-strain diagram such as the yield stress, the ultimate strength, and the ductility.

A material is isotropic at a given point in a member if the properties are the same in every direction. A homogeneous and isotropic material has the same properties at every point and in every direction. A material that is not isotropic is said to be anisotropic. The solid state physicist tells us that a single crystal of a given crystalline material is anisotropic. Because all metals are crystalline, single crystals of metals are anisotropic because each crystal has planes of weakness. Fortunately, the metal members used by the engineer are polycrystalline; that is, they are made up of microscopic crystals. The directions of the planes of weakness in these crystals are randomly oriented so that polycrystalline metals can be considered to have statistical isotropy. The engineer may be called upon to design members made of anisotropic materials; therefore, the stress-strain relations for anisotropic materials will be considered first.

Anisotropic Materials—Generalized Hooke's Law. Let it be assumed that the stress–strain relations are linear. The usual form of Hooke's law assumes that each component of strain is linearly related to each of the six components of stress as follows:

$$\epsilon_x = c_{11}\sigma_x + c_{12}\sigma_y + c_{13}\sigma_z + c_{14}\tau_{xy} + c_{15}\tau_{yz} + c_{16}\tau_{zx}$$

$$\epsilon_y = c_{21}\sigma_x + c_{22}\sigma_y + c_{23}\sigma_z + c_{24}\tau_{xy} + c_{25}\tau_{yz} + c_{26}\tau_{zx}$$

$$\epsilon_z = c_{31}\sigma_x + c_{32}\sigma_y + c_{33}\sigma_z + c_{34}\tau_{xy} + c_{35}\tau_{yz} + c_{36}\tau_{zx}$$

$$\gamma_{xy} = c_{41}\sigma_x + c_{42}\sigma_y + c_{43}\sigma_z + c_{44}\tau_{xy} + c_{45}\tau_{yz} + c_{46}\tau_{zx} \qquad (4\text{--}1)$$

$$\gamma_{yz} = c_{51}\sigma_x + c_{52}\sigma_y + c_{53}\sigma_z + c_{54}\tau_{xy} + c_{55}\tau_{yz} + c_{56}\tau_{zx}$$

$$\gamma_{zx} = c_{61}\sigma_x + c_{62}\sigma_y + c_{63}\sigma_z + c_{64}\tau_{xy} + c_{65}\tau_{yz} + c_{66}\tau_{zx}$$

It is seen from Equations (4–1) that Hooke's law for an anisotropic material requires 36 elastic constants. In certain anisotropic structural materials (wood for instance) the elastic properties for coordinate axes x, y, z would remain unchanged if the positive direction of each axis is reversed. Such a material has elastic symmetry about the xy-, yz-, and zx-planes and is said to be orthotropic.

Orthotropic Materials. Consider the volume element in Figure 4.1 for which all components of stress are positive. Consider the x_1-, y_1-, z_1-coordinate axes for which the positive ends of the x_1- and y_1-axes coincide with the positive x- and y-axes and the positive end of the z_1-axis is in the negative direction. Using the sign convention for stress and strain in

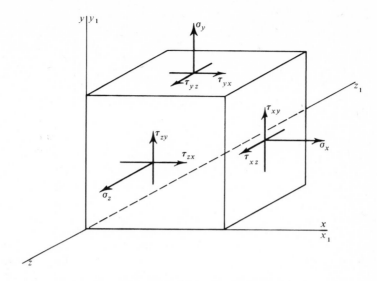

Fig. 4.1.   Stresses on volume element.

Chapters 2 and 3 we have

$$\sigma_x = \sigma_{x_1} \qquad \epsilon_x = \epsilon_{x_1}$$

$$\sigma_y = \sigma_{y_1} \qquad \epsilon_y = \epsilon_{y_1}$$

$$\sigma_z = \sigma_{z_1} \qquad \epsilon_z = \epsilon_{z_1}$$

$$\tau_{xy} = \tau_{x_1y_1} \qquad \gamma_{xy} = \gamma_{x_1y_1} \qquad (4\text{--}2)$$

$$\tau_{yz} = -\tau_{y_1z_1} \qquad \gamma_{yz} = -\gamma_{y_1z_1}$$

$$\tau_{zx} = -\tau_{z_1x_1} \qquad \gamma_{zx} = -\gamma_{z_1x_1}$$

If the elastic properties are identical for x, y, z and x_1, y_1, z_1 coordinate axes, the elastic properties are symmetrical with respect to the xy-plane. By substituting each set of stress and strain components in Equations (4–1), it is seen that Equations (4–1) will be valid only if

$$c_{15} = 0 \qquad c_{35} = 0 \qquad c_{51} = 0 \qquad c_{61} = 0$$

$$c_{16} = 0 \qquad c_{36} = 0 \qquad c_{52} = 0 \qquad c_{62} = 0$$

$$c_{25} = 0 \qquad c_{45} = 0 \qquad c_{53} = 0 \qquad c_{63} = 0$$

$$c_{26} = 0 \qquad c_{46} = 0 \qquad c_{54} = 0 \qquad c_{64} = 0$$

By satisfying the conditions that the elastic properties are also symmetrical with respect to the yz- and zx-planes, Equations (4–1) finally simplify to

$$\epsilon_x = c_{11}\sigma_x + c_{12}\sigma_y + c_{13}\sigma_z \qquad \gamma_{xy} = c_{44}\tau_{xy}$$

$$\epsilon_y = c_{21}\sigma_x + c_{22}\sigma_y + c_{23}\sigma_z \qquad \gamma_{yz} = c_{55}\tau_{yz} \qquad (4\text{–}3)$$

$$\epsilon_z = c_{31}\sigma_x + c_{32}\sigma_y + c_{33}\sigma_z \qquad \gamma_{zx} = c_{66}\tau_{zx}$$

for the orthotropic material. This material requires twelve elastic constants.

In the case of wood, let us take the x-axis in the direction parallel to the grain (parallel to the axis of the tree). The elastic properties listed in Table 1.1 for wood are for compression specimens loaded in the x-direction. For the compression specimen, Equations (4–3) reduce to

$$\epsilon_x = c_{11}\sigma_x$$

where $c_{11} = 1/E_x$ because all components of stress other than σ_x in Equations (4–3) are zero. The state of stress in the compression specimen is uniaxial. The modulus of elasticity E_x is the only elastic constant needed in the elastic design of other wooden members having uniaxial state of stress with the stress in the direction of the grain as is the case for wooden beams discussed in Chapter 7. Others of the elastic constants in Equations (4–3) are needed in case the state of stress is either biaxial or triaxial.

Isotropic Materials. If the material is isotropic, the material has the same properties in all directions. This means that the x, y, z subscripts could be interchanged to y, z, x or z, x, y respectively, without changing the elastic constants. For instance, by interchanging subscripts x and y in the first two of Equations (4–3), we see that $c_{11} = c_{22}$ and $c_{12} = c_{21}$. By continuing such interchanges of subscripts, it can be shown that Equations (4–3) reduce to

$$\epsilon_x = c_{11}\sigma_x + c_{12}(\sigma_y + \sigma_z) \qquad \gamma_{xy} = c_{44}\tau_{xy}$$

$$\epsilon_y = c_{11}\sigma_y + c_{12}(\sigma_x + \sigma_z) \qquad \gamma_{yz} = c_{44}\tau_{yz} \qquad (4\text{–}4)$$

$$\epsilon_z = c_{11}\sigma_z + c_{12}(\sigma_x + \sigma_y) \qquad \gamma_{zx} = c_{44}\tau_{zx}$$

which contain only three elastic constants. In the literature these three constants are defined as follows:

$$c_{11} = \frac{1}{E} \qquad c_{12} = -\frac{v}{E} \qquad c_{44} = \frac{1}{G}, \qquad (4\text{–}5)$$

where E is the modulus of elasticity or Young's modulus, G is the shearing modulus and v is Poisson's ratio.

Hooke's law for an isotropic material can be written in either of the following forms. The first form, Equations (4–6), are obtained by the substitution of Equations (4–5) into Equations (4–4) as follows:

$$\epsilon_x = \frac{\sigma_x}{E} - \frac{v}{E}(\sigma_y + \sigma_z) \qquad \gamma_{xy} = \frac{\tau_{xy}}{G}$$

$$\epsilon_y = \frac{\sigma_y}{E} - \frac{v}{E}(\sigma_x + \sigma_z) \qquad \gamma_{yz} = \frac{\tau_{yz}}{G} \qquad (4\text{–}6)$$

$$\epsilon_z = \frac{\sigma_z}{E} - \frac{v}{E}(\sigma_x + \sigma_y) \qquad \gamma_{zx} = \frac{\tau_{zx}}{G}$$

The second form is obtained when Equations (4–6) are solved for the stresses as follows:

$$\sigma_x = \frac{E}{1+v}\left[\epsilon_x + \frac{v}{1-2v}(\epsilon_x + \epsilon_y + \epsilon_z)\right] \qquad \tau_{xy} = G\gamma_{xy}$$

$$\sigma_y = \frac{E}{1+v}\left[\epsilon_y + \frac{v}{1-2v}(\epsilon_x + \epsilon_y + \epsilon_z)\right] \qquad \tau_{yz} = G\gamma_{yz} \qquad (4\text{–}7)$$

$$\sigma_z = \frac{E}{1+v}\left[\epsilon_z + \frac{v}{1-2v}(\epsilon_x + \epsilon_y + \epsilon_z)\right] \qquad \tau_{zx} = G\gamma_{zx}$$

Either Equations (4–6) or (4–7) are the constitutive relations for all load-carrying members made of linearly elastic isotropic materials.

Values of the three elastic constants in Equations (4–6) and (4–7) for several engineering materials are listed in Table 1.1. Note that, although three elastic constants are indicated in Equations (4–6) and (4–7), there are only two independent elastic constants because in the following paragraph it is shown that

$$E = 2G(1 + v). \qquad (4\text{–}8)$$

In order to derive Equation (4–8) consider a uniaxial state of stress for which $\sigma_1 = \sigma$ and $\sigma_2 = \sigma_3 = 0$. Using either Equation (2–15) or Mohr's circle of stress, it is found that $\tau_{max} = \sigma/2$. Equations (4–6) indicate that

$$\gamma_{max} = \frac{\tau_{max}}{G} = \frac{\sigma}{2G}. \qquad (a)$$

The principal strains for the uniaxial state of stress are given by Equations (4–6) and are $\epsilon_1 = \sigma/E$ and $\epsilon_2 = \epsilon_3 = -v\sigma/E$. Using either Equation (3–17) or Mohr's circle of strain for this state of strain, it is found that

$$\gamma_{max} = \epsilon_1 - \epsilon_2 = \frac{\sigma}{E}(1 + v). \qquad (b)$$

The magnitudes of γ_{max} in Equations (a) and (b) are equal, thus

$$\frac{\sigma}{2G} = \frac{\sigma}{E}(1 + v),$$

$$E = 2G(1 + v).$$

Isotropic Materials and Plane Stress. The state of stress for most of the members considered in this book is plane stress. The nonzero stress components for plane stress are σ_x, σ_y, and τ_{xy}. Thus $\sigma_z = \tau_{zy} = \tau_{zx} = 0$, and Equations (4–6) simplify to

$$\epsilon_x = \frac{\sigma_x}{E} - \frac{v\sigma_y}{E}$$

$$\epsilon_y = \frac{\sigma_y}{E} - \frac{v\sigma_x}{E}, \qquad \gamma_{xy} = \frac{\tau_{xy}}{G} \tag{4–9}$$

$$\epsilon_z = -\frac{v}{E}(\sigma_x + \sigma_y)$$

and Equations (4–7) simplify to

$$\sigma_x = \frac{E}{(1 - v^2)}(\epsilon_x + v\epsilon_y)$$

$$\tau_{xy} = G\gamma_{xy} \tag{4–10}$$

$$\sigma_y = \frac{E}{(1 - v^2)}(\epsilon_y + v\epsilon_x)$$

Illustrative Problem

4.1. The undeformed plate in Figure P4.1 has dimensions $X = 10$ in., $Y = 10$ in., and $Z = \frac{1}{2}$ in. The elastic constants for the material in the plate are $E = 30,000,000$ psi and $v = 0.30$. Let the plate be subjected to plane stress (i.e., $\tau_{zx} = \tau_{zy} = \sigma_z = 0$) as shown in Figure P4.1 with $\sigma_x = 30,000$ psi. If σ_y is of sufficient magnitude so that length Y of the plate remains unchanged, determine the magnitude of σ_y and the final dimensions of the plate.

SOLUTION.   Because the Y-dimension of the plate remains unchanged by the deformation, $\epsilon_y = 0$, and the second of Equations (4–9) gives

$$0 = \frac{\sigma_y}{E} - v\frac{\sigma_x}{E}$$

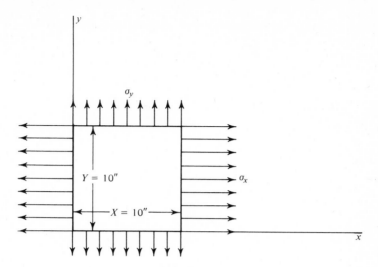

Fig. P 4.1.

from which

$$\sigma_y = v\sigma_x = 0.30(30,000) = 9,000 \text{ psi.}$$

Substituting this value for σ_y in the first and third of Equations (4–9) gives

$$\epsilon_x = \frac{30,000}{30,000,000} - \frac{0.30(9,000)}{30,000,000} = 0.00100 - 0.00009 = 0.00091,$$

$$\epsilon_z = -\frac{0.30(30,000 + 9,000)}{30,000,000} = -0.00039.$$

The final dimensions X', Y', and Z' of the plate are

$$X' = (1 + \epsilon_x)X = 10.0091 \text{ in.}$$

$$Y' = (1 + \epsilon_y)Y = 10.0000 \text{ in.}$$

$$Z' = (1 + \epsilon_z)Z = 0.4998 \text{ in.}$$

Problems

4.2. Derive Equations (4–7) from Equations (4–6) by solving for the stresses in terms of the strains and the elastic constants E, v, and G.

4.3. Defining the state of stress in terms of principal stresses and using Equations (4–9) and (4–10), show that for $v \neq 0$ the state of stress called pure shear is the only state of stress that satisfies the conditions for both plane stress ($\sigma_z = \tau_{zy} = \tau_{zx} = 0$) and plane strain ($\epsilon_z = \gamma_{zy} = \gamma_{zx} = 0$). For pure shear $\sigma_x = \sigma_1$, $\sigma_y = \sigma_2$, $\sigma_z = \sigma_3 = 0$, and $\sigma_1 = -\sigma_2$.

4.4. A steel tension member (see Table 1.1 for elastic properties) has a cross-sectional area of 2 in.^{2} and a length of 10 in. A uniform normal stress of $\sigma_z = 30{,}000$ psi acts on the cross section at each end of the member. Determine the change in volume of the tension member caused by the tension load. Using the value of α from Table 1.2, determine the temperature change needed to keep the volume constant as the load is applied.

ans.   Volume increase $= 0.00839$ in.^{3}; $\Delta t = -21.5°$F.

4.5. A triaxial state of principal stress acts on the faces of a unit cube. Show that these stresses will not produce any volume change (the material is linearly elastic) if $v = \frac{1}{2}$. If $v \neq \frac{1}{2}$, show that the condition necessary for the volume to remain unchanged is for $\sigma_1 + \sigma_2 + \sigma_3 = 0$. Strains are small.

4.6 Through 4.8. In each of the following problems determine the state of strain at the point.

4.6. The state of stress is given in Problem 2.1 and the elastic properties of the material are $E = 15{,}000{,}000$ psi and $v = 0.25$.

4.7. The state of plane stress is given in Problem 2.20 and the elastic properties of the material are $E = 10{,}000{,}000$ psi and $v = 0.32$.

4.8. The state of stress is given in Problem 2.26 and the elastic properties of the material are $E = 30{,}000{,}000$ psi and $v = 0.29$.

ans. $\epsilon_x = 0.000051$; $\epsilon_y = -0.000809$; $\epsilon_z = 0.000309$; $\gamma_{xy} = 0.000862$; $\gamma_{yz} = \gamma_{zx} = 0$.

4.9 Through 4.11. Each of the following problems are problems of plane strain ($\epsilon_z = \gamma_{zy} = \gamma_{zx} = 0$). Determine σ_z, ϵ_x, ϵ_y, and γ_{xy}.

4.9. The known stress components are $\sigma_x = 22{,}000$ psi, $\sigma_y = -12{,}000$ psi, and $\tau_{xy} = 10{,}000$ psi. The elastic properties are $E = 10{,}000{,}000$ psi and $v = 0.32$.

4.10. The known stress components are $\sigma_x = -27{,}000$ psi, $\sigma_y = -13{,}000$ psi, and $\tau_{xy} = -12{,}000$ psi. The elastic properties are $E = 29{,}000{,}000$ psi and $v = 0.28$.

ans. $\sigma_z = -11{,}200$ psi; $\epsilon_x = -0.000697$; $\epsilon_y = -0.000079$; $\gamma_{xy} = -0.001062$.

4.11. The known stress components are $\sigma_x = 22{,}000$ psi, $\sigma_y = 0$, $\tau_{xy} = -11{,}000$ psi. The elastic properties of the material are $E = 15{,}000{,}000$ psi and $v = 0.30$.

4.12 Through 4.14. These are problems of plane stress ($\sigma_z = \tau_{zy} = \tau_{zx} = 0$). Determine ϵ_z, σ_x, σ_y, and τ_{xy}.

4.12. The known strain components are given by Problem 3.34, and the elastic properties are $E = 10{,}400{,}000$ psi and $v = 0.32$.

4.13. The known strain components are given by Problem 3.35 and the elastic properties are $E = 30{,}000{,}000$ psi and $v = 0.29$.

ans. $\epsilon_z = -0.000490$; $\sigma_x = 31{,}160$ psi; $\sigma_y = 19{,}540$ psi; $\tau_{xy} = -10{,}120$ psi.

4.14. The known strain components are given by Problem 3.37 and the elastic properties are $E = 15,000,000$ psi and $v = 0.30$.

4.15. The plate in Problem 4.1 is subjected to plane stress. The elastic constants for the material in the plate are $E = 10,000,000$ psi and $v = 0.32$. Determine the magnitude of σ_y such that $\epsilon_x = 2\epsilon_y$ and $\sigma_x = 30,000$ psi. σ_x and σ_y are principal stresses. Determine the three principal strains.

4.16. The plate in Problem 4.1 is subjected to plane strain. The elastic constants for the material in the plate are $E = 10,000,000$ psi and $v = 0.32$. Determine the magnitudes of σ_y and σ_z such that $\epsilon_x = 2\epsilon_y$ and $\sigma_x = 30,000$ psi. σ_x and σ_y are principal stresses. Determine the three principal strains.

ans. $\sigma_y = 23,570$ psi; $\sigma_z = 17,140$ psi; $\epsilon_x = 0.001697$; $\epsilon_y = 0.000849$; $\epsilon_z = 0$.

4.3.   Linearly Elastic Load and Deformation Analysis

The main emphasis in this book is the derivation and use of the relationship between the loads acting on a member, the dimensions of the member, and either the state of stress at one or more points in the member or the deformations at one or more points of the member. The derivation of load-stress and load-deformation relations for a given member requires that the three conditions in Section 1.5 be satisfied as follows: (1) Each part of the member is in equilibrium (each member considered in this book is assumed to be in static equilibrium). (2) The geometry of deformation must satisfy the condition that each deformed volume element of the member must fit together perfectly with adjacent volume elements. (3) Stress-strain relations for the material are satisfied at every point in the member. Two different procedures are available in satisfying these three conditions.

First Procedure—Simplified Approach. In most of the cases considered in this book, both the type of member and the type of loading for the member are so simple that the procedure followed is to pass a plane perpendicular to the axis of the member and to consider a free-body diagram of the portion of the member to one side of the section. This procedure can be followed if the geometry of deformation is sufficiently simple so that the strain distribution on the cross section can be determined. Exact theories by this procedure can be obtained for straight members subjected to axial centric loading (Chapter 1), pure bending of straight beams (Chapters 7 and 8), and torsion of straight members having circular cross section (Chapter 9). The same procedure is often employed by the so called strength-of-materials approach to obtain approximate solutions of many practical engineering problems.

Second Procedure—Differential Equation Approach. As the type of member and type of loading becomes more complex, the usual procedure is to consider a free-body diagram of an infinitesimal volume element of the member. Differential equations of equilibrium are derived for the volume element. Other differential equations called differential equations of compatibility are derived by considering the geometry of deformation of the volume element. This approach requires that a solution be found for these differential equations that also satisfies stress-strain relations for the material of which the member is made and the boundary conditions specified for the given loading and prescribed deformations at the boundaries of the member. This procedure is usually followed in the more advanced treatment of the subject. In Chapter 9 this approach is used in the analysis of torsion members having noncircular cross sections.

Three Steps in the Derivation of Load-Stress and Load-Deformation Relations. The following three steps are followed when the first procedure (simplified approach) is used in the derivation of load-stress and load-deformation relations for a given member.

Step 1. Assume that the member is in equilibrium. Using the method of sections as discussed in Section 1.1, pass a plane through a cross section of the member so that a portion of the member to one side of the plane can be removed. The portion removed is in equilibrium. The internal forces on the cross section have now become external. Consider a differential area da lying in the cross section; the components of the internal force on the differential area are $\sigma\,da$ and $\tau\,da$. Write the equations of equilibrium for the portion of the member under consideration.

Step 2. In order to solve the equations of equilibrium, it is necessary to determine the distribution of the stress components σ and τ on the cross section. The distribution of each component of the stresses is determined as follows:

(1) The distributions of normal strains and shearing strains on the cross section are determined either by using physical arguments or by using experimental techniques; Note that strains can be observed (and often measured) whereas stresses cannot. The manner in which the strains vary (are distributed) on the cross section depends mainly on the shape (geometry) of the member and on the type of loading (axial, bending, torsion, etc.), but not on the properties of the material of which the member is made.

(2) With the distributions of strains on the cross section known, the distributions of the stresses are obtained by using Equation (4–7) if the material behavior is isotropic and is linearly elastic or is obtained by using plastic stress-strain relations as discussed in Section 4.7 if the material behavior is plastic. Stress-strain time relations for materials whose time-

dependent material properties can be accurately approximated by linear viscoelastic models are considered in Section 4.8.

Step 3.   With the distributions of stresses on the cross section known, the equations of equilibrium can be integrated to obtain the desired relationships between the loads acting on the member and the components of stress at any point on the cross section.

In Section 1.4 the three steps were followed in the derivation of load-stress (Equation 1–10) and load-elongation (Equation 1–18) relations for members subjected to axial centric loading. The three steps are followed in the derivation of similar relations for beams in Chapters 7 and 8 and for torsion of members having circular cross section in Chapter 9.

In a large number of cases exact load-stress and load-deformation relations needed in the design of a given member are not known. Practical solutions are often obtained using the foregoing three-step procedure. Simplifying assumptions are made in order to determine the strain distributions. In this case the approach is usually called the strength-of-materials approach. If at all possible, the magnitude of the error introduced into the theory by these simplifying assumptions should be checked by building either the member of a model of it and loading it to failure. Often the member is too complex to derive a load-stress relationship; the design is then based on trial and error by testing to failure of several different configurations for the member.

4.4.   Rational Procedure in Design

One emphasis of this book will be to derive load-stress and load-deformation relations for several simple types of members, each of which is subjected to specified loads. There are four main steps in a rational procedure in design.

Step 1.   Determine the mode of failure of the member that would most likely take place if the loads acting on the member should become large enough to cause it to fail. Various modes of failure are discussed in Section 4.5. The choice of the material is involved in Step 1 because the type of material may significantly influence the mode of failure that will occur. Note that the choice of material used may often be controlled largely by general factors, such as availability, cost, weight limitations, ease of fabrication, and so forth, rather than primarily by the requirements of design for resisting loads.

Step 2.   In general, the mode of failure can be expressed in terms of some quantity such as the maximum principal stress, the maximum shearing stress, the maximum octahedral* shearing stress, the maximum deformation, and so forth. Independent of what the mode of failure might be, it is generally possible to associate the failure of the member with a particular cross section of the member. For the linearly elastic problem, failure can be interpreted in terms of the state of stress at the point in the cross section where the stresses are maximum. For the plastic problem, failure can be interpreted in terms of the distributions of the various components of the state of stress on the cross section. Therefore, in Step 2, relations are derived between the loads acting on the member, the dimensions of the member, and the distributions of the various components of the state of stress on the cross section of the member. The method of attack for the linearly elastic material was discussed in Section 4.3.

Step 3. By appropriate tests of the material, determine the maximum value of the quantity associated with failure of the member. An appropriate or suitable test is one that will produce in the test specimen or model the same action that results in failure of the actual member. For many operating conditions it is difficult or impossible to formulate tests that are strictly suitable according to this definition. As discussed in Section 4.6, theories of failure are formulated so that results of simple tests (tension and compression specimens) are made to apply to the more complex conditions.

Step 4. By use of experimental observations and analysis, experience with actual structures and machines, judgment, and commercial and legal considerations, select for use in the relation derived in Step 2 a working (allowable or safe) value for the quantity associated with failure of the member. This working value is considerably less than the limiting value determined in Step 3.

The need for selecting a working value less than that found in Step 3 arises mainly from the following uncertainties: (1) uncertainties in the service conditions, especially in the loads, that are affected by a great many conditions that, as a rule, are difficult to control or to predict; (2) uncertainties in the degree of uniformity of the material; (3) uncertainties in the significance or correctness of the relations derived in Step 2. The uncertainties under (3) may be concerned either with the quantity that is assumed to be significant in the failure or with the relations themselves—usually the outcome of simplifying assumptions.

These considerations clearly indicate a need for applying a so-called factor of safety in the design of a given load-carrying member. The function

---

* As discussed in Section 2.11, the octahedral shearing stress acts on a plane making equal angles with the three principal stresses. Test data, from several different types of members (tension, torsion, etc.) made of the same ductile metal, indicate that yielding starts in each member at the same value of the octahedral shearing stress.

of the member is to carry loads; therefore, the factor of safety should be applied to the loads. Using the theory relating the loads to the quantity associated with failure derived in Step 2 and the maximum value of the quantity associated with failure in Step 3, determine the failure loads which we will designate P_f. The factor of safety N is the ratio of the failure load to the working load P_w. Thus

$$N = \frac{P_f}{P_w}. \tag{4–11}$$

If P_f and P_w are each directly proportional to stress, the factor of safety may be based on stress. The magnitude of N may be as low as 1.4 in the aircraft and space vehicle industries where it is essential that the weight of structures be as low as possible. In many applications N will range from 2.0 to 2.5.

4.5. Modes of Failure

If a member is to be designed based on a specified factor of safety, it is necessary that the failure load be calculated. Before the failure load can be calculated, the mode of failure must first be determined. Three modes of failure will be considered as follows: fracture, general yielding, excessive deformation. There is one type of failure that will not be considered here, but will be considered in Chapter 11; this failure is associated with instability of the member and is called a buckling failure.

Because the mode of failure may be influenced by the type of material, consider three different materials, all steels, whose tension stress-strain diagrams are shown in Figure 4.2. Steel A is a brittle material that remains linearly elastic up to fracture so that the proportional limit stress is equal to the ultimate strength. Materials that have a stress-strain diagram similar to steel B are also called brittle because of their limited ductility; the proportional limit for this material may be appreciably below the ultimate strength. Steel C is a high-strength ductile steel for which the proportional limit stress and yield point stress may be equal but the ultimate strength is about 30 per cent greater.

The design of a tension speciman to obtain the data in Figure 4.2 is not a trivial undertaking. The ends of the specimen have to be enlarged so that fixtures can be attached for applying the load. Abrupt changes in cross section result in a stress concentration (see Section 1.7) so that the maximum stress in the specimen at the abrupt change in cross section is appreciably greater than that at locations where the stress is uniformly distributed over the cross section. This difficulty can be overcome with the specimen in Figure 4.3 where

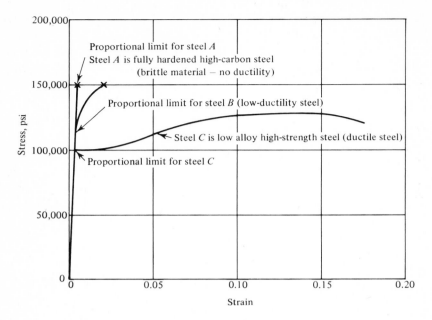

Fig. 4.2. Tension stress-strain diagrams for three steels.

the transition from the test section to the ends of the specimen is very gradual.

In discussing possible modes of failure of load-carrying members made of the three materials whose stress-strain diagrams are shown in Figure 4.2, let us consider load-elongation curves for the tension member shown in Figure 4.4a. It is assumed that the tension member is designed so that the stress concentrations at the points of application of the axial loads are negligible. At present it will be assumed that this member is subjected to gradually applied static loads. The load-elongation curves will be considered for the tension member made of each of the three steels for the case in which there is no stress concentration and for the case in which we have a stress concentration obtained by drilling a small diameter hole through the center

Fig. 4.3. Tension specimen.

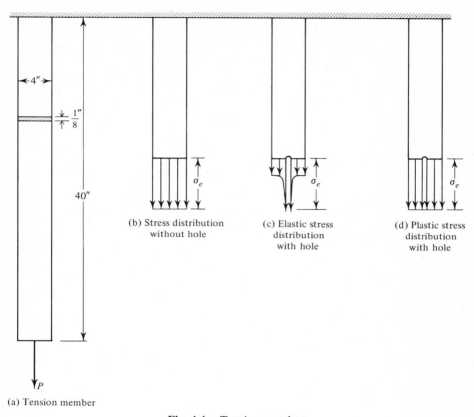

(a) Tension member

Fig. 4.4. Tension member.

of the tension member. In case there is no stress concentration (no hole), the stress distribution for the centrally loaded tension member is uniform, as shown in Figure 4.4b; the stress distribution is uniform for either linearly elastic conditions or plastic conditions. Load-elongation curves for tension members made of the three different steels are shown in Figure 4.5. Note that the shape of the load-elongation curves are similar to the stress-strain diagrams, as shown in Figure 4.2. The one difference is that we assume the load-elongation curve to end at the ultimate load for the tension member made of steel C because fracture would occur at this point if dead* loads are being applied to the member.

* A weight W that is hanging at the end of a tension member is a dead load.

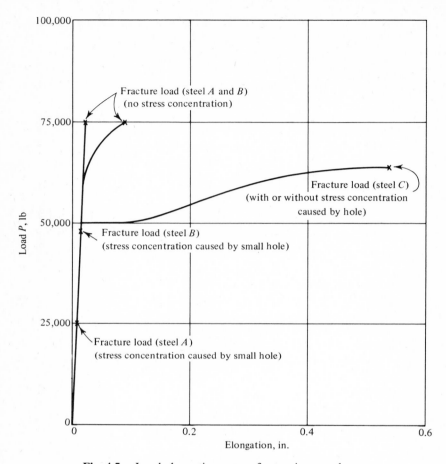

Fig. 4.5.   Load-elongation curves for tension members.

The effect of a stress concentration on the load-elongation curves for the tension member in Figure 4.4a will be illustrated by a small hole drilled in the member; the cross-sectional area of the member removed by drilling the hole is assumed small compared to the area of the cross section of the member. The theoretical stress concentration factor for the hole is known to be equal to 3.00 for linearly elastic behavior to give the stress distribution shown in Figure 4.4c. The effect of the stress concentration on the load-elongation curve for the tension member made of the completely brittle metal (steel A of Fig. 4.2) would be to reduce the fracture load by a factor of 3.00 (Fig. 4.5). On the other hand the stress concentration may not have any effect on the load-elongation curve for the tension member made of a ductile metal (steel C). Although yielding will start at the hole when the load is equal to $A\sigma_e/3$ (where σ_e is the yield point stress for steel C), the yielding which accompanies an increase in load causes a redistribution of stress until at the load $A\sigma_e$ the stress distribution is uniform (Fig. 4.4d). The localized yielding required to cause the redistribution of stress is limited to such a small volume of the tension member that its effect on the load-elongation curve of the member may be negligible. Note that, although the stress distribution is uniform at the load $A\sigma_e$, the strain distribution is not uniform and the maximum strain at the hole may be about nine times greater than the average axial strain in the tension member where yielding is assumed to be impending ($\epsilon_z = \epsilon_e = \sigma_e/E$ away from the hole). In case the material does not have sufficient ductility, the ultimate load may be greatly reduced by the stress concentration as is indicated for the tension member made of steel B in Figure 4.5.

Failure by Fracture.   The one mode of failure recognized by everyone is fracture. When a member fractures, it separates into two or more pieces and its usefulness as a load-carrying member ceases. Fracture is the mode of failure of most members made of brittle materials. Fracture may be the mode of failure of all members made of either brittle or ductile materials if the member is subjected to repeated cycles of loads so as to produce progressive fracture (fatigue failure). If the member is made of a ductile material and is subjected to static loads, fracture may be the mode of failure if there is a defect such as a small undetected crack. The mode of failure of members made of a ductile material and subjected to static loads is usually either general yielding or excessive deformation.

If a member is subjected to repeated cycles of completely reversed load, it may fail by fracture without visual evidence of inelastic deformation. Fracture by repeated loads is commonly referred to as fatigue failure. The material property needed to design these members is the fatigue strength of the material as discussed in Section 1.8.

Failure by General Yielding.   This is not the mode of failure associated with members made of so-called brittle materials (steels A and B in Fig. 4.2 for example). We assume that general yielding will occur only if the member is made of a ductile material (for instance steel C in Fig. 4.2). Because stress concentrations have little effect on the shape of the load-deformation curve for a given member, we will assume that stress concentrations need not be considered if the mode of failure is general yielding.

General yielding mode of failure is not easily defined since it means different things to different engineers. In order to illustrate the problem, consider the dimensionless load-deflection curves for two load-carrying members, member A and member B, shown in Figure 4.6. The characteristic deflection

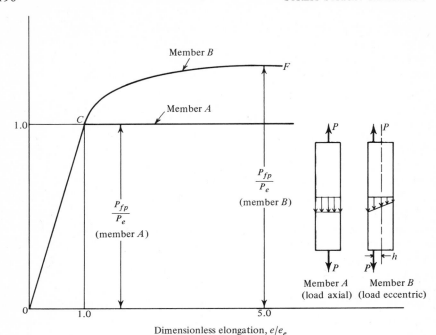

Fig. 4.6.   Dimensionless load-elongation curves for members having uniform and nonuniform stress distributions.

for these members is the elongation of the member. For convenience let both members be made of a ductile steel whose stress-strain diagram is flat topped at the yield point stress (see steel C in Fig. 4.2). Define P_e as the maximum elastic load, the load which initiates yielding at some point in the member other than at a stress concentration. Let e_e be the elongation of the member corresponding to the load P_e. Note that the load-elongation curves for the two members in Figure 4.6 were terminated when the elongation was about $5e_e$. In most cases the failure of the member would occur before this elongation was reached.

Member A in Figure 4.6 is centrally loaded and has a uniform stress distribution such as was the case for the tension member in Figure 4.4a. For this member the load P_e, which initiates yielding, is equal to the fully plastic load P_{fp}, which causes yielding to spread over the cross section of the member. The load-elongation curve for this member has the same shape as the stress-strain diagram and is flat topped at the load P_e for which the uniform stress is equal to the yield point σ_e. The load-deformation curve for most members is similar in shape to the load-elongation curve for member B in Figure 4.6.

Member B is not centrally loaded since the action line of the loads P is at a distance h from the axis through the centroid of each cross section. This load on member B is said to be eccentric and it does not cause a uniform stress distribution over a given cross section of the member (see Chapter 10). The fully plastic load P_{fp}, which causes yielding to spread over a cross section of member B, is greater than the load P_e, which initiates yielding in member B. If we use an elastic analysis (stress-strain relations given by Eqs. 4–6), we are limited to the linearly elastic behavior, and P_e is the maximum elastic load or the failure load for the member. We will assume that failure by general yielding will begin when yielding is initiated at some point in the member other than at a stress concentration. This definition may give a somewhat conservative design for a member as the comments that follow will illustrate.

It is possible to use a plastic analysis (stress-strain relations discussed in Section 4.7) to derive the relation for member B in Figure 4.6 for the curved portion CF of the load-elongation curve from the load P_e, which initiates yielding to the load P_{fp}, which causes fully plastic conditions. For some members failure by general yielding does not occur until the fully plastic load is reached. This definition of failure by general yielding has its limitations because most materials do not have a flat-topped stress-strain diagram of the yield stress, and load-carrying members made of these materials do not have a fully plastic load.

Failure by Excessive Deformation. The maximum load that may be applied to a given member without causing it to cease to function properly may be limited by a permissible deformation of the member. In order to determine the failure load in this case it is necessary that the load-deformation curve for the member be known. In most applications in which the mode of failure is excessive deformation, the stresses in the member are usually sufficiently small so that a linearly elastic analysis can be used. Examples of design problems in which the mode of failure is excessive elastic deformation may be noteworthy. A machine lathe, in order to hold small tolerances on the part being machined, must be designed so that the deformation of the lathe is small. The amplitude of vibration is a measure of the deformation of the vibrating member; these amplitudes have to be sufficiently small so as to eliminate objectional noise, shaking forces, collision of parts, and so forth.

4.6. Theories of Failure

In general, members are designed based on a specified factor of safety. The working load is obtained by dividing the failure load by the factor of safety. As discussed in Sections 4.4 and 4.5, the determination of the failure load requires the use of the mode of failure and the material property associated with it.

Three modes of failure were discussed in Section 4.5 as follows: fracture, general yielding, excessive deformation. The deformations considered in this book are those associated with linearly elastic behavior; thus the only material properties needed to calculate deformations are the elastic constants for the material. The elastic constants depend only on the chemical analysis of the material and not on either the yield stress or ultimate strength of the material. Because the ultimate strength and yield stress of the material are associated with fracture and general yielding modes of failure, it is necessary, when design is limited by specified deformations, to check to see if failure may occur by general yielding or fracture before the specified deformation is reached. Elastic constants are well known for most materials so that special tests are not needed to obtain these constants when the mode of failure is excessive elastic deformation.

The theories of failure that will be presented are those associated with fracture and general yielding modes of failure. These theories of failure have been empirically determined. Test data indicate that different theories of failure are required for fracture than for general yielding modes of failure.

One might question the need for theories of failure. The need for a theory of failure arises from the fact that material properties are obtained from specimens having one state of stress and are used to predict failure of members having another state of stress.

Theory of Failure for Brittle Materials—Maximum Principal Stress Theory of Failure. The maximum principal stress theory of failure, often called Rankine's theory, states that failure begins in all load-carrying members when the maximum principal stress reaches a limiting value. An examination of the failure of members made of brittle materials indicates that fracture occurs on planes on which the maximum principal stress acts. Figure 4.7 shows fractures of two pieces of chalk; the piece in Figure 4.7a is subjected to axial tension loading while the piece in Figure 4.7b is subjected to torsion loading. The maximum principal stress for axial tension loading is on a plane perpendicular to the axis of loading of the chalk, the plane on which fracture occurred. It will be found in Chapter 9 that the state of stress for torsion loading is pure shear; one of the sets of orthogonal planes on which the shearing stresses are acting are the planes perpendicular to the axis of the torsion member. Chapter 2 shows that the maximum principal stress acts on a plane at 45° to the planes on which the maximum shearing stresses are acting. The piece of chalk subjected to torsion in Figure 4.7b fractured on a plane on which the maximum principal stress was acting.

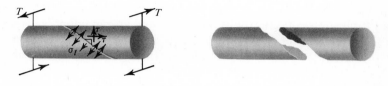

(a) Tension loading and resulting fracture

(b) Torsion loading and resulting fracture

Fig. 4.7. Fractures of pieces of chalk subjected to either tension or torsion loading.

It will be assumed that the maximum principal stress theory of failure can be used to determine the fracture load for all members made of brittle materials. The fracture stress σ_u for a given material can be obtained from tension specimens. The maximum principal stress theory of failure says that fracture will occur in any given member made of that material when the loads are increased to sufficient magnitudes that the maximum principal stress in the member is equal to the fracture stress obtained from the tension specimens. Thus,

$$\sigma_{\max} = \sigma_u, \qquad (4\text{--}12)$$

in which $\sigma_{\max}$ is a tensile stress whose magnitude is approximately as great or greater than the absolute magnitude of the other two principal stresses, which may be compressive in the member. In case $\sigma_{\max}$ is a tensile stress that is small compared to the largest compressive stress, Equation (4–12) may not be valid and the failure load for the member should be obtained by loading the member to failure.

There is one important question that needs to be answered. How do we decide that a given material is brittle? A very limited number of materials behave linearly up to fracture in all members made of these materials; these materials are brittle. Glass is a material that remains linearly elastic to fracture in most applications. Most so-called brittle materials exhibit a limited amount of ductility in a tension test (e.g., steel *B* in Fig. 4.2). The fracture load for members made of materials having limited ductility usually is equal to or greater than that predicted by an elastic analysis using the maximum principal stress theory of failure.

Theory of Failure for General Yielding—Maximum Shearing Stress Theory of Failure and Maximum Octahedral Shearing Stress Theory of Failure. In Section 4.5 the magnitude of the load necessary to produce failure of a member by general yielding was defined as the load required to initiate yielding in regions of the member other than at stress concentrations. Thus, a theory to predict failure of a member by general yielding is identical with a theory to predict initiation of yielding in the main body of the member away from stress concentrations. These theories are commonly referred to in the literature as yield conditions.

Before a theory of failure for general yielding or a yield condition can be developed, it is necessary to investigate how a material fails when yielding takes place. Yielding can be observed in members made of low carbon (mild) steel. The stress-strain diagram of this material exhibits an upper yield-point stress after which yielding proceeds at a lower yield-point stress. Because yielding spreads at a lower stress than that required to initiate it, yielding is heterogeneous and occurs in regions of yielded material adjacent to regions of elastic material. By polishing the surface of the tension specimen before the test load is applied, one can observe these regions that are narrow finger-like bands of yielding material called *Luder's bands*.

Experimental evidence of Luder's bands in tension members having abrupt changes in section is indicated in Figure 4.8 for a tension member

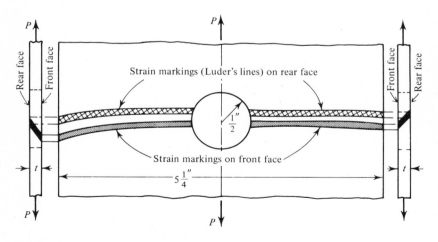

Fig. 4.8. Fully plastic condition in tension steel member containing a hole.

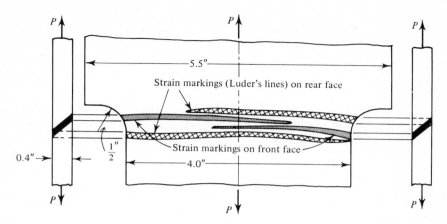

Fig. 4.9. Fully plastic condition in tension steel member containing a fillet.

with a hole and in Figure 4.9 for a tension member with fillets. The sketches were made from photographs of the Luder's bands on surfaces of the two sides of the flat steel members soon after the tensile load P reached the fully plastic value. The Luden's bands on the front and near sides in Figures 4.8 and 4.9 are clearly marked to orient their position in each member. The end or edge views of the material that has yielded are also shown. Observe that yielding occurs on planes making an angle of approximately 45° to the axis of the tension members, as seen from the narrow edge of the right or left side of the members (Figs. 4.8 and 4.9), but on the front and back faces the bands appear to be perpendicular to the axis of the tensile load. In Chapter 2 it was found that these are planes of maximum shearing stress.

Tresca[*] proposed the maximum shearing-stress theory of failure or maximum shearing-stress yield condition, which states that for all members made of the same material, yielding begins at the same limiting magnitude of shearing stress. The limiting value of maximum shearing stress for a given material can be obtained either from tension and compression specimens or from hollow torsion specimens. This theory of failure or yield condition is often used in the design of members made of ductile materials. Mohr's circle of stress indicates that

$$\tau_{max} = \frac{\sigma_{max} - \sigma_{min}}{2} = \frac{\sigma_e}{2}, \tag{4–13}$$

[*] H. Tresca, "Mémoire sure l'écoulement des corpes solides soumis á de fortes peressions," *Comptes Rendus Acad. Sci. Paris* **59** (1864).

where σ_{max} and σ_{min} are the maximum and minimum principal stresses in the member to be designed, and σ_e is the yield stress obtained from tension and compression specimens. The design of members based on Equation (4–13) is conservative because the limiting value of the maximum shearing stress is found to depend on the state of stress and is a minimum for the uniaxial state of stress. The limiting value of the maximum shearing stress for pure shear is about 15 per cent greater than that given by the tension test. This fact led von Mises* to propose a theory of failure or yield condition involving all components of the state of stress. Nadai† interpreted the von Mises theory of failure in terms of the octahedral shearing stress, which is defined in Section 2.11 and is given by Equation (2–31).

The octahedral shearing-stress theory of failure (or yield condition) states that yielding begins in all members made of the same material at the same limiting magnitude of octahedral shearing stress. Equation (2–31) gives the octahedral shearing stress in terms of the three principal stresses. Although the proof is beyond the scope of this book, the octahedral shearing stress can be derived in terms of the six independent components of stress at a point. Thus

$$\tau_G = \tfrac{1}{3}\sqrt{(\sigma_x - \sigma_y)^2 + (\sigma_y - \sigma_z)^2 + (\sigma_z - \sigma_x)^2 + 6(\tau_{xy}^2 + \tau_{yz}^2 + \tau_{zx}^2)}$$

$$= \frac{\sqrt{2}}{3}\,\sigma_e \qquad\qquad\qquad\qquad (4\text{--}14)$$

where σ_x, σ_y, σ_z, τ_{xy}, τ_{yz}, and τ_{zx} are the six known stress components defining the state of stress at the critical point in the member to be designed and σ_e is the yield stress obtained from tension and compression specimens. The octahedral shearing-stress theory of failure is generally accepted as being the most accurate theory of failure for general yielding mode of failure. The reason for this general acceptance is because of the fact that the results of many experimental investigations show that the limiting value of τ_G depends very little upon the kind of test member or loading that is used in the test.

Failure by Progressive Fracture—Repeated Loads. In Section 1.8 it was shown that members subjected to repeated loads generally fail by progressive fracture. This failure is considered to be by brittle fracture because fracture usually occurs without visible evidence of plastic deformation. However, a microscopic examination of the material in the region

* R. von Mises, "Mechanik de festen Körper im plastisch deformablen Zunstand, Nachtichten def Gesellschaft der Wissenschaften Göttingen," *Math-Phys*, Klasse (1913).

† A. Nadai, *Theory of Flow and Fracture of Solids*, Vol. I, 2nd Ed., McGraw-Hill Book Co., New York (1950).

where the progressive fracture originated always indicates that plastic deformation preceded the initiation of the fracture. It has been found that the octahedral shearing-stress theory of failure can be used to predict failure by progressive fracture that occurs under repeated loads. Equation (4–14) can be used in the design of a given load-carrying member subjected to repeated loads if σ_e in Equation (4–14) is replaced by the fatigue strength σ_f of the material for the specified number of load cycles and for the specified range of stress. The fatigue strength for a given material subjected to specified loading conditions can be obtained in Sections 1.8 and 1.9.

Experimental Verification. All three theories of failure considered in this section assume that the material is isotropic. If identical tensile stress-strain curves are obtained from specimens machined from three mutually perpendicular directions in a bar of material it could be said that the material is isotropic. Many materials are not isotropic. The maximum shearing-stress theory of failure and the octahedral shearing-stress theory of failure also assume that the compressive stress-strain curve is identical with the tensile stress-strain curve. It is assumed that these conditions are satisfied for the annealed SAE 1035 steel considered in Figures 4.10 and 4.11.

Additional verification for a theory of failure can be investigated by comparing stress-strain data for uniaxial state of stress obtained from tension

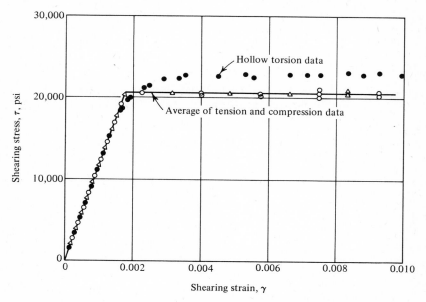

Fig. 4.10. Shearing stress-shearing strain data for annealed SAE 1035 steel.

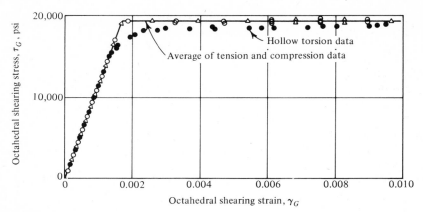

Fig. 4.11. Octahedral shearing stress-octahedral shearing strain data for annealed SAE 1035 steel.

and compression specimens with shearing-stress shearing-strain data for the special case of biaxial state of stress, called pure shear, obtained from hollow torsion specimens. Data from three tension specimens (open circles), three compression specimens (open triangles), and two hollow torsion specimens (solid circles) of annealed SAE 1035 steel are plotted as a shearing-stress shearing-strain diagram in Figure 4.10 and as an octahedral shearing-stress octahedral shearing-strain diagram in Figure 4.11. The method of converting the $\sigma-\epsilon$ data from tension and compression specimens to the $\tau-\gamma$ diagram in Figure 4.10 and to the $\tau_G-\gamma_G$ diagram in Figure 4.11 and the method of converting the $\tau-\gamma$ data from hollow torsion specimens to the $\tau_G-\gamma_G$ diagram in Figure 4.11 are beyond the scope of this book.*

If the maximum shearing-stress theory of failure is valid, all of the data in Figure 4.10 should plot as one $\tau-\gamma$ diagram. Note that the hollow torsion data is about 10 per cent above that obtained from the tension and compression data. If the maximum shearing-stress theory of failure were valid this difference should not exist.

If the octahedral shearing-stress theory of failure is valid, all of the data in Figure 4.11 should plot as one $\tau_G-\gamma_G$ diagram. But this is not true. The hollow torsion data lies about 5 per cent below the average of the tension and compression data for this material.

For the annealed SAE 1035 steel in Figures 4.10 and 4.11 both theories of failure show differences in the values between tension and torsion tests; however, the difference in the octahedral shearing-stress theory of failure is only half the difference of the maximum shearing-stress theory of failure,

* See *Inelastic Behavior of Load-Carrying Members*, J. O. Smith and O. M. Sidebottom, John Wiley and Sons, New York (1965), pp. 87–91.

and this difference is not considered large. In strain-hardening materials (no flat-top curve) even better agreement is found between test data and the octahedral shearing stress theory of failure.

Illustrative Problem

4.17. The most stressed volume element of a certain load-carrying member is located at the free surface (the member has no stress concentrations). With the xy-plane tangent to the free surface, the nonzero components of stress were found to be $\sigma_x = 15,000$ psi, $\sigma_y = -2,000$ psi, and $\tau_{xy} = 7,000$ psi. The load–stress relations for the member are linear so that the factor of safety can be applied either to loads or stresses. Determine the factor of safety used in the design of the member if the member is made of a ductile metal with a tensile yield stress of $\sigma_e = 44,000$ psi.

SOLUTION.   We will consider the solution by using both the octahedral shearing-stress theory of failure and the maximum shearing-stress theory of failure. The stresses on the left side of Equation (4–14) are the stresses in the member when it fails by general yielding. These can be obtained by multiplying the known stresses by the factor of safety N. Thus, Equation (4–14) gives

$$\frac{N}{3}\sqrt{(17,000)^2 + (2,000)^2 + (15,000)^2 + 6(7,000)^2} = \frac{\sqrt{2}}{3}(44,000),$$

$$28,500N = \sqrt{2}(44,000),$$

$$N = 2.18.$$

A factor of safety of 2.18 was used in the design of the member if failure is based on the octahedral shearing-stress theory of failure.

In order to use the maximum shearing-stress theory of failure it is necessary to determine the three principal stresses. These can be obtained from Mohr's circle of stress or by using Equations (2–8) and (2–9).

$$\sigma_1 = \frac{\sigma_x + \sigma_y}{2} + \sqrt{\left[\frac{\sigma_x - \sigma_y}{2}\right]^2 + \tau_{xy}^2}$$

$$= \tfrac{1}{2}(13,000) + \sqrt{\tfrac{1}{4}(17,000)^2 + (7,000)^2}$$

$$= 6,500 + 11,010$$

$$= 17,510 \text{ psi}$$

$$\sigma_2 = 6,500 - 11,010$$

$$= -4,510 \text{ psi}$$

$$\sigma_3 = 0.$$

The third principal stress σ_3 is zero since the surface of the member is a free surface and is free of normal and shearing stresses. At failure the three principal stresses are

$$\sigma_1 = 17,510N \text{ psi,}$$

$$\sigma_2 = -4,510N \text{ psi,}$$

$$\sigma_3 = 0.$$

Substituting these into Equation (4–13) gives

$$\frac{17,510N + 4,510N}{2} = \frac{44,000}{2},$$

$$N = 2.00.$$

A factor of safety of 2.00 was used in the design of the member if failure is based on the maximum shearing stress theory of failure.

Let us now interpret our results for the solution. The working loads that act on the member have produced the stress components given in the statement of the problem. If the octahedral shearing-stress theory of failure is used, the loads can be increased by a factor of 2.18 before failure by general yielding. Assuming this failure load to be correct, the maximum shearing stress theory of failure is conservative since it predicts smaller failure loads.

Problems

4.18. Show that the octahedral shearing stress theory of failure will predict $\tau_e = 0.577\sigma_e$, where σ_e is the yield stress for tension and compression specimens and τ_e is the yield stress for pure shear.

4.19. Show that the maximum principal stress theory of failure will predict $\tau_u = \sigma_u$, where σ_u is the fracture stress for a brittle material from tension tests and τ_u is the fracture stress for pure shear.

4.20 Through 4.24. In each of the problems the most stressed volume element of a given member is located at the free surface (the member has no stress concentrations). With the xy-plane tangent to the free surface, the nonzero stress components are σ_x, σ_y, and τ_{xy}. The load-stress relations for each member are linear so that the factor of safety can be applied to either loads or stresses. Using the octahedral shearing stress theory of failure, determine the factor of safety used in the design of the member.

4.20. The stress components are $\sigma_x = 16,000$ psi, $\sigma_y = 0$, and $\tau_{xy} = 6,000$ psi, and the member is made of a ductile material for which $\sigma_e = 45,000$ psi.

4.21. The stress components are $\sigma_x = 12{,}000$ psi, $\sigma_y = 3{,}000$ psi, and $\tau_{xy} = 8{,}000$ psi, and the member is made of a ductile material for which $\sigma_e = 38{,}000$ psi.

ans. $N = 2.16$.

4.22. The stress components are $\sigma_x = -6{,}000$ psi, $\sigma_y = 8{,}000$ psi, and $\tau_{xy} = 7{,}000$ psi, and the member is made of a ductile material for which $\sigma_e = 40{,}000$ psi.

4.23. The stress components are $\sigma_x = 45{,}000$ psi, $\sigma_y = 0$, and $\tau_{xy} = -28{,}000$ psi, and the member is made of a ductile material for which $\sigma_e = 192{,}000$ psi.

ans. $N = 2.90$.

4.24. The stress components are $\sigma_x = \sigma_y = 0$ and $\tau_{xy} = 33{,}000$ psi, and the member is made of a ductile material for which $\sigma_e = 97{,}000$ psi.

4.25. Solve Problem 4.20 if the maximum shearing stress theory of failure is used.

ans. $N = 2.25$.

4.26. Solve Problem 4.21 if the maximum shearing stress theory of failure is used.
4.27. Solve Problem 4.22 if the maximum shearing stress theory of failure is used.
4.28. Solve Problem 4.23 if the maximum shearing stress theory of failure is used.

ans. $N = 2.67$.

4.29. Solve Problem 4.24 if the maximum shearing stress theory of failure is used.

4.30. The member in Problem 4.20 is made of a brittle material for which the ultimate stress is $\sigma_u = 60{,}000$ psi. Determine the factor of safety used in the design of the member.

ans. $N = 3.33$.

4.31. The member in Problem 4.22 is made of a brittle material for which the ultimate stress is $\sigma_u = 46{,}000$ psi. Determine the factor of safety used in the design of the member.

4.7. Plastic Stress-Strain Relations

As the loads on a given member are increased, yielding will start at one or more points in the member and spread through the member. The engineer is interested in predicting the load-deformation curve for the member after yielding is initiated. Most of the practical problems are those for which part of the member remains elastic whereas the remainder of the member is plastically deformed. These are the so-called elastic-plastic problems. An analysis requires the location of the boundary between the elastic and plastic regions of the member. A yield condition such as either the Tresca yield condition or the octahedral shearing stress yield condition discussed in Section 4.6 is used to locate the elastic-plastic boundary. An elastic analysis using the stress-strain relations of Equations (4–6) is used for the elastic region. A plastic analysis using the stress-strain relations for the plastic material is used in the plastic region. Although Equations (4–6) are valid for all materials and for all members, plastic stress-strain relations may be different for each material and for each state of stress. The plastic stress-strain relations for the general state of stress are beyond the scope of this book.* Plastic stress-strain relations will be considered only for members having either uniaxial state of stress or pure shear state of stress.

Uniaxial State of Stress.   If the state of stress in the member is uniaxial, the plastic stress-strain relation for the material in the member is given by the plastic portion of the stress-strain diagram obtained from tension and compression specimens of the material. Only small strains are considered. The equation of the plastic portion of the stress-strain diagram (curve AB in Fig. 1.6 for instance) for small strains is given by the relation

$$\sigma_z = f(\epsilon_z). \tag{4-15}$$

Equation (4–15) is called the loading function (constitutive relation) for members made of this material if the state of stress in the member is uniaxial. When the stress-strain diagram is flat topped as indicated by AB in Figure 1.7c, Equation (4–15) takes its simplest form and is given by the relation

$$\sigma_z = \sigma_e. \tag{4-16}$$

because σ_z is independent of ϵ_z, once yielding starts, and σ_e is the yield point for the material. In this book Equation (4–16) is assumed to be the loading function (constitutive relation) for plastically deformed members having uniaxial state of stress.

Pure Shear State of Stress.   Material properties can also·be obtained by torsion tests of thin-wall hollow specimens. In Chapter 9 we will find that the state of stress in these specimens is pure shear; the only nonzero stress component is τ_{xy} and the only nonzero strain component is γ_{xy}. A plot of τ_{xy} versus γ_{xy} is the shearing-stress shearing-strain diagram for the material. For small strains, the τ_{xy}–γ_{xy} diagram has a shape similar to the σ_z–ϵ_z diagram. The plastic portion of the shearing-stress shearing-strain diagram for small strains can be approximated by the relation

$$\tau_{xy} = F(\gamma_{xy}). \tag{4-17}$$

---

* See *Inelastic Behavior of Load-Carrying Members*, J. O. Smith and O. M. Sidebottom, New York, John Wiley and Sons, 1965.

It is found that the τ_{xy}–γ_{xy} diagram is flat topped (see Fig. 4.10) for a given material if the σ_z–ϵ_z diagram is also flat topped. Therefore, Equation (4–17) takes its simplest form as the relation

$$\tau_{xy} = \tau_e, \qquad (4\text{–}18)$$

where τ_e is the yield point in pure shear. Hollow torsion specimens are not often tested and Equation (4–18) must be predicted from tension test data. A theory of failure or yield condition is required to make this prediction. Using Tresca's maximum shearing stress theory of failure, Equation (4–13) gives

$$\tau_e = \frac{\sigma_e}{2}. \qquad (4\text{–}19)$$

Using the octahedral shearing stress theory of failure, Equation (4–14) gives

$$\tau_e = \frac{\sigma_e}{\sqrt{3}}. \qquad (4\text{–}20)$$

Obviously both of these values for the shearing yield point can not be valid. Usually test data give a value for the shearing yield point for a given material between the values of $\sigma_e/2$ and $\sigma_e/\sqrt{3}$. In this book it will be assumed that Equation (4–20) is valid.

4.8. Linear Viscoelastic Stress-Strain-Time Relations

When material properties are time and temperature dependent, the material behavior will be approximated by a Maxwell model as discussed in Sections 1.11 and 1.12. Only time effects are considered because the temperature of each member is assumed to remain constant during the life of the loaded member. Stress-strain-time relations for the Maxwell model are considered for members having either uniaxial state of stress or a special case of biaxial state of stress, called pure shear.

Uniaxial State of Stress. The stress-strain-time relation (constitutive relation) for all members having uniaxial state of stress and made of a viscoelastic material, which can be accurately approximated by a Maxwell model, is presented in Section 1.12 and is given by Equation (1–36), which is repeated here:

$$\frac{d\epsilon_z}{dt} = \frac{1}{E_M}\frac{d\sigma_z}{dt} + \frac{\sigma_z}{\mu_M}. \qquad (4\text{–}21)$$

In Equation (4–21) E_M and μ_M are material constants.

Pure Shear State of Stress. Equation (4–21) for uniaxial state of stress relates only one normal stress component σ_z with the corresponding normal strain component ϵ_z. In load-carrying members having pure shear state of stress there is only one nonzero component of shearing stress τ_{xy} and only one nonzero component of shearing strain γ_{xy}. Since only one component of stress and strain must be related with time for both the uniaxial state of stress and pure shear state of stress, it is logical to assume that the shearing stress-shearing strain-time relation (constitutive relation) for members having pure shear state of stress is given by the following relation:

$$\frac{d\gamma_{xy}}{dt} = \frac{1}{G_M} \frac{d\tau_{xy}}{dt} + \frac{\tau_{xy}}{\mu'_M}, \qquad (4\text{–}22)$$

in which G_M and μ'_M are material constants.

Thin-Walled Pressure Vessels

5.1. Introduction

In Chapters 2, 3, and 4 the two-dimensional problem of plane stress and the plane problem of strain have been discussed. Thin-walled pressure vessels that are subjected to internal pressure offer good examples in which states of plane stress occur. Such thin-walled pressure vessels are usually of cylindrical, spherical, or conical shapes and are subjected to internal pressure.

In this chapter the relationship between the stress, the internal pressure, and the dimensions of the vessel is determined for a given point in the wall of the pressure vessel. Futhermore, when a biaxial state of stress exists in the wall of a vessel the question of the significance of the additional stress in causing failure is discussed for the condition that occurs when the load is increased beyond its safe value.

In Section 4.3 it was suggested that three steps should be followed in the derivation of load-stress relations. A thin-walled pressure vessel is an exception to this rule. The stress distribution through the wall is assumed to be uniform when the wall thickness is small compared to other dimensions of the pressure vessel and therefore load-stress relations can be derived using equations of equilibrium alone.

5.2. Stresses in Thin-Walled Circular Cylinders and Spheres

A thin-walled (hollow) circular cylinder subjected to uniform pressure on its inner surface is one in which the thickness of the wall or shell is small in comparison with the inner diameter of the cylinder. When this condition is satisfied, it may be assumed without serious error that the stress σ_θ in the circumferential direction is uniformly distributed throughout the thickness of the shell.

A hoop or tire shrunk on a wheel, an open-ended tank (standpipe), relatively large water, oil, or gas pipe line, and so forth, satisfy rather closely these assumed conditions. In pressure vessels (boilers, tanks), the closed ends give rise to longitudinal stresses and strains on each transverse cross section of the shell in addition to circumferential stresses and strains. For approximate but useful results, however, it may be assumed that the circumferential stress in the shell is not influenced by the longitudinal stress and vice versa. Therefore, the following analysis of the stresses in a thin-walled cylinder will be assumed to be applicable to thin-walled pressure vessels, in addition to hollow open end cylinders in which the state of stress is assumed to be uniaxial.

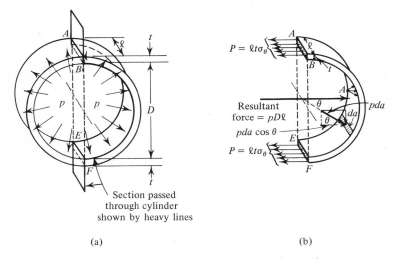

(a)   (b)

Fig. 5.1.   Stress in thin-walled cylinder caused by internal pressure.

Circumferential Stress on Longitudinal Section of Shell.   In accordance with the procedure given in Section 4.3, a section represented by the plane $ABEF$ in Figure 5.1a may be passed through the body. A free-body diagram of the portion of the body to the right of the section (consisting of one half of the shell) is shown in Figure 5.1b. The equations of equilibrium applied to the forces shown in this figure give the relations between the circumferential tensile stress and the internal fluid pressure and dimensions of the hollow cylinder. The result is $\sigma_\theta = pD/2t$, which may be obtained as follows:

Let σ_θ = circumferential tensile stress,

$\quad p$ = uniform pressure (force per unit area) on inner surface of hollow cylinder,

$\quad t$ = thickness of shell,

$\quad D$ = inner diameter of cylinder (also approximately equal to outer diameter because t is small),

$\quad R$ = inner radius of cylinder,

$\quad P$ = resisting circumferential force on the one cross-sectional area of shell.

The pressure of the fluid on the internal surface of the cylinder at any point is normal to the surface at that point, as indicated in Figure 5.1b; the resultant pressure (load) on one half of the shell (Fig. 5.1b) is resisted and held in equilibrium, by the internal forces P, P exerted by the other half of the shell at the areas AB and EF. One condition of equilibrium, therefore, may be expressed as follows:

Resultant horizontal force = total resisting force, or

$$pD\ell = 2P = 2\ell t\sigma_\theta.$$

The expression $pD\ell$ for the resultant horizontal force follows from the fact that it is the sum of the horizontal components of the forces acting on the elementary areas. The force on an elementary area da is $p\,da$, and its horizontal component $p\,da\cos\theta$. The resultant horizontal force, therefore, is $\int p\,da\cos\theta$, which may be written $p\int da\cos\theta$ because the pressure p is the same at all points on the semi-cylindrical area A. But $da\cos\theta$ is the area formed by projecting the area da on a vertical plane; hence $\int da\cos\theta$ is the area formed by projecting the semi-cylindrical area on a vertical plane and is therefore equal to $D\ell$. Thus the resultant horizontal force is $pD\ell$.

Furthermore, the fact that the internal resisting force P in Figure 5.1b is the same at each of the two cross-sectional areas of the shell is obtained from the condition of symmetry or from the moment-equilibrium equation, and the expression $P = \ell t\sigma_\theta$ follows from the condition that σ_θ is uniformly distributed on the area. Hence

$$\sigma_\theta = \frac{pD}{2t} = \frac{pR}{t}, \qquad (5\text{--}1)$$

in which R is the inner radius of the hollow cylinder.

Stress in Transverse Section. The total force of the fluid against the end of the cylinder in Figure 5.2 or against the spherical surface in Figure 5.3 must be held in equilibrium by the total resisting force on a transverse section of the cylinder or sphere, as indicated in Figures 5.2 and 5.3. The

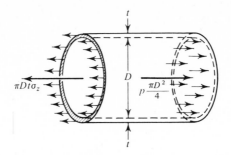

Fig. 5.2.   Stress on transverse sections of thin-walled cylinder.

total force (load) against the end of each body is $p(\pi D^2/4)$, and the total resisting force in each case is $\pi Dt\sigma_z$, where σ_z is the normal stress in the transverse cross section that is perpendicular to the longitudinal axis z of the cylinder or to a diameter of the sphere. Hence the condition of equilibrium requires that

$$p\frac{\pi D^2}{4} = \pi\, Dt\sigma_z.$$

Thus

$$\sigma_z = \frac{pD}{4t} = \frac{pR}{2t}. \tag{5–2}$$

In Equations (5–1) and (5–2), p, σ_θ, and σ_z must be expressed in the same units (usually pounds per square inch), and D, R, and t must be expressed in the same units (usually inches).

A comparison of Equations (5–1) and (5–2) shows that the stress on a longitudinal section of a thin-walled cylinder due to an internal fluid pressure

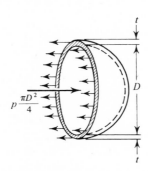

Fig. 5.3.   Stress in thin-walled sphere.

is twice as great as that on a transverse section of the same cylinder. In the sphere it should be noted that the stresses $\sigma_z = \sigma_\theta = pR/2t$ are the same in all cross sections taken through the center of the sphere.

Problems

5.1. A closed-ended thin-walled circular-cylindrical pressure vessel has an internal radius $R = 30$ in., a wall thickness $t = 0.5$ in., and an internal pressure $p = 500$ psi. Determine the magnitude of the circumferential stress σ_θ on the longitudinal cross section and the transverse stress σ_z on the transverse cross section.

ans. $\sigma_\theta = 30,000$ psi,

$\sigma_z = 15,000$ psi.

5.2. A thin-walled spherical pressure vessel has an internal radius of $R = 30$ in., a wall thickness of $t = 0.5$ in., and an internal pressure of $p = 500$ psi. Determine the magnitude of the tensile stress in the wall of the sphere.

ans. $\sigma_\theta = 15,000$ psi.

5.3. Large welded-steel pipe lines, 30 to 34 in. in diameter, are used for the long-distance transmission of gas. Pumping stations are located along this pipe line, usually 75 to 100 miles apart. As the gas leaves a pumping station its pressure may be as high as 700 to 1,000 psi. This pressure decreases as the gas flows at a speed of 15 to 20 miles per hour through the pipe to the next station. One such pipe line has a wall thickness of $\frac{3}{8}$ in. and an outer diameter of 30 in. The maximum gas pressure is 850 psi. What is the maximum circumferential tensile stress in the wall of the pipe by the gas pressure?

ans. $\sigma_\theta = 33,150$ psi.

5.4. A steel standpipe has an inside diameter of 8 ft and a height of 60 ft. When it is full of water ($w = 0.0361$ lb/in.³), what is the circumferential stress in the plate near the bottom of the standpipe if the thickness of the plate is $\frac{3}{8}$ in.?

5.3. Deformation and Strains in Thin-Walled Cylinders and Spheres

Sometimes the increase in diameter of a thin-walled cylinder or sphere caused by the internal pressure must be determined. The deformation of such pressure vessels is influenced by the circumferential and transverse stresses, and hence use must be made of Equations (4–9) and (4–10) to express Hooke's law for plane stress.

Note that the state of stress at the inner surface is triaxial and is not plane stress. The principal stresses of the inner surface are $\sigma_1 = \sigma_\theta$, $\sigma_2 = \sigma_z$, and $\sigma_3 = -p$. However, $\sigma_3 = -p$ is so small compared to σ_1 and σ_2 that it can be neglected when considering strains. The state of stress in thin-walled pressure vessels is usually considered to be plane stress as indicated in Section 5.1.

Let σ_θ, σ_z, ϵ_θ and ϵ_z represent the longitudinal (or transverse) stress and strain, respectively, in the wall. The substitution of these symbols into Equation (4–9) gives

$$\epsilon_\theta = \frac{\sigma_\theta}{E} - v\frac{\sigma_z}{E}, \tag{5–3}$$

$$\epsilon_z = \frac{\sigma_z}{E} - v\frac{\sigma_\theta}{E}, \tag{5–4}$$

in which E is the modulus of elasticity and v in Poisson's ratio.

Closed-End Cylinder.   For the strains in the closed-end cylinder the values of σ_θ and σ_z from Equations (5–1) and (5–2), respectively, are substituted into Equations (5–3) and (5–4) to give the following equations:

$$\epsilon_\theta = \frac{1}{E}\left(\frac{pR}{t} - v\frac{pR}{2t}\right) = \frac{pR}{2Et}(2 - v), \tag{5–5}$$

$$\epsilon_z = \frac{1}{E}\left(\frac{pR}{2t} - v\frac{pR}{t}\right) = \frac{pR}{2Et}(1 - 2v). \tag{5–6}$$

Let the change in length of the internal radius R be ΔR when the internal pressure is applied. Then the change in length of the circumference is $2\pi\,\Delta R$. But the circumferential strain ϵ_θ is, by definition, given by the following equation:

$$\epsilon_\theta = \frac{2\pi\,\Delta R}{2\pi R} = \frac{\Delta R}{R}. \tag{5–7}$$

By combining equations (5–7) and (5–5), the following result for the change in length ΔR of the radius is given:

$$\Delta R = \frac{pR^2}{2Et}(2 - v). \tag{5–8}$$

The change in the diameter of the cylinder caused by the internal pressure p is $2\,\Delta R$. The change in length $\Delta\ell$ for a closed end cylinder is equal to $\epsilon_z\ell$ and is given by the relation (Eq. 5–6)

$$\Delta\ell = \frac{pR\ell}{2Et}(1 - 2v). \tag{5–9}$$

Sphere.   For the strains in the sphere it is noted that the stresses $\sigma_z = \sigma_\theta = pR/2t$. Thus, from Equation 5–3

$$\epsilon_\theta = \frac{1}{E}\left(\frac{pR}{2t} - v\frac{pR}{2t}\right) = \frac{pR}{2Et}(1 - v). \qquad (5\text{--}10)$$

By combining Equation (5–10) with Equation (5–7) the following equation is obtained:

$$\Delta R = \frac{pR^2}{2Et}(1 - v).\qquad (5\text{--}11)$$

The change in diameter of the sphere is $2\,\Delta R$.

Effect of ΔR at End of Closed-Ended Cylinder.   Let Figure 5.4a represent a thin-walled cylindrical pressure vessel with its ends closed by thin-walled hemispherical shells of the same thickness and same material. The hemisphere and cylinder are joined by rivets or welds at AA and BB. For the moment let them remain unjoined. The dashed lines represent the displaced positions of the centerlines, where the change in radius ΔR_c of the cylinder is given by Equation (5–8):

$$\Delta R_c = \frac{pR^2}{2Et}(2 - v),$$

and the change in radius ΔR_s of the sphere is given by Equation (5–11):

$$\Delta R_s = \frac{pR^2}{2Et}(1 - v).$$

The change ΔR_c is more than twice the change ΔR_s and the deformed cylinder

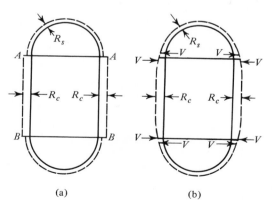

(a)   (b)

Fig. 5.4.

and hemisphere do not match boundaries. Of course this mismatch does not take place when they are joined, as shown in Figure 5.4b. The rather large shearing forces V must develop at the joint between the cylinder and the hemisphere. These shearing forces must be accounted* for in the design and construction of the vessel.

Problems

5.5. Compute the change in length of the diameter of the thin-walled cylinder of Problem 5.1 if $E = 10^7$ psi and $v = 0.30$.

ans. $2\Delta R = 0.153$ in.

5.6. Compute the change in length of the diameter of the sphere in Problem 5.2 if $E = 10^7$ psi and $v = 0.30$.

ans. $2\Delta R = 0.063$ in.

5.7. An aluminum alloy band $\frac{1}{4}$-in. thick and 3-in. wide, is tightened on a steel cylinder (Fig. P5.7) by turning the nuts on the bolts until the tensile stress in each of the

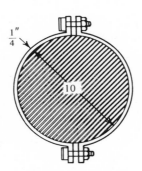

Fig. P 5.7.   Band tightened on smooth cylinder.

two bolts is 15,000 lb. Assume that the aluminum acts elastically and that the cylinder is rigid but has a smooth surface. (1) What is the pressure per unit area of the cylinder on the band? (2) How much does each half-band stretch? (3) What is the stress in the band? Assume $E = 10^7$ psi. (*Hint:* The stress $\sigma_z = 0$ for the band.)

ans.   (1) 1,000 psi; (2) 0.0314 in.; (3) 20,000 psi.

* See, for example, Den Hartog, *Advanced Strength of Materials*, McGraw-Hill, New York, 1952, p. 84.

5.8. Solve for the change in length of the diameter of the steel standpipe of Problem 5.4 at the midheight of the cylinder. Assume that $E = 30 \times 10^6$ psi and $v = 0.3$. (*Hint:* Note that $\sigma_z = 0$, because the cylinder is open at the top end.)

ans. $2\,\Delta R = 0.0053$ in.

5.9. The steel tire for a locomotive driving wheel has an internal diameter $D/1,500$ less than that of the wheel on which the tire is to be shrunk, where D is the diameter of the wheel. The value of D is 60 in., and the value of t (the thickness of the tire) is $\frac{3}{4}$ in. If it is assumed that, after the tire is shrunk on the wheel, the diameter of the wheel is not changed by the pressure of the tire, find (1) the elongation of the tire, (2) the tensile stress (hoop tension) in the tire, and (3) the pressure of the tire on the wheel.

ans. (1) $e = 0.126$ in.; (2) $\sigma_\theta = 20,000$ psi; (3) $p = 500$ psi.

5.10. A high-strength steel ring or hoop, having a proportional limit of 100,000 lb per square inch, an inside diameter of 39.9 in., and a thickness of $\frac{1}{4}$ in. is heated until it just fits over a smooth rigid cylinder, which is at room temperature. The diameter of the cylinder is 40 in. After the ring has cooled to room temperature, (1) what is the stretch of the ring per unit of length, if it is assumed that the diameter of the cylinder does not change; (2) what is the tensile stress in the ring; and (3) what is the pressure of the cylinder on the ring?

ans. (1) 0.0025; (2) 75,000 psi; (3) 937 psi.

5.11. The pressure in the cylinder of a steam engine (Fig. P5.11) is 120 psi and the internal diameter D of the cylinder is 14 in. How many $\frac{3}{4}$-in. bolts are required for strength if the tensile stress in the bolts is not to exceed 8,000 psi? What should be the thickness t of the walls of the gray (cast) iron cylinder to satisfy the requirement for strength if the tensile stress must not exceed 800 psi. (*Note:* The maximum stress specified is taken relatively low, owing to the fact that the load is applied with more or less impact. Moreover, the requirement for strength in many problems is not the governing requirement. In this problem, for example, the bolts should be large enough to prevent a workman, with ordinary tools, from twisting off the heads. Further, the requirement

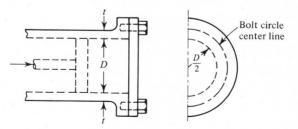

Fig. P 5.11. Steam cylinder and piston.

for tightness of the joint may determine the number of bolts. Similarly, the thickness of the wall may be influenced by the considerations of heat loss or of ease and reliability in casting, and so forth.)

5.4. Prediction of Failure of Closed-End Circular Cylinder Pressure Vessels

In Section 4.6 three methods of predicting the failure of members are presented. These are the maximum principal-stress theory, the maximum shearing-stress theory, and the octahedral shearing-stress theory.

Two of the theories of failure require that the principal stresses be known. The maximum principal stress in pressure vessels is $\sigma_1 = \sigma_\theta$. The intermediate principal stress is $\sigma_2 = \sigma_z$. The third principal stress at the inner surface of the wall is $\sigma_3 = -p$ and is the minimum principal stress; this stress has been neglected in the foregoing discussion but will be included in this section because an assumption that $\sigma_3 = 0$ would introduce an error up to 10 per cent.

Maximum Principal-Stress Theory. According to this theory of failure a pressure vessel would fail when the maximum principal stress becomes equal to some value σ_f as determined from a tension test of the material. Thus, for a thin-walled cylindrical pressure vessel, failure as predicted by this theory would occur when

$$\frac{pR}{t} = \sigma_f, \qquad (5\text{--}12)$$

where pR/t is the maximum principal stress as given by Equation (5–1). Equation (5–12) is rearranged as follows for the purpose of graphical representation:

$$\frac{p}{\sigma_f} = \frac{1}{R/t}. \qquad (5\text{--}13)$$

In Figure 5.5 the ratio p/σ_f is plotted as ordinates and the ratio R/t as abscissas. The middle curve represents points located by plotting corresponding values of p/σ_f and R/t obtained from Equation (5–13).

Maximum Shearing-Stress Theory. According to this theory of failure, a pressure vessel would fail when the maximum shearing stress, as given by Equation (4–13), becomes equal to $\frac{1}{2}\sigma_f$, that is,

$$\tau_{\max} = \frac{\sigma_{\max} - \sigma_{\min}}{2} = \tfrac{1}{2}\sigma_f, \qquad (5\text{--}14)$$

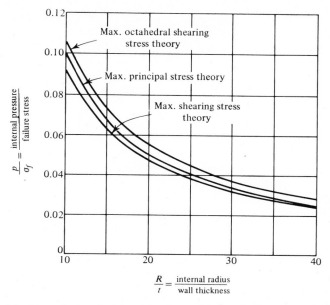

Fig. 5.5.   Maximum internal pressure in closed-ended thin-walled circular cylindrical pressure vessel predicted by various theories of failure.

For a thin-walled cylindrical pressure vessel $\sigma_{max} = pR/t$ and $\sigma_{min} = -p$; these stresses occur at all points on the inner perimeter of each transverse cross section of the cylinder. The substitution of these values of σ_{max} and σ_{min} into Equation (5–14) gives the following equation:

$$\frac{pR}{t} + p = \sigma_f \qquad \text{or} \qquad \frac{p}{\sigma_f} = \frac{1}{R/t + 1}. \qquad (5\text{–}15)$$

In Figure 5.5 the lower curve represents points located by plotting corresponding values of p/σ_f and R/t obtained from Equation (5–15).

Maximum Octahedral Shear-Stress Theory.   According to this theory, failure occurs when the maximum octahedral shearing stress τ_G in the thin-walled pressure vessel becomes equal to $(\sqrt{2}/3)\sigma_f$. The maximum value of τ_G occurs at points on the inner perimeter of the transverse cross section of a cylindrical pressure vessel and is given by Equation (2–31), and thus failure by this theory would be predicted by the following equation:

$$\tau_G = \tfrac{1}{3}\sqrt{(\sigma_1 - \sigma_2)^2 + (\sigma_2 - \sigma_3)^2 + (\sigma_3 - \sigma_1)^2} = \frac{\sqrt{2}}{3}\sigma_f \qquad (5\text{–}16)$$

In Equation (5–16) σ_1, σ_2, and σ_3 are the principal stresses at a point in the thin-walled cylinder. Thus from Equation (5–1) $\sigma_1 = pR/t$; from Equation (5–2) $\sigma_2 = pR/2t$, and the internal pressure p is the third principal stress at points on the inner perimeter, where $\sigma_3 = -p$. These three expressions for σ_1, σ_2, and σ_3 are substituted into Equation (5–16), which gives the following equation:

$$\frac{1}{3}\sqrt{\left(\frac{pR}{t} - \frac{pR}{2t}\right)^2 + \left(\frac{pR}{2t} + p\right)^2 + \left(-p - \frac{pR}{t}\right)^2} = \frac{\sqrt{2}}{3}\sigma_f. \qquad (5\text{–}17)$$

When the terms on the left side of Equation (5–17) are squared and like terms collected, the following equation is obtained:

$$\frac{p}{\sigma_f} = \sqrt{\frac{2}{\frac{3}{2}(R/t)^2 + 3(R/t) + 2}}. \qquad (5\text{–}18)$$

In Figure 5.5 the upper curve represents points located by plotting corresponding values of p/σ_f and R/t obtained from Equation (5–18).

Comparison of Predicted Values of Internal Pressure to Cause Failure of Thin-Walled Cylinder. Figure 5.5 shows that the maximum shearing-stress theory predicts the lowest value of pressure to cause failure and the maximum octahedral shearing stress theory the largest. The maximum principal-stress theory predicts an intermediate value of the pressure to cause failure. However, the maximum difference between the lowest and largest values of the failure pressure is about 15 per cent.

Problems

5.12. For a thin-walled sphere subjected to an internal pressure p show that the pressure to cause failure by the maximum principal stress theory is predicted by the equation

$$\frac{p}{\sigma_f} = \frac{1}{R/2t}.$$

5.13. For a thin-walled sphere subjected to an internal pressure p show that the pressure to cause failure as predicted by the maximum shearing-stress theory is the same as that predicted by the maximum octahedral shearing-stress theory of failure.

$$\text{ans.} \quad \frac{p}{\sigma_f} = \frac{1}{(R/2t) + 1}.$$

5.14. A cylindrical propane gas tank has an inside diameter of 125 in. and a wall thickness of 1 in. The tank is made of a ductile steel having a yield stress of

$\sigma_e = 45,000$ psi. Using the maximum shearing stress theory of failure, determine the working pressure p_w for the tank based on a factor of safety of 2.00.

5.15. Solve Problem 5.14 using the octahedral shearing stress theory of failure.

ans. $p_w = 206$ psi.

5.16. A thin-walled, closed-ended, circular cylinder must be designed to withstand a pressure of 400 psi. The cylinder has a length of 40 in. and an inside diameter of 10 in. The material chosen for manufacturing the pressure vessel is a ductile steel which has a yield stress of $\sigma_e = 36,000$ psi. Determine the thickness of the cylinder based on a factor of safety $N = 2.50$ (1) using the maximum shearing-stress theory of failure and (2) using the octahedral shearing-stress theory of failure.

Analysis of Forces Within a Member

6.1. Preliminary Statement

The major emphasis in this book is to derive load-stress and load-deflection relations for straight load-carrying members because these relations are needed if members are to be designed to carry loads without failure. In this chapter procedures are presented to transform a complicated load system on a straight bar into axial centric, bending, and torsional components. Load-stress and load-deflection relations can be derived for straight members subjected to each separate component. These relations are derived in Chapter 1 for members subjected to axial centric loads, in Chapters 7 and 8 for members subjected to bending loads, and in Chapter 9 for members subjected to torsional loads. Chapter 10 deals with the question of superposing the separate solutions for straight members subjected to combined loads. Let us consider several types of loads before we consider the procedures for transforming a complex load system into simpler components.

Types of Loads. The response of a member to loads and the load-carrying capacity of a member depends on the type of the loading. Loads may be classified as follows:

(1) Static or steady loads are forces that are applied slowly and not repeated, and remain nearly constant after being applied to the member, or are repeated relatively few times, such as the loads on the members of most buildings. Sometimes it is convenient to consider a so-called static load to be composed of two parts—namely, a dead load and a live load. For example, the weight of a bridge is a dead load on the bridge, and the weight of a train moving on the bridge and the wind pressure on the bridge are live loads.

(2) Repeated loads are forces that are applied a very large number of times, causing a stress in the material that is continually changing, often through some definite cycle or range. The loads applied to the crankshaft of an engine that is running and the bending loads that are applied to the axle of a moving locomotive, and to many parts of airplanes in flight, are repeated loads. Repeated loads are discussed in Sections 1.8 and 1.9.

(3) Impact loads are forces that are applied in a relatively short period of time. An impact load is usually applied to a body that is in motion when it comes in contact with the resisting member, and the force exerted by the moving body and the period during which it acts usually cannot be determined. For this reason, in some problems it is more satisfactory to calculate the stresses and deformations produced by an impact load from the energy delivered to the resisting member by the moving body. When this is done, the energy delivered to the resisting member is frequently called an energy load and is expressed in foot-pounds (not in pounds). Impact and energy loads are considered in Chapter 12.

Other Classifications of Loads.   Loads may be classified as distributed loads and concentrated loads. A distributed load may be uniformly distributed or non-uniformly distributed. Thus, if grain of uniform texture is spread on a floor so that its depth is constant, the floor will be subjected to a uniformly distributed load; whereas, if the grain is distributed so that its depth is not constant, the floor is said to carry a nonuniformly distributed load.

A concentrated load is a force distributed on an area that is negligibly small compared to the surface of the resisting member.

Another useful classification of loads may be made in terms of the simpler types of deformational response of the resisting member. Thus, a given member may be subjected to axial centric loads, or to torsional (twisting) loads, or to bending loads. A member, however, may be subjected simultaneously to any two or to all three of these types of loads.

6.2.   Relationship Between External and Internal Forces in a Straight Member

In this book, we assume that the purpose of a member is to transmit loads. Let a member consisting of a straight bar BD in Figure 6.1a have a constant cross section and be fastened securely at end D to a rigid wall. End D is said to be fixed to the wall. The other end B has a flat square plate welded to the bar through which the loads F_z and R are applied to the bar. The end B with the plate is not supported and is free to move (or deflect) under the

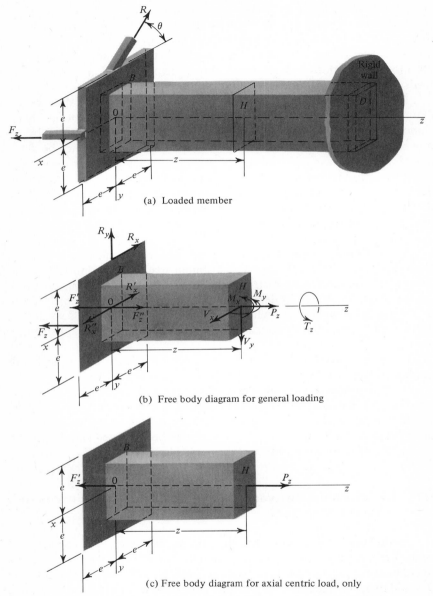

(a) Loaded member

(b) Free body diagram for general loading

(c) Free body diagram for axial centric load, only

Fig. 6.1. Straight member of constant rectangular cross section subjected to general loading.

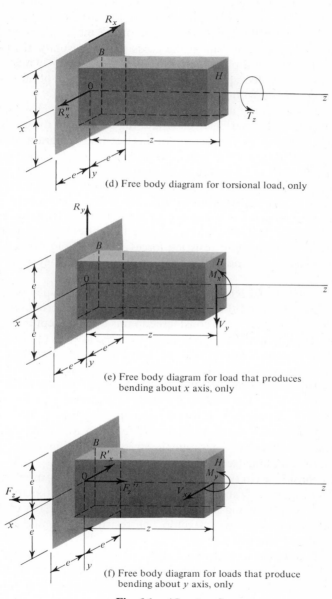

(d) Free body diagram for torsional load, only

(e) Free body diagram for load that produces
bending about x axis, only

(f) Free body diagram for loads that produce
bending about y axis, only

Fig. 6.1. (*Continued*)

action of the loads F_z and R. The problem here is to determine the internal forces in the bar at any cross section, such as H. The analysis is simplified if a set of coordinate axes x, y, z is chosen at one end of the bar so that the z-axis coincides with the longitudinal axis of the member and the x- and y-axes intersect at the centroid of the cross section, usually at one end of the member, and lie in a plane perpendicular to the z-axis. Thus, the cross section H is at a distance z from the end B where the origin of the coordinate axes is located, as shown in Figure 6.1a.

The next step in the analysis is to cut the bar at the cross section H, remove that part of the bar between H and the end B, and draw a free-body diagram of it as shown in Figure 6.1b. In this free-body diagram components of the force R are taken in the directions of the coordinate axes. Thus, R has components $R_x = R \cos \theta$ and $R_y = R \sin \theta$.

The equilibrium of the free-body in Figure 6.1b requires that the loads F_z, R_x, and R_y must be balanced by the internal resisting forces P_z, V_x, V_y that occur at the cross section H as shown in Figure 6.1b. There are also three resisting moments M_x, M_y, and T_z that act on the cross section H and these resisting moments and resisting forces serve to hold the severed part of the bar between B and H in equilibrium because they must balance the loads.

The loading at end B of the member in Figure 6.1b, which produces the three resisting forces and the three resisting moments at cross section H, is the most general loading to be considered in this book, except that loads distributed along the length of the bar are considered later in this chapter. The design of this member requires that the distributions of normal stresses and shearing stresses on cross section H be determined; the stress distributions give the same resultant as the three resisting forces and the three resisting moments on cross section H. It is convenient to consider each of three resisting forces and the three resisting moments separately, determine the distribution of stresses on cross section H for each force or moment, and finally use superposition to determine the stress distributions on cross section H for combined loading (see Chapter 10).

Let us consider each type of resisting force and resisting moment at cross section H in Figure 5.1b and consider the components of the applied loads that produce each resisting force and resisting moment. Each of the loads F_z, R_x, and R_y at end B will develop one resisting force and one or two resisting moments at cross section H.

Axial Component of External Loads. The action line of the resisting axial force P_z in Figure 6.1b coincides with the centroidal axis Oz. The applied load F_z is the only load parallel to the z-axis, but does not coincide with the z-axis; therefore, two equal and opposite forces F_z' and F_z'', each equal to F_z, are applied so that their action lines coincide with the centroidal axis Oz. One of these forces F_z' is in the negative z-direction, has the same line of action as the resisting axial force P_z, and is equal to it. The remaining two forces, F_z, and $F_z'' = F_z$, form a couple, $F_z e$, which produces part of the resisting moment M_y, as discussed later. Note that we have made a simplifying assumption: we have assumed that the deflections are so small that correction of the moment $F_z e$ caused by the product of F_z and the deflection of end B with respect to cross section H can be neglected.

As discussed previously it is convenient to reduce the general loading in Figure 6.1b into several simpler loadings as shown in Figures 6.1c, d, e, and f. Note that the sum of the loads in Figures 6.1c, d, e, and f is identical with the loads in Figure 6.1b. The load $F_z' = F_z$ in Figure 6.1c is an axial load with action line through the centroid of each cross section of the member; therefore, it is an axial centric load and the normal stress distribution on cross section H due to this load is uniform and given by Equation (1–10).

Torsional Components of External Loads. The load R_x at end B in Figure 6.1b produces a resisting transverse shear, a resisting twisting moment, and a resisting bending moment at cross section H. For R_x equal and opposite forces R_x' and R_x'' parallel to R_x are shown in Figure 6.1b acting through the centroid* of the cross section at cross section B. The couple $R_x e$ formed by equal and opposite forces $R_x = R_x''$ in Figure 6.1b lies in the xy-plane; this is the only torsional load acting at cross section B and is equal and opposite to the resisting twisting moment T_z at cross section H. These loads are shown acting on the member in Figure 6.1d. The topics relating to the distribution of shearing stresses on cross section H caused by the torque T_z are developed in Chapter 9.

Transverse Shear Components and Bending Components of External Loads. The axial centric component F_z and the torsional component $R_x e$ of the external loads that act at cross section B in Figure 6.1b have been discussed in the preceding paragraphs and are shown acting on the member in Figures 6.1c and d, respectively. The remaining loads are called bending

---

* The forces R_x' and R_x'' must pass through the shear center which, for the rectangular cross section, is located at the centroid. The shear center is defined as the point in the cross section of the member through which the action line of a transverse load must pass if the load is to produce bending of the member without torsion. Methods of determining the location of the shear center are given in most books on advanced mechanics of materials, for example, in Chapter 4 *Advanced Mechanics of Materials*, Seely and Smith, John Wiley and Sons, Second Edition, 1952. In a member having a cross section with one axis of symmetry, the shear center lies in the plane of symmetry. If there are two axes of symmetry (see Fig. 6.1) or if there is point symmetry with respect to the centroid (e.g., a Z-shaped section), the shear center coincides with the centroid of the cross section. An axis of the member through the shear center of every cross section of the member is called the bending axis of the member.

loads. It is convenient to break these up into components that produce bending in the yz-plane about an axis in the cross section H that is parallel to the x-axis as indicated in Figure 6.1e and that produce bending in the xz-plane about an axis in the cross section H that is parallel to the y-axis as indicated in Figure 6.1f. The load R_y in Figure 6.1e is the only load in the yz-plane that produces bending about an axis parallel to the x-axis; R_y is the y-component of the transverse shear and is equal and opposite to the resisting transverse shear V_y, which acts through the centroid of cross section H. The couple $R_y z$ formed by equal and opposite forces $R_y = V_y$ is a bending moment and is equal and opposite to the resisting bending moment M_x in the yz-plane at the cross section H. Topics relating to the determination of the normal stress distribution on cross section H caused by the bending moment M_x and the determination of the shearing stress distribution on cross section H caused by the transverse shear V_y are developed in Chapter 7.

The loads in Figure 6.1f are those that produce bending in the xz-plane about an axis in cross section H parallel to the y-axis. The load R_x' is the x-component of the transverse shear and is equal and opposite to the resisting transverse shear V_x, which acts at cross section H. The sum of the two couples $F_z e$ and $R_x' z$ is a bending moment and is equal and opposite to the resisting bending moment M_y in cross section H. Most of the problems considered in this book will be those for which $V_x = M_y = 0$.

Use of Equilibrium Equations. The magnitudes of the three internal resisting forces P_z, V_x, and V_y and the three internal resisting moments M_x, M_y, and T_z at cross section H in Figure 6.1b are obtained using equations of equilibrium. These equations are as follows:

$$\sum F_z = 0 \qquad\qquad P_z = F_z \tag{6-1}$$

$$\sum F_x = 0 \qquad\qquad V_x = R_x \tag{6-2}$$

$$\sum F_x = 0 \qquad\qquad V_y = R_y \tag{6-3}$$

$$\sum M_x = 0 \qquad\qquad M_x = V_y z = R_y z \tag{6-4}$$

$$\sum M_y = 0 \qquad\qquad M_y = V_x z + F_z e = R_x' z + F_z e \tag{6-5}$$

$$\sum M_z = 0 \qquad\qquad T_z = V_x e = R_x e \tag{6-6}$$

The term on the left side of each of Equations (6–1) through (6–6) represents a resisting force or moment. In Equation (6–1), P_z is the resisting axial force and F_z is the external axial centric load. In Equations (6–2) and (6–3) the terms V_x and V_y represent resisting transverse shears whereas R_x

and R_y represent external transverse shear loads. In Equations (6–4) and (6–5) the terms M_x and M_y are resisting bending moments, but the right side of these equations represents the corresponding external bending moments. In Equation (6–6) the term T_z is the resisting torsional moment and the right side represents the external torsional load. Because the resisting quantity is always equal to the external quantity (load) we shall usually refer to them as axial centric load, transverse shears, bending moments, or torsional loads or the latter three simply as shears, moments, or torques.

Sign Convention for Transverse Shears and Bending and Torsional Moments. When the origin of the x, y, z axis is taken at one end of a load-carrying member, the positive end of the z-axis is toward the other end of the member as shown in Figure 6.1.

The resisting transverse shearing forces at any cross section are V_x and V_y, which are parallel to the x- and y-axes, respectively, and thus each lie in a plane perpendicular to the z-axis. Any cutting plane perpendicular to the z-axis produces two lengths of the member with faces that join at that section. The sign convention for transverse shears depends on which of the two faces is considered. The face we consider is the one for which the positive end of the z-axis protrudes as indicated in Figure 6.1b. The transverse shear V_x is positive when its sense is in the positive direction of the x-axis as shown in Figure 6.1b (and negative when its sense is in the negative direction of the x-axis). The transverse shear V_y is positive when its sense is in the positive direction of the y-axis as shown in Figure 6.1b (and negative when its sense is in the negative direction of the y-axis).

The bending moments M_x and M_y in Figure 6.1b lie in the yz- and xz-planes, respectively. M_x is positive when it tends to put tensile stresses in that part of the cross section of the beam adjacent to the positive end of the y-axis as shown in Figure 6.1b (and negative when it tends to put compressive stresses on the part adjacent to the positive end of the y-axis). M_y is positive when it tends to put tensile stresses on that part of the cross section of the beam adjacent to the positive end of the x-axis as shown in Figure 6.1b (and negative when it tends to put compressive stresses on that part adjacent to the positive end of the x-axis).

The torsional resisting moment T_z in Figure 6.1b lies in a plane perpendicular to the z-axis and is positive when its action would tend to move a right-hand screw in the positive direction of the z-axis.

Problems

6.1. A wheel and axle are loaded (Fig. P6.1). Determine the values of the quantities P_z, V_x, V_y, M_x, M_y, and T_z with respect to the cross section at point D.

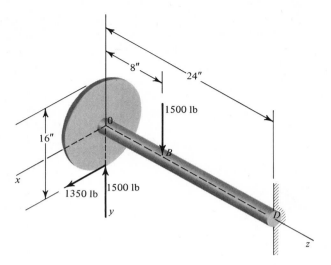

Fig. P 6.1.

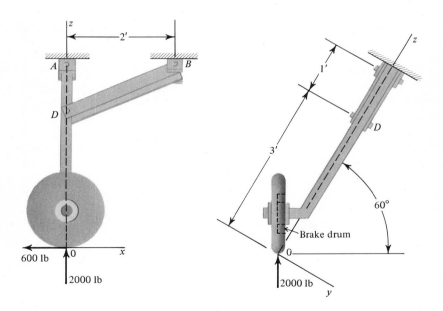

Fig. P 6.2.

6.2. A portion of the landing gear for a light plane is shown in Figure P6.2. Determine the values of the quantities P_z, V_x, V_y, M_x, M_y, and T_z with respect to the cross section at point D.

ans. $P_z = -1,732$ lb; $V_x = 600$ lb; $V_y = 1,000$ lb; $M_x = 36,000$ lb-in;

$M_y = 21,600$ lb-in.; $T_z = 0$.

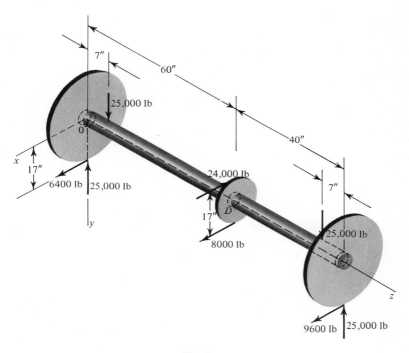

Fig. P 6.3.

6.3. The loads shown acting on the three wheels and axle in Figure P6.3 hold the assembly in equilibrium. Determine the values of the quantities P_z, V_x, V_y, M_x, M_y, and T_z with respect to the cross section at point D.

ans. $P_z = 0$; $V_x = -6,400$ lb; $V_y = 0$; $M_x = 175,000$ lb-in.;

$M_y = -384,000$ lb-in.; $T_z = 108,800$ in.-lb.

6.4. For the member in Figure P6.4 determine the values of the quantities P_z, V_x, V_y, M_x, M_y, and T_z with respect to the cross section at point D. The coordinates

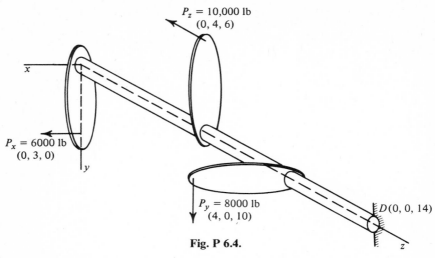

Fig. P 6.4.

of point D and of the points of application of the loads are given in parentheses in Figure P6.4.

6.3.   Analysis of Transverse Forces in Beams

Let the external forces or loads that act on the member in Figure 6.1 all be forces whose action lines intersect the bending axis Oz and are per-pendicular to it. A member that is subjected only to such a system of trans-verse forces is called a beam.*

For the purpose of making an analysis of the forces acting on a beam, all forces are resolved into components lying either in the yz-plane as indicated in Figure 6.1e or in the xz-plane as indicated in Figure 6.1f. It is assumed here that both the yz-plane and the xz-plane are planes of symmetry for the beam. The transverse forces all lie in one plane for most beams. Therefore, further consideration of beam loads in this chapter will be based on the assumption that all of the transverse forces lie in the yz-plane.

Several common types of beams are considered and we should become familiar with their names. A *simple* beam is one that rests on two supports at the ends of the beam; the distance between the supports is called the *span* of the beam.

* If the beam acts as it is assumed to act, in this and the following chapters, its length must be at least five times its maximum distance across the cross section. Furthermore, the minimum distance across the cross section of the beam must be sufficient to prevent collapse by twisting or wrinkling (buckling); thus, extremely deep, thin rectangular beams and I beams with very wide thin flanges, and so forth, are excluded from consideration.

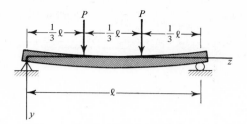

Fig. 6.2. Simple beam.

Figure 6.2 shows a horizontal simple beam subjected to two equal concentrated loads lying in the yz-plane at the third points. The curve assumed by
the central longitudinal axis of the deformed beam is called the *elastic curve*
of the beam. The ordinate y to a point on the elastic curve is called the deflection of the beam (analysis of deflections of beams is given in Chapter 8). The

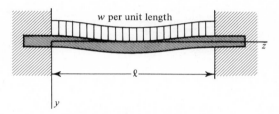

Fig. 6.3. Fixed-ended beam.

deflections shown in Figures 6.2 to 6.7 are exaggerated in order to show the
form assumed by the beams in response to the loads.

A *fixed or fixed-ended* beam is one so restrained at its end that the slope
of the elastic curve of the beam at the restrained end does not change when the

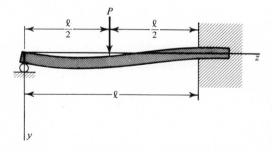

Fig. 6.4. Beam fixed at one end, supported at other end.

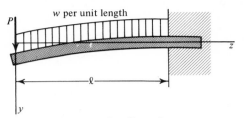

Fig. 6.5. Cantilever beam.

load is applied. Figure 6.3 shows a beam fixed at both ends and subjected to a uniformly distributed load of w pounds per unit length; Figure 6.4 represents a beam fixed at one end, supported at the other, and subjected to a concentrated load at midspan. The end connections of beams in structures and machines frequently offer considerable restraint but not sufficient to establish

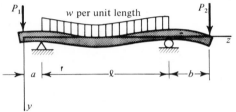

Fig. 6.6. Overhanging beam.

the conditions required for fixed-ended beams; such beams are then intermediate between simply supported beams and fixed-ended beams.

A *cantilever* beam is one that is fixed at one end and free at the other end. Figure 6.5 shows a cantilever beam subjected to a uniformly distributed load over its entire length and to a concentrated load at its free end.

Figure 6.6 shows an overhanging beam that overhangs both supports and that carries concentrated loads at the ends of the beam and a uniformly distributed load over the span between supports.

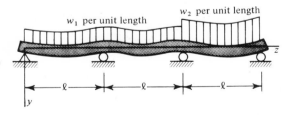

Fig. 6.7. Continuous beam.

A *continuous* beam is one that rests on more than two supports. Figure 6.7 shows a continuous beam with three equal spans carrying a uniformly distributed load of w_1 pounds per unit of length over two spans and a uniformly distributed load of w_2 pounds per unit of length over the third span.

Fibers of a beam.   It is frequently convenient to consider that a beam is composed of a large number of longitudinal rods or filaments called fibers whose cross sections are very small (differential areas). Some of these very slender elements or fibers shorten when the loads are applied (are in compression), and others stretch (are in tension). Study Figures 6.2–6.7 and determine whether the fibers stretch or shorten in the upper and lower portions of the beams at various sections along the beams, in order to permit the beams to deflect as shown. Such a qualitative analysis of beam behavior will be very useful in Chapter 8.

Pure bending is bending caused by couples. Thus, the middle third of the beam in Figure 6.2 is subjected to pure bending. Bending produced by forces that do not form couples is called ordinary bending. As is shown later, that part of the length of a beam that is subjected to pure bending has no transverse shearing stresses developed in it—the stresses on any transverse section are normal (tensile or compressive) stresses, whereas in ordinary bending the loads develop shearing stresses as well as normal stresses on a transverse section.

Reactions.   For convenience the forces exerted on a beam by the supports are called reactions, and the other forces are called loads, but both loads and reactions are merely external forces that act on the beam and hold the beam in equilibrium.

Statically Determinate and Statically Indeterminate Beams.   Beams for which the reactions can be found from the equations of equilibrium are called statically determinate beams, and those for which the number of unknown reactions is greater than the number of equilibrium equations are called statically indeterminate beams. Simple and cantilever beams and over-hanging beams that rest on two supports are statically determinate beams. Fixed-ended beams and continuous beams are statically indeterminate, and hence equations in addition to the equilibrium equations are required for determining the reactions, as will be discussed in Chapter 8.

Problems

6.5.   Find the reactions of the supports for the beam shown in Figure P6.5; neglect the weight of the beam.

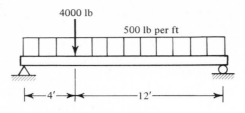

Fig. P 6.5.

6.6. Determine the reactions of the supports for the beam shown in Figure P6.6; neglect the weight of the beam.

ans. $R_1 = 4,267$ lb; $R_2 = 8,133$ lb.

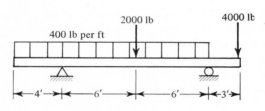

Fig. P 6.6.

6.7. In Figure 6.6, let $P_1 = 2,000$, $P_2 = 1,000$, $w = 200$ lb per ft, $a = 3$ ft, $b = 6$ ft, and $\ell = 20$ ft. Calculate the reactions of the supports.

6.8. The floor in a room supports a uniformly distributed load of 300 lb per sq. ft. The room is 30-ft wide, and the floor rests on simple beams having supports directly beneath the walls; that is, the span of the beams is 30 ft. If the beams are spaced 2-ft apart, what are the reactions at the ends of the beams?

ans. $R_1 = R_2 = 9,000$ lb.

6.9. In Figure 6.5, let $P = 2,000$ lb, $w = 300$ lb per ft, and $\ell = 12$ ft. Calculate the reactions (couple and vertical force) exerted by the wall on the beam.

6.4.   Shear and Moment Diagram

In the case of the member in Figure 6.1, all of the loads were applied at one section of the member. Usually the loads are applied at many locations along the member (Figs. P6.1 through P6.4). In this case, the general loading is broken up into four simpler loadings, which include either axial-centric loads only, torsional loads only, bending loads in the yz-plane only, or bending loads in the xz-plane only, as discussed in Section 6.2. Each type of loading is considered separately. The distribution of either the axial-centric loads or the torsional loads along the member is usually not considered sufficiently complex to warrant the consideration of a diagram representing the distribution of either the resisting axial force P_z or the resisting torque T_z along the member. However, the distribution of transverse shears and bending moments in beams are so complex that special consideration is given to the problem of constructing diagrams of resisting transverse shears and resisting bending moments along the beam. It is convenient in the remainder of this chapter to assume that all of the loads acting on the beam lie in the yz plane.

A *shear diagram* for a beam is a curve in which the abscissas represent distances along the beam and the ordinates represent the resisting transverse shears V_y for the cross sections of the beam at which the ordinates are drawn. A *moment diagram* for a beam is a curve in which the abscissas represent distances along the beam and the ordinates represent the resisting bending moments M_x for the cross sections of the beam at which the ordinates are drawn. These curves can be represented either as graphs or as mathematical relations as demonstrated by the following two examples.

Beam with Concentrated Load. Figure 6.8a shows a simply supported beam of length ℓ subjected to a concentrated load P in the yz plane at a distance $z = a$ from the left end. Equations of equilibrium are used to determine the reactions R_1 and R_2 in terms of the known load P. The concentrated load P causes both the shear and moment diagrams to be discontinuous at $z = a$. In order to obtain the equations for the resisting transverse shears V_y and the resisting bending moments M_x it is necessary to draw two free-body diagrams as shown in Figures 6.8b and c because there is a discontinuity at the concentrated load P. One free body is obtained by passing a cutting plane within the length from $z = 0$ to $z = a$ and another within the length from $z = a$ to $z = \ell$. The transverse shear is the algebraic sum of all the loads and reactions acting on the beam to the left of the section and the resisting moment is the algebraic sum of the moments with respect to the section of all the loads and reactions acting on the beam to the left of the section.

Equations of equilibrium for the free-body diagram in Figure 6.8b give equations for both V_y and M_x as functions of z in the length from $z = 0$ to $z = a$.

$$V_y = R_1, \tag{6-7}$$

$$M_x = R_1 z. \tag{6-8}$$

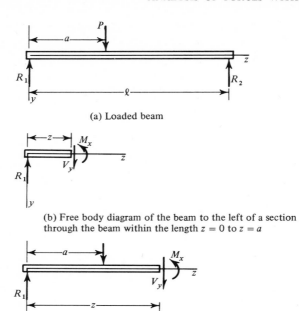

(a) Loaded beam

(b) Free body diagram of the beam to the left of a section
through the beam within the length $z = 0$ to $z = a$

(c) Free body diagram of the beam to the left of a section
through the beam within the length $z = a$ to $z = \ell$

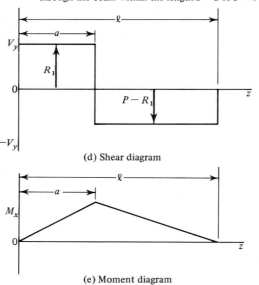

(d) Shear diagram

(e) Moment diagram

Fig. 6.8. Simple beam loaded by concentrated load.

Similar equations are obtained for the free-body diagram in Figure 6.8c:

$$V_y = R_1 - P, \qquad (6\text{--}9)$$

$$M_x = R_1 z - P(z - a). \qquad (6\text{--}10)$$

Equations (6–7) and (6–9) taken together represent the shear diagram for the beam in Figure 6.8a over its length. Thus

$$\begin{aligned} V_y &= R_1 & 0 \le z \le a \\ V_y &= R_1 - P & a \le z \le \ell, \end{aligned} \qquad (6\text{--}11)$$

is a mathematical representation of the shear diagram for the beam in Figure 6.8a. These equations are plotted to give the shear diagram as a graph in Figure 6.8d.

Equations (6–8) and (6–10) taken together represent the bending moment diagram for the beam in Figure 6.8a over its length. Thus

$$\begin{aligned} M_x &= R_1 z & 0 \le z \le a \\ M_x &= R_1 z - P(z - a) & a \le z \le \ell \end{aligned} \qquad (6\text{--}12)$$

is a mathematical representation of the moment diagram for the beam and was used to plot the moment diagram as a graph in Figure 6.8e.

Beam with Distributed Load and Concentrated Moment. Figure 6.9a shows a simply supported beam of length ℓ subjected to a concentrated moment M_0 at location $z = a$ and to a uniformly distributed load w from $z = 0$ to $z = b$. The reactions R_1 and R_2 are obtained using equations of equilibrium. The shear diagram suddenly changes its slope at $z = b$ and the moment diagram is discontinuous at location $z = a$ because its slope becomes infinite at that section. The free-body diagrams in Figures 6.9b, c, and d were obtained by passing cutting planes through the beam within each of the three lengths where both the shear and moment diagrams are continuous.

Using equations of equilibrium, V_y and M_x are found for the free-body diagram in Figure 6.9b, to be given by the relations

$$V_y = R_1 - wz, \qquad (6\text{--}13)$$

$$M_x = R_1 z - \frac{wz^2}{2}. \qquad (6\text{--}14)$$

For the free-body diagram in Figure 6.9c,

$$V_y = R_1 - wz \qquad (6\text{--}15)$$

$$M_x = R_1 z - \frac{wz^2}{2} + M_0 \qquad (6\text{--}16)$$

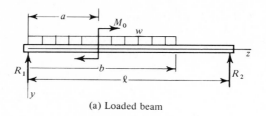

(a) Loaded beam

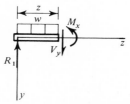

(b) Free body diagram of the beam
to the left of a section through the
beam within the length $z = 0$ to
$z = a$

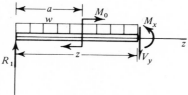

(c) Free body diagram of the beam
to the left of a section through the
beam within the length $z = a$ to
$z = b$

Fig. 6.9.   Simple beam loaded by couple and uniformly distributed load.

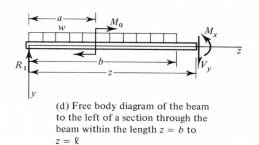

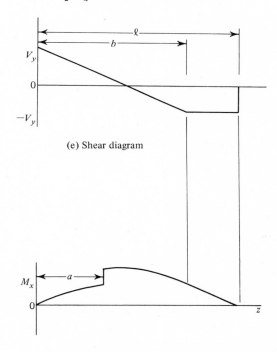

(d) Free body diagram of the beam
to the left of a section through the
beam within the length $z = b$ to
$z = \ell$

(e) Shear diagram

(f) Moment diagram

Fig. 6.9. (*Continued*)

For the free-body diagram in Figure 6.9d,

$$V_y = R_1 - wb \tag{6-17}$$

$$M_x = R_1 z - wb\left(z - \frac{b}{2}\right) + M_0 \tag{6-18}$$

Equations (6-13), (6-15), and (6-17) taken together represent the shear diagram for the beam in Figure 6.9a over its entire length. Thus

$$V_y = R_1 - wz \qquad 0 \le z \le b$$
$$V_y = R_1 - wb \qquad b \le z \le \ell \tag{6-19}$$

is a mathematical representation of the shear diagram for the beam and was used to plot the graphical representation of the shear diagram in Figure 6.9e.

Equations (6-14), (6-16), and (6-18) taken together represent the bending moment diagram for the beam in Figure 6.9a over its entire length. Thus

$$M_x = R_1 z - \frac{wz^2}{2} \qquad\qquad 0 \le z \le a$$

$$M_x = R_1 z - \frac{wz^2}{2} + M_0 \qquad\qquad a \le z \le b \tag{6-20}$$

$$M_x = R_1 z - wb\left(z - \frac{b}{2}\right) + M_0 \qquad b \le z \le \ell$$

is a mathematical representation of the moment diagram for the beam and was used to plot the moment diagram as a graph (Fig. 6.9f).

The foregoing examples have indicated that the shear and moment diagrams may have sudden changes in shape at one or more locations along the length of a beam. The mathematical representation of the moment diagram is needed in Chapter 8 where the deflections of beams are considered. We will find that the fact that several different equations are needed to represent the moment diagram will greatly increase the work required to determine the deflections of a given beam subjected to known loads. Much of this work is eliminated if the moment diagram can be expressed by a single mathematical relation. This can be done by the use of step functions as explained in the following section.

6.5. Step Function

Special functions called step functions (sometimes called singularity functions) were originally introduced by A. Clebsch* in 1862. A step function of z starting at a discontinuity at location z_0 is written $\langle z - z_0 \rangle^n$ where n is any positive integer including zero. This function has the following properties.

$$\langle z - z_0 \rangle^n = \begin{cases} (z - z_0)^n & \text{when } n > 0 \text{ and } z \geq z_0 \\ 0 & \text{when } n > 0 \text{ and } z < z_0 \end{cases}$$

(6–21)

$$\langle z - z_0 \rangle^0 = \begin{cases} 1 & \text{when } z \geq z_0 \\ 0 & \text{when } z < z_0 \end{cases}$$

In many applications, differentiation and integration of step functions are required:

$$\frac{d}{dz} \langle z - z_0 \rangle^n = n \langle z - z_0 \rangle^{n-1} \qquad \text{when } n \geq 1 \quad (6\text{–}22)$$

$$\int \langle z - z_0 \rangle^n \, dz = \frac{1}{n + 1} \langle z - z_0 \rangle^{n+1} + C \qquad \text{when } n \geq 0 \quad (6\text{–}23)$$

in Equation (6–23) C is a constant of integration.

The use of step functions to represent the shear and moment diagrams for beams will be illustrated using the two beams in Figures 6.8a and 6.9a. The shear and moment diagrams for the beam in Figure 6.8a are given by Equations (6–11) and (6–12), respectively. In terms of step functions these relations become

$$V_y = R_1 - P\langle z - a \rangle^0, \tag{6–24}$$

$$M_x = R_1 z - P\langle z - a \rangle^1. \tag{6–25}$$

The loads shown acting on the beam in Figure 6.9a have to be modified when step functions are used to represent the shear and moment diagrams. It is necessary that a distributed load continue to the right end ($z = \ell$). To do this a fictitious distributed load w is applied on both the top and bottom surfaces of the beam from $z = b$ to $z = \ell$ as indicated in Figure 6.10a. The loading in Figure 6.10a is identical with that shown in Figure 6.9a from

* For discussion of the Clebsch method see "Clebsch's Method for Beam Deflections," W. D. Pilkey, *Journal of Engineering Education*, p. 170, 1964. Our notation is patterned after that used by W. H. Macauley, "Note on the Deflection of Beams," *Messenger of Mathematics*, Vol. 48, pp. 129–130, 1919.

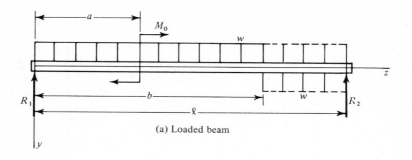

(a) Loaded beam

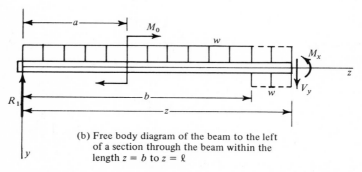

(b) Free body diagram of the beam to the left
of a section through the beam within the
length $z = b$ to $z = \ell$

Fig. 6.10. Simple beam with loading equivalent to that in Fig. 6.9.

$z = 0$ to $z = b$ and is equivalent from $z = b$ to $z = \ell$. Pass a cutting plane
through the beam in Figure 6.10*a* within the length from $z = b$ to $z = \ell$
to give the free-body diagram shown in Figure 6.10*b*. Equations of equilibrium
give

$$V_y = R_1 - wz + w(z - b) \qquad\qquad b \leq z \leq \ell \qquad (6\text{--}26)$$

$$M_x = R_1 z - \frac{wz^2}{2} + M_0 + w(z - b)^2/2 \qquad b \leq z \leq \ell \qquad (6\text{--}27)$$

If step functions are not used, Equations (6–13), (6–15), and (6–26) represent
the shear diagram and Equations (6–14), (6–16), and (6–27) represent the
moment diagram for the beam in Figure 6.10*a*. Using step functions, the
shear and moment diagrams for the loading in Figure 6.10*a* are given by
the relations

$$V_y = R_1 - wz + w\langle z - b\rangle^1 \qquad\qquad (6\text{--}28)$$

$$M_x = R_1 z - \frac{wz^2}{2} + M_0\langle z - a\rangle^0 + \frac{w}{2}\langle z - b\rangle^2. \qquad (6\text{--}29)$$

It is easy to show that Equations (6–28) and (6–29) give the same shear and moment diagrams as Equations (6–19) and (6–20). Equations (6–28) and (6–29) are more compact and are easier to use than Equations (6–19) and (6–20) for shear and bending moment.

Problems

6.10 Through 6.21. For the beams shown in Figures P6.10 through P6.21 use the method illustrated in Figures 6.8 and 6.9 to make a diagram that shows the resisting transverse shear V_y and the resisting moment M_x at any cross section of the beam; also write the equations that represent V_y and M_x at any cross section.

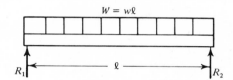

Fig. P 6.10.

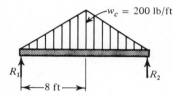 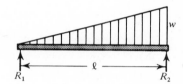

Fig. P 6.11.   **Fig. P 6.12.**

ans. to problem 6.12. $R_1 = w\ell/6$; $R_2 = w\ell/3$.

The shear and moment diagrams are given by the relations

$$V_y = R_1 - \frac{wz^2}{2\ell} = \frac{w\ell}{6} - \frac{wz^2}{2\ell},$$

$$M_x = R_1 z - \frac{wz^3}{6\ell} = \frac{w\ell z}{6} - \frac{wz^3}{6\ell}.$$

Fig. P 6.13.

ans. to problem 6.13. $R_1 = 1{,}500$ lb: $R_2 = 1{,}500$ lb. (continued on page 243)

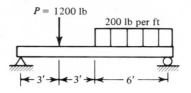

Fig. P 6.14.

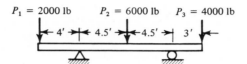

Fig. P 6.15.

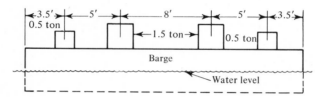

Fig. P 6.16.

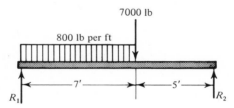

Fig. P 6.17.

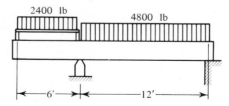

Fig. P 6.18.

The shear and moment diagrams are given by the relations (ans. to P. 6.13)

$$V_y = R_1 - wz = 1{,}500 - 100z \qquad\qquad 0 \le z \le 4$$

$$V_y = R_1 - wz - P = 500 - 100z \qquad\qquad 4 \le z \le 16$$

$$V_y = R_1 - wz - P + R_2 = 2{,}000 - 100z \qquad 16 \le z \le 20$$

$$M_x = R_1 z - \frac{wz^2}{2} = 1{,}500z - 50z^2 \qquad\qquad 0 \le z \le 4$$

$$M_x = R_1 z - \frac{wz^2}{2} - P(z-4) = 4{,}000 + 500z - 50z^2 \qquad 4 \le z \le 16$$

$$M_x = R_1 z - \frac{wz^2}{2} - P(z-4) + R_2(z-16)$$

$$= -20{,}000 + 2{,}000z - 50z^2 \qquad\qquad 16 \le z \le 20$$

The shear and moment diagrams using step functions are (ans. to P. 6.13)

$$V_y = R_1 - wz - P\langle z-4 \rangle^0 + R_2\langle z-16 \rangle^0$$

$$= 1{,}500 - 100z - 1{,}000\langle z-4 \rangle^0 + 1{,}500\langle z-16 \rangle^0,$$

$$M_x = R_1 z - \frac{wz^2}{2} - P\langle z-4 \rangle^1 + R_2\langle z-16 \rangle^1,$$

$$= 1{,}500z - 50z^2 - 1{,}000\langle z-4 \rangle^1 + 1{,}500\langle z-16 \rangle^1.$$

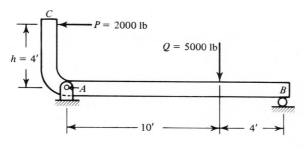

Fig. P 6.19.

ans. to problem 6.19. $R_{Az} = 2{,}000\ \text{lb}$; $R_{Ay} = 2{,}000\ \text{lb}$; $R_B = 3{,}000\ \text{lb}$. (continued on page 244).

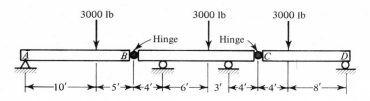

Fig. P 6.20.

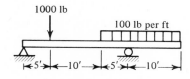

Fig. P 6.21.

The shear and moment diagrams are given by the relations (ans. to P. 6.19)

$$V_y = R_{Ay} = 2,000 \qquad\qquad\qquad\qquad 0 \le z \le 10$$

$$V_y = R_{Ay} - Q = 3,000 \qquad\qquad\qquad 10 \le z \le 14$$

$$M_x = -Ph + R_{Ay}z = -8,000 + 2,000z \qquad\qquad 0 \le z \le 10$$

$$M_x = -Ph + R_{Ay}z - Q(z - 10) = 42,000 - 3,000z \qquad 10 \le z \le 14$$

The shear and moment diagrams using step functions are (ans. to P 6.19)

$$V_y = R_{Ay} - Q\langle z - 10 \rangle^0 = 2,000 - 5,000\langle z - 10 \rangle^0,$$

$$M_x = -Ph + R_{Ay}z - Q\langle z - 10 \rangle^1 = -8,000 + 2,000z - 5,000\langle z - 10 \rangle^1.$$

6.6. Relationship Between Bending Moment and Transverse Shear

There is a useful relationship between the bending moment and the transverse shear that we can use to determine one in terms of the other as follows:

$$V_y \, dz = dM_x \qquad\qquad\qquad (6\text{--}30a)$$

or

$$V_y = \frac{dM_x}{dz} \qquad\qquad\qquad (6\text{--}30b)$$

We shall now prove the validity of Equations (6–30). Let Figure 6.11 represent an infinitesimal length dz of a beam loaded by a distributed load w (not necessarily uniformly distributed). The transverse shearing forces and bending moments on each end of the short length dz of the beam are as shown. The beam is assumed to be in a state of equilibrium. We, therefore, may write the following equation of equilibrium:

$$\sum M_0 = 0; \qquad M_x + V_y\, dz - w\, dz(\tfrac{1}{2}\, dz) - (M_x + dM_x) = 0. \qquad (6\text{--}31)$$

In Equation (6–31), the term $\tfrac{1}{2}w\,(dz)^2$ can be neglected as a higher order term and the equation reduces to Equation (6–30a) or (b).

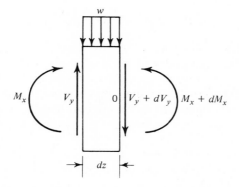

Fig. 6.11.

Interpretation and Use of Equations (6–30a) and (b).   Two important uses may be made of Equations (6–30). First, by taking the integral of each side of Equation (6–30a) of a finite length of the beam, let us say from $z = z_a$ to $z = z_b$, we have the following equation:

$$\int_{z_a}^{z_b} dM_x = \int_{z_a}^{z_b} V_y\, dz. \qquad (6\text{--}32)$$

The left side of Equation (6–32) represents the difference between the moment at $z = z_b$ and at $z = z_a$ and the right side of Equation (6–32) represents the area enclosed under the transverse shear diagram between the ordinates at $z = z_a$ and $z = z_b$ and the z-axis. This fact means that we may use the area under the diagram representing transverse shear between any two cross sections of a beam to determine the change in bending moment between the same two cross sections of a beam, as will be illustrated later in this section.

Second, the condition for the bending moment to have a maximum (or minimum) is that the derivative

$$\frac{dM_x}{dz} = 0. \tag{6-33}$$

From Equations (6–30b) we note that the shear V_y must be zero to fulfill this latter condition. Hence, at the cross section (or cross sections) in a beam at which the transverse shear V_y is zero, the bending moment M_x must be a maximum (or a minimum).

Illustrative Problem

6.22. Let a beam of length 17 ft be simply supported 3 ft from the left end and at the right end and be loaded as shown in Figure P6.22a. Construct the bending moment diagram for the beam by making use of the area under the transverse shear diagram (Eq. 6–32) and locate the cross section at which the maximum and minimum bending moment occurs by making use of the conditions expressed by Equation (6–30b) and Equation (6–33).

SOLUTION. We determine the reactions as follows: Taking the sum of the moments of all the external loads with respect to A, $\sum M_A = 0$ gives $R_B = 6,000$ lb; taking $\sum M_B = 0$ gives $R_A = 6,000$ lb; and taking the sum of the vertical external forces $\sum F_y = 0$ gives a check on the values found for R_A and R_B.

The shear diagram shown in Figure P6.22b was constructed using the procedure developed in Section 6.4.

The moment diagram as shown in Figure P6.22c is obtained by making use of Figure P6.22b and Equation (6–32). The bending moment at the left end is zero. By making use of Equation (6–32), we find that the change in bending moment from O to Q is equal to the area under the transverse shear diagram from O to Q; that is, the change is $-6,000$ lb-ft, which is the ordinate at Q in Figure P6.22c.

From Q to S in Figure P6.22b the area under the transverse shear diagram is $+16,000$ lb-ft. We add this change in bending moment, algebraically, to the $-6,000$ lb-ft ordinate at Q in Figure P6.22c to obtain the ordinate $+10,000$ lb-ft at S in Figure P6.22c.

From S to T in Figure P6.22b the area under the transverse shear diagram is $+8,000$ lb-ft. We add this change in bending moment, algebraically, to the $+10,000$ lb-ft ordinate at S in Figure P6.22c to obtain the ordinate $+18,000$ lb-ft at T in Figure P6.22c.

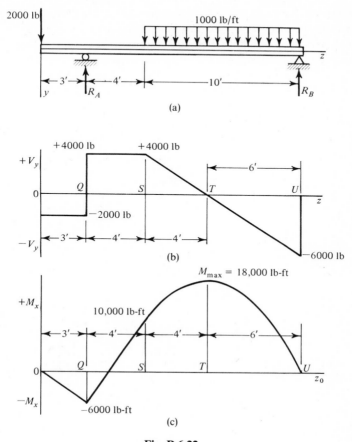

Fig. P 6.22.

From T to U in Figure P6.22b the area under the transverse shear diagram is $-18,000$ lb-ft. We add this change in bending moment to the $+18,000$ lb-ft ordinate at T in Figure P6.22c to obtain the ordinate zero at U in Figure P6.22c.

With the ordinates at Q, S, T, and U in Figure P6.22c thus determined we draw a smooth curve, which represents the bending moment diagram.

Note that the maximum negative bending moment $-6,000$ lb-ft (i.e., the minimum algebraic value) occurs at Q where the transverse shear has a value of zero; likewise the maximum positive bending moment occurs at T where the transverse shear is again equal to zero. These facts verify the conditions of Equation (6–30b) and Equation (6–33).

Note also that from O to S, where there are rectangular areas in the shear diagram, the bending moment diagram consists of straight line segments. However, from S to U, where there are triangular areas in the shear diagram, the bending moment diagram is curved.

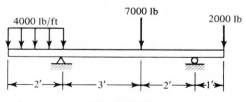

Fig. P 6.23.

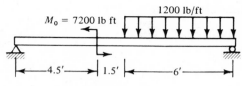

Fig. P 6.24.

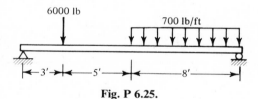

Fig. P 6.25.

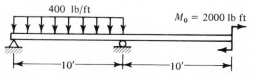

Fig. P 6.26.

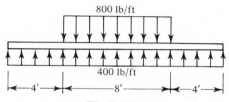

Fig. P 6.27.

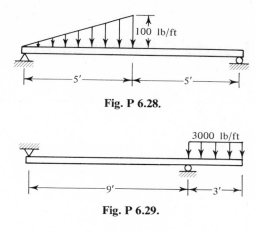

Fig. P 6.28.

3000 lb/ft

Fig. P 6.29.

Problems

6.23 Through 6.29. For the beams supported and loaded as shown in Figures P6.23 through P6.29 construct the bending moment diagram of the beam by making use of the area under the transverse shear diagram (Eq. 6–32), and locate the cross section where the bending moment has a maximum or minimum value by making use of the conditions as expressed by Equation (6–30b) and Equation (6–33).

6.30 Through 6.33. For the beams that are shown in Figures P6.1 through P6.4 construct diagrams showing the transverse shear V_y and V_x over the entire length of the beam. Also construct bending moment diagrams that represent the bending moments M_x and M_y over the entire length of the beam.

Bending Loads—Stresses in Beams

7.1. Introduction

In Chapter 6 it was shown how any system of external loads acting on a straight bar can be resisted (see Fig. 6.1b) at any cross section of the member by an axial centric force P_z, two transverse shears V_x and V_y, two bending moments M_x and M_y, and a torsional moment T_z.

For the member that resists an axial centric load $P = P_z$ only, that is, $M_x = M_y = V_x = V_y = T_z = 0$ at all cross sections (see Section 1.4), the relationship for the longitudinal normal stress is $\sigma_z = P/A$ as given by Equation (1–10).

Chapter 9 gives the relationship between the distribution of the shearing stresses at any cross section and the load for the member that resists a torsional moment $T = T_z$ only: that is, $M_x = M_y = V_x = V_y = P_z = 0$ at all cross sections.

This chapter deals with the relationship between the distribution of the normal stresses at any cross section and the load for the member that resists bending moments M_x and M_y only; that is, $V_x = V_y = P_z = T_z = 0$ at all cross sections. Such a member is said to be subjected to *pure bending*.

After completing the derivation of expressions for the distribution of the normal stresses for pure bending, the relationship will be derived between the transverse shears V_x and V_y, which (as shown in Sections 6.4 and 6.6) are related to the bending moments M_x and M_y.

Before proceeding to derive these relationships between the stresses and the external loads we shall discuss a general procedure that can be used in all cases.

7.2. Simplified Procedure for Deriving Load-Stress Relationship

The method or procedure used throughout this book for obtaining the relationship between the loads and the normal and shearing stresses at any cross section has been given in Section 4.3. A brief outline of this procedure is repeated here.

Step 1. By use of the method presented in Chapter 6, express the relation between the loads acting on the member and the internal forces or moments at the cross section of the member.

Step 2. Express the internal or resisting forces or moments at the cross section in terms of the normal and shearing stresses at the section; this requires that the distribution of the stresses on the section must be found. This distribution of the stresses may be determined as follows: (1) The distribution of strains in the longitudinal fibers of the member at the cross section is determined. The conclusions arrived at in this step are usually supported by some experimental results. (2) The stress-strain relationship must be obtained for the material of which the member is made. The stress–strain relation and known distribution of strains determine the distribution of stresses.

Step 3. By substituting the results found in Step 2 into the equations obtained from Step 1, the desired relationships are obtained between the loads acting on the member and the stresses at any point on the cross section considered.

Most of the emphasis in this chapter is concerned with bending stresses in beams for which all of the loads lie in a plane of symmetry for the beam. Many practical beams are subjected to symmetrical loading. Many beams, particularly in the aircraft industry, do not have a plane of symmetry and are subjected to unsymmetrical loading. Bending stresses in beams of arbitrary cross section are treated in Section 7.5. If you prefer to treat symmetrical bending as a special case of unsymmetrical bending, continue with Section 7.5, 7.6, and 7.7 and return to Section 7.4, omitting Section 7.3.

7.3. Bending Stresses in Beams Subjected to Symmetrical Loading

Let Figure 7.1a represent a straight beam of constant cross section for which the yz-plane is a plane of symmetry. Let the external loads acting on the free end of the beam be the couple Qs that lies in the yz-plane. The only load acting on the beam is a couple lying in the plane of symmetry; therefore,

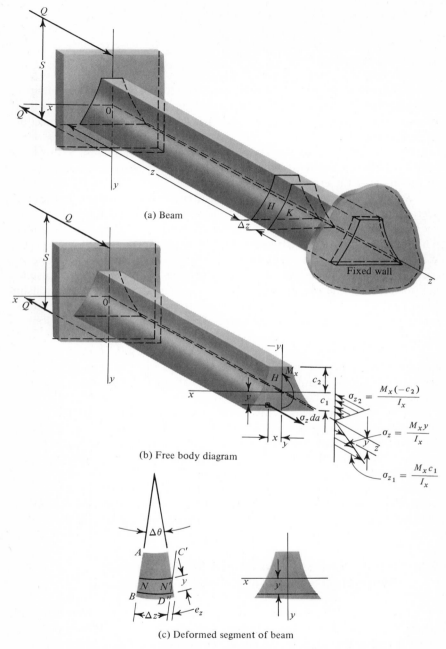

(a) Beam

$$\sigma_{z2} = \frac{M_x(-c_2)}{I_x}$$

$$\sigma_z = \frac{M_x y}{I_x}$$

$$\sigma_{z1} = \frac{M_x c_1}{I_x}$$

(b) Free body diagram

(c) Deformed segment of beam

Fig. 7.1. Pure bending of beam subjected to symmetrical bending.

the beam is subjected to pure bending, the bending moment is positive, and the loading is symmetrical.

The problem is to determine the distribution of stresses on a cross section of the beam caused by the external loads. A cutting plane perpendicular to the z-axis is passed through the beam at cross section H to remove the free-body diagram in Figure 7.1b. At cross section H, $P_z = V_x = V_y = M_y = T_z = 0$; therefore, the length OH of the beam in Figure 7.1b is put in equilibrium by the resisting moment M_x. Now follow the general procedure given in Section 7.2.

Step 1. Apply the equations of equilibrium to the loads acting on the free-body diagram in Figure 7.1b as follows:

$$\sum M_x = 0 \qquad M_x = Qs, \tag{7-1}$$

$$\sum F_z = 0 \qquad Q - Q = P_z = 0. \tag{7-2}$$

Step 2. A distribution is sought for the internal forces, which are now external forces on cross section H, in Figure 7.1b whose resultant is equal to M_x. The intensity of these forces at any point (x, y) is the normal stress σ_z. Multiply this stress by the infinitesimal part da of the area surrounding the point (x, y). The force $\sigma_z\, da$ acts on the infinitesimal area da. Some of the $\sigma_z\, da$ forces will be tensile forces and some must be compressive forces, because Equation (7-2) shows that the resultant axial force P_z is zero.

The right-hand members of Equations (7-1) and (7-2) are expressed in terms of the forces $\sigma_z\, da$ by using the principle that the resultant is equal to the sum of its components as follows:

$$M_x = \int y\sigma_z\, da, \tag{7-3}$$

$$0 = \int \sigma_z\, da. \tag{7-4}$$

Step 2a. Step 2a requires that the geometry of deformation be investigated to determine the strain distribution in the beam. Physical arguments, which can be easily checked experimentally, can be used to prove that plane sections of the unloaded beam remain plane after pure bending loads are applied to the beam. Pass a cutting plane perpendicular to the z-axis to give cross section K in Figure 7.1a at a short distance Δz from cross section H. A side view of the deformed segment of the beam of length Δz is shown in Figure 7.1c. The deformations are greatly exaggerated so that they can be observed. Cross section H designated by line AB and cross section K designated by line CD are inclined to each other by the angle $\Delta\theta$. Because plane sections remain plane, the top of the segment of the beam shortens whereas the bottom elongates. Obviously, there is a longitudinal surface designated by NN' along which the undeformed length Δz does not change during the deformation; this is called the neutral surface of the beam and the plane cross sections always remain perpendicular to the neutral surface (Fig. 7.1c). The intersection of the neutral surface with the cross section is called the neutral axis. Let the x-axis in cross section H in Figure 7.1c be the neutral axis. The distance y to the force $\sigma_z\, da$ is then measured from the neutral axis.

Draw a line $C'D'$ parallel to AB through N' as indicated in Figure 7.1c. At distance y from the neutral surface, the undeformed gage length Δz has elongated an amount e_z caused by the deformation of the beam. From geometry, the elongation e_z is given by the relation

$$e_z = y\, \Delta\theta.$$

Dividing both sides by the gage length Δz and noting that $e_z/\Delta z = \epsilon_z$, we get

$$\epsilon_z = y\frac{\Delta\theta}{\Delta z}. \tag{7-5}$$

Because both $\Delta\theta$ and Δz are independent of y, Equation (7–5) can be written

$$\frac{\epsilon_z}{y} = \frac{\Delta\theta}{\Delta z} = \text{constant.} \tag{7-6}$$

It has not been necessary thus far to assume any specific type of stress-strain relationship.

Step 2b. Let it now be assumed that the stress-strain relation for the material is linearly elastic, that is, use the third of Equations (4–6) in which the values of $\sigma_x = \sigma_y = 0$. Thus, $\sigma_z = E\epsilon_z$ and Equation (7–6) becomes, by multiplying both sides by the modulus of elasticity E,

$$\frac{E\epsilon_z}{y} = E\,(\text{constant}) = C,$$

or

$$\sigma_z = Cy, \tag{7-7}$$

where C is a constant.

Step 3. The expression for σ_z obtained from Step 2 and given by Equation (7–7) is substituted into Equations (7–3) and (7–4), which give the following results:

$$M_x = \int Cy^2\, da = C\int y^2\, da, \tag{7-8}$$

$$0 = \int Cy\, da = C\int y\, da. \tag{7-9}$$

Because the constant C is not zero, the integral in Equation (7–9) is zero.

But

$$\int y \, da = A\bar{y} = 0$$

where A is the cross-sectional area of the beam and $\bar{y}$ is the distance from the x-axis to the centroid. It is noted that $\bar{y} = 0$ and that the x-axis is a centroidal axis of the cross section. Thus, the neutral x-axis and the centroidal axis coincide when linear elastic behavior is assumed to occur.

The integral $\int y^2 \, da$ in Equation (7–8) is the second moment of the area A with respect to the x-axis (commonly called the moment of inertia of the area with respect to the x-axis); the integral is described in Appendix A where it is given the symbol I_x. Setting the integral in Equation (7–8) equal to I_x, Equation (7–8) becomes

$$M_x = CI_x = \frac{\sigma_z I_x}{y} \quad \text{or} \quad \sigma_z = \frac{M_x y}{I_x}, \tag{7–10}$$

which is the load-stress relation called the *flexure formula for symmetrically loaded beams made of linearly elastic materials.*

Note. Equation (7–10) has been derived assuming that the beam is subjected to pure bending only. This equation is exact for pure bending. Most beams are subjected to transverse shear loads in addition to the bending loads as discussed in Section 6.2. Although plane sections do not remain plane (one of the conditions used in the derivation of Eq. 7–10), when the beam is subjected to transverse shear loads, Equation (7–10) is assumed to be valid for beams subjected to transverse shear loads. Both experimental data and more exact theories support this conclusion, particularly if the beam has a length of at least five times its depth. As indicated in Section 7.9, a cross section of the beam will have a shearing stress distribution in addition to the normal stress distribution given by Equation (7–10) if the transverse shear is not zero.

7.4. Flexure Formula for Symmetrical Bending

The flexure formula

$$\sigma_z = \frac{M_x y}{I_x} \tag{7–11}$$

for symmetrical bending of an elastic beam has been derived both in Section 7.3 (see Eq. 7–10) and as a special case of unsymmetrical bending in Section 7.7 (see Eq. 7–43).

Figure 7.1b shows the distribution of the bending stress σ_z along the y-axis. As indicated by Equation (7–11), σ_z varies directly with the distance y measured from the x-axis. When the bending moment is positive (sign convention for bending moment is given in Section 6.2), the maximum tensile bending stress is obtained by the substitution of $y = c_1$ into Equation (7–11), which gives

$$\sigma_{z_1} = \frac{M_x c_1}{I_x}; \tag{7–12}$$

and the maximum compressive bending stress is obtained by the substitution of $y = -c_2$ into Equation (7–11), which gives

$$\sigma_{z_2} = \frac{M_x(-c_2)}{I_x}. \tag{7–13}$$

Equations (7–12) and (7–13) are rewritten as follows:

$$\sigma_{z_1} = \frac{M_x}{I_x/c_1} \tag{7–14}$$

and

$$\sigma_{z_2} = \frac{-M_x}{I_x/c_2}. \tag{7–15}$$

The smallest of the denominator terms I_x/c_1 and I_x/c_2 in Equations (7–14) and (7–15) is called the *section modulus* Z and is expressed in inches to the third power. Thus

$$Z = \frac{I_x}{c_1} \quad \text{or} \quad Z = \frac{I_x}{c_2}, \tag{7–16}$$

whichever is the smaller, is the section modulus.

Figure 7.2 shows the physical significance of the value of Z. Each cross section in Figure 7.2 has an area of 4 in.^{2} The value of $Z = I_x/c$ varies from 1.33 for the square (Fig. 7.2a) to 6.10 for the I-section of Figure 7.2d, and

$$\sigma_{z(max)} = \frac{M_x}{Z}. \tag{7–17}$$

Therefore, for a given bending moment M_x, the maximum bending stress $\sigma_{z(max)}$ in the square cross section of Figure 7.2a would be $6.10/1.33 = 4.58$ times what it would be for the I-beam in Figure 7.2d. Or, to state it differently, the beam with the I-section of Figure 7.2d will resist 4.58 times as much load for the same maximum bending stress σ_z as the square of Figure

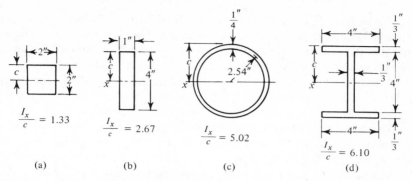

Fig. 7.2.   Cross section having the same areas but widely different values of I_x/c.

7.2a, which has the same cross-sectional area and therefore the same amount of material per foot length in the beam.

Limitations of the Flexure Formula.   As the flexure formula (Eq. 7–11) is being used in the design of beams, there are several limitations that should be noted as follows:

(1) The loads on the beam must be slowly applied or must be static loads. The stresses in the beam are not given by this formula when impact loads produce accelerations in the beam while the stresses and strains are being developed.

(2) The value of σ_z given by Equation (7–11) at a given point in a loaded beam is the normal stress at that point due to external forces only. If this value of σ_z is to be equal to the actual stress in the beam at that point, the beam must be free from initial or residual stresses due to temperature gradients, uneven cooling during heat treatment, cold working, and so forth.

(3) As the beam is being loaded, the deformations of the beam must be such that the movement of a given beam cross section will be a translation in the y-direction and a rotation about the x-axis. The beam must fail by bending and not by twisting, lateral buckling, or local wrinkling. A rectangular section beam $\frac{1}{8}$-in. wide and 6-in. deep would probably fail by twisting, and an I-beam having wide and thin flanges would probably fail by local buckling or wrinkling of the outer portion of the compression flanges.

(4) The undeformed beam must either be straight or have a relatively small initial curvature. Plane sections of straight and curved beams remain plane; therefore the total strain distribution is linear for both beams. The gage length for a given fiber in either beam is the distance measured along the fiber between the two plane sections. Every fiber has the same gage length for the straight beam but will not have the same gage length for the curved beam. Because strains are obtained by dividing each total strain by the

corresponding gage length, the strain distribution will be linear for the straight beam but not for the curved beam. The flexure formula requires that the stress distribution be linear; this requirement is satisfied for linearly elastic behavior of straight beams but not of curved beams.

(5) The beam must not have abrupt changes in section in the portion of the beam in which the stress σ_z is to be found because plane sections do not remain plane at or near such changes in sections (see Section 7.8).

(6) Not only must the material in the beam be linearly elastic but the modulus of elasticity of all the material in the beam must have the same magnitude. The flexure formula is not valid for a two material beam unless E is the same for the two materials. Composite beams of two materials are discussed in Section 7.17.

(7) The stresses σ_z in the neighborhood of a point of application of a concentrated load are quite different from the values calculated using the flexure formula; however, the formula is assumed to be valid for the side of the beam opposite the point of application of the concentrated load.

Illustrative Problems

7.1.   A simply supported 6-in. by 12-in. yellow pine wood (see Table 1.1) beam of length $\ell = 16$ ft, is loaded by a uniformly distributed load of 400 lb/ft (including the weight of the beam) over the full length, and a concentrated load of 1,000 lb at a distance of 4 ft from the left support. All loads lie in the yz-plane which is a plane of symmetry as shown in Figure P7.1a. Determine the maximum tensile and compressive values of the bending stresses in the beam.

SOLUTION.   Using equations of equilibrium on the free-body diagram in Figure 7.1a, the reactions R_1 and R_2 are found to be

$$R_1 = 3,950 \text{ lb}, \qquad R_2 = 3,450 \text{ lb}.$$

The shear diagram in Figure P7.1b and the moment diagram in Figure P7.1c were constructed using the procedure in Chapter 6.

Maximum Bending Stresses.   Equations (7–12) and (7–13) are used to compute the bending stresses. The value of I_x is (see Appendix A)

$$I_x = \frac{bh^3}{12} = \frac{6(12)^3}{12} = 864 \text{ in.}^4$$

From Equation (7–12)

$$\sigma_{z_1} = \frac{M_{x(\text{max})}c_1}{I_x} = \frac{14,880(12)(6)}{864} = 1,240 \text{ psi tension (bottom fiber).}$$

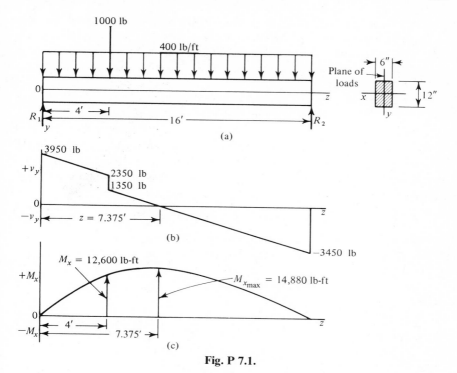

Fig. P 7.1.

From Equation (7–13)

$$\sigma_{z_2} = \frac{M_{x(max)}(-c_2)}{I_x} = \frac{14,880(12)(-6)}{864} = -1,240 \text{ psi compression (top fiber).}$$

Both of these values of maximum bending stresses are much less than the yield strength of yellow pine as given in Table 1.1.

Problems

Note: In the problems that follow three important assumptions are made: (1) The stress-strain relationship of the material is linear. (2) The loads acting on the beam all lie in one plane, and furthermore the plane of the loads coincides with the axis of symmetry in every cross section. (3) The beams are assumed to be supported in the direction perpendicular to the plane of the loads so that failure by lateral buckling (see Chapter 11) does not occur.

7.2. The cantilever beam in Figure P7.2 is made by nailing three 2-in. by 6-in. boards together as shown. (1) Determine the magnitude and location of the maximum

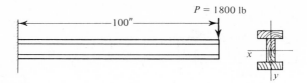

Fig. P 7.2.

tensile bending stress σ_z in the beam. (2) What is the maximum tensile bending stress in the center board on which the two flanges of the beam are nailed? (3) If the boards are yellow pine with yield strength $\sigma_e = 5,000$ psi (see Table 1.1), what is the factor of safety used in the design of the beam? (Creep occurs at this stress level.)

ans.   (1) $\sigma_z = 2,100$ psi (top of beam at wall); (2) $\sigma_z = 1,260$ psi; (3) $N = 2.38$.

7.3.   The T-section simple beam in Figure P7.3 is made of gray cast iron whose ultimate strengths in tension and compression are $\sigma_{ut} = 21,000$ psi and $\sigma_{uc} = 66,000$ psi,

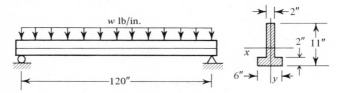

Fig. P 7.3.

respectively. The material is assumed to be linearly elastic up to fracture. (1) Determine the magnitude of w based on a factor of safety of $N = 2.50$. (2) What would be the magnitude of w if the flange of the T-section is located at the top of the beam instead of at the bottom as shown?

ans.   (1) $w = 373$ lb/in.; (2) $w = 239$ lb/in.

7.4.   The beam in Figure P7.4 is made by glueing 1-in. by 2-in. oak boards together to form a rectangular section beam having a width of 2 in. The yield strength of the

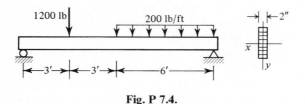

Fig. P 7.4.

oak is $\sigma_e = 4{,}300$ psi (see Table 1.1). If the minimum factor of safety for the beam is 2.00, determine the number of boards that must be glued together to form the beam.

ans.   Use 8 boards. (Creep is neglected.)

7.5.   The beam in Figure P7.5 has a circular cross section as shown. The beam is made of an alloy steel that has a yield strength of $\sigma_e = 140{,}000$ psi. Determine the minimum value for the diameter D of the beam based on a factor of safety of $N = 2.00$.

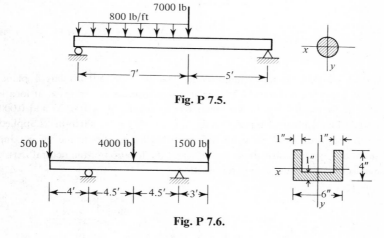

Fig. P 7.5.

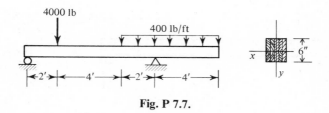

Fig. P 7.6.

7.6.   The channel section beam in Figure P7.6 is made of a cast iron whose stress-strain diagrams can be assumed to be linear up to the ultimate strengths of $\sigma_{ut} = 25{,}000$ psi in tension and $\sigma_{uc} = 75{,}000$ psi in compression. (1) Determine the maximum values of the tensile and compressive stresses in the beam. (2) What is the factor of safety for the beam?

7.7.   The beam in Figure P7.7 is built up by nailing 1-in. by 6-in. yellow pine boards together to form a rectangular section beam having a depth of 6 in. The yield strength of the yellow pine is $\sigma_e = 5{,}000$ psi. Determine the number of boards needed to make the beam if the factor of safety is $N = 2.20$. (Creep is neglected.)

Fig. P 7.7.

262 BENDING LOADS—STRESSES IN BEAMS

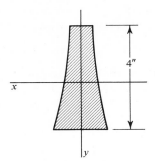

Fig. P 7.8.

7.8. An extruded beam of aluminum alloy ($\sigma_e = 44{,}000$ psi) has a plane of symmetry as indicated in Figure P7.8. Strain gages to measure strains ϵ_z at locations 1-in. and 3-in. below the top of the beam record strains of -0.00120 and 0.00080, respectively, when a positive pure bending moment $M_x = 56{,}000$ lb-in. is applied to the beam. If the modulus of elasticity is $E = 10{,}000{,}000$ psi, determine the maximum tensile stress and compressive stress in the beam, the location of the neutral axis, and the moment of inertia of the beam cross section.

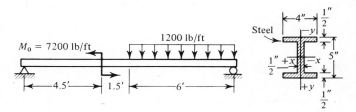

Fig. P 7.9.

7.9. The beam in Figure P7.9 is built up by welding three $\frac{1}{2}$-in. by 4 in. steel bars together to form the I-section shown. (1) Determine the maximum tensile stress in the beam. (2) If the yield stress for the steel is $\sigma_e = 32{,}000$ psi, determine the factor of safety for the beam.

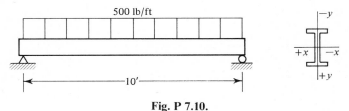

Fig. P 7.10.

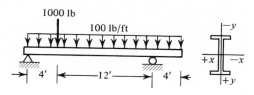

Fig. P 7.11.

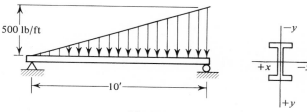

Fig. P 7.12.

7.10 Through 7.12. It is required that the beams shown in Figures P7.10 through P7.12 are to be standard I-beams made of rolled steel. Assuming that the maximum bending tensile and compressive stress σ_z must not exceed 20,000 psi, choose an I-beam cross section from the tables listed in Appendix B.

ans.   Problem 7.12.   3 in.—7.5 lb I-beam.

7.13 Through 7.23. The beams shown in Figures P7.13 through P7.23 have the cross section as described at the right end of each beam. Determine the magnitude and

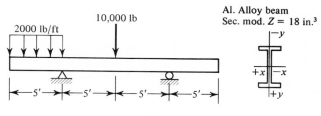

Fig. P 7.13.

location of the maximum tensile and compressive bending stress σ_z in each beam. Where the cross section is described as a combination of plates with I-beams or a channel and an I-beam, the properties of the channels and I-beams are given in tables in Appendix B.

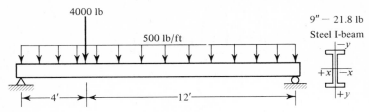

Fig. P 7.14.

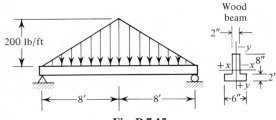

Fig. P 7.15.

ans.   Problem 7.15. $\sigma_{z(ten.)}$ = 1,130 psi (bottom of beam 8 ft from left end).

$\sigma_{z(comp.)} = -1,880$ psi (top of beam 8 ft from left end).

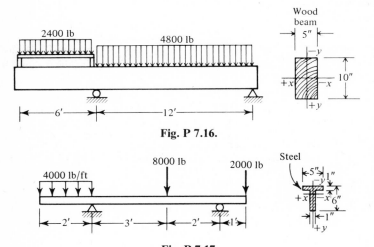

Fig. P 7.16.

Fig. P 7.17.

ans.   Problem 7.17. $\sigma_{z(ten.)}$ = 7,490 psi (bottom of beam 5 ft from left end).

$\sigma_{z(comp.)} = -11,500$ psi (bottom of beam 2 ft from left end).

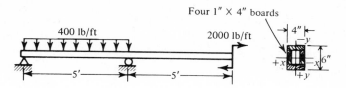

Fig. P 7.18.

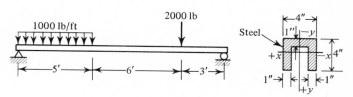

Fig. P 7.19.

ans.   Problem 7.19. $\sigma_{z(ten.)}$ = 19,700 psi (bottom of beam 4.54 ft from left end).

$\sigma_{z(comp.)}$ = $-14,500$ psi (top of beam 4.54 ft from left end).

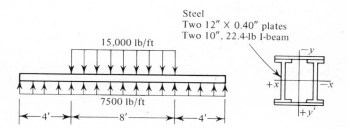

Fig. P 7.20.

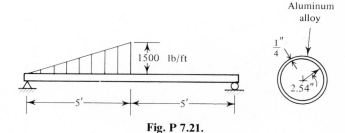

Fig. P 7.21.

ans.   Problem 7.21. $\sigma_{z(ten.)}$ = 15,300 psi (bottom of beam 4.08 ft from left end).

$\sigma_{z(comp.)}$ = $-15,300$ psi (top of beam 4.08 ft from left end).

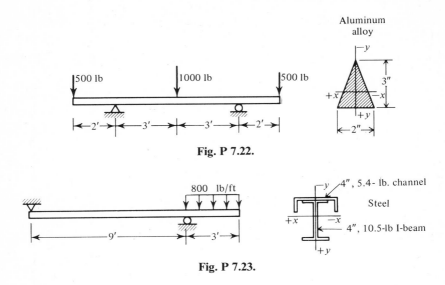

Fig. P 7.22.

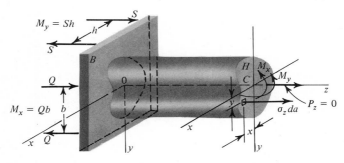

Fig. P 7.23.

7.5.   Bending Stresses in Beams of Arbitrary Cross Section

Let Figure 7.3 represent the segment BH of a beam that has a constant cross section of arbitrary shape, and let the external forces (loads) be the couples Qb, lying in a plane parallel to the yz-plane, and Sh, lying in a plane parallel to the xz-plane. Thus the external bending moments are Qb and Sh, each has a positive sense in Figure 7.3, and the beam is subjected to pure bending. The internal or resisting bending moments are M_x and M_y as shown on a cross section H in Figure 7.3. The general procedure given in Section 7.2 will be followed.

Fig. 7.3.   Straight member of constant cross section subjected to pure bending.

Step 1. The equations of equilibrium are applied to the loads acting on the free-body diagram of Figure 7.3 as follows:

$$\sum M_x = 0 \qquad\qquad M_x = Qb \qquad\qquad (7\text{-}18)$$

$$\sum M_y = 0 \qquad\qquad M_y = Sh \qquad\qquad (7\text{-}19)$$

$$\sum F_z = 0 \qquad Q - Q + S - S = P_z = 0 \qquad\qquad (7\text{-}20)$$

Step 2. A distribution of internal forces, which are now external on cross section H, in Figure 7.3 must be found whose resultant is equal to M_x and M_y. The intensity of these forces at any point (x, y) is the normal stress σ_z. Multiply this stress by the infinitesimal part da of the area surrounding the point (x, y). The force acts on the infinitesimal area da. A force such as $\sigma_z\, da$ will act on all such increments of area da of the total area A of the cross section H. Some of the $\sigma_z\, da$ forces will be tensile forces and some must be compressive forces, because Equation (7–20) shows that the resultant axial force P_z is zero.

The right-hand members of Equations (7–18) through (7–20) are expressed in terms of the force $\sigma_z\, da$ by using the principle that the resultant is equal to the sum of its components as follows:

$$M_x = \int y\sigma_z\, da, \qquad\qquad (7\text{-}21)$$

$$M_y = \int x\sigma_z\, da, \qquad\qquad (7\text{-}22)$$

$$0 = \int \sigma_z\, da. \qquad\qquad (7\text{-}23)$$

Step 2a. Step 2a requires that the geometry of deformation be investigated to determine the strain distribution in the beam. Physical arguments, which can be easily checked experimentally, can be used to prove that plane sections of the unloaded beam remain plane after pure bending loads are applied to the beam. Consider any two sections perpendicular to the bending axis of the beam (bending axis is parallel to the z-axis) at a distance Δz apart. Because plane sections remain plane, the total strain e_z of the longitudinal fibers of the beam between the two planes can be represented by a plane. Each fiber of the beam between the two planes has the same gage length Δz; therefore, the longitudinal strain $\epsilon_z = e_z/\Delta z$ of the longitudinal fibers can also be represented by a plane. Let the coordinates (x, y) locate the position in the cross section of the longitudinal fiber. The following equation in which a', b', and c' are constants represents the plane:

$$\epsilon_z = a'x + b'y + c'. \qquad\qquad (7\text{-}24)$$

The longitudinal z-axis is taken also as the axis for the longitudinal strain ϵ_z, the centroid C in cross section H is used as the origin of ϵ_z, and the plane represented by Equation (7–24) will intersect cross section H, because some strains are tensile and some are compressive.

Step 2b.   It is assumed that the stress-strain relation for the material is linearly elastic; that is, the third of Equations (4–6) is used. Because the values of $\sigma_x = \sigma_y = 0$, it follows that

$$\epsilon_z = \frac{\sigma_z}{E}. \qquad (7–25)$$

When the expression for ϵ_z from Equation (7–25) is substituted into Equation (7–24), the following relationship is obtained:

$$\sigma_z = ax + by + c \qquad (7–26)$$

where $Ea' = a$, $Eb' = b$, and $Ec' = c$.

Step 3.   The expression for σ_z, obtained from Step 2 and given by Equation (7–26), is substituted into Equations (7–21) through (7–23) which give the following results:

$$M_x = \int (axy + by^2 + cy)\, da = a \int xy\, da + b \int y^2\, da + c \int y\, da, \quad (7–27)$$

$$M_y = \int (ax^2 + bxy + cx)\, da = a \int x^2\, da + b \int xy\, da + c \int x\, da, \quad (7–28)$$

$$0 = \int (ax + by + c)\, da = a \int x\, da + b \int y\, da + c \int da \qquad (7–29)$$

The integrals in Equations (7–27) through (7–29) are as follows:

$$\int y^2\, da = I_x \qquad \int x^2\, da = I_y \qquad (7–30)$$

$$\int y\, da = Q_x \qquad \int x\, da = Q_y \qquad (7–31)$$

$$\int xy\, da = I_{xy} \qquad (7–32)$$

The integrals in Equations (7–30) and (7–32) are described in Appendix A.

The symbols I_x and I_y in Equation (7–30) represent the moment of inertia of the area of the cross section with respect to the x- and y-axes, respectively. The symbols Q_x and Q_y represent the first moment of the area of the cross section with respect to the x- and y-axes, respectively. Since the x- and y-axes have been chosen as centroidal axes, the values of $Q_x = Q_y = 0$. The symbol I_{xy} represents the product of inertia of the cross section with respect to the axes x and y.

The symbols given in Equations (7–30) through (7–32), except for Q_x and Q_y which are each equal to zero, are substituted into Equations (7–27) through (7–29) to give the following equations:

$$M_x = aI_{xy} + bI_x, \qquad (7–33)$$

$$M_y = aI_y + bI_{xy}, \qquad (7–34)$$

$$0 = cA. \qquad (7–35)$$

By solving Equations (7–33) through (7–35) for the constants a, b, and c, the following results are found:

$$a = \frac{M_y I_x - M_x I_{xy}}{I_x I_y - I_{xy}^2},$$
(7–36)

$$b = \frac{M_x I_y - M_y I_{xy}}{I_x I_y - I_{xy}^2},$$
(7–37)

$$c = 0 \text{ (because } A \neq 0).$$
(7–38)

The substitution of the values of the constants a, b, and c given by Equations (7–36) through (7–38) into Equation (7–26) gives the final result as

$$\sigma_z = \frac{M_y I_x - M_x I_{xy}}{I_x I_y - I_{xy}^2} x + \frac{M_x I_y - M_y I_{xy}}{I_x I_y - I_{xy}^2} y.$$
(7–39)

Neutral Axis.   As stated before, part of the area of the cross section is subjected to tensile stresses σ_z whereas another part is subjected to compressive stresses σ_z. The line in the cross section that divides these two parts of the area is called the neutral axis, for the stress $\sigma_z = 0$ at all points on this line. Thus, the location of the neutral axis is found by setting the right side of Equation (7–39) equal to zero, which gives the following equation:

$$y = \left(\frac{M_x I_{xy} - M_y I_x}{M_x I_y - M_y I_{xy}} \right) x.$$
(7–40)

Equation (7–40) is the equation of the neutral axis.

Note.   Equations (7–39) and (7–40) have been derived assuming that the beam is subjected to pure bending only. These equations are exact for pure bending. Most beams are subjected to transverse shear loads in addition to the bending loads as discussed in Section 6.2. Although plane sections do not remain plane (one of the conditions used in the derivation of Equations (7–39) and (7–40)) when the beam is subjected to transverse shear loads, Equations (7–39) and (7–40) are assumed to be valid for beams subjected to transverse loads. Both experimental data and more exact theories support this conclusion, particularly if the beam has a length of at least five times its depth. As indicated in Section 7.9, a cross section of the beam will have a shearing stress distribution in addition to the normal stress distribution given by Equation (7–39).

Illustrative Problems

7.24.   Let the cross section of the beam of Figure 7.3 be a right triangular shape whose dimensions are shown in Figure P7.24a in which the x-axis

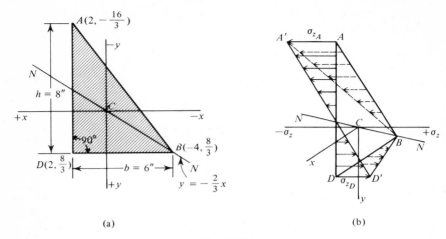

(a)   (b)

Fig. P 7.24.

and the y-axis intersect at the centroid C and are parallel to the legs of the right triangle. Let $M_x = +15{,}000$ lb-in. and $M_y = 0$. Determine the location of the neutral axis of the bending stresses and compute the maximum tensile and compressive bending stresses σ_z in the cross section.

SOLUTION.   The properties I_x and I_y are obtained by using $I_x = \frac{1}{36}bh^3$ and $I_y = \frac{1}{36}hb^3$ (as given in Problem A.3 in Appendix A), and I_{xy} is found from the equation $I_{xy} = -\frac{1}{72}b^2h^2$ (see Prob. A.15 in Appendix A). Thus

$$I_x = \tfrac{1}{36}6(8)^3 = 85.33 \text{ in.}^4, \qquad I_y = \tfrac{1}{36}8(6)^3 = 48 \text{ in.}^4$$

$$I_{xy} = -\tfrac{1}{72}(6)^2(8)^2 = -32 \text{ in.}^4$$

The substitution of these values along with $M_x = 15{,}000$ lb-in. and $M_y = 0$ into Equation (7–40) gives the following equation for the neutral axis:

$$y = \left(\frac{15{,}000(-32) - 0(85.33)}{15{,}000(48) - 0(-32)} \right) x.$$

Therefore

$$y = -\tfrac{2}{3}x \qquad\qquad\qquad\qquad\qquad (a)$$

is the equation of the N–N axis as shown in Figure P7.24a. Note that N–N passes through the vertex $B(-4, \frac{8}{3})$ at one end of the hypotenuse. If one of the bending moments M_x or M_y is zero (here it is $M_y = 0$), the neutral axis will pass through one end of the hypotenuse of the right triangle.

The substitution of the values of I_x, I_y, I_{xy}, M_x, and M_y into Equation (7–39) gives the following equation for the bending stress at any point (x, y) in the cross section:

$$\sigma_z = \left(\frac{0(85.33) - 15,000(-32)}{85.33(48) - (-32)^2}\right)x + \left(\frac{15,000(48) - 0(-32)}{85.33(48) - (-32)^2}\right)y$$

which reduces to

$$\sigma_z = 156.2x + 234.3y. \tag{b}$$

In Fig. P7.24b the triangular cross section is drawn in perspective as represented by the plane ABD. The abscissa σ_z to any point in the plane $A'BD'$ represents the stress σ_z as given by Equation (b) for any point in the cross section as described by its coordinates (x, y) in the cross-section plane ABD. Note that the intersection of plane $A'BD'$ with the cross section plane ABD is the neutral axis N–N.

Maximum Tensile and Compressive Bending Stresses. In Figure P7.24 note that the points A and D are located at the greatest distances on either side of the neutral axis N–N. The point D has coordinates $(2, +\frac{8}{3})$ and A, $(2, -\frac{16}{3})$. Therefore, with M_x positive, the bending stress is tensile at D and is compressive at A. These facts are confirmed by the substitution of the coordinates in Equation (b) as follows:
For point $D(2, \frac{8}{3})$:

$$\sigma_{zD} = 156.2(2) + 234.2(+\tfrac{8}{3}) = +937 \text{ psi (tension)}.$$

For point $A(2, -\frac{16}{3})$:

$$\sigma_{zA} = 156.2(2) + 234.3(-\tfrac{16}{3}) = -937 \text{ psi (compression)}.$$

7.25. Let the cross section of the beam of Figure 7.3 be a 5-in. by $3\frac{1}{4}$-in. by $\frac{5}{16}$-in. Z-bar as shown in Figure P7.25a. Let the bending moments $M_x = +13,400$ lb-in. and $M_y = +6,710$ lb-in. Determine the location of the neutral axis of the bending stresses σ_z by using Equation (7–40) and use Equation (7–39) to obtain the equation for the value of the stress σ_z at any point in the cross section. Determine the magnitude and location of the maximum compressive and the maximum tensile stresses σ_z.

SOLUTION. The properties with respect to the centroidal axes x and y of the area of the cross section of the Z-bar in Figure P7.25a are obtained in Illustrative Problem PA.19 in Appendix A. They are

$$I_x = 13.35 \text{ in.}^4, \quad I_y = 6.19 \text{ in.}^4, \quad \text{and} \quad I_{xy} = 7.00 \text{ in}^4.$$

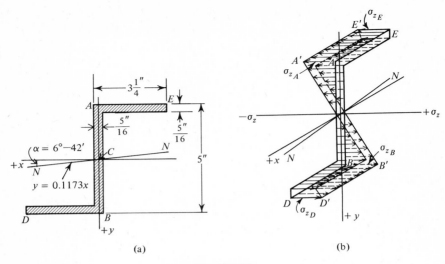

Fig. P 7.25.

The substitution of these values into Equation (7–40), along with the given values of M_x and M_y, gives

$$y = \left(\frac{13{,}400(7.00) - 6{,}710(13.35)}{13{,}400(6.19) - 6{,}710(7.00)}\right) x = \frac{4{,}221}{35{,}980} x,$$

which reduces to

$$y = 0.1173x. \tag{a}$$

Equation (a) represents the neutral axis N–N that makes the angle $\alpha = 6°\ 42'$ with the x-axis as shown in Fig. P7.25a.

The substitution of the values of I_x, I_y, I_{xy}, M_x, and M_y into Equation 7–39 gives the following result:

$$\sigma_z = \left(\frac{6{,}710(13.35) - 13{,}400(7.00)}{13.35(6.19) - \overline{7.00}^2}\right) x + \left(\frac{13{,}400(6.19) - 6{,}710(7.00)}{13.35(6.19) - \overline{7.00}^2}\right) y,$$

which reduces to

$$\sigma_z = \frac{-4{,}221}{33.64} x + \frac{35{,}980}{33.64} y,$$

and finally to

$$\sigma_z = -125.5x + 1070y. \tag{b}$$

In Figure P7.25b the Z-bar cross section is drawn in perspective as shown by the plane $DBAE$. At the centroid C of the Z-bar, the axis σ_z is taken perpendicular to the plane of the cross section and to the x- and y-axes. The location of any point in the area or on the boundary of the area of the cross section of the Z-bar is described by the coordinates (x, y). When the coordinates (x, y) of any such point are substituted into Equation (b), the value of the bending stress σ_z at that point is determined. Thus, the coordinates of the points D, B, A, and E were substituted into Equation (b) and the corresponding values of $\sigma_{z_D} = 2{,}287$ psi, $\sigma_{z_B} = 2{,}695$ psi, $\sigma_{z_A} = -2{,}695$ psi, and $\sigma_{z_E} = -2{,}287$ psi were obtained. The coordinates of the points D', B', A' and E' in Figure P7.25b are as follows:

$D'(\frac{99}{32}, 2.5, 2{,}287)$, $B'(-\frac{5}{32}, 2.5, 2{,}695)$, $A'(\frac{5}{32}, -2.5, -2{,}695)$,

and $E'(-\frac{99}{32}, -2.5, -2{,}287)$

The points D', B', A', E' lie in a plane that contains the neutral axis N–N and the centroid C of the Z-bar cross section.

From Figure P7.25a it is observed that the points A and B in the cross section are at the greatest distances from the neutral axis N–N. In Figure P7.25b the abscissas, σ_z to the plane $D'B'A'E'$ show that the stress σ_z increases in direct proportion to the distance from the neutral axis N–N. Thus the maximum tensile bending stress is $\sigma_{z_B} = 2{,}695$ psi and the maximum compressive bending stress is $\sigma_{z_A} = 2{,}695$ psi, as obtained before.

Problems

7.26. Let the beam of Figure 7.3 be a steel angle cross section whose dimensions are given in Figure P7.26. Let $M_x = -50{,}000$ lb-in. and $M_y = 20{,}000$ lb-in. and

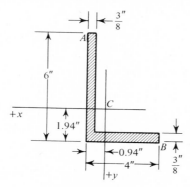

Fig. P 7.26.

determine the location of the neutral axis and the magnitude and location of the maximum values of the tensile and compressive bending stress σ_z. (*Hint*: See Problem PA.23 in Appendix A for properties I_x, I_y, and I_{xy} for cross section.)

ans. $y = 0.210x$ is equation of neutral axis.

$\sigma_{z_A} = 14{,}750$ psi tension; $\sigma_{z_B} = -8{,}900$ psi compression.

7.27.   Let the beam of Figure 7.3 be a wood beam that has the cross section *ABDE* with dimensions as shown in Figure P7.27. Let the beam be loaded by a bending

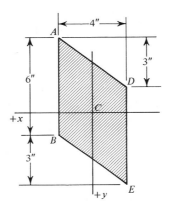

Fig. P 7.27.

moment $M = 15{,}000$ lb-in. that lies in the longitudinal plane of the beam through the points *A* and *E*. Let the sense of the bending moment be such that it tends to produce compressive σ_z stress at *E* and tensile σ_z stress at *A*. Determine the location of the neutral axis and the magnitude and location of the maximum values of the tensile and compressive bending stresses σ_z.

ans. $I_x = 90$ in.^{4}, $I_y = 32$ in.^{4}, $I_{xy} = -24$ in.^{4}

$y = 0.249x$ is equation of neutral axis.

$\sigma_{z_A} = 962$ psi tension, $\sigma_{z_E} = -962$ psi compression.

7.6.   Bending Stresses in Beams Referred to Principal Axes

In Sections A.7 and A.8 in Appendix A it is shown that for any cross-sectional area of a beam there is one set of axes x, y through the centroid for which $I_{xy} = 0$. These axes are called the principal axes, because I_x and I_y

with respect to these axes are the maximum and minimum values of moments of inertia of the area.

Let the x, y-axes be chosen so that they are principal axes, that is, $I_{xy} = 0$. When this value of $I_{xy} = 0$ is substituted into Equation (7–39) the result is as follows:

$$\sigma_z = \frac{M_y x}{I_y} + \frac{M_x y}{I_x} \tag{7-41}$$

and, by setting $\sigma_z = 0$ in Equation (7–41), the neutral axis is represented by

$$y = -\frac{M_y I_x}{M_x I_y} x. \tag{7-42}$$

Equations (7–41) and (7–42) are somewhat simpler to use than Equations (7–39) and (7–40). Therefore, in problems where it is easy to select principal axes in the beam cross section there is much advantage in doing so.

Axes of Symmetry. In Section A.8 of Appendix A it is shown that when a cross section has an axis of symmetry it is a principal axis, and the axis perpendicular to it is the other principal axis.

Let Figure 7.4 represent a beam with an axis of symmetry, yy. Equations (7–41) and (7–42) can be used for solving for the bending stresses σ_z in the beam. The procedure is shown in the following illustrative problems.

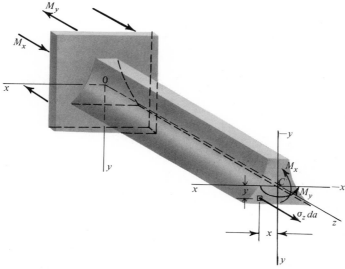

Fig. 7.4. Straight member of constant cross section with one plane of symmetry and subjected to pure bending.

Illustrative Problems

7.28. A wood beam of rectangular cross section $b = 6$ in. by $h = 10$ in. is loaded as a simply supported beam in a roof structure as shown by AB in Figure P7.28a. The simple supports are a distance $\ell = 15$-ft apart. The vertical load $w = 145$ lb/ft is distributed uniformly over the entire length of the beam and makes an angle of 26° with the yy axis of symmetry as shown in Fig. P7.28b. Determine the location and magnitude of the maximum tensile and compressive bending stresses σ_z in the beam.

SOLUTION. From the dimensions in Figure P7.28b $I_x = \frac{1}{12}6(10)^3 = 500$ in.^{4}, $I_y = \frac{1}{12}10(6)^3 = 180$ in.^{4}, and $I_{xy} = 0$ because the x- and y-axes are axes of symmetry. The transverse shear diagrams and the bending moment diagrams (Sections 6.4 and 6.6) in planes yz and xz are shown in Figures P7.28c and d, respectively. From Figure P7.28c and d the maximum bending moments M_y and M_x are as follows:

$$M_y = \frac{w \sin 26° \ell^2(12)}{8} = 21,500 \text{ lb-in.}$$

$$M_x = \frac{w \cos 26° \ell^2(12)}{8} = 44,000 \text{ lb-in.}$$

The neutral axis is obtained from Equation (7–42) by the substitution of these bending moments, along with $I_x = 500$ in.^{4} and $I_y = 180$ in.^{4}, and is given by the following equation:

$$y = -\frac{21,500(500)}{44,000(180)}x = -1.36x. \tag{a}$$

The straight line represented by N–N in Figure P7.28b is a plot of Equation (a) and is the neutral axis of bending. Hence, the bending stress σ_z varies directly as the distance from the N-N axis. The points $D(3, 5)$ and $E(-3, -5)$ are the two points most distant from the N-N axis. Hence, the coordinates of D and E are substituted into Equation (7–41), which is as follows, with the values of M_x, M_y, I_x, and I_y substituted:

$$\sigma_z = \frac{21,500}{180}x + \frac{44,000}{500}y = 119x + 88y, \tag{b}$$

Bending stress at D(3, 5):

$$\sigma_{z_D} = 119(3) + 88(5) = 797 \text{ psi (tension)}.$$

Bending stress at E(−3, −5):

$$\sigma_{z_E} = 119(-3) + 88(-5) = -797 \text{ psi compression}.$$

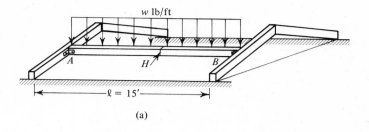

(a)

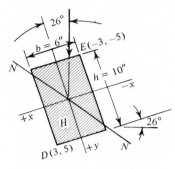

(b) Section H at $z = \dfrac{\ell}{2}$

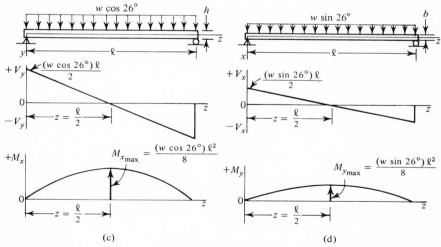

(c)   (d)

Fig. P 7.28.

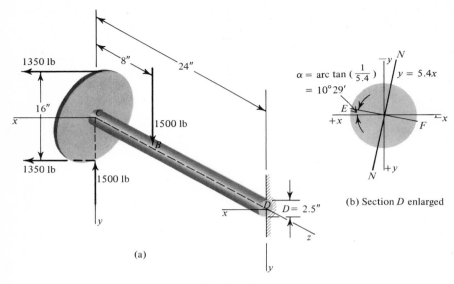

Fig. P 7.29.

7.29. In Figure P7.29a the circular cross section of the beam CBD has a constant diameter $D = 2.5$ in. The beam is made of a high-strength steel with an elastic limit greater than 90,000 psi. Disregarding the effect of the stress concentration factor caused by the fixture at the end D on the magnitude of the bending stresses, determine the magnitude and location of the maximum tensile and compressive bending stresses at the fixed end D.

SOLUTION. The bending moment M_y at the fixed end D is $M_y = -2{,}700 \times 24 = -64{,}800$ lb-in., whereas the bending moment M_x at D is $M_x = 1{,}500 \times 8 = 12{,}000$ lb-in. The properties of the cross sectional area are

$$I_x = I_y = \frac{\pi D^4}{64} = \frac{\pi R^4}{4} = \frac{\pi(1.25)^4}{4} = 1.917 \text{ in}^4, \quad \text{and} \quad I_{xy} = 0.$$

Use Equations (7–41) and (7–42) for this problem. First, substitute the appropriate quantities I_x, I_y, M_x, and M_y into Equation (7–42), which gives

$$y = -\frac{(-64{,}800)}{(12{,}000)}\frac{(1.917)}{(1.917)}x$$

or

$$y = +5.4x. \tag{a}$$

Equation (a) represents the neutral axis N-N as shown in Figure P7.29b.

We now refer to Equation (7–41) and substitute these same values of I_x, I_y, M_x, and M_y into it which gives the equation for the bending stress at every point in the cross section:

$$\sigma_z = \frac{-64{,}800}{1.917}x + \frac{12{,}000}{1.917}y = -33{,}800x + 6{,}260y. \tag{b}$$

The bending stress σ_z is directly proportioned to the distance from the neutral axis N-N. The most distant points from the axis N-N are E and F at the ends of a diameter that is perpendicular to the neutral axis N-N. The coordinates of E and F are found from the angle $\alpha = \arctan \frac{1}{5.4}$ as shown in Figure P7.29b. Thus for point E

$$x_E = R \cos \alpha = 1.25 \cos 10° 29' = 1.229,$$

$$y_E = -R \sin \alpha = -1.25 \sin 10° 29' = -0.2274.$$

For the point F

$$x_F = -R \cos \alpha = -1.25 \cos 10° 29' = -1.229,$$

$$y_F = R \sin \alpha = 1.25 \sin 10° 29' = 0.2274.$$

Bending stress at E: From Equation (b)

$$\sigma_{z_E} = -33{,}800(x_E) + 6260(y_E) = -33{,}800(1.229) + 6{,}260(-0.2274),$$

$$= -43{,}000 \text{ psi, compression.}$$

Bending stress at F: From Equation (b),

$$\sigma_{z_F} = -33{,}800(x_F) + 6260(y_F) = -33{,}800(-1.229) + 6{,}260(0.2274),$$

$$= +43{,}000 \text{ psi, tension.}$$

Problems

7.30. A circular cylindrical bar of high-strength steel of constant diameter of $D = 2.5$ in. is used as a simply supported beam of length $\ell = 9$ ft between supports. The beam is subjected to two equal concentrated transverse loads $P_x = P_y = 2{,}000$ lb that are applied at the third points of the length $\ell = 9$ ft, as shown in Figure P7.30. Determine the magnitude and location of the maximum tensile and compressive bending stresses σ_z in the beam.

ans. $\sigma_z = 34{,}900$ psi in tension and compression.

Location: Under either load.

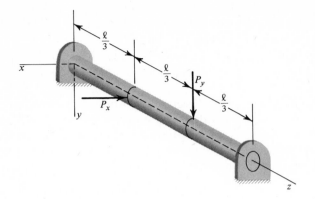

Fig. P 7.30.

7.31.   A wood beam of rectangular cross section 8-in. by 4-in. as shown in Figure P7.31 has a length $\ell = 10$ ft and is simply supported at the ends. The beam is loaded transversely in the principal plane yz by a concentrated load $P_y = 1,000$ lb at $z = \ell/4$

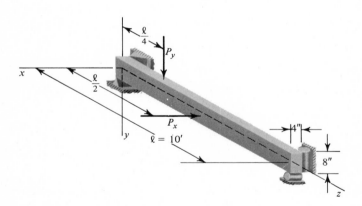

Fig. P 7.31.

and in the principal plane xz at $z = \ell/2$ by a conceatrated load $P_x = 500$ lb. Determine the magnitude and location of the maximum tensile and compressive bending stresses σ_z in the beam.

ans. $\sigma_z = 1,055$ psi in tension and compression at $z = \ell/4$.

7.7. Bending Stresses in Beams Loaded in One Principal Plane Only

In Section 7.6 it has already been stated that sometimes there is much advantage in selecting the principal planes of the beam for location of reference axes x and y. In most cases where straight bars are to be used as beams it is also possible to have all the transverse loads lie in one plane, which is called the *plane of the loads*. As will be seen later in this section, there is also much advantage to be gained in efficient use of the material in the beam by placing the plane of the loads in a principal plane of the beam.

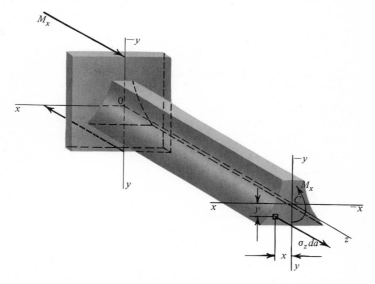

Fig. 7.5.   Straight member of constant cross section subjected to pure bending with plane of loads coinciding with plane of symmetry.

Let Figure 7.5 represent a beam that has a cross section with one plane of symmetry, namely, the plane containing the yy-axis. Thus, the x- and y-axes are principal axes, as discussed in Section A.8 in Appendix A. The beam of Figure 7.5 is subjected to a bending moment M_x, which lies in the principal plane containing the y-axis. The external bending moment is resisted by the bending moment M_x.

The properties of the cross section at the section are I_x, I_y, $I_{xy} = 0$. The resisting bending moment $M_y = 0$. Substitute these quantities in Equation (7–39), which reduces to the following equation for the longitudinal bending stress σ_z:

$$\sigma_z = \frac{M_x y}{I_x}. \tag{7-43}$$

The neutral axis is obtained by the substitution of the same quantities into Equation (7–40), which is reduced to

$$y = 0, \tag{7-44}$$

which is the equation of the x-axis. Equation (7–43) is called the flexure formula.

If you omitted Sections 7.3 and 7.4 of this chapter you should now return to Section 7.4 where further consideration is given to the flexure formula for symmetrical bending.

7.8. Elastic-Stress Concentration in a Beam

If a beam has an abrupt change in cross section such as a fillet or a groove (Fig. 7.6) the section at the abrupt change in area does not remain plane when the loads are applied; hence the bending- (normal-) stress distribution

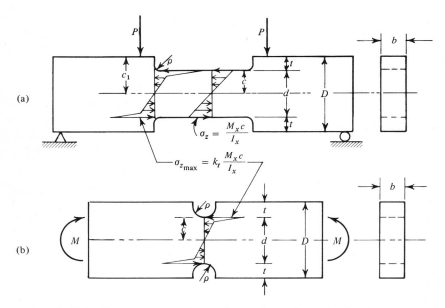

Fig. 7.6. Stress concentration at abrupt change in section in a beam.

at the section is not linear. The elastic-strain and hence the elastic-stress distribution is represented in Figure 7.6a and b, in which the maximum bending stress is given by the expression

$$\sigma_{z_{max}} = k_t \frac{M_x c}{I_x},$$ (7–45)

where k_t is the elastic (theoretical or ideal) stress concentration factor (for a similar expression for axial loads, see Section 1.7; for torsion loads see Section 9.2).

Values for k_t in Equation (7–45), as found by the photoelastic (polarized-light) method, are given in Table 7.1 for a beam with a fillet (Fig. 7.6a). [For values of k_t for other abrupt changes in section (such as the groove in Fig. 7.6b) see *Advanced Mechanics of Materials*, Seely and Smith, John Wiley and Sons.]

Table 7.1
Values of Stress-Concentration Factor k_t for Beam with Fillet
(Fig. 7.6a)

VALUES OF ρ/d	VALUES OF t/ρ					
	0.25	0.5	1.0	2.0	4	8
0.5	1.15	1.20	1.22	1.22	1.22	1.22
0.2	1.27	1.37	1.46	1.50	1.52	1.55
0.1	1.32	1.50	1.67	1.72	1.75	1.89
0.05	1.35	1.62	1.90	2.05	2.23	2.30

The maximum bending (normal) stress as given by Equation (7–45) is the significant stress in the beam under certain conditions as, for example, when the material is brittle or when the loads are applied and released repeatedly for many times (see Section 1.8 for discussion of repeated loads). However, when the material is ductile and when the loads are not repeated many times, the effects of the stress concentration are usually disregarded and the stress is computed by the ordinary flexure formula ($k_t = 1$ in Eq. 7–45). This fact is discussed in Section 4.5.

Illustrative Problem

7.32. A cantilever beam is made of a ductile steel, has a rectangular cross section, and has fillets as shown in Figure P7.32. The beam is subjected

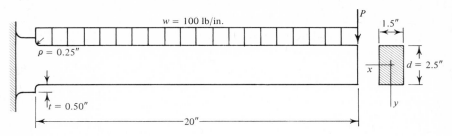

Fig. P 7.32.

to a distributed load $w = 100$ lb/in., which remains constant (dead load), and to a concentrated load P at the free end, which is cycled between 0 and P_{max}. The material properties for the steel are $\sigma_e = 45{,}000$ psi, $\sigma_u = 86{,}000$ psi, and $\sigma_f = 32{,}000$ psi for 1,000,000 completely reversed cycles of stress. (1) Assuming that failure of the beam will be a fatigue failure, determine the magnitude of the working value of P_{max} that can safely be cycled 1,000,000 times based on a factor of safety $N = 2.00$ for both w and P_{max}. Assume that $k_f = k_t$. Also determine σ_{max} and σ_{min}. (2) Assuming that failure of the beam will be due to general yielding, determine the magnitude of the working value of P_{max} based on a factor of safety of $N = 2.00$.

SOLUTION. *Part (1)* Using the dimensions of the beam in Figure P7.32,

$$\frac{\rho}{d} = \frac{0.25}{2.5} = 0.10,$$

$$\frac{t}{\rho} = \frac{0.50}{0.25} = 2.00.$$

For these values of ρ/d and t/ρ, Table 7.1 gives

$$k_t = k_f = 1.72.$$

The moment of inertia of the area of the cross section is

$$I_x = \frac{bh^3}{12} = \frac{1.5(2.5)^3}{12} = 1.953 \text{ in}^4.$$

The nominal value of the minimum normal stress σ_{min-n} in the beam is obtained by using the maximum bending moment, M_x produced by the distributed load w, as follows:

$$\sigma_{min-n} = \frac{M_x c}{I_x} = N\left(\frac{-w\ell^2}{2}\right)\left(\frac{-d}{2I_x}\right) = \frac{2.00(-100)(20)(20)(-2.5)}{4(1.953)} = 25{,}600 \text{ psi.}$$

The magnitude of the nominal value of the maximum normal stress σ_{max-n} can be determined once r is determined because $\sigma_{max-n} = \sigma_{min-n}/r$. Substituting this value for σ_{max-n} and values for σ_f, σ_u, and k_f in Equation (1-22) gives the following equation from which the range of stress ratio r can be determined:

$$\frac{25,600}{r} = \frac{2(32,000)/1.72}{1 - r + [32,000/1.72(86,000)](1 + r)},$$

$$r = 0.544.$$

The magnitude of σ_{max-n} is given by the relation

$$\sigma_{max-n} = \frac{\sigma_{min-n}}{r} = \frac{25,600}{0.544} = 47,100 \text{ psi.}$$

The magnitude of P_{max} to produce fracture in 1,000,000 cycles of load is obtained by using the foregoing value of σ_{max-n} and is given by the relation

$$M_{x(max)} = -P_{max}\ell + \frac{-Nw\ell^2}{2} = \frac{\sigma_{max-n}I_x}{c} = \frac{47,100(1.953)}{-1.25} = -73,600 \text{ lb-in.,}$$

$$P_{max} = \frac{73,600}{20} - \frac{2.00(100)(20)}{2} = 3,680 - 2,000 = 1,680 \text{ lb.}$$

Let P_w be the working value of P_{max}:

$$P_w = \frac{P_{max}}{N} = \frac{1,680}{2.00} = 840 \text{ lb.}$$

The magnitudes of σ_{max} and σ_{min} are given by Equations (1-23) and (1-24):

$$\sigma_{max} = \frac{k_f + 1}{2}\sigma_{max-n} - \frac{k_f - 1}{2}\sigma_{min-n}$$

$$= \frac{1.72 + 1}{2}(47,100) - \frac{1.72 - 1}{2}(25,600) = 54,800 \text{ psi,}$$

$$\sigma_{min} = -\frac{k_f - 1}{2}\sigma_{max-n} + \frac{k_f + 1}{2}\sigma_{min-n}$$

$$= -0.36(47,100) + 1.36(25,600) = 17,900 \text{ psi.}$$

PART (2). As discussed in Section 4.5, stress concentrations are neglected when considering failure by general yielding. The magnitude of P_{max} to produce general yielding in the beam is given by the relation

$$M_{x(max)} = -P_{max}\ell - \frac{Nw\ell^2}{2} = \frac{\sigma_e I_x}{c} = \frac{45,000(1.953)}{-1.25} = -70,300 \text{ lb-in.},$$

$$P_{max} = \frac{70,300}{20} - \frac{2.00(100)(20)}{2} = 3,515 - 2,000 = 1,515 \text{ lb.}$$

Let P_w be the working value of P_{max}:

$$P_w = \frac{P_{max}}{N} = \frac{1,515}{2.00} = 757.5 \text{ lb.}$$

Note from the solutions of Parts (1) and (2) that failure of the beam is by general yielding rather than by fatigue fracture and that $P_w = 757.5$ lb.

Problems

In the problems that follow it is assumed that the strength reduction factor k_f is equal to the theoretical stress concentration factor k_t.

7.33. Let the beam in Problem 7.32 be subjected to the concentrated load P only at the free end which is cycled between 0 and P_{max}. Determine the magnitude of P_w that can safely be cycled 1,000,000 times based on a factor of safety of $N = 2.50$.

7.34. Let the beam in Problem 7.32 be subjected to a distributed load $w = 30$ lb/in. which remains constant and to a concentrated load P at the free end, which is cycled between 0 and P_{max}. Determine the magnitude of P_w that can safely be cycled 1,000,000 times based on a factor of safety of $N = 2.00$ for both w and P_{max}. Does the beam fail by fatigue or general yielding?

ans. $P_w = 1,090$ lb; the beam fails by fatigue.

7.35. The beam in Problem 7.32 is made of a brittle material for which $\sigma_u = 28,000$ psi. The beam has a rectangular cross section. The dimensions of the beam are as follows: $\ell = 10$ in., width $= 1.25$ in., $d = 1.25$ in., $t = 0.25$ in., $\rho = 0.25$ in. The beam is subjected to a distributed load $w = 10$ lb/in. and to a concentrated load P at the free end; both loads are static loads. Determine the magnitude of P if the beam is designed using a factor of safety of $N = 4.00$ for both w and P.

ans. $P = 106$ lb.

7.36. The dimensions of the beam in Figure 7.6a are as follows: $b = 2$ in., $D = 4.2$ in., $d = 3$ in., $\rho = 0.60$ in. The beam has a length of 60 in. and the two loads P are located 20 in. from the left and right supports, respectively. The loads P are cycled between 0 and P_{max}. The beam is made of 2024-T4 aluminum alloy, which has the following material properties: $\sigma_e = 46,000$ psi, $\sigma_u = 66,000$ psi, and $\sigma_f = 28,000$ psi for 1,000,000 completely reversed cycles of stress. Determine the working value of P_{max} that can safely be cycled 1,000,000 times based on a factor of safety of $N = 2.50$.

7.37. Solve Problem 7.36 if the loads P are cycled between 1,000 lb and P_{max}. Does the beam fail by fatigue or general yielding?

7.9. Significance of the Shearing Stresses in Beams

In Section 7.4 it was shown that for elastic behavior of a beam the tensile (or compressive) stress σ_z in the outer fibers at a transverse cross section of a beam is given by the expression $\sigma_z = M_x c/I_x$ as indicated at Section AB in Figure 7.7a and c. An elastic shearing stress also occurs at the same point on any diagonal plane passing through the point; the maximum value $\tau_{max} = \frac{1}{2}\sigma_z$ (see Section 4.6, Eq. 4–13).

Even though τ_{max} is only one half the value of σ_z, it may be the cause of failure of beams that are made of a material that is relatively weak in shear. In Section 4.6 general yielding failure of members subjected to static loads and made of ductile materials is predicted using either τ_{max} or the maximum value $\tau_{G_{max}}$ of the octahedral shearing stress.

At a section of a beam that is subjected to vertical shear in addition to bending, as at section CD in Figure 7.7a and b, there are also shearing stresses $\tau_{zy} = \tau_{yz}$ in the transverse (vertical) and longitudinal (horizontal) planes, respectively, at the point. Furthermore, as indicated in Figure 7.7d, these shearing stresses are zero at the outer fibers ($\gamma_{zy} = 0$) and have their maximum values at the neutral axis where the shearing strain γ_{zy} is a maximum; this statement will be proved in the next section. The fact that $\tau_{zy} = \tau_{yz}$ at any point follows from Section 2.2.

The Problem Defined. The problem now to be considered is to express the elastic shearing stress $\tau_{zy} = \tau_{yz}$ at any point in the beam in terms of the external forces acting on the beam and the dimensions of the cross section of the beam. The shearing stress is of special importance in timber beams (see Fig. P7.41), in concrete beams, and in certain built-up metal beams used in airplane structures, bridges, and so forth. Physical evidence that vertical and horizontal shearing stresses are present in a beam (except for pure bending) is obtained from a study of the behavior of a beam composed of two parts (Fig. P7.45). If the two parts act as a unit (as a single beam) as in Figure P7.45b, shearing stresses must exist between the two parts.

If the method outlined in Section 4.3 were used in solving the foregoing problem, the procedure would be as follows in obtaining an expression for τ_{zy}: the transverse shear V_y for the section CD in Figure 7.7b is $V_y = R_1 = P$. Now if V_y can be expressed in terms of τ_{zy} at any point on the section CD, and

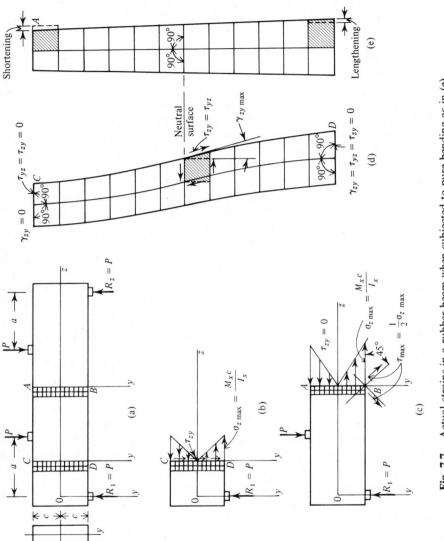

Fig. 7.7. Actual strains in a rubber beam when subjected to pure bending as in (e), and when subjected to ordinary bending as in (d).

the dimensions of the area, our problem will be solved; this step, of course, requires that the shearing-stress distribution be known. In order to determine the shearing stress distribution, the shearing-strain distribution must first be found. Unfortunately the distribution of shearing strains over the area is unknown and is difficult to determine quantitatively by an experimental method; this is in marked contrast to the satisfactory method of determining the strains normal to the area. Therefore, the method outlined in Section 4.3 and used for determining the expression $\sigma_z = M_x y / I_x$ will not be used in obtaining the expression for $\tau_{zy} = \tau_{yz}$ in terms of the loads acting on the beam.

It is possible and desirable, however, to qualitatively determine the distribution of elastic shearing strains (and elastic shearing stresses τ_{zy}) as indicated in Figure 7.7d. The beam in Figure 7.7a was made of rubber, which permitted strains to be produced that were sufficiently large to be observed with the naked eye. Before the beam was loaded, squares $\frac{1}{2}$ in. on a side were ruled on the vertical face of the beam, and after the loads were applied, these squares were deformed as shown in Figure 7.7d and e.

Observe that in the central portion of the beam (AB) where pure bending occurs, and hence where no transverse shear exists, the tensile and compressive (longitudinal) strains of the fibers vary directly with the distances of the fibers from the neutral surface, as shown in Figure 7.7e. However, at a section, such as CD, for which transverse shear exists in addition to some bending, plane sections do not remain plane, and the deformations of the squares in Figure 7.7d show that shearing deformation, and therefore the shearing stresses $\tau_{zy} = \tau_{yz}$ occur, in addition to normal (tensile and compressive) strains.

The shearing strains γ_{zy} increase in value from zero at the outer fibers to a maximum at the neutral axis, but it is difficult to quantitatively determine the law of variation, and furthermore the law of variation depends on the shape of the cross section. Because, for elastic behavior of the beam, the elastic shearing stresses are proportional to the elastic shearing strains, it follows that the values of the shearing stresses $\tau_{zy} = \tau_{yz}$ are equal to zero at the outer fibers, and their maximum values occur at the neutral axis. A quantitative expression for $\tau_{zy} = \tau_{yz}$ will now be obtained by use of the equation $V_y = dM_x / dz$ (see Section 6.6).

7.10. Relation Between Loads and Transverse and Longitudinal Shearing Stress

Consider the beam in Figure 7.8a. Let a block B having a small length dz (Fig. 7.8b) be removed from the beam. The forces that the block exerted

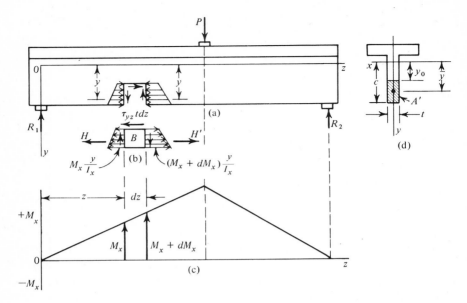

Fig. 7.8.   Method of determining expression for longitudinal shearing stress in beam.

on the beam are shown. These forces must have been exerted, of course, on the faces that were in contact with the beam. As shown in Section 7.3, the compressive (or tensile) stress at any point on any cross section of the beam varies directly as the distance of the point from the neutral axis, being zero at the neutral axis. Thus, the block B must have pulled longitudinally on its two end faces, and in addition exerted transverse shearing forces on the beam, downward at its left end and upward at its right end. Figure 7.8b is a free-body diagram of B. The equilibrium of block B will be used to determine τ_{yz}.

Because the bending moments at the two sections are not equal as shown in Figure 7.8c, the tensile forces H and H' on the two faces of the block (Fig. 7.8b) are not equal, and hence there must be shearing forces on the top face of the block and also on the left and right faces of the block. A free-body diagram (Fig. 7.8b) of the block B shows that these forces constitute two couples of equal magnitude and opposite sense that hold the block in equilibrium.

If H' and H represent the total force on the right and left faces, respectively, the total shearing force on the top face is equal to $H'-H$ (Fig. 7.8b). Furthermore, because the area $t\,dz$ on which the shearing stress occurs is small, the shearing stress τ_{yz} may be assumed to be constant over the area of the top face of B and hence the total shearing force is $\tau_{yz} t\, dz$. Therefore,

$$\tau_{yz} t\, dz = H' - H. \tag{7–46}$$

But

$$H' = \int_{y_0}^{c} (M_x + dM_x) \frac{y}{I_x}\, da,$$

and similarly

$$H = \int_{y_0}^{c} \frac{M_x\, y\, da}{I_x}.$$

Thus, the substitution of these two expressions for H' and H into Equation (7–46) gives

$$\tau_{yz} t\, dz = \frac{dM_x}{I_x} \int_{y_0}^{c} y\, da.$$

Therefore,

$$\tau_{yz} = \frac{dM_x}{dz} \cdot \frac{1}{I_x t} \int_{y_0}^{c} y\, da,$$

and, from Equation (6–30b), $dM_x/dz = V_y$. Therefore,

$$\tau_{yz} = \frac{V_y}{I_x t} \int_{y_0}^{c} y\, da, \tag{7–47}$$

in which τ_{yz} is the longitudinal shearing stress (and also the transverse shearing stress τ_{zy}) in a cross section for which the transverse shear is V_y, and at a point whose distance from the neutral axis is y_0; the thickness of the beam at the distance y_0 from the neutral axis is t, and I_x is the moment of inertia of the whole cross section of the beam about the neutral axis. The expression $\int_{y_0}^{c} y\, da$ is the first moment (often called the statical moment) about the neutral axis of that part of the cross-sectional area of the beam between the plane on which the longitudinal shearing stress τ_{yz} occurs and the outer face of the beam (i.e., between y_0 and c). This area is the cross-hatched area A' in the end view in Figure 7.6d. Furthermore, if the distance $\bar{y}$ of the centroid of the area A' from the neutral axis is known, the moment of this area may be found from the product $A'\bar{y}$ because $\int_{y_0}^{c} y\, da = A'\bar{y}$. Hence, the foregoing equation may be written

$$\tau_{yz} = \frac{V_y}{I_x t} \cdot A'\bar{y} = \frac{V_y Q}{I_x t}, \tag{7–48}$$

in which $Q = \int_{y_0}^{c} y\,da = A'\bar{y}$ and, as already noted, is called the statical moment about the neutral axis of that portion of the whole area between $y = y_0$ and $y = c$.

Equation (7–48) is valid only when the flexure formula is valid because the flexure formula was used in the derivation of Equation (7–48).

Maximum Value of $\tau_{zy} = \tau_{yz}$.   It is important, next, to locate the point in a beam at which the shearing stress $\tau_{zy} = \tau_{yz}$ is a maximum. If the beam has a constant cross section, with constant width, I_x and t are constant, and hence the maximum value of $\tau_{zy} = \tau_{yz}$ in Equations (7–47) and (7–48) will occur in the section of the beam for which V_y is maximum; for a simple beam subjected to a uniform load, V_y is maximum close to one support. Furthermore, in any section of constant thickness, $\tau_{zy} = \tau_{yz}$ will be a maximum when $\int_{y_0}^{c} y\,da$ or $A'\bar{y}$ is maximum, which occurs when y_0 is zero; that is, $\tau_{zy} = \tau_{yz}$ is maximum at the neutral surface. Thus, in a simple beam of rectangular cross section subjected to a uniformly distributed load, the longitudinal and transverse shearing stresses vary throughout the beam as shown in Figure 7.9.

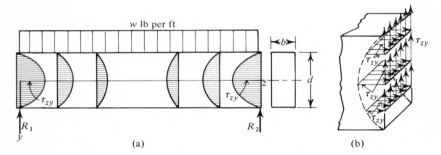

Fig. 7.9.   Variation of shearing stress in beam.

Thus, the maximum value of the longitudinal and transverse shearing stresses in any section of a beam having a rectangular cross section bd (Fig. 7.9) is

$$\tau_{zy} = \tau_{yz} = \frac{V_y}{I_x t}A'\bar{y} = \frac{V_y}{\frac{1}{12}bd^3 \cdot b}b\frac{d}{2}\frac{d}{4} = \frac{3V_y}{2bd} = \frac{3V_y}{2A}, \qquad (7\text{–}49)$$

in which A is the area of the whole cross section. Hence, the maximum value of $\tau_{zy} = \tau_{yz}$ in any section of a rectangular beam is 50 per cent greater than the average transverse shearing stress in the section. If a beam has a circular cross section, the maximum value is $33\frac{1}{3}$ per cent greater than V_y/A; that is, $\frac{4}{3}V_y/A$. If the beam is a thin circular tube the maximum value is $2V_y/A$.

7.11. Transverse and Longitudinal Shear in Flanged-Type Beams

In a beam having relatively thin flanges such as channel and I-sections and certain shapes used in airplane construction, it is frequently assumed that the flanges offer no resistance to the transverse shear V_y; all the resistance to transverse shear is assumed to be offered by the web of the I-section, and so forth. Furthermore, the transverse shearing stress on the area of the web is considered to be constant, the web being regarded as extending the entire depth of the beam. The justification for the foregoing simplifying assumption about an I-section may be found in a study of Figure 7.10.

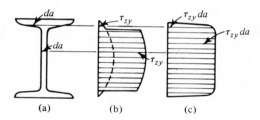

Fig. 7.10. Variation of shearing stress on cross section of I beam.

In any section of an I-beam, τ_{zy}, according to Equation (7–48), will be large where t is small, and small where t is large, the effect on τ_{zy} of the term Q being relatively small in the case of an I-section. Furthermore, τ_{zy} will change abruptly where t changes abruptly. Hence, the longitudinal (and transverse) shearing stress at a section in an I-beam varies approximately as shown in Figure 7.10b, and the shearing force $\tau_{zy}\,da$ on the elementary strips of the section is approximately constant per unit of depth for the whole depth of the section as shown in Figure 7.10c.

7.12. Lateral Shear in Flanges of Channel or I-Section

Let Figure 7.11a represent a rolled channel used as a horizontal canti-lever beam subjected to a vertical concentrated load at its free end. Let a small block B (Fig. 7.11b) be removed from the upper flange of the beam between sections DE and FG. The forces that hold the block B in equilibrium are shown in Figure 7.11c. These forces represent two couples equal in magnitude but opposite in sense lying in the longitudinal central plane of the flange. This fact shows that the longitudinal shearing stress τ_{xz} is equal to a

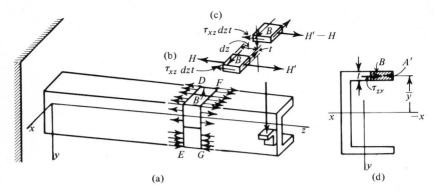

Fig. 7.11. Lateral shearing stress in flanges of channel beam.

lateral shearing stress τ_{zx} that acts laterally along the center line of the flange as shown in the cross section (enlarged) in Figure 7.11d. Furthermore, the magnitude of τ_{xz} and of τ_{zx} is computed by Equation (7–48) in which the quantities t, A', and $\bar{y}$ are shown in Figure 7.11d.

Significance of Lateral Shear in Flanges.   The lateral shearing forces in the flanges of I- and channel sections are as shown in Figure 7.12a and b. Note that in an I-section these lateral shearing forces act to the right and left in each flange and are balanced because of the symmetry of the section. However, in the channel section the lateral shearing forces act to the left in the lower flange and to the right in the upper flange, and therefore create an unbalanced twisting couple, which must be balanced by locating the load to the left of the centroid, to keep the beam from twisting as it bends. The location of the action line of the load V is through the shear center O.

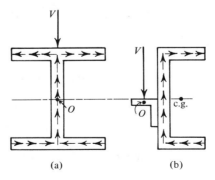

Fig. 7.12.   Load must pass through the shear center O to prevent twist of beams as it bends.

The shear center is discussed further in Chapter IV of *Advanced Mechanics of Materials*, 2nd Ed., F. B. Seely and J. O. Smith, 1952, John Wiley and Sons.

7.13.   Shear Flow

The shearing force along a transverse or longitudinal surface in a beam is $t\tau_{zy}$ and $t\tau_{yz}$, respectively, along the beam. This shearing force per unit length in the transverse direction or along a longitudinal section of the beam is called the shear flow and is usually designated by q. For example, in Figure 7.13 the shear flow along the longitudinal surface $ABCD$ is $(H'-H)/dz$ where

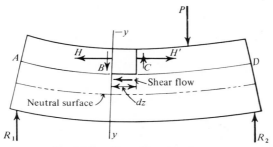

Fig. 7.13.   Shear flow in a beam.

H and H' are the longitudinal forces exerted in the beam by the rectangular block. If we let $H' - H = dH$ at the section yy in Figure 7.13, then $q = dH/dz$. Hence, by making use of the foregoing expressions for H' and H as developed in the derivation of Equation (7–47), we obtain

$$q = \frac{V_y Q}{I_x}.$$ (7–50)

It is convenient to calculate the shear flow and then obtain the shearing stress by dividing the shear flow by the thickness t of the beam at the location where q is determined. Hence,

$$\tau = \frac{q}{t} = \frac{V_y Q}{I_x t}.$$ (7–51)

Illustrative Problem

7.38.   Compute the maximum shearing stress in a simple beam composed of two 15-in. 45-lb channels placed back to back and covered with

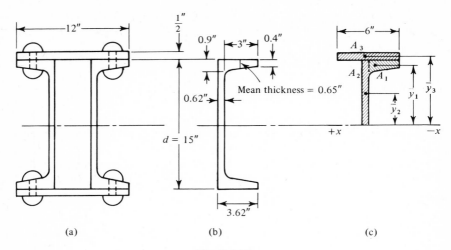

Fig. P 7.38.

two 12-in. by $\frac{1}{2}$-in. steel plates fastened to the channels by $\frac{7}{8}$-in. rivets (Fig. P7.38a) and simply supported on a 12-ft span. The beam is subjected to a concentrated load of 100,000 lb at the center of the span. (Neglect the weight of the beam). The dimensions of each channel are shown in Figure P7.38b. Also compute the spacing of the $\frac{7}{8}$ in. rivets if each rivet is allowed to resist a 9,000-lb shearing force between the plate and the channel.

SOLUTION. A steelmaker's handbook gives the following values for each channel in addition to those shown in Figure P7.38b.

$$I_x = 375 \text{ in.}^4, \qquad A = 13.2 \text{ in.}^2$$

$$I_x \text{ for the two cover plates} = 2(12)(\tfrac{1}{2})(7.75^2) = 720 \text{ in.}^4$$

Thus I_x for two channels and two cover plates is 1,470 in.^{4} The maximum shearing stress is $\tau_{zy} = V_y A' \bar{y} / I_x t$.

$$V_y = 50,000 \text{ lb}, \qquad I_x = 1,470 \text{ in.}^4, \qquad t = 1.24 \text{ in.}$$

The value of $A'\bar{y}$ is most easily found as the sum of the moments of the areas A_1, A_2, and A_3 (Fig. P7.38c) for both channel sections and plates. Thus,

$$A'\bar{y} = 2A_1\bar{y}_1 + 2A_2\bar{y}_2 + 2A_3\bar{y}_3$$

$$= 2(3)(0.65)\left(7.5 - \frac{0.65}{2}\right) + 2(0.62)(7.5)(3.75)$$

$$+ 2(6)(0.5)(7.75) = 109.5 \text{ in.}$$

Therefore,

$$\max \tau_{zy} = \frac{50,000(109.5)}{1,470(1.24)} = 3,000 \text{ psi.}$$

The maximum bending stress ($\sigma_z = M_x c / I_x$) is found to be 19,600 psi. Thus the maximum shearing stress is small in this section (and in nearly all other rolled steel sections, except when used on very short spans), even though the bending (normal) stress is nearly the full allowable value.

The average shearing stress over the entire cross section is

$$\tau_{avg} = \frac{V_y}{A} = \frac{50,000}{38.4} = 1,300 \text{ psi,}$$

and hence the maximum shearing stress is 2.3 times the average.

The shearing stress assuming that it is uniformly distributed only over the web area of the two channels is

$$\tau_{avg} = \frac{V_y}{A_w} = \frac{50,000}{15(2)(0.62)} = 2,690 \text{ psi.}$$

The rivet spacing is obtained from the shear flow q between one half of one plate and one of the channels; that is, since each rivet can resist a 9,000-lb shear load, the spacing is $9,000/q$. But $q = V_y Q / I_x$, where Q is the first moment of A_3 in Figure P7.38c.

Therefore,

$$Q = A_3 \bar{y}_3 = 6(0.5)(7.75) = 23.25 \text{ in.}^3$$

and

$$q = \frac{50,000(23.25)}{1,470} = 791 \text{ lb per in. of length}$$

$$\text{Rivet spacing} = \frac{9,000}{791} = 11.4 \text{ in.}$$

Problems

7.39. A simply supported horizontal beam is made of wood and has a cross-sectional area 6-in. wide by 10-in. deep. A concentrated vertical load of 18,000 lb acts at the midspan section, and the span is 10 ft. (1) Calculate the maximum longitudinal (or transverse) shearing stress in the beam. (2) Calculate also the longitudinal shearing stress at a point 3 in. from the top of the beam at a section 2 ft from the left support.

7.40. A simply supported horizontal timber beam that has a hollow square cross section is made by fastening together four 2-in. by 8-in. planks with screws as shown in Figure P7.40. The span of the beam is 10 ft, and the beam is subjected to a concentrated vertical load of 6,000 lb that acts 3 ft from the left end. (1) Calculate the maximum longitudinal shearing stress and state where in the beam this stress occurs. (2) Determine

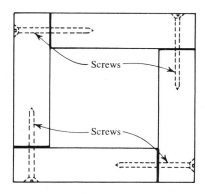

Fig. P 7.40.

the spacing of the screws along the beam between the left support and the load if each screw is capable of resisting a direct shearing force of 460 lb.

ans.   2 in.

7.41. A Douglas-fir beam (Fig. P7.41) having a rectangular cross section 1-in. by 2-in. when tested as a cantilever beam with a concentrated load at the free end failed by longitudinal shear (as shown in Fig. P7.41) when the total load on the beam was

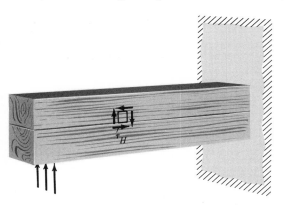

Fig. P 7.41.   Cantilever timber beam that failed by longitudinal shear.

381 lb. Calculate the maximum longitudinal shearing stress when the failure occurred. Assume that shearing stress is proportional to shearing strain (elastic behavior) until rupture occurs; this assumption will give approximate but useful results.

$$\text{ans.} \quad \tau_{zy} = 286 \text{ psi.}$$

7.42. A simply supported horizontal beam is subjected to two equal concentrated vertical loads $P = 115,000$ lb that are applied at the quarter points of the beam. The beam span is $\ell = 10$ ft, and the cross section consists of an I-beam with four hollow tubular cylinders welded continuously longitudinally along the edges of the four flanges as shown in Figure P7.42. Determine the magnitude of the longitudinal shearing

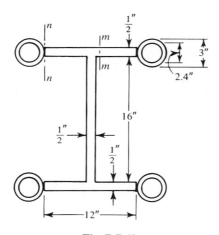

Fig. P 7.42.

stress on each of the following longitudinal planes: (1) the plane nn through the throat of weld joining a tube to a flange edge, (2) the plane mm at the juncture of the flange and web, (3) the maximum longitudinal (or transverse) shearing stress.

$$\text{ans.} \quad \tau_{nn} = 2,860 \text{ psi}; \tau_{mm} = 6,080 \text{ psi};$$

$$\tau_{max} = 14,600 \text{ psi.}$$

7.43. A horizontal cantilever beam of length $\ell = 6$ ft is loaded by a vertical load $P = 560$ lb at its free end. The beam consists of three 2-in. by 4-in. pieces of timber glued together with their longitudinal axes parallel as indicated by the cross-sectional view shown in Figure P7.43. Compute the maximum longitudinal (or transverse) shearing stress in the beam, and determine its location in the beam.

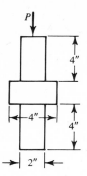

Fig. P 7.43.

7.44. A horizontal simply supported beam is 10 ft in length and is loaded at its center by a concentrated load $P = 6,000$ lb. The beam is made by fastening four 2-in. by 4-in. timbers to a 2-in by 16-in. timber, as shown in Figure P7.44, by steel bolts $\frac{1}{2}$ in. in diameter spaced 8 in. apart along the length. The longitudinal axes of all the timbers are parallel. Compute the following stresses: (1) the maximum bending stress, (2) the maximum longitudinal shearing stress in the beam, (3) the shearing stress in the steel bolts.

ans.   (1) $\sigma_z = 767$ psi;   (2) $\tau_{max} = 128$ psi;

(3) $\tau = 3,130$ psi.

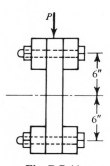

Fig. P 7.44.

7.45. Compare the flexural strengths of the two beams illustrated in Figure P7.45; the beams have rectangular cross sections. In (a) the beam is composed of two equal parts of the same material; one part slides over the other, if no shearing resistance is developed on the surfaces of contact, and hence the bending resistance of the beam is the sum of the resistances of the two beams acting independently. In (b) shearing

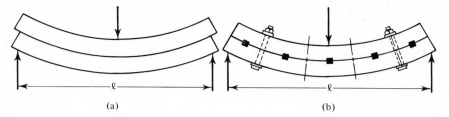

Fig. P 7.45.   Effect of shearing resistance in a beam composed of two parts.

resistance is exerted by the keys and bolts, and hence the two parts of the beam act as one beam.

7.46.   A railroad rail having the cross section shown in Figure P7.46 is used as a simple beam. If a concentrated load of 40,000 lb is applied at the center of the span in

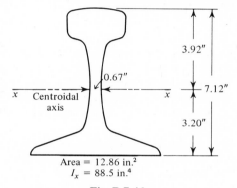

Fig. P 7.46.

the axis of symmetry, what is the maximum value of the transverse and longitudinal shearing stresses in the beam? The moment about the centroidal axis of the area of the cross section of the rail, on either side of the axis, is found to be 16.0 in.[3] If the maximum bending stress is $\sigma_z = 24{,}000$ psi, what is the span length of the beam?

7.14.   Manner in Which Plastic Strains Develop in Beam of Ductile Metal

When the loads on a beam are increased to sufficient magnitudes, the material in the beam yields and the linearly elastic load-stress relations derived in Sections 7.3, 7.5, 7.6, and 7.7 are not valid. Plastic load-stress relations for beams are based on one of the same assumptions used in deriving

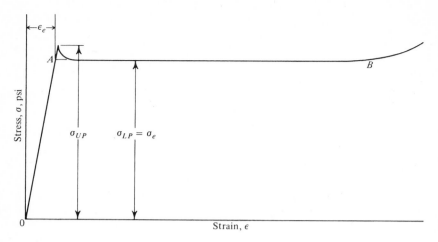

Fig. 7.14.

the elastic relations, namely plane sections before deformation are assumed to remain plane after deformation. This assumption is verified by experiment for beams made of strain-hardening materials but is not strictly valid for beams made of materials whose stress-strain diagrams are flat topped at the lower yield point as indicated by the diagram in Figure 7.14 for low carbon or structural grade steel.

In Figure 7.15 is shown a rectangular section beam subjected to pure bending. The beam is made of structural steel whose stress-strain diagram is shown in Figure 7.14. When the bending moment on such a beam is increased

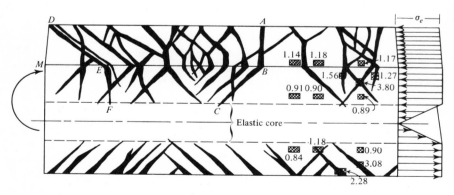

Fig. 7.15.   Manner in which inelastic deformation (yielding) develops in a beam of rectangular cross section made of structural steel.

in magnitude, yielding is initiated in one or more points in the beam when the stress in the most stressed fibers is equal to the upper yield point σ_{UP} (see Fig. 7.14). Once yielding starts at a given location, the stress in the most stressed fibers in both the yielded region and the elastic material adjacent to the yielded region decreases to the lower yield point stress $\sigma_{LP} = \sigma_e$. Yielding spreads into the beam to redistribute the stress by increasing the stress in the fibers below the most stressed fibers until the applied moment is balanced.

By polishing the beam before testing, the yielded material appears as plastic strain markings called Luder's bands; these are shown as shaded bands or wedges in Figure 7.15. Markings such as DE and AB are on top; EF and BC are on the side of the beam. The testing of the beam in Figure 7.15 was not terminated at the first sign of Luder's bands, but the bending moment was increased until the Luder's bands had penetrated to the depth shown.

In Section 4.6 it was stated that experimental evidence indicates that yielding occurs on planes of maximum shearing stress. Because the state of stress in the beam is uniaxial, there are an infinite number of planes of maximum shearing stress, each of which makes an angle of 45° with the direction of the normal stress. However, most of the Luder's bands in Figure 7.15 occur on one or the other of two planes. Bands ABC and DEF are typical. The plane of band ABC is perpendicular to the front and back faces of the beam and intersects the top face at about 45°; all of the bands on the tension (bottom) half of the beam were of this type. The plane of band DEF is perpendicular to the top face of the beam and makes an angle of about 45° with the front and back faces.

Obviously, plane sections cannot remain plane for the beam in Figure 7.15. The material behavior remained elastic outside the shaded bands and the axial strain was less than or equal to the upper yield point strain $\epsilon_{UP} = \sigma_{UP}/E$. Within the Luder's bands, the strains can have any value from ϵ_{UP} to that indicated by point B in Figure 7.14. In order to indicate the variation in strains at various locations on the surface of the beam, wire-resistance electrical strain gages having gage lengths of either $\frac{1}{8}$ in. or $\frac{1}{4}$ in. were cemented to the beam. After testing the beam, the paper surrounding the gage element was removed, leaving the areas over which the strains were measured; these are shown as cross-hatched areas in Figure 7.15. The numbers beside each gage show the ratio of the measured strain to the lower yield point strain $\epsilon_e = \epsilon_{LP} = \sigma_{LP}/E$. In each instance the strain reading was increased appreciably when one or more Luder's bands passed under the gage.

Although plane sections do not remain plane for the beam in Figure 7.15, the average strain obtained by using strain gages with a gage length at least as long as the depth of the beam indicates that the average strain varies linearly with the depth of the beam. Based on the average strain a predicted strain equal to the yield strain ϵ_e is located at the depths indicated by the dashed lines. Between the dashed lines, the average strains are less than ϵ_e and the material behaves elastically; this region of the beam is called the *elastic core* of the beam. Outside the dashed lines, the average strains are expected to be greater than ϵ_e, but several short-length strain gages just outside show values that are slightly smaller. The stress distribution on the right end of the beam in Figure 7.15 is found to give a bending moment that closely approximated the applied moment.

7.15. Fully Plastic Bending Moment—Ultimate or Fracture Moment

When the loads on the beam have increased sufficiently to cause one or more of the yielded portions (wedges), such as BC or EF in Figure 7.15, to penetrate from the outer surfaces through the entire depth of the beam, the value of the bending moment is called the fully plastic bending moment and is denoted by M_{fp}. Thus, when this bending moment is acting, there is no elastic core of material remaining at the section to restrain the yielding, and hence the beam is said to have a plastic hinge at this section. This condition means that if a portion of the beam is subjected to a constant bending moment the beam will continue to deflect approximately at a constant value of M_{fp} as the yielding spreads longitudinally and fills the gaps between the markings. Thus the beam will fail by general (unrestrained) yielding, provided that the material has a yield point. Hence, for a statically determinate beam, the loads on the beam which produce a fully plastic moment at any section of the beam are the ultimate loads for the beam; plastic behavior of statically indeterminate beams is discussed in Chapter 8.

The value of the fully plastic moment for the rectangular beam shown in Figure 7.16 may be found as follows: The forces acting on the portion of the beam that lies to one side (left side) of a section are shown in Figure 7.16. The equations of equilibrium applied to these forces give

$$\sum F_z = 0; \qquad \int \sigma \, da = 0 \quad \text{or} \quad T = C = \sigma_e \frac{bh}{2}; \qquad (7\text{--}52)$$

$$\sum M_x = 0; \qquad M_{fp} = \int y\sigma_e \, da = \sigma_e \frac{bh^2}{4}. \qquad (7\text{--}53)$$

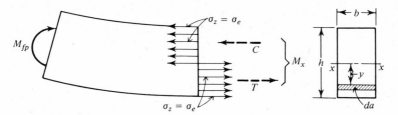

Fig. 7.16.   Method of determining the fully plastic bending moment.

Hence the fully plastic moment is given by the expression

$$M_{fp} = \sigma_e \frac{bh^2}{4}. \tag{7–54}$$

Because the bending moment M_e that would cause the stress in the outer fibers just to reach the value σ_e is

$$M_e = \frac{\sigma_e I_x}{c} = \sigma_e \frac{bh^2}{6} \tag{7–55}$$

we may write

$$M_{fp} = 1.5M_e. \tag{7–56}$$

The moment M_e is often called the elastic-limit moment. Hence, the fully plastic bending moment for this beam is 50 per cent greater than the elastic-limit bending moment, provided that the beam has a rectangular cross section and is made of material having a yield point that has the same value for tension and compression.

Influence of Shape of Cross Section.   Note that the shape of the cross section has an important influence on the value of the fully plastic bending moment. We note that in Equation (7–56) one-and-a-half times M_e is equal to M_{fp} for a rectangular cross section. This factor, which is designated by K, to be multiplied into M_e to obtain M_{fp} is given in Table 7.2 for several cross sections. (For other cross sections, see *Advanced Mechanics of Materials,* F. B. Seely and J. O. Smith, John Wiley and Sons, 1952.) Hence, Equation (7–56) for any cross section may be written

$$M_{fp} = KM_e \qquad \text{or} \qquad M_{fp} = K\frac{\sigma_e I_x}{c}. \tag{7–57}$$

The values of K in Table 7.2 reveal two very important facts: (1) if a beam has certain common types of cross sections, such as rectangular or circular cross sections,

Table 7.2

CROSS SECTION	VALUES OF K IN FULLY PLASTIC BENDING MOMENT: $M_{fp} = KM_e$
Rectangular	1.5
Circular	1.7
Circular tube (inner diam. $\frac{3}{4}$ outer diam.)	1.4
I- or [- sections	1.1 to 1.2

and is used where small plastic strains are permissible, the maximum static loads that the beam can resist are much larger than those found by restricting the loads to values that produce stresses and strains within or at the elastic limit. Thus, by taking advantage of the greater moment resulting from small inelastic strains in the beam, the maximum moment that can be applied to the beam without causing structural failure is greatly increased. (2) But the strength of beams having I- and channel cross sections can be increased very little by permitting small inelastic strains to occur.

In the usual method of design of beams made of ductile metals and used in so-called heavy structures for resisting static loads at ordinary temperatures, the moment M_e that causes a maximum stress in the outer fibers equal to the yield stress σ_e is assumed to be the moment that causes failure of the beam, even though the beams in such structures would usually function satisfactorily if subjected to small inelastic strains.

In this method of design, some beams (with rectangular, circular, etc., cross sections) will have excessive reserve strength whereas beams with some other types of cross sections (I-sections, etc.) will have very little excessive reserve strength.

Ductile Material Without a Yield Point. Throughout the discussion in Sections 7.14 and 7.15, it was assumed that the material was ideally plastic; that is, the material had a yield point and the stress-strain diagram in tension was the same as that for compression. If, however, the stress-strain diagrams in tension and compression are not identical, and the material does not have a yield point, there is no fully plastic bending moment because there is no yield point; when there is no yield point, the resisting moment will continue to increase to the ultimate value that occurs when the external fiber fractures. Fortunately, an appropriate and useful value for the ultimate resisting moment is $K(\sigma_u I_x/c)$, where σ_u is the ultimate strength and values of K are given in Table 7.2.

Brittle Material—Ultimate or Fracture Moment—Modulus of Rupture.
For beams made of brittle material it is usually assumed that the material
behaves elastically up to the load that causes fracture of the beam, and hence
the bending moment corresponding to facture would be

$$M_{\text{ult}} = \frac{\sigma_u I_x}{c}, \tag{7-58}$$

where σ_u is the ultimate tensile strength of the material. However, when such
beams are tested to fracture in bending, it is found that the value of M_{ult}
from tests is 20 to 100 per cent greater than that given by Equation (7–58).
The fact is explained by the change in the stress distribution in bending which
occurs as a result of the inelastic behavior that takes place beyond the proportional limit of the material. Consequently, when beams of brittle material
such as gray iron, terra cotta, building stone, and timber are used, a fictitious
value σ_r of the stress (known as the modulus of rupture) is employed in
Equation (7–58). The value of σ_r is obtained from bending tests of beams of the
material from the formula

$$\sigma_r = \frac{M_{\text{ult}} \cdot c}{I_x}. \tag{7-59}$$

Values of σ_r are greater than the ultimate tensile strength σ_u. The value
of σ_r will depend on the shape of the cross section of the beam used in the
tests; for example, values of σ_r obtained from tests of beams of circular cross
section are greater than those obtained from tests of beams with an I-section.

Illustrative Problem

7.47. A simply supported horizontal beam has a span of $\ell = 50$ in.
and is loaded by two equal vertical forces P applied at equal distances of
10 in. from each end. The cross section of the beam is an area in the shape of
a T whose dimensions are as shown in Figure P7.47a. The loads P lie in the
plane of symmetry of the T-section. Compute the value of the ultimate loads
P for the beam if it is made of a structural grade steel having a yield point σ_e
in tension and compression of 35,000 psi. The resisting moment in the beam
is the fully plastic moment when the ultimate load is reached, as explained in
Section 7.15.

SOLUTION. The maximum bending moment in the beam is $M_{\text{max}} = 10P$.
This bending moment is resisted by the fully plastic moment M_{fp}, as indicated
in Figure P7.47. The stress distribution on any cross section yy between the

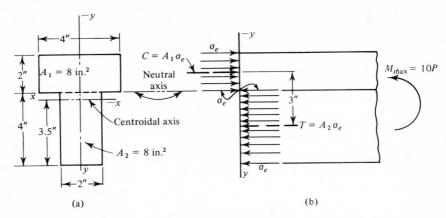

Fig. P 7.47. Fully plastic bending moment in T beam.

loads is indicated in Figure P7.47a and b, where the neutral axis is located so as to divide the cross section into two equal areas A_1 and A_2 and is not the centroidal axis as in the case of elastic bending. The proof of this fact is as follows. From equilibrium conditions:

Sum of the horizontal forces on the beam $= 0$.

Therefore,

$$C = T \qquad \text{or} \qquad A_1 \sigma_e = A_2 \sigma_e. \tag{a}$$

Because σ_e in compression is equal to σ_e in tension, it follows from Figure P7.47a that $A_1 = A_2$.

Also, from equilibrium conditions,

$$M_{\max} = M_{fp}. \tag{b}$$

The value of M_{fp} is equal to the moment of the couple which consists of the forces T and C, each of which passes through the centroid of the areas A_1 and A_2, respectively, since the stress is uniformly distributed on these areas. Therefore, $M_{fp} = A_1 \sigma_e(3) = 8(35,000)(3) = 840,000$ lb-in. Hence, from Equation (b),

$$M_{\max} = 10 P_{\text{ult}} = 840,000 \text{ lb-in.}$$

$$P_{\text{ult}} = 84,000 \text{ lb.}$$

Comparison with Elastic-limit Load. The load P_e at which the extreme fiber stress first reaches the yield point σ_e is obtained as follows:

$$M_e = M_{\max} = 10 P_e = \frac{\sigma_e I_{x'}}{c_1}, \tag{c}$$

in which I_x is the moment of inertia with respect to the centroidal axis (which is also the neutral axis for elastic conditions in bending). The value of $I_x = 49.0$ in.[4] Therefore, from Equation (c),

$$10P_e = \frac{35,000 \times 49.0}{3.5} = 490,000,$$

$$P_e = 49,000 \text{ lb.}$$

Hence, the ultimate load P_{ult} is 1.71 times the elastic-limit load P_e. The fact that $M_{fp} = 1.71 M_e$ for the cross section given in this problem indicates that $K = 1.71$ for this cross section; this value of K could be put in Table 7.2.

Problems

7.48. A beam made of a ductile material having a yield point in tension and in compression of $\sigma_e = 40,000$ psi has a trapezoidal cross section (Fig. P7.48). If the beam is subjected to pure bending by loads that lie in the plane of symmetry of the cross section, compute the values of the elastic-limit moment M_e and the fully plastic moment M_{fp} for the beam.

ans. $M_e = 377,000$ lb-in.; $M_{fp} = 677,000$ lb-in.

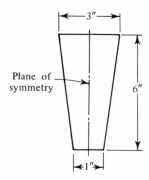

Fig. P 7.48.

7.49. Calculate the load P acting on the steel beam shown in Figure P7.49 when the fully plastic moment is developed in the beam. Assume that the yield point of the steel is $\sigma_e = 35,000$ psi.

ans.   26,250 lb.

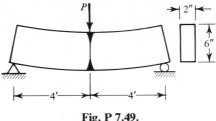

Fig. P 7.49.

7.50. Calculate the maximum bending moment that can be applied to the beam shown in Figure P7.50 if it is specified that an elastic core must exist in the middle half of the depth of the beam. The yield point of the material is σ_e and the cross section has the dimensions b and h.

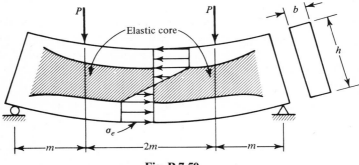

Fig. P 7.50.

7.51. Show that the expression for the fully plastic bending moment for a simply supported beam having a circular cross section is $1.7M_e$ as given in Table 7.2.

7.52. Let the beam in Figure P7.49 be made of dry yellow pine whose modulus of rupture is $\sigma_r = 11,000$ psi. Compute the ultimate fracture load for the beam.

7.16. Composite (Two-Material) Beam

In the derivation of the flexure formula $M_x = \sigma_z I_x / y$, it was assumed that the material of the beam was homogeneous. The formula, therefore, does not apply directly to a composite beam as, for example, a two-material beam such as a timber beam reinforced by steel plates, or a reinforced-concrete beam. It is sometimes convenient, however, to transform the section of such a beam to an equivalent section of a one-material (homogeneous) beam and to apply the flexure formula.

7.17. Timber Beam Reinforced by Steel Plates

Plate on Both Tension and Compression Faces. Let it be required to find the stress in the timber and in the steel plates at any section of the beam shown in Figure 7.17, in which the thickness of the plates is small compared to the depth of the beam. The plates are attached to the timber so that the timber and plates act together as a unit. In other words, it is assumed that

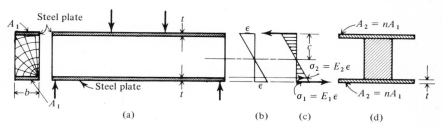

Fig. 7.17. Beam reinforced on top and bottom.

plane sections remain plane after bending, the same as in homogeneous beams, and hence the strains of the fibers vary directly as the distances of the fibers from the neutral axis, as indicated in Figure 7.17b. Further, since the plates are thin, the strains of the steel plates and of the outer fibers of the timber at any section are nearly equal—denoted by ϵ in Figure 7.17. The stress in the steel, however, is much greater than that in the outer fibers of the timber, owing to the difference in the moduli of elasticity of the two materials. The stress in the steel is $E_1\epsilon$, and that in the outer fibers of the timber is $E_2\epsilon$, where E_1 and E_2 are the moduli of elasticity of the steel and timber, respectively.

The total internal force in each steel plate then is $E_1\epsilon A_1$, where A_1 is the area of cross section of one steel plate. If, now, the steel is replaced by timber so that the internal force in the added timber is equal to that in the steel and acts at the same distance from the neutral axis, the result will be a one-material or so-called homogeneous beam having the transformed section area shown in Figure 7.17d. The total internal force in each added timber area A_2 is $E_2\epsilon A_2$; hence,

$$E_2\epsilon A_2 = E_1\epsilon A_1 \qquad \text{or} \qquad A_2 = \frac{E_1}{E_2}A_1 = nA_1 \qquad (7\text{--}60)$$

Thus the area of the timber to be added in place of the steel is n times the area replaced, where n is the ratio of the modulus of elasticity of the material replaced to that of the material added. The flexure formula may now be applied to the homogeneous beam having this transformed section. The solution of this simple problem, however, may be reached more conveniently perhaps by use of Figure 7.17c rather than by the method of the transformed section.

Steel Plate on Tension Side Only.   Let it be required to determine the maximum bending stress in the steel plate and in the outer fibers of the timber at any section of the beam shown in Figure 7.18. Because the timber and steel are assumed to act together as a beam, the strains of the fibers vary directly as the distances of the fibers from the neutral axis of the beam.

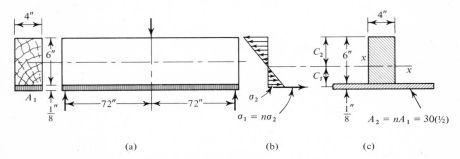

$$(a) \qquad\qquad (b) \qquad\qquad (c)$$

Fig. 7.18.   Beam reinforced on bottom face only.

But the location of the neutral axis is not known; it may be found conveniently by locating the centroidal axis of the transformed section since the neutral axis and centroidal axis are coincident in a homogeneous beam.

The transformed section is obtained by replacing the area A_1 of the steel by an area A_2 equal to nA_1, as previously discussed, where n is the ratio of the modulus of elasticity of the material replaced to that of the material added. The transformed section is shown in Figure 7.18c. The stress in the beam with this section may be found from the flexure formula.

Illustrative Problem

7.53.   Let the beam in Figure 7.17a be a simple beam with a span of 12 ft, supporting a concentrated load of 4,000 lb at the center of the span instead of two loads as shown in the figure. Let the width of the beam be 4 in. and its depth $6\frac{1}{4}$ in., and let the thickness of each steel plate be $\frac{1}{8}$ in. Calculate the maximum stress in the steel and in the timber. The moduli of elasticity of the timber and steel are 10^6 and 30×10^6 psi, respectively; therefore $n = 30$.

SOLUTION. σ_1 = stress in steel, σ_2 = stress in outer fiber of timber, $\sigma_1 = n\sigma_2 = 30\sigma_2$.

Bending moment = resisting moment

$$2{,}000 \times 72 = \frac{\sigma_2 I_x}{c} + \sigma_1 A_1 \times 6\tfrac{1}{8}$$

$$= \frac{\sigma_2 \tfrac{1}{12} \times 4 \times 6^3}{3} + 30\sigma_2 \times 4 \times \tfrac{1}{8} \times 6\tfrac{1}{8}$$

$$= 24\sigma_2 + 91.8\sigma_2 = 115.8\sigma_2.$$

Therefore, $\sigma_2 = 1{,}240$ psi, and $\sigma_1 = 30\sigma_2 = 37{,}200$ psi. Or, instead of obtaining the resisting moment in the timber from $\sigma_2 I_x/c$, it may be found as

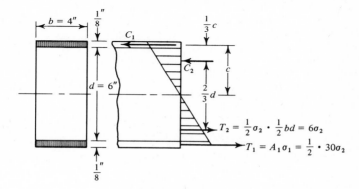

Fig. P 7.53.

the moment $T_2 \times \tfrac{2}{3}d$ (or $C_2 \times \tfrac{2}{3}d$) of the couple T_2 and C_2, as indicated in Figure P7.53, where T_2 is the total tensile force in the timber below the neutral axis. Thus the moment in the timber is

$$(\tfrac{1}{2}\sigma_2 \times \tfrac{1}{2}bd) \times \tfrac{2}{3}d = \tfrac{1}{6}\sigma_2 bd^2 = 24\sigma_2.$$

Problems

7.54. Solve Problem 7.53 by the method of the transformed cross section.

7.55. A rectangular timber member having a width of 6 in. and a depth of 10 in. is used as a horizontal cantilever beam having a free length of 8 ft. Steel plates $\tfrac{1}{4}$ in. thick are firmly attached to the top and bottom faces of the beam. The beam supports a uniformly distributed load. If the maximum stress in the timber is 1,000 psi, what is the maximum stress in the steel, and what is the total load on the beam? The modulus of elasticity for the timber is 2×10^6 and for steel 30×10^6 psi.

ans.   6,830 lb.

7.56.   If in Problem 7.53 steel plates $\frac{1}{4}$-in. thick are attached to the vertical sides of the timber beam instead of to the top and bottom faces, what will be the maximum stress in the steel and in the timber? The steel plates cover the sides of the beam completely, and the composite beam acts as a unit.

7.57.   Let the working stress be 600 psi for the timber beam of Problem 7.53 and determine the proper thickness of the steel plates. Use $n = 30$.

ans. $t = 0.275$ in.

7.58.   In Problem 7.53 let it be assumed that the steel plate is removed from the top face of the beam, leaving the beam reinforced only on the bottom or tension face. Let it be required to find the maximum moment the beam can resist without causing an elastic stress in the timber greater than 1,000 psi. What will be the corresponding stress in the steel?

Deflection of Beams

8.1. Introduction

As noted in Section 4.5, the maximum load that can be applied to a beam sometimes may be limited by an elastic deflection, beyond which the beam would not function satisfactorily under the given service conditions. This means that the stiffness rather than the strength of the beam is the governing condition that the beam must satisfy. Thus it is important that we find a relationship between the loads acting on a beam and the elastic deformation or deflection caused by the loads (load-deflection relation for the beam); this relationship will also include the stiffness of the material of which the beam is made (as indicated by the modulus of elasticity) and the dimensions of the beam. The general form of this relationship is expressed by the elastic-curve equation for the beam. These results are also used to solve for the redundant reactions for statically indeterminate beams.

The Main Problem. The main purpose of this chapter is to derive the equation of the elastic curve for a beam (see Fig. 8.1a) and to use the equation for determining the deflection at any point of the elastic curve (especially the maximum elastic deflection) of beams of various types.

Elastic Curve Defined. The elastic curve of an originally straight beam is the curve of the longitudinal bending axis (footnote, page 223) of the stressed beam, provided that the maximum stress in the beam does not exceed the proportional limit of the material. For beams of usual proportions and materials, this means that the deflections are small; the deflections in the subsequent figures are greatly exaggerated in order to indicate the form of the elastic curve. Since the elastic curve lies in the neutral surface of the beam, it does not change its length as the beam is bent. Furthermore, because the

315

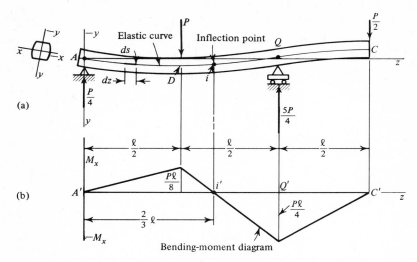

Fig. 8.1. General characteristics of elastic curve of beam.

elastic deformations are small, a differential length ds along the elastic curve of an originally horizontal straight beam usually may be assumed to be equal to the horizontal differential length dz (see Figs. 8.1, 8.2, and 8.3); and the change in slope at two points on the curve at the distance ds apart may be assumed to be equal to the change in the angle $d\theta$ itself (tan $\theta = \theta = dy/dz$). The deflection y of any point of the elastic curve and especially the maximum deflection $y_{\max}$ (Fig. 8.3) will be found later in this chapter.

8.2.   General Features of Elastic Behavior of a Beam

The general shape of the elastic curve of a given beam can be determined from the bending-moment diagram. For example, let Figure 8.1*a* represent a horizontal simply supported beam that overhangs its right-hand support; the cross section has one plane of symmetry,* the $y–y$ axis, and the loads also

---

* In unsymmetrical bending, determine the principal axes of inertia u and v for the beam cross section (see Appendix A). Determine components of each load acting on the beam parallel to u- and v-axes. Treat each set of loads separately. The load components parallel to the u-axis cause deflection in the u-direction with the v-axis as the neutral axis. Theories developed in this chapter are valid for this loading and will give the component of the deflections of the beam in the u-direction. Similarly treating the components of the loads parallel to the v-axis will give the component of the deflections of the beam in the v-direction. The deflection of the beam at any point is obtained by adding vectorially the u- and v-components of the deflection at that point.

lie in the plane of symmetry. The bending-moment diagram is shown in Figure 8.1*b*. The elastic curve of the beam is represented in Figure 8.1*a*; the curve from *A* to *i* is concave upward because the bending moment is positive at all sections of the beam from *A* to *i*, whereas the curve is concave downward from *i* to *C* because the bending moment at all sections from *i* to *C* is negative. The point of the elastic curve at which the curvature changes from concave upward to concave downward, or vice versa, is called the *inflection point*, and it occurs at the section of the beam for which the bending moment is equal to zero, as indicated in Figure 8.1.

Angle Change. In the solution of the main problem, previously stated, it will be convenient to consider the beam to be made up of elements consisting of thin slices of length $ds = dz$. One such element is shown as $GHFQ$ in Figure 8.2. The bending moments M_x and $M_x + dM_x$ acting on the vertical

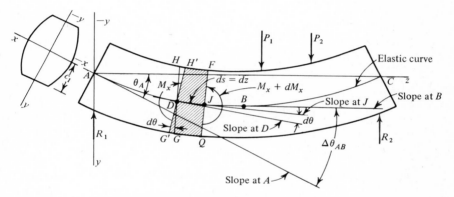

Fig. 8.2. Change of slope to elastic curve of beam.

faces of any element cause one face of the element to rotate with respect to the other face through an angle $d\theta$; the value of M_x, of course, varies with the position of the element in the beam. The angle change $d\theta$ is equal to the change of slope of the elastic curve in the length ds, and the change of slope $\Delta\theta$ over a finite length of the curve, as from *A* to *B*, is the summation of the angle changes in all the elements from *A* to *B*. Thus,

$$\Delta\theta_{AB} = \int_A^B d\theta. \tag{8-1}$$

In order to determine the elastic curve of the beam we now need to find an expression for $d\theta$ in terms of M_x, E, I_x, and dz so that the integral in Equation (8–1) can be evaluated.

8.3. Equation of Elastic Curve in Terms of Angle Change

Figure 8.3 shows a deflected beam similar to that in Figure 8.2. The line HG is drawn parallel to $F'Q'$ to show the angle change $d\theta$ through which $H'G'$ has rotated relative to $Q'F'$. In the triangle DGG' let the elongation GG'

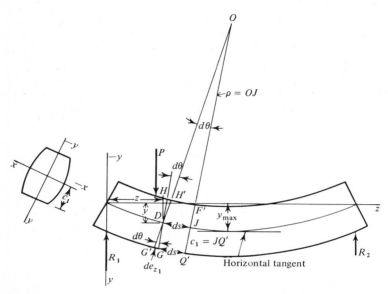

Fig. 8.3.   Analysis of strains in beam for determining deflection of beam.

of the extreme fiber GQ' be denoted by de_{z_1}. Because GG' is small in comparison with the distance $c_1(DG)$ from the neutral axis to the extreme fiber, the angle GDG' may be obtained from the following equation

$$\text{angle } GDG' = d\theta = -de_{z_1}/c_1. \tag{8-2}$$

The negative sign appears on the right side of Equation (8–2) because the change in slope $d\theta$ between D and J in Figure 8.3 is negative and because de_{z_1} and c_1 are positive quantities. But the elongation de_{z_1} of the extreme fiber is equal to $\epsilon_{z_1} ds$ in which ϵ_{z_1} is the strain in the fiber and $ds = dz$ is the fiber length. Furthermore, as previously shown, $\epsilon_{z_1} = \sigma_{z_1}/E$ and $\sigma_{z_1} = M_x c_1/I_x$, where σ_{z_1} is the stress in the extreme fiber. By making these substitutions in Equation (8–2), we have

$$d\theta = -\frac{\epsilon_{z_1} dz}{c_1} = -\frac{\sigma_{z_1} dz}{Ec_1} = -\frac{(M_x c_1/I_x)\, dz}{Ec_1} = -\frac{M_x\, dz}{EI_x}, \tag{8-3}$$

in which M_x is the bending moment (the change dM_x is neglected as a higher order term) in the element of length dz for which the angle change is $d\theta$, I_x is the moment of inertia of the cross section, and E is the modulus of elasticity of the material. The negative sign is retained in front of the right side of Equation (8–3) because all of the other quantities ϵ_{z_1}, σ_{z_1}, dz, E, M_x, and I_x introduced in Equation (8–3) are positive quantities in Figure 8.3. Equation (8–3) is the elastic-curve equation for the beam expressed in terms of the change in slope $d\theta$ between the two tangents drawn at the ends of the element of length dz of the curve in terms of M_x, E, I_x, and dz. The expression for $d\theta$ from Equation (8–3) is substituted in Equation (8–1), which gives

$$\Delta\theta = -\int \frac{M_x}{EI_x}\,dz. \tag{8–4}$$

This equation may be used to great advantage in determining the deflection of a beam, as will be seen later in this chapter, and you should become familiar with its derivation and use.

Illustrative Problems

8.1. A cantilever beam (Fig. P8.1) of length ℓ is fixed at its right end and supports a concentrated load P at its free end. Let E be the modulus of elasticity of the material and I_x the moment of inertia of the cross section. Compute the change in slope $\Delta\theta$ between the fixed end and the free end in terms of P, ℓ, E, and I_x.

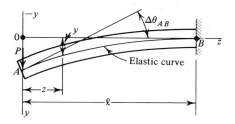

Fig. P 8.1.

SOLUTION. From Equation (8–4)

$$\Delta\theta_{AB} = -\int_A^B \frac{M_x}{EI_x}\,dz = -\int_0^\ell \frac{M_x}{EI_x}\,dz.$$

Because the changes in slope are assumed to be small (greatly exaggerated in Figure P8.1), $ds = dz$, and the bending moment $M_x = -Pz$. Hence,

$$\Delta\theta_{AB} = -\int_0^\ell -\frac{Pz\,dz}{EI_x} = +\left[\frac{Pz^2}{2EI_x}\right]_0^\ell = +\frac{Pl^2}{2EI_x}.$$

Note that the slope of the beam at its fixed end does not change when the beam is loaded. Because $\Delta\theta_{AB} = \theta_B - \theta_A = -\theta_A$, the slope of the beam at the free end is $\theta_A = -\Delta\theta_{AB}$.

8.2. A beam of constant cross section is made of an aluminum alloy (see Table 1.1) and is supported and loaded as shown in Figure P8.2. The cross section of the beam is a rectangle 2-in. wide and 8-in. deep. By making use of the sketch of the elastic curve of the beam and the bending-moment diagram, compute the following values: (1) maximum bending stress in the beam; (2) change in slope from A to B; (3) change in slope from B to C; (4) change in slope from A to C.

SOLUTION. (1) $I_x = \frac{1}{12}$ (2) $(8^3) = 85.33$ in.^{4}.

$$\sigma_{\max} = \frac{M_{\max}c}{I_x} = \frac{(-192,000)(-4)}{85.33} = 9,000 \text{ psi}.$$

This stress is less than the proportional limit.

In solving Equation (8–4) it is necessary to express M_x as a function of z. The moment diagram is shown in Figure 8.2b. Using the method outlined in Section 6.4,

$$M_x = -2,000z \qquad\qquad 0 \le z \le 96'' \qquad\qquad \text{(a)}$$

$$M_x = -2,000z + 6,000(z - 96) \qquad 96'' \le z \le 144'' \qquad \text{(b)}$$

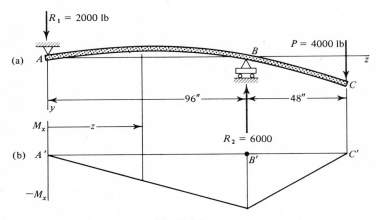

Fig. P 8.2.

In the range from A to B, Equation (a) is valid and

$$(2) \quad \Delta\theta_{AB} = -\int_A^B \frac{M_x}{EI_x} dz = -\int_0^{96} -\frac{2,000z}{EI_x} dz$$

$$= \left[+\frac{1,000z^2}{EI_x} \right]_0^{96} = \frac{+1,000 \times \overline{96}^2}{10^7 \times 85.33} = +0.0108 \text{ rad.}$$

In the range from B to C, Equation (b) is valid and

$$(3) \quad \Delta\theta_{CB} = -\int_B^C \frac{M_x\, dz}{EI_x} = -\int_{96}^{144} \frac{-2,000z + 6,000(z - 96)}{EI_x} dz$$

$$= -\frac{1}{EI_x} \left[-1,000z^2 + 6,000\frac{(z - 96)^2}{2} \right]_{96}^{144} = +0.0054 \text{ rad.}$$

$$(4) \quad \Delta\theta_{AC} = \Delta\theta_{AB} + \Delta\theta_{CB} = +0.0162 \text{ rad.}$$

Problems

8.3. A simply supported beam carries a uniformly distributed load of w lb per unit length of the beam. Determine the change in slope of the elastic curve between the left end and the midpoint of the span in terms of w, ℓ, E, and I_x.

8.4. A simply supported beam with a span of 12 ft supports equal concentrated loads of 4,000 lb at the third points. If the beam is made of an aluminum alloy (see Table 1.1) and has a rectangular cross section 3-in. wide and 6-in. deep, compute the change in slope $\Delta\theta$ between the left end and the midpoint of the span. Justify the assumption that the beam acts elastically.

ans. -0.0171 rad.

8.5. In Figure 8.1 determine the change in slope between tangents drawn at the points A and D of the elastic curve in terms of P, ℓ, E, and I_x.

8.6. In Figure 8.1 determine the change in slope between tangents drawn at points Q and C of the elastic curve in terms of P, ℓ, E, and I_x.

8.4. Elastic-Curve Equation in Terms of Radius of Curvature

Equation (8–3) may be interpreted in a slightly different way to derive a relationship between the radius of curvature at any point of the elastic curve and the values of M_x, E, and I_x. In Figure 8.3 let O be the center of curvature of the elastic curve at section $Q'F'$, and let ρ be the radius of curvature (which is assumed to be constant at each point of the length dz). From triangle

OJD we see that $ds = dz = \rho\,d\theta$. If this value of dz is substituted in the right member of Equation (8–3), we obtain

$$\frac{1}{\rho} = \frac{-M_x}{EI_x} \quad \text{or} \quad \rho = \frac{-EI_x}{M_x} \tag{8–5}$$

in which ρ is the radius of curvature of the elastic curve at a section and M_x, E, and I_x have the same meaning as in Equation (8–3).

It should be recalled that by definition $1/\rho$ represents the curvature of the beam at the cross section where the radius of curvature is ρ. Thus Equation (8–5) indicates a very important fact: namely, that the bending moment at any section of a beam (and hence the maximum stress at the section) is directly related to the curvature at that section.

We should note also from Equation (8–5) that, if a beam of constant cross section is so loaded that the bending moment M_x is constant over a portion of the beam, the radius of curvature of the elastic curve of this portion also will be constant (because E and I_x are constant); hence the elastic curve for this portion is an arc of a circle. Conversely, if a beam is bent in an arc of a circle, the bending moments for all sections of the beam are equal. Furthermore, the preceding equation also shows that, when M_x is equal to zero, ρ is equal to infinity; thus, at the inflection point (Section 8.2) the center of curvature is at an infinite distance from the beam.

Problems

8.7. In Figure P8.7 is shown a thin strip of brass (see Table 1.1) bent around a portion AB of a stationary cylindrical surface of radius $R = 20$ in. The dimensions of the cross section are $b = 0.5$ in. and $h = 0.05$ in. Calculate the bending moment at section B (and at all sections between A and B), and then calculate the value of P if $\ell = 12$ in.

ans. $M_x = -3.125$ in.-lb; $P = 0.260$ lb.

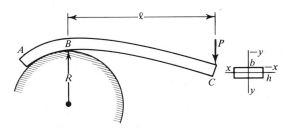

Fig. P 8.7.

8.8. A simple beam (Fig. P8.8) is composed of two rectangular bars of the same width and of the same material. The depth of the top bar is $\frac{1}{2}$ in. and that of the bottom bar is 1 in. The beam is subjected to loads causing no stress greater than the proportional limit of the material. Compare the maximum bending stresses in the two bars. Assume that shearing stresses do not develop between the two beams. (*Hint:* The radii of curvature of the two beams at any section are equal.)

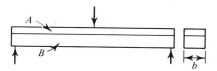

Fig. P 8.8.

8.9. In Problem 8.8 let the two bars have the same cross-sectional dimensions, but let the top beam be made of steel and the other of an aluminum alloy (see Table 1.1). Compare the maximum bending stresses in the two bars.

8.5. Differential Equation of the Elastic Curve in Terms of Rectangular Coordinates

An expression for the elastic-curve equation in terms of the rectangular coordinates z and y, where the z- and y-axes are as shown in Figure 8.3, is obtained from Equation (8–5) by expressing the radius of curvature in terms of the rectangular coordinates. This equation is (see any book on calculus)

$$\frac{1}{\rho} = \frac{d^2y/dz^2}{[1 + (dy/dz)^2]^{3/2}}. \tag{8–6}$$

The denominator of the right side of Equation (8–6) may be assumed with negligible error to be equal to unity for beams that are straight before being loaded and that are given only small deflections. For such beams the value of the slope dy/dz to the elastic curve at any point is always small compared to unity, and hence $(dy/dz)^2$ is sufficiently small to be neglected without introducing serious errors. Thus the expression in Equation (8–6) becomes

$$1/\rho = d^2y/dz^2. \tag{8–7}$$

If the quantity $1/\rho$ is eliminated from Equations (8–5) and (8–7), the following equation is found:

$$\frac{d^2y}{dz^2} = \frac{-M_x}{EI_x}. \tag{8–8}$$

8.6.   Use of the Various Equations of the Elastic Curve for Determining Deflection

Equations (8–3), (8–5), and (8–8) are three different expressions of the elastic-curve equation for a beam. They are alike in that each contains the term M_x/EI_x and they differ only in the fact that this quantity M_x/EI_x is related to different variables in each equation. To summarize these facts, note that from Equation (8–3), $-M_x/EI_x = d\theta/dz$; from Equation (8–5), $-M_x/EI_x = 1/\rho$; and from Equation (8–8), $-M_x/EI_x = d^2y/dz^2$. The quantity M_x/EI_x, therefore, has special physical significance and deserves further consideration. It is, in fact, the curvature of the elastic curve (see any book on calculus) or, to state it in terms of the slope dy/dz of the elastic curve, it is the rate of change in slope of the elastic curve of the beam at the section where the bending moment is M_x.

Equation (8–8) is solved by using a method known as the double-integration method. Equation (8–3) is solved by making use of definite integrals instead of obtaining the general solution of a differential equation. This method, called the moment-area method, has the advantage of having a rather easy physical interpretation, which makes possible the computation of the definite integrals by using semigraphical means. This method is derived in Section 8.8 and is used later in solving problems in this chapter.

8.7.   Double-Integration Method

In Sections 8.1 through 8.6, the problem of relating the loads on a beam to the deflection of the beam was discussed, and the elastic-curve equation for a beam subjected to loads was derived. This equation (Eq. 8–8 with the negative sign on the left side) is

$$-\frac{d^2y}{dz^2} = \frac{M_x}{EI_x} \tag{8–9}$$

This is the differential equation (in terms of rectangular coordinates) of the elastic curve of an originally straight beam. In this equation, M_x is the bending moment as defined in Section 6.2 and as used in Chapter 7. The origin O of the y-, z-axes is a fixed point, and hence does not move when the loads are applied to the beam. Therefore, y is the deflection of the elastic curve at any section (Fig. 8.4).

Signs M_x and d^2y/dz^2.   In using the preceding differential equation of the elastic curve, it is important to understand the significance of the signs of M_x and d^2y/dz^2; E and I_x are positive and may be regarded merely as

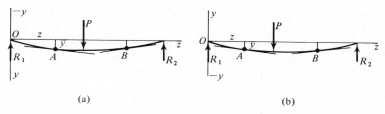

Fig. 8.4. Effect of direction of axes on sign of d^2y/dz^2.

magnitudes. The sign of M_x already has been discussed (Section 6.2); it is positive for a horizontal beam when it produces tensile stress in the bottom fibers of the beam or when it causes the center of curvature to lie above the beam, and is negative when it causes compressive stress on the bottom fibers, and so forth. The sign of d^2y/dz^2, however, depends on the choice of the positive directions of the axes. For example, Figure 8.4a represents a horizontal simply supported beam subjected to a load that gives a positive bending moment. The positive directions for y- and z-axes are downward and to the right, respectively.

The slope dy/dz at a point A on the curve is positive, whereas at a point B the slope is negative, and thus as z increases dy/dz decreases. Therefore, the rate of change of dy/dz with respect to z (i.e., d^2y/dz^2) is negative, and because M_x is positive, the equation must be written $M_x = -EI_x(d^2y/dz^2)$.

If, however, the positive direction of the y-axis is chosen upward as shown in Figure 8.4b, the slope at A is negative and increases as z increases; thus d^2y/dz^2 is positive. But M_x is positive,* and the right side of the equation then must also be positive, which requires that the equation shall be written $M_x = +EI_x(d^2y/dz^2)$. If, then, for any horizontal beam the z-axis is positive to the right and the positive direction of the y-axis is chosen downward, the negative sign in Equation (8–9) should be used. In this book the positive direction of the y-axis is chosen downward for horizontal beams, and hence the negative sign in Equation (8–9) is used.

In using the double integration method, the bending moment M_x in the equation

$$-EI_x(d^2y/dz^2) = M_x \qquad (8\text{--}10)$$

is expressed as a function of z as described in Section 6.4, where this function of z is always a polynomial in z if there are no axial components of load. Furthermore, this expression for M_x in terms of z is valid for the entire length

* In keeping with the sign convention for bending moment as discussed in Chapters 6 and 7, the bending moment should really be negative in Figure 8.4b if the y-coordinate of the points in the beam cross section are also positive when above the neutral axis.

of the beam when step functions are used as illustrated in Section 6.5. Thus Equation (8–10) is a linear differential equation of the second order whose solution gives the deflection y of the beam.

The term d^2y/dz^2 is stated in the following form $d(dy/dz)/dz$ so that Equation (8–10) is as follows:

$$-EI_x \, d\left(\frac{dy}{dz}\right) = M_x \, dz. \qquad (8–11)$$

As already stated the bending moment M_x is usually a polynomial in z and therefore every term on both sides of Equation (8–11) is a differential that is readily integrated.

Several illustrative problems are given to show how Equation (8–11) is used to solve for the deflection of a beam. In each problem the expression M_x for the bending moment is derived as shown in Section 6.4 and is substituted into Equation (8–11). Each term on both sides of the equation is integrated twice to find the deflection. With each integration is added a constant of integration, the values for which are found by making use of the physical conditions imposed by the nature of the supports; these conditions are called boundary conditions.

Illustrative Problems

8.10. Derive the elastic curve equation for the cantilever beam shown in Figure P8.10 by solving the differential equation of Equation (8–10). Show that the deflection at the free end is $y_{max} = P\ell^3/3EI_x$. The beam has a constant cross section with at least one axis of symmetry, and the load P lies in an axis of symmetry. The moment of inertia I_x is computed with respect to the neutral axis x–x of bending that is through the centroid of the cross

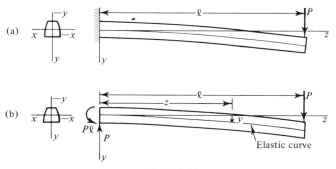

Fig. P 8.10.

section and is perpendicular to the axis of symmetry containing the load P as shown in Figure P8–10b.

SOLUTION. We draw the free-body diagram of the beam as shown in Figure P8.10b. The bending moment M_x at any cross section of the beam is $M_x = Pz - P\ell$. Thus Equation (8–10) is as follows:

$$-EI_x\frac{d^2y}{dz^2} = Pz - P\ell. \tag{a}$$

Equation (a) is integrated as indicated by the method described by Equation (8–11). Thus

$$-EI_x\frac{dy}{dz} = \tfrac{1}{2}Pz^2 - P\ell z + C_1, \tag{b}$$

and

$$-EI_x y = \tfrac{1}{6}Pz^3 - \tfrac{1}{2}P\ell z^2 + C_1 z + C_2. \tag{c}$$

Two boundary conditions at the fixed end of the beam are used to determine the values of the constants of integration C_1 and C_2. These two boundary conditions are as follows: at $z = 0$, the slope of the beam is $dy/dz = 0$; and at $z = 0$, the deflection $y = 0$. The first boundary condition is applied to Equation (b), which gives

$$EI_x(0) = \tfrac{1}{2}P(0)^2 - P\ell(0) + C_1$$

and hence

$$C_1 = 0.$$

The second boundary condition is applied to Equation (c), which gives

$$EI_x(0) = \tfrac{1}{6}P(0)^3 - \tfrac{1}{2}P\ell(0)^2 + 0(0) + C_2,$$

and hence $C_2 = 0$. Therefore, with $C_1 = C_2 = 0$ substituted into Equation (c) it becomes

$$-EI_x y = \tfrac{1}{6}Pz^3 - \tfrac{1}{2}P\ell z^2. \tag{d}$$

Equation (d) gives the deflection y at any cross section of the beam at the distance z from the fixed end. At the free end $z = \ell$, and substituting this value in Equation (d) gives

$$-EI_x y_{z=\ell} = \tfrac{1}{6}P\ell^3 - \tfrac{1}{2}P\ell^3$$

or

$$y_{z=\ell} = \frac{1}{3}\frac{P\ell^3}{EI_x}.$$

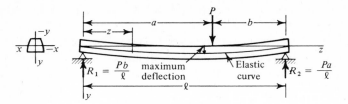

Fig. P 8.11.

8.11. For the simply supported beam loaded as shown in Figure P8.11, derive the elastic curve equation (1) without using step functions and (2) using step functions (see Section 6.5). (3) Assuming that a is greater than b, locate the cross section where the maximum deflection of the beam occurs.

SOLUTION—PART (1). The free-body diagram for the beam is shown in Figure P8.11. Using the procedure developed in Section 6.4, the bending moment diagram is given by the relations

$$M_x = \frac{Pb}{\ell}z \qquad\qquad 0 \le z \le a \qquad\qquad (a)$$

$$M_x = \frac{Pb}{\ell}z - P(z - a) \qquad\qquad a \le z \le \ell \qquad\qquad (b)$$

Thus, Equation (8–10) is as follows:

$$-EI_x\frac{d^2y}{dz^2} = \frac{Pb}{\ell}z \qquad\qquad 0 \le z \le a \qquad\qquad (c)$$

$$-EI_x\frac{d^2y}{dz^2} = \frac{Pb}{\ell}z - P(z - a) \qquad\qquad a \le z \le \ell \qquad\qquad (d)$$

Equations (c) and (d) are integrated by the method described in Equation (8–11) with the following results:

$$-EI_x\frac{dy}{dz} = \frac{Pb}{2\ell}z^2 + C_1 \qquad\qquad (e)$$

$$-EI_xy = \frac{Pb}{6\ell}z^3 + C_1z + C_2 \qquad\qquad (f)$$

when Equation (c) is integrated; and

$$-EI_x\frac{dy}{dz} = \frac{Pb}{2\ell}z^2 - \frac{P}{2}(z - a)^2 + C_3 \qquad\qquad (g)$$

$$-EI_xy = \frac{Pb}{6\ell}z^3 - \frac{P}{6}(z - a)^3 + C_3z + C_4 \qquad\qquad (h)$$

when Equation (d) is integrated. Four boundary conditions are required to determine the values of the constants of integration C_1, C_2, C_3, and C_4. Two of these are given by the conditions that $y = 0$ when $z = 0$ and when $z = \ell$. The other two boundary conditions are given by the facts that the slope and deflection of the elastic curve must be continuous at every point along the beam, including the point under the load P. This means that the right sides of Equations (e) and (g) must be equal when $z = a$ and that the right sides of Equations (f) and (h) must be equal when $z = a$.

When the first boundary condition, $y = 0$ when $z = 0$, is substituted into Equation (f), the following equation is obtained:

$$-EI_x(0) = \frac{Pb}{6\ell}(0) + C_1(0) + C_2,$$

$$C_2 = 0 \tag{i}$$

When the second boundary condition $y = 0$ when $z = \ell$ is substituted into Equation (h) $(a \le z \le \ell)$ the following equation is obtained:

$$-EI_x(0) = \frac{Pb\ell^2}{6} - \frac{P}{6}(\ell - a)^3 + C_3\ell + C_4.$$

Because $\ell - a = b$, this equation simplifies to

$$C_3\ell + C_4 = \frac{Pb}{6\ell}(b^2 - \ell^2). \tag{j}$$

The third boundary condition states that the right side of Equation (e) is equal to the right side of Equation (g) when $z = a$.
Thus,

$$\frac{Pba^2}{2\ell} + C_1 = \frac{Pba^2}{2\ell} - \frac{P}{2}(a - a) + C_3,$$

$$C_1 = C_3. \tag{k}$$

The fourth boundary condition states that the right side of Equation (f) (note that $C_2 = 0$) is equal to the right side of Equation (g) when $z = a$.
Thus,

$$\frac{Pba^3}{6\ell} + C_1\ell = \frac{Pba^3}{6\ell} - \frac{P}{6}(a - a)^3 + C_3\ell + C_4,$$

$$C_1\ell = C_3\ell + C_4.$$

Because Equation (k) states that $C_1 = C_3$,

$$C_4 = 0. \tag{m}$$

Equations (j), (k), and (m) give

$$C_1 = C_3 = \frac{Pb}{6\ell}(b^2 - \ell^2). \tag{n}$$

When the constants of integration given by Equations (i), (m), and (n) are substituted into Equations (f) and (h), the elastic curve equation is obtained as follows:

$$-EI_xy = \frac{Pb}{6\ell}z^3 + \frac{Pb}{6\ell}(b^2 - \ell^2)z \qquad\qquad 0 \le z \le a$$

$$-EI_xy = \frac{Pb}{6\ell}z^3 - \frac{P}{6}(z - a)^3 + \frac{Pb}{6\ell}(b^2 - \ell^2)z \qquad a \le z \le \ell \tag{o}$$

Note that two separate equations are required for the elastic curve.

PART (2). When step functions are used, the two equations for the moment diagram given by Equations (a) and (b) can be written as one:

$$M_x = \frac{Pb}{\ell}z - P\langle z - a\rangle^1. \tag{p}$$

Equation (8–10) is as follows:

$$-EI_x\frac{d^2y}{dz^2} = \frac{Pb}{\ell}z - P\langle z - a\rangle^1, \tag{q}$$

which can be integrated twice to give, first

$$-EI_x\frac{dy}{dz} = \frac{Pb}{2\ell}z^2 - \frac{P}{2}\langle z - a\rangle^2 + C_5 \tag{r}$$

and, second

$$-EI_xy = \frac{Pb}{6\ell}z^3 - \frac{P}{6}\langle z - a\rangle^3 + C_5z + C_6. \tag{s}$$

Two boundary conditions are required to determine the values of the constants of integration C_5 and C_6. These are given by the conditions that $y = 0$ when $z = 0$ and when $z = \ell$.

When the first boundary condition, $y = 0$ when $z = 0$, is substituted into Equation (s), the following equation is obtained:

$$-EI_x(0) = \frac{Pb}{6\ell}(0) - \frac{P}{6}(0) + C_5(0) + C_6,$$

$$C_6 = 0. \tag{t}$$

When the second boundary condition, $y = 0$ when $z = \ell$, is substituted into Equation (s), the following equation is obtained:

$$-EI_x(0) = \frac{Pb\ell^2}{6} - \frac{P}{6}(\ell - a)^3 + C_5\ell.$$

Noting that $\ell - a = b$, this equation gives

$$C_5 = \frac{Pb}{6\ell}(b^2 - \ell^2). \tag{u}$$

When the constants of integration given by Equations (t) and (u) are substituted into Equation (s), the elastic curve equation is obtained as follows:

$$-EI_xy = \frac{Pb}{6\ell}z^3 - \frac{P}{6}\langle z - a\rangle^3 + \frac{Pb}{6\ell}(b^2 - \ell^2)z. \tag{v}$$

The advantage of using step functions in solving beam-deflection problems by double integration is clearly demonstrated by the solution of the elastic curve equation for the beam in Figure P8.11. Only two constants of integration were required to solve for the elastic curve equation given by Equation (v) whereas four constants of integration were required to solve for Equations (o). Note that Equations (o) and (v) give the same elastic curve for the beam. The ratio of the time required to solve for the elastic curve equation when using step functions and when not using step functions is equal approximately to $1/n^2$, where n is the number of independent equations needed to represent the moment equation for the beam when step functions are not used. Equations (a) and (b) indicate that $n = 2$ for this problem.

PART (3). The location in the beam at which the maximum deflection occurs is at the location at which the slope $dy/dz = 0$. Because $b < a$, the cross section at which the slope is zero would be expected to be located within the length $z = 0$ to $z = a$. The value of z at this cross section is given either by Equation (e) with the value of C_1 given by Equation (n) or by Equation (r) with the value of C_5 given by Equation (u) as follows:

$$-EI_x\frac{dy}{dz} = \frac{Pb}{2\ell}z^2 + \frac{Pb}{6\ell}(b^2 - \ell^2) = 0.$$

Solving for z,

$$z = \sqrt{\frac{\ell^2 - b^2}{3}} = \sqrt{\frac{a(a + 2b)}{3}}. \tag{w}$$

Note that Equation (w) confirms that for $a > b$ the value of $z < a$. The value of z given by Equation (w) can be substituted into either the first of Equations (o) or Equation (v) to obtain the maximum deflection for the beam.

Problems

Note. In the problems that follow five important assumptions are made. (1) The stress-strain relationship of the material is linear. (2) The loads acting on the beam all lie in one plane; furthermore, the plane of the loads coincides with the principal axis of inertia in every cross section. (3) The beams are assumed to be supported in the direction perpendicular to the plane of the loads so that failure by lateral buckling (see Chapter 11) does not occur. (4) Unless otherwise specified the beams are assumed to have constant cross section. (5) The weights of the beams are neglected unless otherwise specified.

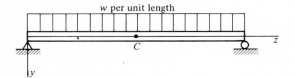

Fig. P 8.12.

8.12. The simple beam shown in Figure P8.12 is subjected to a uniformly distributed load. Derive the elastic curve equation for the beam and determine the maximum deflection Δ in terms of w, ℓ, E, and I_x.

$$\text{ans.} \quad \Delta = \frac{5}{384} \frac{w\ell^4}{EI_x}.$$

8.13. Let the beam in Problem 8.12 have a length of 20 ft and let $w = 800$ lb/ft. Select a rolled steel I-beam from Appendix B to be used as the beam, if the working stress for the beam is $\sigma_z = 20{,}000$ psi and the maximum deflection for the beam is limited to 0.750 in.

8.14. Several 6-in. I-beams ($I_x = 26.0$ in.^{4}) are placed side by side to form a simple beam with a span of 15 ft. A load of 80,000 lb is uniformly distributed over the beams. The working stress for the material in the beams is 24,000 psi and the allowable deflection for the beams is 1.5 in. (1) Determine the number of steel ($E = 30{,}000{,}000$ psi) beams required. (2) Determine the number of aluminum alloy ($E = 10{,}800{,}000$ psi) beams required.

ans.   (1) 9 steel beams; (2) 15 aluminum alloy beams.

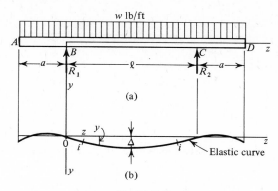

Fig. P 8.15.

8.15. Derive the elastic curve equation for length ℓ of the beam shown in Figure P8.15 and determine the maximum deflection Δ in length ℓ in terms of w, ℓ, a, E, and I_x.

$$\text{ans.} \quad \Delta = \frac{5}{384} \frac{w\ell^4}{EI_x} - \frac{1}{16} \frac{w\ell^2 a^2}{EI_x}.$$

8.16. Derive the elastic curve equation for the cantilever beam shown in Figure P8.16 and determine the maximum deflection Δ of the beam in terms of w, ℓ, E, and I_x.

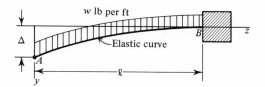

Fig. P 8.16.

8.17. Find the slope of the midpoint B of the cantilever beam shown in Figure P8.17 and the deflection Δ of the free end A of the beam in terms of w, ℓ, E, and I_x.

$$\text{ans.} \quad \theta_B = -\frac{1}{48} \frac{w\ell^3}{EI_x}; \; \Delta_A = \frac{7}{384} \frac{w\ell^4}{EI_x}.$$

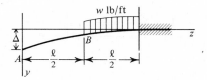

Fig. P 8.17.

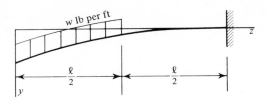

Fig. P 8.18.

8.18. Derive the elastic curve equation for the cantilever beam shown in Figure P8.18.

8.19. A yellow pine timber member is used as a cantilever beam with a span of 10 ft and is loaded as shown in Figure P8.19. The depth of the rectangular section is 12 in. and its width is 6 in. Determine the maximum value of P if the deflection of the beam at the free end must not exceed 0.40 in. Does this load cause the maximum bending stress to exceed the elastic limit of the material? $E = 1.8 \times 10^6$ psi.

ans. $P = 770$ lb.

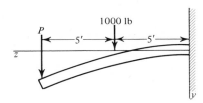

Fig. P 8.19.

8.20. Two oak boards 2-in. by 4-in. are loaded as cantilever beams as shown in Figure P8.20. The working stress for the oak is 2,000 psi. (1) If the shearing stress (friction) between the two boards can be neglected, determine the maximum value of P and the maximum deflection of the beams when this load is applied. (2) Determine the maximum value that P can have if the two boards are glued together to form a composite beam. What is the maximum deflection of the composite beam? $E = 1.5 \times 10^6$ psi.

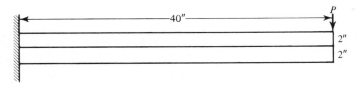

Fig. P 8.20.

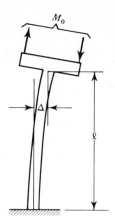

Fig. P 8.21.

8.21. A vertical cantilever beam is subjected to a bending couple M_0 at its free end as shown in Figure P8.21. Determine the deflection Δ at the free end in terms of M_0, ℓ, E, and I_x.

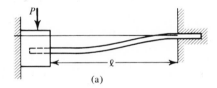

(a)

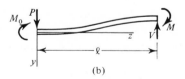

(b)

Fig. P 8.22. Concentrated load and a bending couple at each end of a beam.

8.22. The cantilever beam in Figure P8.22a is loaded at its free end by a concentrated load P and moment M_0 as indicated in Figure P8.22b such that the slope of the free end is zero. Determine the magnitude of M_0 and the deflection Δ of the free end in terms of P, ℓ, E, and I_x. (*Hint*: Three boundary conditions are available. Two can be used to obtain the constants of integration and the third to find M_0.)

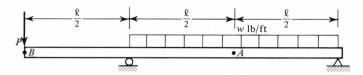

Fig. P 8.23.

8.23. For the beam in Figure P8.23, (1) determine the magnitude of P in terms of w and ℓ such that the deflection of the beam at A is zero. (2) What is the deflection of the beam at B in terms of w, ℓ, P, E, and I_x when these loads are applied to the beam?

8.24. A diving board often is supported as indicated in Figure P8.24. Determine the relation for the deflection Δ of the beam under the load P in terms of P, ℓ_1, ℓ_2, E, and I_x.

$$\text{ans.} \quad \Delta = \frac{P\ell_2^3}{3EI_x}(1 + \ell_1/\ell_2).$$

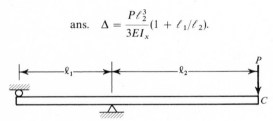

Fig. P 8.24.

8.25. The diving board in Problem 8.24 is made of hickory, for which $E = 1{,}800{,}000$ psi. Let $\ell_1 = 4$ ft, $\ell_2 = 7$ ft, and the depth of the beam be 2 in. What must be the width of the diving board if the deflection of the free end of the board is to be 2 in. when a 180 lb man is standing at the free end?

8.26. One application of beams is to use them as rotational springs. In Figure P8.26 the moment M_A applied at the end A is proportional to the slope θ_A at A. The quantity β_A is the rotational spring constant having dimensions lb-in./rad. Determine β_A for the beam in terms of ℓ, E, and I_x.

$$\text{ans.} \quad \beta_A = \frac{3EI_x}{\ell}.$$

$$\ell \qquad M_A = -\beta_A\,\theta_A$$

$B \qquad\qquad A$

Fig. P 8.26.

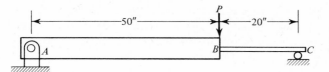

Fig. P 8.27.

8.27. Member AB in Figure P8.27 can be considered rigid and is pivoted at A. Beam BC is fixed to member AB at B; the beam BC is an aluminum alloy tube ($E = 10.4 \times 10^6$ psi) having an outside diameter of 1.000 in. and an inside diameter of 0.800 in. Determine the magnitude of P necessary to cause AB to rotate through an angle of 0.010 rad. Will the material in the beam remain elastic under this condition if $\sigma_e = 42,000$ psi.

ans. $P = 111$ lb.

8.28. A pointer AB (Fig. P8.28) is attached at A to the simple beam that supports concentrated loads P at the quarter points. Determine the slope ($\tan \theta_A = \theta_A$) of the pointer $A'B'$ and the deflection $B_1 B'$ of the end B of the pointer in terms of P, ℓ, E, and I_x.

ans. $\theta_A = P\ell^2/16EI_x$; $B_1 B' = 5P\ell^3/96EI_x$.

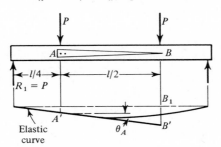

Fig. P 8.28.

8.29. A pointer of length ℓ is attached to the free end of the beam shown in Figure P8.29. A concentrated load P and moment M_0 are applied to the free end of the beam. Determine the magnitude of M_0 in terms of P and ℓ such that the deflection of the free end of the pointer is zero.

ans. $M_0 = P\ell/3$.

Fig. P 8.29.

8.30. Before loading the beam in Figure P8.30 a pointer of length ℓ was attached to the beam over the roller; its free end is at the same elevation as the centroid of each cross section of the beam. When load P is applied, the free end of the pointer is found to move downward a distance of $P\ell^3/4EI_x$. (1) Determine the deflection Δ of the free end of the beam. (2) What is the magnitude of a in terms of ℓ?

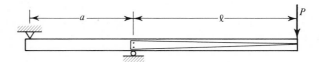

Fig. P 8.30.

8.31. A beam is 20-ft long and is simply supported at one end and at the middle. It carries a uniformly distributed load of $w = 400$ lb/ft between supports. What will be the deflection of the free end of the beam if the beam is made of steel and has a circular cross section 4 in. in diameter?

8.32. A 10-in. 40-lb steel I-beam is used as a simple beam on a span ℓ of 16 ft. A concentrated load P of 14,000 lb is applied at a point $\ell/4$ from the right support. Determine the deflection at the middle of the beam.

ans.   0.299 in.

8.33. Calculate the maximum deflection of a steel shaft 4 in. in diameter used as a simple beam on a span of 10 ft to support a uniformly distributed load that causes a maximum bending stress of 16,000 psi.

ans.   0.400 in.

8.34. Determine the deflection of the point B of the beam shown in Figure P8.34 in terms of P, ℓ, a, E, and I_x.

ans. $\Delta_B = Pa^2(\ell - 2a)^2/6\ell EI_x$.

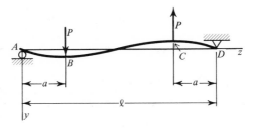

Fig. P 8.34.

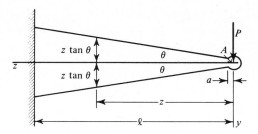

Fig. P 8.35.

8.35. A cantilever beam has a rectangular section of constant width b and varying depth as shown by the taper in Figure P8.35. Show that the value of M_x/EI_x at any distance z from the load is $-3P/2Ebz^2 \tan^3\theta$ and that the deflection of the point A (a short distance a from the load P) is

$$\Delta_A = 3P\left(\log_e\frac{\ell}{a} + \frac{a}{\ell} - 1\right)/2Eb \tan^3\theta.$$

8.36. A flat plate in the shape of an isosceles triangle ABC (see Fig. P8.36a) is used as a cantilever beam with side AB fixed and vertex C the free end. A concentrated load P is applied at C perpendicular to the plane ABC. Show that the M_x/EI_x diagram for the beam is a rectangle as indicated in Figure P8.36b and that the deflection at the load is $\Delta_C = 3P\ell^2/(Ed^3 \tan\theta)$.

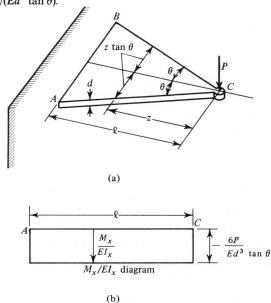

(a)

(b)

Fig. P 8.36.

8.37. Through 8.51. The beams shown in Figures P8.37 through P8.51 have the cross sections as described at the right end of each beam. The material of which the beam is made is also indicated in each figure. In each figure a cross section is designated by the point marked A. For each beam solve for the deflection of point A. The values of the modulus of elasticity E to be used are as follows: for steel, $E = 30,000,000$ psi; for aluminum alloy $E = 10,500,000$ psi; for wood $E = 1,500,000$ psi.

ans.   Problem 8.37 $\Delta_A = -0.0161$ in.

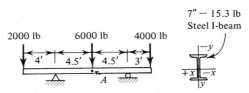

Fig. P 8.37.

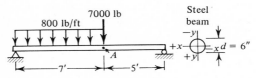

Fig. P 8.38.

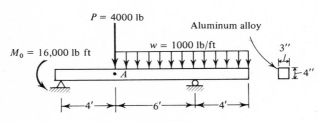

Fig. P 8.39.

ans.   Problem 8.39 $\Delta_A = 0.0905$ in.

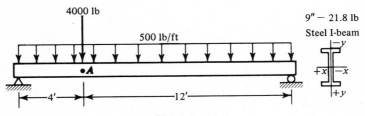

Fig. P 8.40.

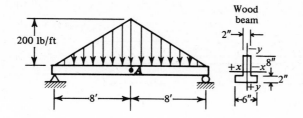

Fig. P 8.41.

ans.   Problem 8.41 $\Delta_A = 0.926$ in.

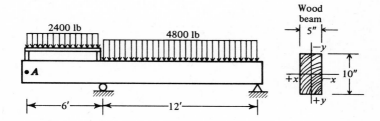

Fig. P 8.42.

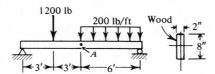

Fig. P 8.43.

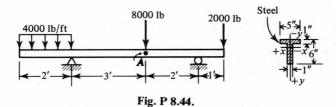

Fig. P 8.44.

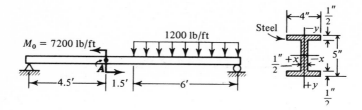

Fig. P 8.45.

ans.   Problem 8.45 $\Delta_A = 0.307$ in.

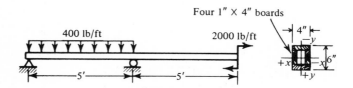

Fig. P 8.46.

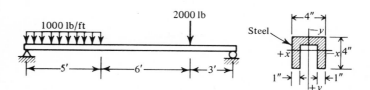

Fig. P 8.47.

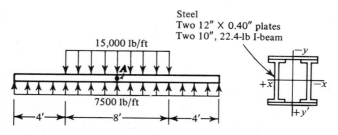

Fig. P 8.48.

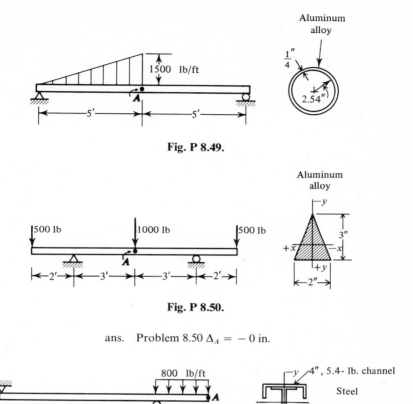

Fig. P 8.49.

ans.   Problem 8.50 $\Delta_A = -0$ in.

Fig. P 8.50.

Fig. P 8.51.

8.8.   Moment-Area Method

A convenient semigraphical interpretation and procedure, called the moment-area method,* leads to two theorems for determining the slope and deflection at any point of the elastic curve of a beam. The first step in

---

* Sometimes this method is called the slope-deviation method. We suggest that the name curvature-area moment method be given to it, because the area referred to is always the area under the curve whose ordinate represents the curvature of the beam at the section, and the moment referred to is the moment of the curvature area.

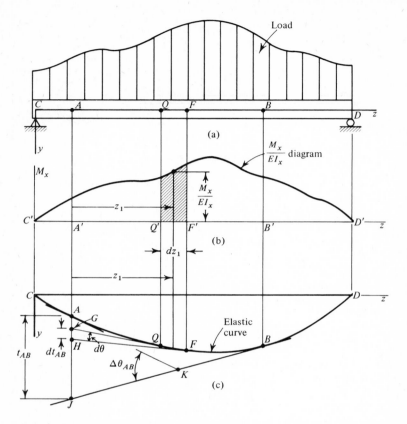

Fig. 8.5. Graphical constructions used in the derivation and interpretation of the moment-area method for determining deflections of beams.

the method involves an interpretation of Equation (8–4):

$$\Delta\theta = -\int \frac{M_x}{EI_x}\, dz.$$

For example, Figure 8.5a represents a beam subjected to a distributed load; Figure 8.5b represents the M_x/EI_x (curvature) diagram for the beam, any ordinate in which is the bending moment divided by EI_x at the section where the ordinate is erected; that is, the ordinate represents the curvature of the beam at the section. If EI_x is a constant, the M_x/EI_x diagram has the same form as the moment diagram.

In Figure 8.5c, $CAQFBD$ represents the elastic curve of the beam, with deflections greatly exaggerated. As indicated in Figure 8.5b $(M_x/EI_x)\,dz_1$ is represented by a differential area under the M_x/EI_x diagram, as shown between the ordinates at Q' and F'. But, from Equation (8–3), the angle $d\theta$ between any two tangent lines QG and HF in Figure 8.5c drawn at points Q and F on the elastic curve, a differential distance dz_1 apart, is equal to the quantity $(M_x/EI_x)\,dz_1$. Let the total change in slope between tangent lines drawn to the elastic curve at any two points such as A and B be $\Delta\theta_{AB}$. Then

$$\Delta\theta_{AB} = \int_A^B d\theta = -\int_A^B \frac{M_x}{EI_x}\,dz_1 \tag{8–12}$$

and is represented by the total area under the M_x/EI_x diagram between the specified ordinates, such as ordinates erected at A' and B'. Therefore, the following theorem may be stated:

Theorem I. When a straight beam is subjected to bending, the difference $\Delta\theta_{AB}$ in the slopes of the elastic curve at any two points is equal in magnitude to the area of the M_x/EI_x diagram between ordinates at the corresponding points. The sign of $\Delta\theta_{AB}$ will be negative when the sum of the areas is positive and $\Delta\theta_{AB}$ will be positive when the sum of the areas is negative, as shown by Equation (8–12).

A second theorem stating the procedure for determining deflections may be obtained as follows. In Figure 8.5c, let t_{AB} denote the distance of any point A on the elastic curve, measured in a direction perpendicular to the original position of the beam from a tangent drawn at any other point B on the elastic curve. The distance t_{AB} will be called the tangential deviation of the point. Let z_1 be the distance along the length of the beam from the point A' to ordinate at the centroid of the cross-hatched area between Q' and F', as shown in Figure 8.5b. Let dt_{AB} be defined as the tangential deviation between the points Q and F as shown in Figure 8.5c. The value of t_{AB} is found as the summation of the distance dt_{AB} corresponding to the changes in slope over the differential distances dz_1 between A and B. These dt_{AB} deviations are caused by the bending moments in the various dz_1 lengths of the beam. The sign of dt_{AB} in Figure 8.5 is positive because it is in the direction of the positive y-axis. The magnitude of dt_{AB} is equal to $z_1\,d\theta$, since an arc is equal to the product of the radius and the angle. Because $d\theta$ is negative,

$$t_{AB} = \int dt_{AB} = -\int z_1\,d\theta. \tag{8–13}$$

But, as previously shown, $d\theta = -(M_x/EI_x)\,dz_1$, hence

$$t_{AB} = \int_A^B \frac{M_x z_1}{EI_x}\,dz_1. \tag{8-14}$$

It is very important to note that in the preceding equations z_1 is the distance of any point on the elastic curve (or of any ordinate in the M_x/EI_x diagram) from the point whose tangential deviation is to be found; it is not the distance from the origin and is therefore not to be thought of as a coordinate.

As is evident from Figure 8.5b, however, $(M_x/EI_x)\,dz_1$ is the moment of the differential area $M_x\,dz_1/EI_x$ of the M_x/EI_x diagram about the ordinate through point A whose tangential deviation is t_{AB}; hence $\int(M_x z_1/EI_x)\,dz_1$ is the moment of that part of the M_x/EI_x diagram that lies between the two ordinates considered—the moment being taken about the ordinate through the point whose tangential deviation is desired. The following theorem may therefore be stated:

> *Theorem II. When a straight beam is subjected to bending, the tangential deviation t_{AB} of any point A on the elastic curve measured normal to the original position of the beam, from a tangent drawn to the elastic curve at any other point B, is represented in magnitude by the moment of the area of the M_x/EI_x diagram between the ordinates at the two points about an ordinate through A.*

The sign convention of the tangential deviation t_{AB} is given in the next paragraph.

Sign Convention. In many problems the sign or direction of the tangential deviation can be determined by inspection. It is helpful to note, however, that if moments of positive areas are considered as positive, point A lies above the tangent drawn at point B for positive moments (Fig. 8.6a) and below the tangent at B for negative moments (Fig. 8.6b). For example, in Figure 8.6a,

$$t_{AB} = (\tfrac{2}{3}z_1)\left(\frac{1}{4}\frac{Pz_1^2}{EI_x}\right) = \frac{1}{6}\frac{Pz_1^3}{EI_x},$$

and

$$t_{BA} = (\tfrac{1}{3}z_1)\left(\frac{1}{4}\frac{Pz_1^2}{EI_x}\right) = \frac{1}{12}\frac{Pz_1^3}{EI_x},$$

Note that t_{AB} is not equal to t_{BA}. In Figure 8.6b,

$$t_{AB} = (\tfrac{2}{3}z_1)\left(-\frac{1}{4}\frac{Pz_1^2}{EI_x}\right) = -\frac{1}{6}\frac{Pz_1^3}{EI_x},$$

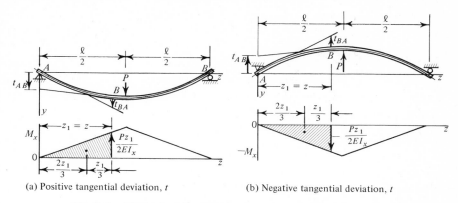

(a) Positive tangential deviation, t (b) Negative tangential deviation, t

Fig. 8.6.   Method of determining sign of tangential derivation.

and

$$t_{BA} = (\tfrac{1}{3}z_1)\left(-\frac{1}{4}\frac{Pz_1^2}{EI_x}\right) = -\frac{1}{12}\frac{Pz_1^3}{EI_x}.$$

Furthermore, in solving Equation (8–14) mathematically for t_{AB}, if it is assumed that the y-axis is positive downward, t_{AB} will be positive (downward) when the $\int_A^B (M_x z_1/EI_x)\,dz_1$ is positive and t_{AB} will be negative (upward) when this integral is negative. In evaluating $\int_A^B (M_x z_1/EI_x)\,dz_1$, the terms z_1, E, and I_x are always positive and the bending moment M_x has the sign convention as described in Section 6.2 and as shown in Figure 8.6a and b.

8.9.   Cantilever Beam; Concentrated Load at Free End

In Figure 8.7, AB represents the elastic curve of the beam, and $A'B'H$ represents the M_x/EI_x diagram. The beam is assumed to have a constant cross section, and the weight of the beam is neglected.

Maximum Deflection.   The maximum deflection of the beam may be found as follows. The tangential deviation t_{AB} of A from a tangent drawn at B is equal in magnitude to the maximum deflection Δ of the cantilever beam. Thus, from Theorem II, the value of t_{AB} is

t_{AB} = moment of area $A'B'H$ about ordinate through A',

   = area $A'B'H$ times distance to centroid,

$$= \left(-\frac{1}{2}\frac{P\ell^2}{EI_x}\right)\left(\frac{2}{3}\right)\ell = -\frac{1}{3}\frac{P\ell^3}{EI_x}. \tag{8–15}$$

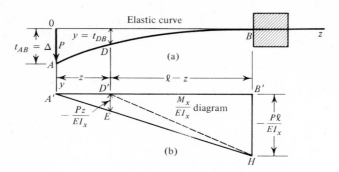

Fig. 8.7.

The negative sign of t_{AB} indicates that the tangent to the elastic curve at the point B lies above the point A. Because the tangent at B coincides with the centerline of the beam before it was loaded, we note that the distance t_{AB} is equal in magnitude to the deflection Δ of point A of the beam. Because the deflection of point A is in the direction of the y-axis, the deflection is positive and $\Delta = -t_{AB}$.

Deflection of Any Point. The deflection y of a point D at the distance z from the free end of the beam may be found as follows. The tangential deviation t_{DB} of D from a tangent at B has the same magnitude as y; thus, if we use Theorem II, $y = -t_{DB}$ = the negative of the moment of area $B'D'EH$ about $D'E$. Let the area $B'D'EH$ (Fig. 8.7b) be divided into two triangular areas as indicated by the dashed line. Then,

$$y = -t_{DB} = -\left[-\frac{Pz}{2EI_x}\frac{(\ell - z)^2}{3} - \frac{P\ell}{2EI_x}\frac{2}{3}(\ell - z)^2 \right].$$

Hence,

$$6EI_x y = P(z^3 - 3\ell^2 z + 2\ell^3), \tag{8-16}$$

which is the elastic curve equation.

8.10. Simple Beam; Cross Section Not Constant

Let a concentrated load P act at the center of a simply supported beam (Fig. 8.8a), and let the moment of inertia of each cross section in the central half of the beam be I_x and each section in the outer quarters be $I_x/2$. The M_x/EI_x diagram is shown in Figure 8.8b. Let it be required to determine Δ, the maximum deflection of the beam.

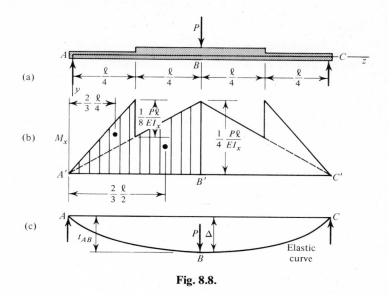

Fig. 8.8.

By using Theorem II in connection with Figure 8.8b, the magnitude of the maximum deflection shown in Figure 8.8c may be found as follows:

$$\Delta = t_{AB} = \text{moment about ordinate through } A' \text{ of shaded area of } M_x/EI_x \text{ diagram,}$$

$$= \frac{1}{2} \frac{1}{4} \frac{P\ell}{EI_x} \frac{\ell}{2} \left(\frac{2}{3} \frac{\ell}{2}\right) + \frac{1}{2} \frac{1}{8} \frac{P\ell}{EI_x} \frac{\ell}{4} \left(\frac{2}{3} \frac{\ell}{4}\right),$$

$$= \frac{P\ell^3}{48EI_x} + \frac{P\ell^3}{384EI_x} = \frac{3P\ell^3}{128EI_x}. \tag{8-17}$$

8.11. Beam with General Loading

The beam in Figure 8.9a is subjected to concentrated loads at the reactions, a concentrated couple at the left end, a uniformly distributed load, and a linearly increasing distributed load. Thus, every type of beam load considered in this book is acting on the beam in Figure 8.9a. The elastic curve of the beam assumes a shape similar to that shown in Figure 8.9b. Let it be required to determine the maximum deflection of that portion of the beam between the supports. It is assumed that the slope of the beam at

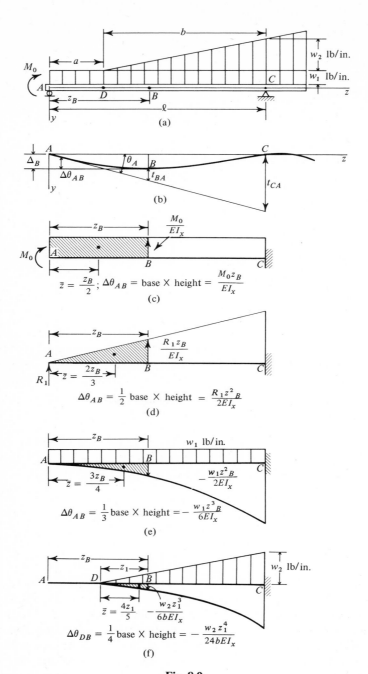

$\bar{z} = \dfrac{z_B}{2}$; $\Delta\theta_{AB} = \text{base} \times \text{height} = \dfrac{M_0 z_B}{EI_x}$

(c)

$\bar{z} = \dfrac{2z_B}{3}$

$\Delta\theta_{AB} = \dfrac{1}{2} \text{ base} \times \text{height} = \dfrac{R_1 z^2{}_B}{2EI_x}$

(d)

$\bar{z} = \dfrac{3z_B}{4}$

$\Delta\theta_{AB} = \dfrac{1}{3} \text{base} \times \text{height} = -\dfrac{w_1 z^3{}_B}{6EI_x}$

(e)

$\bar{z} = \dfrac{4z_1}{5}$

$\Delta\theta_{DB} = \dfrac{1}{4} \text{base} \times \text{height} = -\dfrac{w_2 z_1^4}{24bEI_x}$

(f)

Fig. 8.9.

point C is negative; therefore, the beam will have only one point (point B) within length ℓ where the slope of the beam is zero and the maximum deflection of the beam is Δ_B. Distance z_B to point B must first be obtained before the maximum deflection Δ_B can be determined. Using Theorems I and II and Figure 8.9b, the following relations can be determined:

$$\Delta\theta_{AB} = \theta_A = \tan\theta_A = \frac{t_{CA}}{\ell}, \tag{8–18}$$

$$\Delta_B = z_B\theta_A - t_{BA} = \frac{z_B t_{CA}}{\ell} - t_{BA}. \tag{8–19}$$

The change in slope $\Delta\theta_{AB}$ in Equation (8–18) is given by Equation (8–12) whereas the tangential deviations t_{CA} and t_{BA} in Equations (8–18) and (8–19) are given by Equation (8–14). The integrals in Equations (8–12) and (8–14) can be solved by writing M_x/EI_x as discontinuous functions of z as discussed in Section 6.4 or as one function of z using step functions as discussed in Section 6.5; however, the amount of computational work can usually be reduced by breaking the M_x/EI_x diagram down into several simple parts. There are many ways in which the M_x/EI_x diagram can be broken down into simple parts; the procedure followed here is to apply each of the loads, acting on the beam over the length ℓ, to a separate cantilever beam as indicated in Figures 8.9c, d, e, and f. The sum of the M_x/EI_x diagrams in Figures 8.9c, d, e, and f is equal to the actual M_x/EI_x diagram for the length ℓ of the beam. The angle change and two tangential deviations in Equations (8–18) and (8–19) require that the area under the M_x/EI_x diagram and the location of the centroid of this area be known. These quantities are given for each M_x/EI_x diagram shown in Figures 8.9c, d, e, and f. The quantities $\Delta\theta_{AB}$, t_{BA}, and t_{CA} required in Equations (8–18) and (8–19) are given by the following relations:

$$\Delta\theta_{AB} = \frac{M_0 z_B}{EI_x} + \frac{R_1 z_B^2}{2EI_x} - \frac{w_1 z_B^3}{6EI_x} - \frac{w_2 z_1^4}{24bEI_x},$$

$$t_{BA} = \frac{M_0 z_B^2}{2EI_x} + \frac{R_1 z_B^3}{6EI_x} - \frac{w_1 z_B^4}{24EI_x} - \frac{w_2 z_1^5}{120bEI_x},$$

$$t_{CA} = \frac{M_0 \ell^2}{2EI_x} + \frac{R_1 \ell^3}{6EI_x} - \frac{w_1 \ell^4}{24EI_x} - \frac{w_2 b^4}{120EI_x}.$$

When the foregoing expressions for $\Delta\theta_{AB}$ and t_{CA} are substituted into Equation (8–18), the value of z_B can be determined. With this value of z_B and the values of t_{CA} and t_{BA}, the maximum deflection ΔB is found from Equation (8–19).

Illustrative Problems

8.52.   A 10-in., 40-lb-per-ft steel I-beam is used as a horizontal cantilever beam as shown in Figure P8.52. The beam supports a uniformly distributed load of 200 lb/ft, including the beam weight, and two concentrated loads: one load of 1,000 lb acts 2 ft from the free end and the other of 2,500 lb acts at the midpoint. Compute the maximum bending stress and the maximum deflection of the beam.

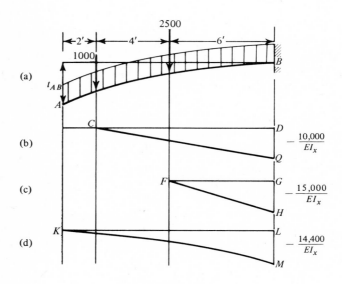

Fig. P 8.52.

SOLUTION.   From the appropriate table in Appendix B we find $I_x = 158.0$ in.[4] The maximum bending moment, including the weight of the beam, is $-39,400$ lb-ft. Hence, the maximum bending stress is

$$\sigma_{max} = \frac{M_x c}{I_x} = \frac{(-39,400(12)(-5)}{158.0} = 15,000 \text{ psi.}$$

Using the procedure presented in Section 8.11, the M_x/EI_x diagram for the beam is given in three parts as shown in Figure P8.52b, c, and d, where part b is for the 1,000-lb load, part c is for the 2,500-lb load, and part d is for the distributed load. The area under the M_x/EI_x diagrams and the location of the centroid of the areas are given in Figure 8.9d and e. By using Theorem II, the magnitude of the maximum deflection Δ is found to be

$\Delta = -t_{AB}$ = the negative of the sum of moments of areas CDQ, FGH, and KLM about the ordinate through A,

$$= \tfrac{1}{2}(10)\left(\frac{10,000}{EI_x}\right)(2 + \tfrac{2}{3}10) + \tfrac{1}{2}(6)\left(\frac{15,000}{EI_x}\right)(6 + \tfrac{2}{3}6) + \tfrac{1}{3}(12)\left(\frac{14,400}{EI_x}\right)(\tfrac{3}{4}12),$$

$$= \frac{1,402,000}{EI_x}.$$

But $E = 30,000,000$ psi and $I_x = 158.0$ in.[4] in which the length units are inches. In obtaining the foregoing results for the deflection, the length units were feet. Hence, the numerator quantity 1,402,000 is in lb-ft³. To keep the units consistent, we must therefore multiply the numerator by the quantity 12^3 to convert the units to lb-in.³ Hence,

$$= \frac{1,402,000(12^3)}{30,000,000(158)} = 0.511 \text{ in.}$$

8.53. A simply supported horizontal beam is loaded as shown in Figure P8.53a. The beam is a 9-in., 10.68-lb-per-ft aluminum alloy I-beam. The beam has values for E and I_x as follows: $E = 10,000,000$ psi and $I_x = 102.4$ in.[4] Compute the maximum deflection Δ of the beam.

SOLUTION. Using Theorems I and II, and Figure P8.53b, the following relations can be determined (Equations 8–18 and 8–19):

$$\Delta\theta_{AB} = \theta_A = \frac{t_{CA}}{\ell}, \tag{a}$$

$$\Delta_B = z_B\theta_A - t_{BA} = \frac{z_B t_{CA}}{\ell} - t_{BA}. \tag{b}$$

Using the procedure presented in Section 8.11, the M_x/EI_x diagram for the beam is given in three parts as shown in Figure P8.53c, d, and e, where part c is for the reaction $R_1 = 9,750$ lb at the left end, part d is for the 10,000 lb load, and part e is for the distributed load. The area under the M_x/EI_x diagrams and the location of the centroid of the areas are given in Figure 8.9d and e. By using Theorems I and II, the quantities $\Delta\theta_{AB}$, t_{BA}, and t_{CA} needed in Equations (a) and (b) are determined as follows:

$\Delta\theta_{AB}$ = the sum of areas $A'B'O'$ and $LB''O''$

$$= \frac{9,750z_B^2}{2EI_x} - \frac{10,000(z_B - 3)^2}{2EI_x}, \tag{c}$$

t_{BA} = the sum of moments of areas $A'B'O'$ and $LB''O''$ about ordinate through B,

$$= \frac{9{,}750z_B^2}{2EI_x}\left(\frac{z_B}{3}\right) - \frac{10{,}000(z_B - 3)^2}{2EI_x}\left(\frac{z_B - 3}{3}\right), \tag{d}$$

t_{CA} = the sum of moments of areas $A'KH$, LNM, and RST about ordinate through C,

$$= \tfrac{1}{2}(20)\left(\frac{195{,}000}{EI_x}\right)(\tfrac{20}{3}) - \tfrac{1}{2}(17)\left(\frac{170{,}000}{EI_x}\right)(\tfrac{17}{3}) - \tfrac{1}{3}(10)\left(\frac{25{,}000}{EI_x}\right)(\tfrac{10}{4}),$$

$$= \frac{4{,}600{,}000}{EI_x}. \tag{e}$$

The substitution of Equations (c) and (e) into Equation (a) gives the magnitude of z_B, which locates the point of maximum deflection. Thus,

$$\frac{9{,}750z_B^2}{2EI_x} - \frac{10{,}000(z_B - 3)^2}{2EI_x} = \frac{4{,}600{,}000}{20EI_x},$$

$$z_B^2 - 240z_B + 2{,}200 = 0,$$

and

$$z_B = 9.54 \text{ ft.}$$

Substituting this value of z_B in Equation (d) gives

$$t_{BA} = \frac{9{,}750(9.54)^3}{6EI_x} - \frac{10{,}000(6.54)^3}{6EI_x} = \frac{945{,}000}{EI_x}.$$

This value of t_{BA}, the value of t_{CA} given by Equation (e), and values of z_B and ℓ when substituted into Equation (b) gives

$$\Delta_B = \frac{4{,}600{,}000(9)}{20EI_x} - \frac{945{,}000}{EI_x} = \frac{1{,}249{,}000}{EI_x}.$$

When the values of E and I_x are substituted in this equation, and the factor 12^3 is multiplied into the numerator (see solution of Problem 8.52), the result is

$$\Delta_B = \frac{1{,}249{,}000(12)^3}{10{,}000{,}000(102.4)} = 2.11 \text{ in.}$$

The maximum bending moment is 29,250 lb-ft. Therefore, the maximum bending stress is

$$\sigma_{max} = \frac{29{,}250(12)(4.5)}{102.4} = 15{,}400 \text{ psi.}$$

This stress is less than the elastic limit of the aluminum alloy (see Table 1.1).

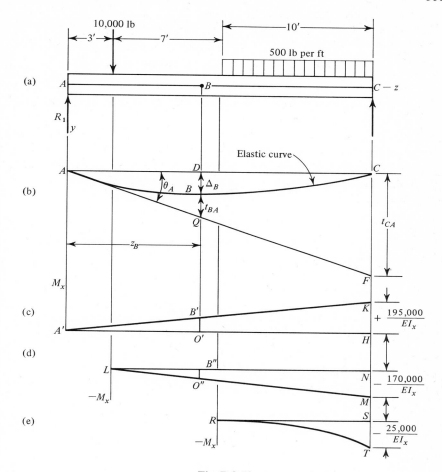

Fig. P 8.53.

Problems

8.54. Derive the elastic curve equation for the beam in Figure P8.54 in terms of M_0, ℓ, E, and I_x.

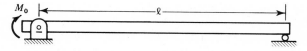

Fig. P 8.54.

8.55. For the beam in Problem 8.54 determine the location z_B of the point of maximum deflection and the maximum deflection Δ_B.

$$\text{ans.} \quad z_B = 0.423\ell\,; \Delta_B = \frac{0.0642 M_0 \ell^2}{EI_x}.$$

8.56. Determine the elastic curve equation for the beam in Figure P8.12 in terms of w, ℓ, E, and I_x.

8.57. The beam in Figure P8.18 is made by nailing 1-in. by 6-in. boards together to form a rectangular section beam having a depth of 6 in. The beam has a length of 8 ft and $w = 200$ lb/ft. The modulus of elasticity for the wood is $E = 1,500\,000$ psi and the working stress for the wood is $\sigma_w = 2,000$ psi. Determine the minimum number of boards to make the beam and the deflection Δ of the free end of the beam.

$$\text{ans.} \quad \text{number of boards} = 5\,; \Delta = 1.12 \text{ in.}$$

8.58. Determine the deflection of point C at the location where the load P is applied to the beam in Figure P8.24 in terms of P, ℓ_1, ℓ_2, E, and I_x. Note that

$$\Delta_C = t_{CA} - \frac{t_{BA}(\ell_1 + \ell_2)}{\ell_1}.$$

8.59. Determine the deflection of the free end of the cantilever beam in Figure P8.59 in terms of w, ℓ, E, and I_x.

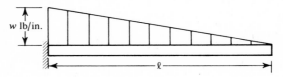

Fig. P 8.59.

8.60 Through 8.88. Solve Problems 8.23 through 8.51 using the moment-area method.

8.12. Relationship Between Maximum Deflection and Maximum Stress

It will be well at this point to summarize some of the results obtained in this and the preceding chapter and to call attention to the relationship between the maximum bending moment (and hence the maximum elastic stress) and the maximum deflection for a beam. Such a summary may be convenient for use in the design of a beam to resist elastic deflection.

In Table 8.1, W is the total load on the beam having a span ℓ, E is the modulus of elasticity of the material, and I_x is the moment of inertia of the cross section of the beam about the centroidal axis, the cross section being assumed constant.

Table 8.1

TYPE OF BEAM AND OF LOADING	MAXIMUM BENDING MOMENT, M_x	MAXIMUM DEFLECTION
Cantilever, load at end	$1W\ell$	$\dfrac{1}{3}\dfrac{W\ell^3}{EI_x}$
Cantilever, uniform load	$\frac{1}{2}W\ell$	$\dfrac{1}{8}\dfrac{W\ell^3}{EI_x}$
Simple beam, load at center	$\frac{1}{4}W\ell$	$\dfrac{1}{48}\dfrac{W\ell^3}{EI_x}$
Simple beam, uniform load	$\frac{1}{8}W\ell$	$\dfrac{5}{384}\dfrac{W\ell^3}{EI_x}$

Tables similar to Table 8.1 for additional types of beams and of loadings may be found in various handbooks dealing with load-resisting members, such as Steel Construction, American Institute of Steel Construction, and the Aluminum Company of America Structural Handbook.

It is seen from this table that for a cantilever or simple beam subjected to any type of static loading general expressions for M_x and Δ may be written as follows:

$$M_x = \alpha W\ell, \qquad \Delta = \beta\frac{W\ell^3}{EI_x},$$

in which α and β are constants depending on the type of beam and of loading. If W is eliminated from the preceding general expressions, the result is

$$\Delta = \frac{\beta}{\alpha}\frac{M_x\ell^2}{EI_x}, \qquad \text{but} \qquad M_x = \frac{\sigma_{z_1}I_x}{c_1}$$

$$\Delta = \frac{\beta}{\alpha}\frac{\sigma_{z_1}}{E}\frac{\ell^2}{c_1}. \tag{8-20}$$

One way of interpreting this equation is as follows: If several beams, each having a constant cross section, are of the same type, are made of the same material, and are subjected to the same type of loading (in other words, if $\beta/\alpha E$ = a constant), then the deflections of the beams will vary directly with the maximum stress, with the square of the spans, and inversely with the distances from the neutral axis to the most remote fibers.

Design of a Beam.   Thus if a beam is to be designed to resist a specified maximum elastic deflection, it is possible to limit the maximum deflection of a beam by the choice of a maximum value of the bending stress. For example, let a simply supported 10-in., 30-lb steel I-beam of 15-ft span length be subjected to a uniformly distributed load. For this beam Equation (8–20) becomes, when values of α, β, E, ℓ, and c_1 are substituted,

$$\Delta_{max} = \frac{225}{10^7}\sigma_{z_1}. \tag{8–21}$$

In case $c_1 > c_2$, $\sigma_{z_1} = \sigma_{max}$.

Illustrative Problem

8.89.   A beam is simply supported at its ends and is subjected to a uniformly distributed load. The beam is made of steel and is 12-in. deep. It is specified that the maximum elastic deflection of the beam must not exceed $\frac{1}{360}$ of the length ℓ and that the maximum elastic tensile or compressive bending stress must not exceed 20,000 psi; determine the maximum length ℓ that the beam may have and still satisfy both the foregoing conditions.

SOLUTIONS.   From Equation (8–20), we have

$$\frac{\ell}{360} = \left(\frac{\frac{5}{384}}{\frac{1}{8}}\right)\frac{20,000}{30 \times 10^6}\frac{\ell^2}{6}.$$

Therefore, $\ell = 240$ in. $= 20$ ft.

Problems

8.90.   If the beam in Problem 8.89 must be 24 ft in length and 12 in. in depth, determine the maximum elastic tensile or compressive bending stress if it is assumed that the deflection must not exceed $\frac{1}{360}$ of its length.

ans.   16,660 psi.

8.91.   A cantilever beam to be subjected to a concentrated load at its free end must be made so that the following conditions are fulfilled: The length must be 2 ft, the depth must be 3 in., the elastic deflection must not exceed 0.3 in., and the maximum tensile or compressive bending stress must not exceed 20,000 psi. Can the beam be made of magnesium alloy? aluminum alloy? (See Table 1.1.)

8.92. If the length and depth of a beam made of steel are given, can the maximum elastic deflection be controlled (limited to a specified amount) by choosing a limiting value of the maximum tensile or compressive bending stress? (*Hint:* Use Eq. 8–20.)

8.13. Deflection of Beam Caused by Shear

The deflection of a beam caused by the shearing stresses in the beam was assumed in the preceding discussions to be negligible. In relatively short, deep beams, however, the deflection caused by shear may require consideration. An approximate value for the deflection caused by the shearing stresses may be found as follows:

The shear deformation dy_τ of a small block of length dz in the beam in Figure 8.10 is

$$dy_\tau = \gamma_{zy}\, dz = \frac{\tau_{zy}}{G}\, dz$$

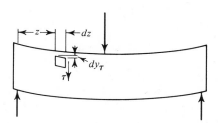

Fig. 8.10.

in which τ_{zy} is the shearing stress on the face of the block; the deflection of a fiber of length z (Fig. 8.10) is

$$y_\tau = \frac{1}{G} \int_0^z \tau_{zy}\, dz. \tag{8–22}$$

Because τ_{zy} varies in magnitude over each cross section, only one of the infinite number of values of τ_{zy} at each cross section can be substituted into Equation (8–22) to give the correct value of the component of the beam deflection caused by shearing stresses. One approach is to use the average value of the shearing stress, $\tau_{zy(ave)} = V_y/A$, where V_y is the vertical shear and A is the cross-sectional area of the beam, and introduce a correction factor η as follows:

$$y_\tau = \frac{\eta}{G} \int_0^{z} \frac{V_y}{A} \, dz. \tag{8-23}$$

A reliable value for η for a given beam is the ratio of $\tau_{zy(max)}$ to $\tau_{zy(ave)}$. Values of η for several beam cross sections are listed in Table 8.2.

The exact solution for the component of beam deflection due to shearing stresses of a rectangular section cantilever beam with concentrated load at the free end can be obtained and is identical with that given by Equation (8-23) with $\eta = 1.5$ (see Table 8.2).

Table 8.2

Beam cross section	η
Rectangle	1.5
Circle	1.33
Thin-wall circular	2.0
I-section*	1.0

* The area A for the I-section is the area of the web, ht where h is the beam depth and t is the web thickness.

Problems

8.93. A rectangular section cantilever beam has a width of 2 in. a depth of 6 in. and a length of 24 in. The beam is made of structural steel ($E = 30,000,000$ psi and $G = 11,600,000$ psi). Determine the magnitude of a concentrated load P acting through the centroid and parallel to the 6-in. dimension at the free end of the beam which will develop a working stress of 20,000 psi. Also determine the components of deflection of the free end of the beam due to bending (normal) stresses and due to transverse shearing stresses.

ans. $P = 10,000 \, lb$; $\Delta_\sigma = 0.04267 \, in.$; $\Delta_\tau = 0.00259 \, in.$

8.94. Let the beam in Problem 8.93 be replaced by a 6-in. 12.5 lb/ft I-beam. Note that when short I-beams are used in design, it may be necessary to stiffen some sections particularly the section where the loads are applied; this may be accomplished at the free end by welding a plate on the end of the beam. Determine the load P if the maximum stress given by the flexure formula is 20,000 psi. Also determine the component of deflection of the free end of the beam due to bending stresses and transverse shearing stresses.

ans. $P = 6,060 \, lb$; $\Delta_\sigma = 0.0426 \, in.$; $\Delta_\tau = 0.00909 \, in.$

8.14.   Deflection of Linear Viscoelastic Beam

As discussed in Sections 1.11 and 1.12, material behavior under certain environmental conditions may be time dependent. Beams made of these materials continue to deflect with time. The prediction of the time-dependent deflection requires that the constitutive relation for the material and for the beam be specified. The only viscoelastic model considered here is the Maxwell model. Because the state of stress in the beam is assumed to be uniaxial, the constitutive relation for a beam made of a material approximated by a Maxwell model is the same as for axial centric loading as given by Equation (1–36). The relation is

$$\dot{\epsilon}_z = \frac{\dot{\sigma}_z}{E_M} + \frac{\sigma_z}{\mu_M} \tag{8–24}$$

in which E_M and μ_M are material constants and the dot designates differentiation with respect to time.

Let the beam in Figure 8.3 be made of a time-dependent material that can be accurately approximated by a Maxwell model. At some time t, the length $ds = dz$ takes the deformed shape indicated by $F'Q'G'H'$ with center of curvature at O and with radius of curvature ρ; this deformed length is redrawn in Figure 8.11. Because of the time-dependent deformation and

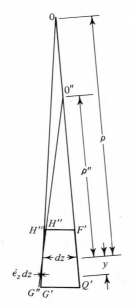

Fig. 8.11.

because plane sections remain plane, face $H'G'$ rotates with respect to face $F'Q'$ in a time interval dt to a new position $H''G''$ with new center of curvature O'' and new radius of curvature ρ''. The change in geometry with time indicates that

$$\frac{d\rho}{dt} = \dot{\rho} = \frac{y}{\dot{\epsilon}_z} \qquad (8\text{--}25)$$

which states that the strain rate varies linearly with the distance y from the neutral axis of the beam.

The stress distribution in the linear viscoelastic beam can be determined using Equations (8–24) and (8–25). Let the loads that produce the deformations indicated by $F'Q'G'H'$ in Figure 8.11 be applied in sufficiently short time so that the viscous element (dashpot) of the Maxwell model does not have time to react. The material is linearly elastic at that time; let zero time be specified at that time. The stress distribution at zero time is linear and given by the flexure formula, Equation (7–11). During the first increment of time dt (after the time-dependent deformation starts), the strain rate $\dot{\epsilon}_z$ varies linearly with y as indicated by Equation (8–25). Divide Equation (8–24) by y and note that the stress σ_z at the end of time dt will be $\sigma'_z + d\sigma_z$ where σ'_z is the stress at zero time calculated using the flexure formula. The resulting equation is

$$\frac{\dot{\epsilon}_z}{y} = \frac{d\sigma_z}{yE_M\,dt} + \frac{\sigma'_z + d\sigma_z}{y\mu_M}$$

which can be rewritten as

$$\frac{\dot{\epsilon}_z}{y} - \frac{\sigma'_z}{y\mu_M} = \frac{d\sigma_z}{y}\left[\frac{1}{E_M\,dt} + \frac{1}{\mu_M}\right]. \qquad (8\text{--}26)$$

The two terms on the left side of Equation (8–26) are constants since both $\dot{\epsilon}_z$ and σ'_z vary linearly with y. For a specified increment of time dt the bracket term on the right side of Equation (8–26) is a constant; therefore, $d\sigma_z/y$ is also a constant and $d\sigma_z$ varies linearly with y. Thus, the stress distribution in a beam whose time-dependent material behavior is represented by a Maxwell model is linear and given by the flexure formula. The stress increment $d\sigma_z$ during the increment of time dt will be zero unless the loads on the beam change in magnitude during time dt.

Because the flexure formula is valid for the linear viscoelastic beam, the stress σ_z in Equation (8–24) is given by the relation $\sigma_z = M_x y/I_x$ and the stress rate $\dot{\sigma}_z$ is given by the relation $\dot{\sigma}_z = \dot{M}_x y/I_x$. These two relations along with Equations (8–24) and (8–25) give the following relation:

$$\frac{1}{\dot{\rho}} = -\frac{d^2\dot{y}}{dz^2} = \frac{\dot{M}_x}{E_M I_x} + \frac{M_x}{\mu_M I_x}. \qquad (8\text{--}27)$$

In case the loads on the beam remain constant, $\dot{M}_x = 0$ and Equation (8–27) can be integrated to give

$$-\frac{d^2y}{dz^2} = \frac{M_x t}{\mu_M I_x} + C_1.$$

The constant of integration C_1 is determined by the boundary condition

$$-\frac{d^2y}{dz^2} = \frac{M_x}{E_M I_x} \qquad \text{when} \qquad t = 0.$$

Thus,

$$-\frac{d^2y}{dz^2} = \frac{M_x}{E_M I_x}\left[1 + \frac{E_M t}{\mu_M}\right]. \tag{8–28}$$

At zero time it will be noted that Equation (8–28) reduces to Equation (8–10). The deflection y at a specified point in the beam for zero time can be determined using either the double-integration method of Section 8.7 or the moment-area method of Section 8.8. The deflection at the specified point for any time t is obtained by the product of y and the bracket term in Equation (8–28). The deflection rate for the given point in the beam is equal to $y E_M/\mu_M$.

Illustrative Problem

8.95. A cantilever beam has a circular cross section with a diameter of 1 in. and has a length of 10 in. The beam is made of nylon plastic whose time-dependent material behavior is assumed to be accurately approximated by a Maxwell model. A constant stress tension creep test of this nylon at 75°F and 50 per cent relative humidity indicated that the relation between strain ϵ_z and time was nearly linear from 300 hr to 1,000 hr. At a stress $\sigma_z = 1,000$ psi, the strains were found to be $\epsilon_z = 0.0083$ at 300 hr and $\epsilon_z = 0.0090$ at 1,000 hr. The beam is subjected to a concentrated load $P = 10$ lb at the free end in a room maintained at 75°F and 50 per cent relative humidity. (1) Determine the maximum stress in the beam. (2) Determine the creep rate for the free end of the beam for steady state conditions and the total deflection at 600 hr.

SOLUTION: PART (1). The maximum stress in the beam is given by the flexure formula Equation (7–11).

$$\sigma_{z(max)} = \frac{M_x c}{I_x} = \frac{10P(\tfrac{1}{2})}{\pi(1)^4/64} = 1,020 \text{ psi.}$$

PART (2).   The material constants E_M and μ_M have to be determined for the material. The creep rate for the tension specimen at $\sigma_z = 1{,}000$ psi is

$$\dot{\epsilon}_z = \frac{0.0090 - 0.0083}{1{,}000 - 300} = 10^{-6} \, 1/\text{hr}.$$

Since the load P remains constant, the value of $\dot{\sigma}_z = 0$ in Equation (8–24) and $\dot{\epsilon}_z = \sigma_z/\mu_M$; therefore,

$$\mu_M = \frac{\sigma_z}{\dot{\epsilon}_z} = \frac{1{,}000}{10^{-6}} = 10^9 \, \text{lb-hr/in.}^2$$

Substituting this value of μ_M in Equation (1–37) along with $\epsilon_z = 0.0090$, $\sigma_1 = \sigma_z = 1{,}000$ psi, and $t = 1{,}000$ hr gives

$$E_M = \frac{\sigma_z}{\epsilon_z - \sigma_z t/\mu_M} = \frac{1{,}000}{0.0090 - [1{,}000(1{,}000)/10^9]} = 125{,}000 \text{ psi.}$$

The deflection rate for the free end of the beam requires that the deflection Δ_e for the free end of the beam for linearly elastic conditions be determined. From Problem 8.10,

$$\Delta_e = \frac{P\ell^3}{3E_M I_x} = \frac{10(1{,}000)(64)}{3(125{,}000)\pi} = 0.544 \text{ in.}$$

The deflection rate $\dot{\Delta}$ for the free end of the beam is given by Equation (8–28):

$$\dot{\Delta} = \frac{\Delta_e E_M}{\mu_M} = \frac{0.544(125{,}000)}{10^9} = 0.000068 \text{ in./hr.}$$

The total deflection at 600 hr is

$$\Delta = \Delta_e + t\dot{\Delta} = 0.544 + 0.000068(600) = 0.585 \text{ in.}$$

Problems

8.96.   A rectangular section beam is made of canvas laminate for which the material constants are $E_M = 9.27 \times 10^5$ psi and $\mu_M = 3.52 \times 10^9$ lb-hr/in.^{2} The beam has a depth of 1 in. a width of $\frac{1}{2}$ in. and a length of 16 in. It is loaded as a simple beam with a concentrated load P applied at a distance of 6 in. from the left support. If $\sigma_{z(max)} = 5{,}000$ psi, determine P, the deflection rate, and the total deflection at 800 hr.

8.97.   Solve Problem 8.96 for the condition that the beam is subjected to a distributed load w lb/in. instead of the concentrated load P.

8.15. Deflection of Beam by Castigliano's Theorem

Castigliano's theorem for deflection has been derived in Sections 1.15 and 1.16 for pin-connected structures in which the members are axially loaded. The same procedure can be used to show* that the theorem is also valid when applied to solve for the deflection of beams. In this section the method of applying Castigliano's theorem to the problem of the deflection of a beam will be developed.

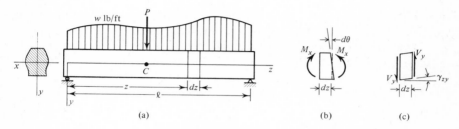

Fig. 8.12.

Let Figure 8.12 represent a simply supported straight beam resting on rigid supports and subjected to a distributed load. Let it be required that the elastic deflection of a point C in the beam be determined by the use of Castigliano's theorem. Let a concentrated load P be applied to the beam at C. From Castigliano's theorem the deflection y_P at the load P is given by Equation (1–54) which is $y_P = \partial\Phi/\partial P$. Because only linear elastic beams are considered in this chapter, the value of the complementary energy Φ may be replaced by its equivalent U, the strain energy. Hence,

$$y_P = \frac{\partial U}{\partial P}. \qquad (8-29)$$

In Equation (8–29) the strain energy U is the total strain energy in the beam due to the work of the loads, including P (although P may be equal to zero).

The strain energy U is determined by considering the beam to be made up of differential portions, each of length dz as shown in Figure 8.12a. The strain energy is determined for each element and the sum of the strain energies of all the elements gives the total strain energy U for the beam. Each element of the beam stores strain energy due to the bending moment M_x, which deforms it by the angle $d\theta$ as shown in Figure 8.12b, and also

* See *Advanced Mechanics of Materials* F. B. Seely and J. O. Smith, pages 442–451, 2nd ed., John Wiley and Sons, 1952.

due to the shearing force V_y, that deforms it by the angle represented by γ_{zy}, which is the shearing strain as shown in Figure 8.12c. Let dU represent the total strain energy in one element of the beam of length dz. Then

$$dU = \tfrac{1}{2}M_x\, d\theta + \tfrac{1}{2}V_y\gamma_{zy}\, dz. \tag{8–30}$$

The angular deformation $d\theta$, from Equation (8–3) is

$$d\theta = \frac{M_x\, dz}{EI_x}$$

where the positive sign is used because positive work is done on the beam element in Figure 8.12b; this is possible only if M_x and $d\theta$ have the same sign.

Also, the shearing strain γ_{zy} is equal to $\tau_{max}/G = \eta V_y/AG$, in which η is a factor whose value depends on the shape of the cross section (see Table 8.2), A is the cross-sectional area of the beam, and G is the shearing modulus of elasticity. The substitution of these values of $d\theta$ and γ_{zy} into Equation (8–30) gives

$$dU = \frac{1}{2}\frac{M_x^2\, dz}{EI_x} + \frac{1}{2}\frac{\eta V_y^2}{AG}\, dz. \tag{8–31}$$

But

$$U = \int_0^{\ell} dU \tag{8–32}$$

because the total strain energy is equal to the sum of its parts. The substitution of Equation (8–31) into Equation (8–32) gives

$$U = \int_0^{\ell} \frac{1}{2}\frac{M_x^2}{EI_x}\, dz + \int_0^{\ell} \frac{1}{2}\frac{\eta V_y^2}{AG}\, dz. \tag{8–33}$$

From Equation (8–29), the partial differentiation* of both sides of Equation (8–33) gives

$$y_P = \frac{\partial U}{\partial P} = \int_0^{\ell} \frac{M_x}{EI_x}\frac{\partial M_x}{\partial P}\, dz + \int_0^{\ell} \frac{\eta V_y}{AG}\frac{\partial V_y}{\partial P}\, dz. \tag{8–34}$$

Illustrative Problems

8.98. A horizontal cantilever beam of length ℓ is subjected to a concentrated load P at the free end as shown in Figure P8.98. The load P

---

* Because the limits of the integrals are constants, the partial differentiation can be performed under the integrals as if no integrals were involved.

is perpendicular to a principal axis of the cross-sectional area and passes through the shear center of the cross section. By making use of Castigliano's theorem derive an expression for the deflection of the beam in terms of the load P, ℓ, A, I_x, E, G, and η.

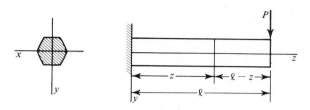

Fig. P 8.98.

SOLUTION. We make use of Equation (8–34) to solve the problem. From Figure P8.98 the bending moment at any cross section is

$$M_x = -P(\ell - z) \tag{a}$$

and the transverse shear is

$$V_y = P. \tag{b}$$

The partial derivatives needed in Equation (8–34) are found from Equations (a) and (b) as follows:

$$\frac{\partial M_x}{\partial P} = -(\ell - z) \quad \text{and} \quad \frac{\partial V_y}{\partial P} = 1. \tag{c}$$

The expressions in Equations (a), (b), and (c) are substituted into Equation (8–34) as follows:

$$y_P = \int_0^\ell \frac{P(\ell - z)^2}{EI_x} dz + \eta \int_0^\ell \frac{P\,dz}{AG}. \tag{d}$$

When the integrals in Equation (d) are evaluated the result is as follows:

$$y_P = \left[\frac{-\dfrac{P}{3}(\ell - z)^3}{EI_x} \right]_0^\ell + \eta \left[\frac{Pz}{AG} \right]_0^\ell \tag{e}$$

and finally,

$$y_P = \frac{P\ell^3}{3EI_x} + \eta \frac{P\ell}{AG}. \tag{f}$$

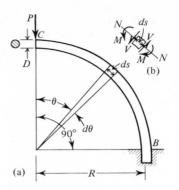

Fig. P 8.99.

8.99.   A cylindrical rod of diameter D is manufactured in the shape of a quarter circle of radius R, where R is much greater than D. The rod is used as a bracket as shown in Figure P8.99a fixed at one end B and is subjected to a concentrated load P at the other end. The action line of P is through the center of the quarter circle. Figure P8.99b shows an infinitesimal length ds of the rod with the bending moment M, transverse shearing force V, and axial force N acting on each end. Derive the expression for the deflection at P by making use of Castigliano's theorem. (*Hint:* Because R is much larger than D it can be assumed that the expressions for the strain energy in Equation (8–33) may be used without introducing much error. Also, the term $\int_0^\ell \frac{1}{2}(N^2/EA)\, ds$ (see Eq. 1–13) is added to Equation (8–33) for expressing the strain energy due to the axial component N.)

SOLUTION.   The deflection y_P is obtained by using Castigliano's theorem. The total strain energy U is obtained as follows:

$$U = \int_0^{\pi/2} \frac{M^2}{2EI}\, ds + \int_0^{\pi/2} \frac{\eta V^2}{2AG}\, ds + \int_0^{\pi/2} \frac{N^2}{2AE}\, ds. \tag{a}$$

Then, from Equation (8–29), by differentiation of Equation (a), we get

$$y_P = \int_0^{\pi/2} \frac{M}{EI} \frac{\partial M}{\partial P}\, ds + \int_0^{\pi/2} \frac{\eta V}{AG} \frac{\partial V}{\partial P}\, ds + \int_0^{\pi/2} \frac{N}{AE} \frac{\partial N}{\partial P}\, ds. \tag{b}$$

From Figure P8.99a we derive the following expressions* :

$$M = PR \sin \theta, \qquad V = P \cos \theta, \qquad N = P \sin \theta, \tag{c}$$

* The sign conventions for M, V, and N are unimportant here for the reason that each of these terms will have the same sign as its partial derivative; hence when these quantities are substituted into Equations (a) or (b), all terms are positive.

and, differentiating these expressions, we have

$$\frac{\partial M}{\partial P} = R \sin\theta, \qquad \frac{\partial V_y}{\partial P} = \cos\theta, \qquad \frac{\partial N}{\partial P} = \sin\theta. \tag{d}$$

The substitution of $ds = R\, d\theta$ and $\eta = 1.33$ (see Table 8.2) along with the expressions of Equations (c) and (d) in Equation (b), gives

$$y_P = \int_0^{\pi/2} \frac{PR^3 \sin^2\theta\, d\theta}{EI} + 1.33 \int_0^{\pi/2} \frac{PR \cos^2\theta\, d\theta}{AG} + \int_0^{\pi/2} \frac{PR \sin^2\theta\, d\theta}{AE}. \tag{e}$$

In order to complete the solution of Equation (e) we take $\sin^2\theta = (1 - \cos 2\theta)/2$ and $\cos^2\theta = (1 + \cos 2\theta)/2$. Equation (e), with these substitutions, becomes

$$y_P = \frac{PR^3}{EI} \int_0^{\pi/2} \left(\frac{d\theta}{2} - \frac{\cos 2\theta\, d\theta}{2} \right) + 1.33 \frac{PR}{AG} \int_0^{\pi/2} \left(\frac{d\theta}{2} + \frac{\cos 2\theta\, d\theta}{2} \right)$$

$$+ \frac{PR}{AE} \int_0^{\pi/2} \left(\frac{d\theta}{2} - \frac{\cos 2\theta\, d\theta}{2} \right)$$

$$= \frac{PR^3}{EI} \left[\frac{\theta}{2} - \frac{\sin 2\theta}{4} \right]_0^{\pi/2} + 1.33 \frac{PR}{AG} \left[\frac{\theta}{2} + \frac{\sin 2\theta}{4} \right]_0^{\pi/2} + \frac{PR}{AE} \left[\frac{\theta}{2} - \frac{\sin 2\theta}{4} \right]_0^{\pi/2}$$

$$= \frac{\pi}{4} \frac{PR^3}{EI} + 1.33 \frac{\pi}{4} \frac{PR}{AG} + \frac{\pi}{4} \frac{PR}{AE}. \tag{f}$$

Because the area A of the cross section is $\pi D^2/4$ and the moment of inertia $I = \pi D^4/64$, Equation (f) gives

$$y_P = \frac{16PR^3}{ED^4} + 1.33 \frac{PR}{GD^2} + \frac{PR}{ED^2}. \tag{g}$$

In Equation (f) it can be seen that the first term, which is due to the bending moment, predominates. For example, let $D = 1$ in. and $R = 10$ in. Then Equation (f) gives the following, by terms

$$y_P = 16{,}000 \frac{P}{E} + 13.3 \frac{P}{G} + 10 \frac{P}{E}. \tag{h}$$

Thus, Equation (h) shows that the second and third terms, the deflection caused by transverse shear V and axial force N can be neglected.

Problems

8.100. Find by use of Castigliano's theorem the maximum deflection y_P of a simple beam of span ℓ and constant cross section subjected to a concentrated load P at the midlength of the beam.

8.101. For the cantilever beam of Figure P8.98 determine the deflection of the point at the midlength of the beam in terms of P, ℓ, E, and I_x. (*Hint:* apply a fictitious load Q at the midlength and, after determining the deflection in terms of P, Q, ℓ, E, and I_x, set $Q = 0$.)

8.102. A bracket is manufactured by bending a circular cylindrical rod into a semicircular shape of radius R and of circular cross-section with diameter D as shown in Figure P8.102. The bracket is fixed at one end B and is subjected to a concentrated load P

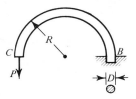

Fig. P 8.102.

at the free end C. The action line of P is tangent to the circle of radius R. By using Castigliano's theorem derive an expression for the deflection y_P of the bracket at the load P. Neglect the effect of the transverse shear V and the axial component N on the deflection.

8.103. A bracket BCD is manufactured in the shape shown in Figure P8.103. The cross section of the bracket is circular and has a constant diameter D. The bracket

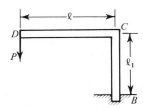

Fig. P 8.103.

is fixed at B and is subjected to a concentrated load P at the free end D, which is perpendicular to the length ℓ. Determine the deflection y_P at the load P in terms of P, ℓ, ℓ_1, D, E, and G. (*Hint:* Include the effect of transverse shear in the length ℓ and the axial force in the length ℓ_1.)

8.16. Statically Indeterminate Beams

In determining the stresses in beams (see Chapter 7) and the deflections of beams as discussed in the previous sections, it was assumed that all the forces (loads and reactions) acting on the beam were known or that they could be found by making use of the equations of equilibrium. Sometimes a beam is supported in a manner such that the number of reactive forces and couples that support the beam is greater than the number of equations of equilibrium that are available for solving for them. Such a beam is said to be statically indeterminate.

All beams that are considered in this chapter are subjected to a system of external loads, including the reactive (supporting) forces and couples, that lie in the longitudinal plane of the beam and all forces are perpendicular to the longitudinal axis of the beam. Hence, there are only two equations of equilibrium for any given beam. Thus, any beam with more than two reactive forces or couples is a statically indeterminate beam. The degree of statical indeterminacy is equal to the number of reactive forces and couples in excess of two. For example, the beam shown in Figure 8.13a, which is

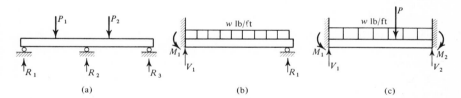

(a) (b) (c)

Fig. 8.13. Statically indeterminate beams.

subjected to two known loads P_1 and P_2, has three reactions R_1, R_2, and R_3; hence, the degree of indeterminacy is one, because there are three unknown reactions. The beam shown in Figure 8.13b is subjected to a known uniformly distributed load w lb/ft and is supported by the fixed end moment M_1 and shear V_1 at the left end and at the right end by the reaction R_1 at the roller. Again, the degree of indeterminacy is one, because there are three unknown reactions. In Figure 8.13c the beam is subjected to a known concentrated load P and a known uniformly distributed load w lb/ft and is supported by a fixed end moment M_1 and shear V_1 at the left end and a fixed end moment M_2 and shear V_2 at the right end. Thus, the degree of indeterminacy is two, because there are four unknown reactions.

Redundants. All the unknown reactions must be determined for the statically indeterminate beam. Two equations of equilibrium are always available. The degree of indeterminacy represents the number of additional conditions (equations) that must be set up in order to complete the solution. An interpretation of the physical behavior of the beam in response to the unknown reactions is of great assistance in setting up these additional equations. An inspection of the beams of Figure 8.13 shows that in Figure 8.13a the reaction R_2 could be removed without upsetting the equilibrium of the beam, assuming that the beam has enough resistance to the increased bending stresses caused by the removal of R_2. Such a reaction as R_2 that can be thus removed is called a redundant. Every statically indeterminate beam has a number of redundant reactions (forces or couples) equal to the degree of redundancy or indeterminacy. In Figure 8.13b either M_1 or R_1 can be chosen as the redundant. In Figure 8.13c, where there are two re-dundants, several choices are possible: V_1 and M_1, V_2 and M_2, or M_1 and M_2. Note that in every choice of redundants, the remaining reactions will assure the equilibrium of the beam. A little experience will show that where several choices can be made, one particular choice of redundants is the most con-venient to use in setting up the additional equations.

   Methods of Setting up Additional Equations for Redundants.   There are two major approaches used for determining the additional equations for the redundants. The first approach makes use of the differential equation (Eq. 8–10) of the elastic curve of the beam and is referred to as the differential equation method. The boundary conditions on the beam that are directly related to the effects that the redundants have on the deformation of the beam are used in the differential equation to obtain the additional equations.

   The second method makes use of the principle of least-complementary work, discussed in Section 1.17.

   Both of these methods will now be developed and illustrated in the sections that follow.

8.17.   Differential Equations Method: Beam Fixed at Both Ends—Concentrated Load

   The beam in Figure 8.14a is fixed at each end so that the ends cannot deflect vertically or rotate when the concentrated load P is applied. Load P lies in a plane that contains the bending axis and intersects each cross section of the beam on a line parallel to the y-axis; the y-axis is a principal axis of inertia for the cross section. The problem is to determine all of the reactions on the beam. The known quantities are P, ℓ, a, I_x, and E. Assume linearly elastic behavior for the material. The five steps of solution given in Chapter 1 (Section 1.5) are followed.

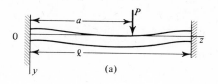

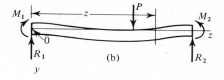

Fig. 8.14.

Step 1 is the construction of the free body-diagram in Figure 8.14b. In Step 2, note that there are four unknown reactions and only two equations of equilibrium; the degree of redundancy is two. Step 3 is satisfied by finding four boundary conditions on the deformations of the beam in order to determine the two constants of integration for Equation (8–10) and to obtain the two additional equations to determine the two redundant reactions. The deformations of the beam in Figure 8.14a have been greatly exaggerated in order to be observable. The four boundary conditions are that both the slope and deflection are zero at each end of the beam. In Step 4 the equations of equilibrium are as follows:

$$\sum F_y = 0 = P - R_1 - R_2,$$
$$\sum M_0 = R_2\ell - Pa + M_2 - M_1 = 0.$$

These two equations reduce to the following:

$$R_2 = P - R_1, \tag{a}$$
$$M_2 = M_1 + Pa - R_2\ell. \tag{b}$$

The magnitudes of R_1, R_2, M_1, and M_2 are obtained in Step 5 by using Equation (8–10), Equations (a), (b), and the four boundary conditions in Step 3. The bending moment M_x at any distance z from the left end of the beam is

$$M_x = M_1 + R_1z - P\langle z - a\rangle^1.$$

Equation (8–10) becomes

$$EI_x \frac{d^2y}{dz^2} = -M_x = -M_1 - R_1z + P\langle z - a\rangle^1,$$

which is integrated to give

$$EI_x \frac{dy}{dz} = -M_1 z - \frac{R_1 z^2}{2} + \tfrac{1}{2}P\langle z - a\rangle^2 + C_1. \tag{c}$$

The constant of integration C_1 equals zero because $dy/dz = 0$ when $z = 0$. One of the relations for determining the redundant reactions is given by the boundary condition $dy/dz = 0$ when $z = \ell$. The substitution of these quantities into Equation (c) gives

$$0 = -M_1 \ell - \frac{R_1 \ell^2}{2} + \tfrac{1}{2}P(\ell - a)^2. \tag{d}$$

Integrating Equation (c) again gives

$$EI_x y = -\frac{M_1 z^2}{2} - \frac{R_1 z^3}{6} + \tfrac{1}{6}P\langle z - a\rangle^3 + C_2.$$

The constant of integration C_2 equals zero because $y = 0$ when $z = 0$. The second relation for determining the redundant reactions is given by the boundary condition $y = 0$ when $z = \ell$.

$$0 = -\frac{M_1 \ell^2}{2} - \frac{R_1 \ell^3}{6} + \tfrac{1}{6}P(\ell - a)^3. \tag{e}$$

The two simultaneous equations (d) and (e), can be solved for R_1 and M_1:

$$R_1 = P\left(1 - 3\frac{a^2}{\ell^2} + 2\frac{a^3}{\ell^3}\right),$$

$$M_1 = -P\ell\left(\frac{a}{\ell} - \frac{2a^2}{\ell^2} + \frac{a^3}{\ell^3}\right).$$

Substituting these values of R_1 and M_1 in Equations (a) and (b) give

$$R_2 = P\left(\frac{3a^2}{\ell^2} - \frac{2a^3}{\ell^3}\right),$$

$$M_2 = -P\ell\left(\frac{a^2}{\ell^2} - \frac{a^3}{\ell^3}\right).$$

The fact that the expressions for M_1 and M_2 are negative means that the sense of each is opposite to that shown in Figure 8.14b.

8.18. Beam Fixed at One End, Supported at Other End; Uniform Load

The steel ($E = 30,000,000$ psi) beam in Figure 8.15a has a length of 80 in. and a rectangular cross section with a depth of 4 in. and a width of 3 in. The beam is supported at the right end by an aluminum alloy ($E = 10,000,000$ psi) tension member which has a cross-sectional area of 0.20 in.^{2} and a length of 100 in. The tension member is unstressed when the beam is unloaded. Determine the maximum normal stress in the beam and in the tension member if $w = 100$ lb/in. The five steps are again used in the solution, but a different procedure is used to accomplish Step 5.

The problem includes interaction between two different load-carrying members. Step 1 requires the two free-body diagrams in Figures 8.15b and c. It is assumed that the tension member AB does not produce a bending moment at the pin B. Hence, there are three reactions acting on the beam and only two equations of equilibrium, and the degree of redundancy is one (Step 2). Step 3 is satisfied by finding one boundary condition from the geometry of deformation of the two members. This condition is satisfied by noting that the elongation e of the tension member is equal to the deflection Δ_B of the right end of the beam.

In Step 4 the equations of equilibrium for the beam give

$$\sum F_y = 0 = w\ell - P - R,$$

$$\sum M_0 = 0 = P\ell - \tfrac{1}{2}w\ell^2 - M_1.$$

These two equations reduce to the following, when the values of ℓ and w are substituted:

$$R = 8,000 - P, \tag{a}$$

$$M_1 = -320,000 + 80P. \tag{b}$$

In Step 5 the magnitude of P can be obtained using Equation (1–13), Equation (8–10), Equation (a), and the boundary condition in Step 3. Instead of using the differential equation (8–10), we will use the fact that the deflection of the free end of a cantilever beam is known to be $\Delta_1 = w\ell^4/(8EI_x)$ if the beam is subjected to a uniformly distributed load acting alone, that is, if P is removed from Figure 8.15c; and if the beam is subjected to a concentrated load at the end acting alone, that is, the distributed load w is removed from Figure 8.15c, $\Delta_2 = P\ell^3/3EI_x$, where $I_x = bh^3/12 = 16$ in.^{4} Using the principle of superposition, the deflection Δ of the right end of the

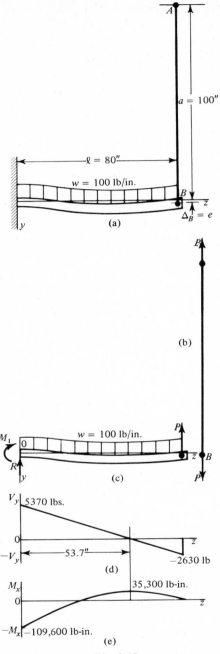

A

$a = 100''$

$\ell = 80''$

$w = 100$ lb/in.

B

z

$\Delta_B = e$

y

(a)

P

(b)

M_1

0

$w = 100$ lb/in.

P

z B

R

y

(c)

P

V_y 5370 lbs.

0

z

$-V_y$

$53.7''$

-2630 lb

(d)

M_x

$35,300$ lb-in.

0

z

$-M_x$ $-109,600$ lb-in.

(e)

Fig. 8.15.

beam is

$$\Delta_B = \Delta_1 - \Delta_2 = \frac{100(80)^4}{8(30,000,000)(16)} - \frac{P(80)^3}{3(30,000,000)(16)},$$

$$= 1.607 - 0.000356P.$$

The deflection Δ_B of the right end of the beam is equal to the elongation e of the tension member

$$e = \frac{Pa}{AE} = \frac{100P}{0.20(10,000,000)} = 0.000050P,$$

$$\Delta_B = e,$$

$$1.067 - 0.000356P = 0.000050P,$$

$$P = \frac{1.067}{0.000406} = 2,630 \text{ lb.}$$

The stress in the tension member is given by Equation (1–10):

$$\sigma = \frac{P}{A} = \frac{2,630}{0.20} = 13,150 \text{ psi}$$

The shear and moment diagrams for the beam are shown in Figures 8.15d and e. The bending moment M_1 at the left end of the beam is the maximum moment and is given by Equation (b):

$$M_1 = -320,000 + 80P = -109,600 \text{ lb-in.}$$

The maximum normal stress in the beam is given by Equation (7–11):

$$\sigma = \frac{M_1 c}{I_x} = \frac{-109,600(-2)}{16} = 13,700 \text{ psi.}$$

Problems

8.104. A horizontal cantilever beam rests at its free end on a spring so that, when there is no load applied, the beam and spring are just barely in contact (no force exerted on beam by the spring). The downward load P then is applied at the free end of the beam. The spring is deflected the same amount Δ as is the free end of the beam. If the reaction R of the spring on the beam is $R = k\Delta$, where k is the spring constant, determine the deflection Δ and the force R in terms of k, ℓ, E, I_x, and P.

$$\text{ans.} \quad R = \frac{P\ell^3}{(3EI_x/k + \ell^3)}.$$

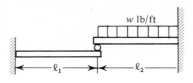

Fig. P 8.105.

8.105. Two cantilever beams of identical cross sections and materials are arranged as shown in Figure P8.105. The roller fits snugly between the two beams when the beams are unloaded. Determine the reaction that the roller exerts on the two beams when the uniformly distributed load w is applied to the upper beam. Known quantities are w, ℓ_1, ℓ_2, E, and I_x.

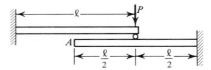

Fig. P 8.106.

8.106. Two identical cantilever beams (same E and I_x) are arranged as shown in Figure P8.106. When $P = 0$, the roller R fits snugly between the beams. Determine the downward deflection of point A at the free end of the lower beam in terms of P, ℓ, E, and I_x.

$$\text{ans.} \quad \Delta_A = \frac{5P\ell^3}{54EI_x}.$$

8.107. For the beam in Figure P8.107 determine the reaction R of the roller on the beam in terms of P, w, and ℓ.

$$\text{ans.} \quad R = 5P/16 + 41w\ell/128.$$

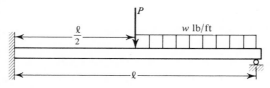

Fig. P 8.107.

8.108.   The beam in Problem 8.107 has a square cross section 2 in. on a side and has a length of 32 in. If $w = 80$ lb/in., determine the magnitude of P if the working stress for the beam is 20,000 psi.

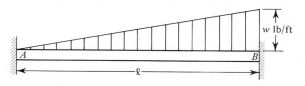

Fig. P 8.109.

8.109.   For the beam in Figure P8.109 determine the reaction R_A and the moment M_A at the wall at the left end of the beam in terms of w and ℓ.

ans. $R_A = 3w\ell/20; M_A = -w\ell^2/30$.

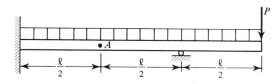

Fig. P 8.110.

8.110.   The beam in Figure P8.110 is loaded as shown. Determine the reaction R at the roller support and the deflection of point A in terms of P, w, ℓ, E, and I_x.

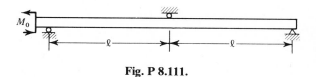

Fig. P 8.111.

8.111.   For the beam in Figure P8.111 determine the three reactions in terms of M_0 and ℓ.

ans. $R_1 = 5M_0/4\ell; R_2 = 3M_0/2\ell; R_3 = M_0/4\ell$.

8.112.   Determine the deflection at midspan for the right span of the beam in Problem 8.111.

8.113.   The beam in Figure P8.113 was made by nailing four 1-in. by 4-in. yellow pine boards together as shown. (See Table 1.1 for material properties of yellow pine.)

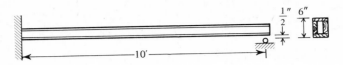

Fig. P 8.113.

When the beam is unloaded, the roller support at the right end of the beam is $\frac{1}{2}$-in. below the beam. Determine the reaction R at the roller support and the maximum bending stress in the beam when the beam is subjected to a uniformly distributed load $w = 120$ lb/ft.

8.19. Beam on Three or More Supports—Three-Moment Theorem

Frequently, beams have three or more simple supports. Such beams are called continuous beams. It is convenient to let the internal moments over the supports be the redundant reactions. Rather than treat each continuous

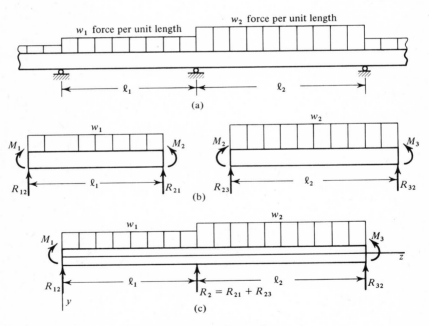

Fig. 8.16. Continuous beam.

beam problem separately it is possible to derive an equation called the three-moment equation, which relates three internal moments over three consecutive supports, and the loads acting on the two spans between these supports. Refer to the five steps to be used in the solution (see Section 1.5).

Consider two consecutive spans of a continuous beam subjected to uniformly distributed loads as shown in Figure 8.16a. To take Step 1, free-body diagrams of the two spans are drawn, as shown in Figure 8.16b. In Step 2 it is determined that the redundants are the moments M_1, M_2, and M_3 over the three consecutive supports and these have been assumed to be positive. In Step 3 note that the deflection at the three supports are assumed to be equal to zero. In Step 4 two equations of equilibrium are written out of the four possible equations of equilibrium. The moment equilibrium equation about the right end of the left span gives

$$R_{12}\ell_1 + M_1 - M_2 - \frac{w_1\ell_1^2}{2} = 0. \tag{a}$$

A free-body diagram of the two spans, taken together, where $R_2 = R_{21} + R_{23}$, is shown in Figure 8.16c. The moment equilibrium equation about the right end gives

$$R_{12}(\ell_1 + \ell_2) + R_2\ell_2 + M_1 - M_3 - \frac{w_1(\ell_1 + \ell_2)^2}{2} - \frac{(w_2 - w_1)\ell_2^2}{2} = 0. \tag{b}$$

For Step 5 we use Equation (8–10) and, by making use of the free-body diagram in Figure 8.16c, we obtain the differential equation

$$-EI_x\frac{d^2y}{dz^2} = M_x = M_1 + R_{12}z - \frac{w_1z^2}{2} - \frac{w_2 - w_1}{2}\langle z - \ell_1\rangle^2$$

$$+ R_2\langle z - \ell_1\rangle^1. \tag{c}$$

Integrating Equation (c) twice gives the two equations that follow:

$$-EI_x\frac{dy}{dz} = M_1z + \frac{R_{12}z^2}{2} - \frac{w_1z^3}{6} - \frac{w_2 - w_1}{6}\langle z - \ell_1\rangle^3$$

$$+ \frac{R_2}{2}\langle z - \ell_1\rangle^2 + C_1, \tag{d}$$

$$-EI_xy = \frac{M_1z^2}{2} + \frac{R_{12}z^3}{6} - \frac{w_1z^4}{24} - \frac{w_2 - w_1}{24}\langle z - \ell_1\rangle^4$$

$$+ \frac{R_2}{6}\langle z - \ell_1\rangle^3 + C_1z + C_2. \tag{e}$$

The boundary condition $y = 0$, when $z = 0$, gives $C_2 = 0$. The boundary condition $y = 0$, when $z = \ell_1$, gives

$$C_1 = -\frac{M_1 \ell_1}{2} - \frac{R_{12} \ell_1^2}{6} + \frac{w_1 \ell_1^3}{24}.$$

When these values of C_1 and C_2 and the boundary condition $y = 0$ when $z = \ell_1 + \ell_2$ are substituted into Equation (e) we get

$$0 = \frac{M_1}{2}(\ell_1 + \ell_2)^2 + \frac{R_{12}(\ell_1 + \ell_2)^3}{6} - \frac{w_1(\ell_1 + \ell_2)^4}{24} - \frac{w_2 - w_1}{24}(\ell_2)^4$$

$$+ \frac{R_2 \ell_2^3}{6} - \frac{M_1 \ell_1}{2}(\ell_1 + \ell_2) - \frac{R_{12} \ell_1^2}{6}(\ell_1 + \ell_2) + \frac{w_1 \ell_1^3}{24}(\ell_1 + \ell_2). \quad \text{(f)}$$

The three-moment theorem for continuous beams subjected to uniformly distributed loads is obtained by eliminating R_{12} and R_2 from Equations (a), (b), and (f):

$$M_1 \ell_1 + 2M_2(\ell_1 + \ell_2) + M_3 \ell_2 = -\frac{w_1 \ell_1^3}{4} - \frac{w_2 \ell_2^3}{4}. \quad (8\text{--}35)$$

The three-moment theorem for more general loading can be derived by using the moment-area method (Section 8.8) instead of the differential equation method and takes the form

$$M_1 \ell_1 + 2M_2(\ell_1 + \ell_2) + M_3 \ell_2 = -\frac{6Q_1}{\ell_1} - \frac{6Q_2}{\ell_2}, \quad (8\text{--}36)$$

where Q_1 is the first moment, with respect to the left end of span 1, of the area under the moment diagram for span 1 when $M_1 = M_2 = 0$; and Q_2 is the first moment, with respect to the right end of span 2, of the area under the moment diagram for span 2 when $M_2 = M_3 = 0$. Note that Equation (8–36) reduces to (8–35) when the load over each span is uniformly distributed.

Equation (8–35) takes its simplest form when all the spans have equal length and the distributed load is uniformly distributed over all spans. It is of considerable interest to determine the effect of number of spans on the magnitude of the negative moment over the supports and the magnitude of the vertical shears at either side of each support. For this purpose the moment coefficients are given in Figure 8.17 for beams having equal spans of one, two, three, four, and five and subjected to uniform load on all spans. The values directly above the supports in Figure 8.17 are the moment coefficients—that is, the numbers by which $-w\ell^2$ must be multiplied in order to obtain the bending moments over the supports. Similarly, the numbers on either side of the supports are the shear coefficients: that is,

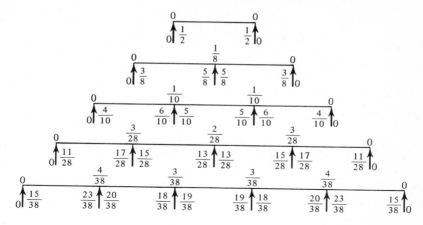

Fig. 8.17. Values of shear and moment coefficients of continuous beams of equal spans subjected to equal uniformly distributed loads on all spans.

the numbers by which $w\ell$ must be multiplied to obtain the magnitude of the vertical shear for the section; the vertical shear is negative for the section to the left of each support and positive for the section to the right of each support. The reaction at each support is the arithmetic sum of the vertical shears on the two sides of the support.

Significance of Negative Moments.   In continuous beams, the negative moments over the supports reduce the moments (and hence stresses) near the centers of the spans, and hence continuous beams in general are stronger and stiffer than similarly loaded simply supported beams of equal spans. On the other hand, the uneven settlement of supports may change the moments at the supports and throughout the beam from those found by the preceding analysis; furthermore, the stiffer the beams, the greater is the change in the moments. Partly for this reason and partly because the loads on the various spans of continuous beams in structures may vary considerably from those assumed in the design, it frequently is assumed that, in uniformly loaded beams of four or more equal spans, all the spans (except the end spans) are subjected to the same maximum bending moment, a common value being $\frac{1}{12} w\ell^2$; the maximum moment in the end spans is somewhat greater ($\frac{1}{10}w\ell^2$ is frequently used). Compare these values with those given in Figure 8.17 for beams having more than four spans, and note that the moments do not vary greatly over the inner supports. Two-span and three-span beams are stressed higher than beams of four or more spans, and for such beams the maximum moment in each span frequently is assumed to be $\frac{1}{10} w\ell^2$.

Problems

8.114. A continuous wooden beam consists of four equal spans, each 12-ft long, and is subjected to a uniform load of 200 lb/ft over its entire length. (1) Find the reaction of the second support. (2) If the beam has a rectangular cross section, the depth being one-and-one-half the width, what is the depth if the maximum fiber stress in the beam is 1,000 psi?

ans.   (1) $R_2 = 2,740$ lb; (2) $h = 6.95$ in.

8.115. A 12-in. 40.8-lb steel I-beam is used as a horizontal continuous beam over four spans. The lengths of the spans are 20, 12, 20 and 12 ft, respectively, from left to right. The loads are uniformly distributed over each span, the loads per foot of length on the four spans being 2,000, 1,600, 2,000, and 1,600 lb/ft, respectively. Compute the maximum bending stress in the beam.

ans. $M_2 = -65,400$ lb-ft; $M_3 = -42,300$ lb-ft;

$M_4 = 60,100$ lb-ft; $\sigma = 17,500$ psi.

8.116. A continuous beam has three spans of 12-ft each. The first span is subjected to a uniformly distributed load of 2,000 lb/ft. The other spans each have a 10,000-lb load at midspan. Compute the four reactions, assuming the elastic limit is not exceeded. (*Hint:* Use Eq. 8–36.)

ans. $R_1 = 9,900$ lb; $R_2 = 19,850$ lb.

8.117. What should be the depth of a rectangular section pine continuous beam having four equal spans of 10 ft, in order to resist a uniformly distributed load of 300 lb/ft over each span? Use a working stress of 1,000 psi, and make the depth of the beam twice the width.

8.118. A continuous beam of two spans, 15 ft and 20 ft, carries a uniformly distributed load of 1,500 lb/ft over the longer span and no load on the shorter span. Compute the maximum positive and negative bending moments and the reactions at the three supports. Assume that the elastic limit is not exceeded.

ans. $M_2 = -42,800$ lb-ft; $M_{max} = 55,100$ lb-ft.

8.20. Principle of Least Complementary Work for Beams

The principle of least-complementary work states that the complementary work W_c, which is equal to the total internal complementary energy Φ in a statically indeterminate beam, is a minimum. Physically, this means that of all the possible values that the redundant forces and moments can take as the beam deforms under the action of the external loads and reactions, the values that they take will make Φ a minimum. In this chapter the principle is applied only to beams made of linearly elastic materials. For such beams the total complementary energy Φ is equal to the total internal strain energy U. Hence, the total strain energy U will be used here. The application of this principle will now be illustrated. The five steps are used, but Steps 3 and 5 take a different form as will be seen.

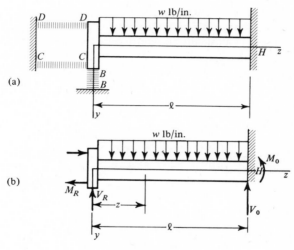

Fig. 8.18.

Let Figure 8.18 represent a horizontal beam of length ℓ that is fixed at the right end and is supported by elastic coil springs BB, CC, and DD at the left end. Spring BB exerts a vertical force $V_R = ky_B$, where y_B is the deflection of the left end and k is the elastic constant for the spring. Springs CC and DD are identical and are mounted horizontally so that they will exert equal horizontal forces on the left end of the beam, one force causing tension in the spring and the other a compression. Thus, springs CC and DD have the effect of exerting a moment M_R on the left end of the beam. Let $M_R = \beta\theta$, where θ is the angle through which the plane section of the left end of the beam rotates when the uniformly distributed load w is applied and β is the rotational spring constant for the two springs CC and DD. (Note that β has units of lb-in./rad since θ is in radians and also note that the value of β will not only depend on the size and length of springs CC and DD but will also depend on the distance between the center lines of the coils of the two springs.)

Figure 8.18*b* shows a free-body diagram of the beam as required by Step 1. Steps 2 and 4 are taken together here; Step 4 is accomplished by writing the two independent equations of equilibrium as follows:

$$\sum F_y = V_R + V_O - w\ell = 0, \tag{a}$$

$$\sum M_H = V_R\ell - M_R - \frac{w\ell^2}{2} - M_O = 0. \tag{b}$$

There are four unknown quantities, namely V_R, M_R, V_O, and M_O. Step 2 is taken by noting that only two equations of equilibrium are available, and therefore the beam is statically indeterminate to the second degree. Let V_R and M_R be chosen as the redundant quantities. Therefore two additional equations are required. These are obtained by using Step 5 which is accomplished by deriving the expression U for the total strain energy in the beam and the springs and setting the partial derivatives of U with respect to V_R and M_R, respectively, equal to zero as follows:

$$\frac{\partial U}{\partial V_R} = 0, \tag{c}$$

$$\frac{\partial U}{\partial M_R} = 0. \tag{d}$$

Note that Step 3, which involves a direct use of boundary conditions (see Sections 8.17 through 8.19), is complied with automatically when the principle of least-complementary work is used.

By referring to Equation (8–33), which includes the energy from the bending moment M_x and also that from the transverse shear V_y, the expression for U for the total strain energy in the beam and the supporting springs is obtained as follows:

$$U = \int_0^\ell \frac{M_x^2}{2EI_x} \, dz + \int_0^\ell \frac{\eta V_y^2}{2AG} \, dz + \frac{1}{2} \frac{V_R^2}{k} + \frac{1}{2} \frac{M_R^2}{\beta}. \tag{e}$$

In Equation (e) the bending moment M_x and its partial derivatives are

$$M_x = V_R z + M_R - \frac{wz^2}{2}; \qquad \frac{\partial M_x}{\partial V_R} = z; \qquad \frac{\partial M_x}{\partial M_R} = 1. \tag{f}$$

The transverse shear V_y and its partial derivatives are

$$V_y = V_R - wz; \qquad \frac{\partial V_y}{\partial V_R} = 1; \qquad \frac{\partial V_y}{\partial M_R} = 0. \tag{g}$$

Equations (c) and (d) are now obtained by the partial differentiation of Equation (e) with respect to the redundant V_R and the partial differentiation of Equation (e) with respect to the redundant M_R as follows:

$$\frac{\partial U}{\partial V_R} = \int_0^\ell \frac{M_x}{EI_x} \frac{\partial M_x}{\partial V_R} dz + \int_0^\ell \frac{\eta V_y}{AG} \frac{\partial V_y}{\partial V_R} dz + \frac{V_R}{k} = 0, \tag{h}$$

$$\frac{\partial U}{\partial M_R} = \int_0^\ell \frac{M_x}{EI_x} \frac{\partial M_x}{\partial M_R} dz + \int_0^\ell \frac{\eta V_y}{AG} \frac{\partial V_y}{\partial M_R} dz + \frac{M_R}{\beta} = 0. \tag{i}$$

The expressions for M_x and V_y and their partial derivatives as given in Equations (f) and (g) are substituted into Equations (h) and (i), and the integrals are evaluated, with the results given in the following two equations, respectively:

$$\frac{1}{3} \frac{V_R \ell^3}{EI_x} + \frac{1}{2} \frac{M_R \ell^2}{EI_x} - \frac{1}{8} \frac{w\ell^4}{EI_x} + \frac{\eta V_R \ell}{AG} - \frac{1}{2} \frac{\eta w\ell^2}{AG} + \frac{V_R}{k} = 0, \tag{j}$$

$$\frac{1}{2} \frac{V_R \ell^2}{EI_x} + \frac{M_R \ell}{EI_x} - \frac{1}{6} \frac{w\ell^3}{EI_x} + \frac{M_R}{\beta} = 0. \tag{k}$$

By solving Equations (j) and (k) simultaneously for the values of M_R and V_R the following expressions are obtained:

$$M_R = \frac{\beta \ell^2}{EI_x + \beta \ell}(-\tfrac{1}{2}V_R + \tfrac{1}{6}w\ell) \tag{l}$$

$$V_R = \frac{\dfrac{1}{2} \dfrac{\eta w\ell^2}{AG} + \dfrac{1}{8} \dfrac{w\ell^4}{EI_x} - \dfrac{1}{12} \dfrac{\beta w\ell^5}{EI_x(EI_x + \beta\ell)}}{\dfrac{1}{3} \dfrac{\ell^3}{EI_x} - \dfrac{1}{4} \dfrac{\beta\ell^4}{EI_x(EI_x + \beta\ell)} + \dfrac{\eta\ell}{AG} + \dfrac{1}{k}}. \tag{m}$$

Problems

8.119. For the beam of Figure 8.18 let $\beta = 0$ and use Equations (l) and (m) to solve for M_R and V_R.

8.120. For the beam of Figure 8.18 let $k = 0$ and solve for V_R and M_R by making use of Equations (l) and (m).

8.121. For the beam of Figure 8.18 let β and k approach infinity; that is, let the end of the beam supported by the springs be rigidly fixed and use Equations (l) and (m) to solve for M_R and V_R.

8.122. Make use of Equations (l) and (m) to solve for the axial force in the aluminum tension member that supports the right end of the beam described in Section 8.18 and as shown in Figure 8.15.

8.21. Effect of Plastic Deformation on the Load-Deflection Curve of Statically Indeterminate Beams

In discussing the plastic behavior of statically indeterminate beams we will limit our consideration to beams made of a material that has a flat-topped stress-strain diagram at the yield point such as that of structural steel. A typical load-deflection curve for a statically indeterminate beam is shown in Figure 8.19 where the load is a concentrated load P and Δ is the deflection of P. From O to A the material in the beam remains linearly elastic and the

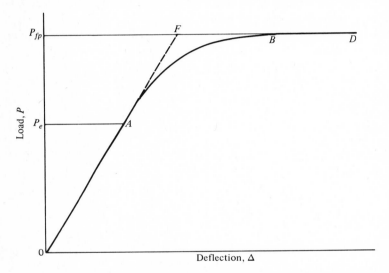

Fig. 8.19. Load-deflection curve for statically indeterminate member.

theory presented in the foregoing sections is valid. The elastic-plastic behavior of the beam occurs from A to B; the derivation of curve AB is beyond the scope of this book.* The load-deflection curve in Figure 8.19 is horizontal from B to D at the fully-plastic load for the statically indeterminate beam.

The shape of the load-deflection curve is similar for statically determinate and statically indeterminate beams. The major difference is indicated by the fact that the ratio of the fully plastic load P_{fp} to the maximum elastic load P_e is appreciably greater for a given statically indeterminate beam than

---

* J. O. Smith and O. M. Sidebottom, *Inelastic Behavior of Load Carrying Members*, John Wiley and Sons, Inc., 1965.

for the same beam loaded as a statically determinate beam. For statically determinate beams this ratio was found to be dependent on the shape of the cross section of the beams and lies in the range from 1.10 for light-weight I-beams to 2.00 for diamond-shaped cross sections.

If one is limited to an elastic analysis, design is based on the maximum elastic load P_e in Figure 8.19 because failure of the member by general yielding is assumed (see Section 4.5) to begin at the load P_e. Extend the straight line OA (dashed) until it intersects at F the horizontal line at the fully plastic load; note that the actual load-deflection curve does not deviate appreciably from the line OAF until the load approaches the fully plastic load. In many engineering applications of beams the allowable deflection may be such that failure of the beam will not occur until the fully plastic load is applied. In such beams extreme care must be taken to prevent the beam from failing by lateral buckling. It is seen, therefore, that both the elastic analysis and the fully plastic analysis are important in determining the significant load-carrying capacity of a beam. The value of P_e is one limiting value of the maximum load (a lower limit) and P_{fp} is another limiting value (an upper limit) that may be applied to the beam before destroying its load-carrying function. The specifications in various design codes are often determined by requiring that the maximum load the beam can be expected to resist shall lie between these two limits.

8.22. Fully Plastic Load for Statically Indeterminate Beams

The fully plastic load analysis for a statically indeterminate beam is much simpler than the elastic analysis for the beam. The simplicity in the fully plastic analysis arises from the fact that when the fully plastic condition exists in the beam, the fully plastic load can be determined by the equations of equilibrium. To illustrate this fact let the beam in Figure 8.20 be fixed at each end so that the ends cannot deflect vertically or rotate when the concentrated load P is applied at the quarter point. The cross section of the beam has a plane of symmetry and the load P is assumed to lie in this plane. The beam is made of a ductile material whose yield point is σ_e. Determine the elastic-limit load P_e in terms of c_1, ℓ, I_x, and σ_e and the fully plastic load P_{fp} for the beam in terms of σ_e, c_1, ℓ, I_x, and K, which is a factor from Table 7.2 that depends on the shape of the cross section of the beam. Also determine the ratio of the fully plastic load to the maximum elastic load. It will be assumed that the extreme fiber distances are such that $c_1 > c_2$.

Elastic-Limit Load P_e. The elastic solution of this problem is given in Section 8.17, the results of which are shown in Figure 8.20b. The maximum

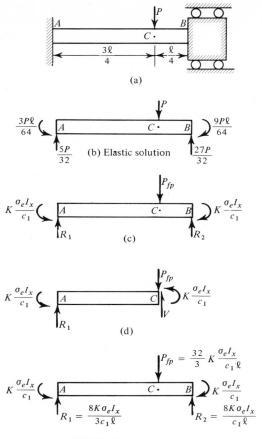

(a)

$\dfrac{3P\ell}{64}$ ⟲ $\dfrac{5P}{32}$ (b) Elastic solution $\dfrac{27P}{32}$ $\dfrac{9P\ell}{64}$

$K\dfrac{\sigma_e I_x}{c_1}$ ⟲ R_1 (c) R_2 $K\dfrac{\sigma_e I_x}{c_1}$

$K\dfrac{\sigma_e I_x}{c_1}$ ⟲ R_1 (d) V $K\dfrac{\sigma_e I_x}{c_1}$

$P_{fp} = \dfrac{32}{3}K\dfrac{\sigma_e I_x}{c_1 \ell}$

$K\dfrac{\sigma_e I_x}{c_1}$ ⟲ $R_1 = \dfrac{8K\sigma_e I_x}{3c_1 \ell}$ $R_2 = \dfrac{8K\sigma_e I_x}{c_1 \ell}$ $K\dfrac{\sigma_e I_x}{c_1}$

(e) Fully plastic solution

Fig. 8.20.

bending moment in the beam is $M_{\max} = 9P\ell/64$, which occurs at the right end. When the maximum bending stress at the right end reaches the value σ_e, the following equation holds if we neglect the stress concentration caused by the grip at the fixed end:

$$M_{\max} = \frac{\sigma_e I_x}{c_1} = \frac{9}{64}P_e \ell$$

$$P_e = \frac{64}{9}\frac{\sigma_e I_x}{c_1 \ell} \tag{a}$$

Fully Plastic Load P_{fp}. The fully plastic load P_{fp} is the value of the load P when the fully plastic moment $K(\sigma_e I_x/c_1)$ (see Section 7.15) occurs at the three sections A, B, and C, as shown by the free-body diagrams in Figure 8.20c and d. When fully plastic hinges form at A, B, and C, the deflection of point C (the point of application of the load P_{fp}) can continue to increase at constant load. Thus, the deflections are indeterminate when $P = P_{fp}$; this is the condition that must be satisfied at the fully plastic load. The forces and moments in each of Figures 8.20c and d must satisfy the equilibrium equations. From Figure 8.20d the equation $\sum M_C = 0$ gives

$$\sum M_C = 0 = \frac{3}{4}R_1\ell - 2K\frac{\sigma_e I_x}{c_1}; \qquad R_1 = \frac{8}{3}K\frac{\sigma_e I_x}{c_1 \ell}.$$

From Figure 8.20c the equation $\sum M_B = 0$ gives

$$\sum M_B = 0 = R_1\ell - \frac{P_{fp}\ell}{4},$$

from which we get

$$P_{fp} = 4R_1 = \frac{32}{3}K\left(\frac{\sigma_e I_x}{c_1 \ell}\right). \tag{b}$$

Also, from Figure 8.20c, the equation $\sum F_y = 0$ gives

$$R_1 + R_2 = P_{fp} \qquad \text{whence} \qquad R_2 = P_{fp} - R_1 = 8K\frac{\sigma_e I_x}{c_1 \ell}.$$

In Figure 8.20e are shown the moments and loads on the beam when the fully plastic load is applied.

Ratio of P_{fp} to P_e. The ratio of the fully plastic load to the maximum elastic load can be obtained dividing Equation (a) by Equation (b) as follows:

$$\frac{P_{fp}}{P_e} = \frac{32K\sigma_e I_x}{3c_1 \ell}\frac{9c_1 \ell}{64\sigma_e I_x} = 1.5K.$$

If the beam has a rectangular cross section, the magnitude of K is 1.5 and the ratio is found to be 2.25.

Problems

8.123. A beam of span length $\ell = 24$ in. has each end fixed and is subjected to a concentrated load P at 10 in. from the left end. The beam is a solid circular cylinder with a diameter of 2 in. and is made of a steel with a yield point of $\sigma_e = 50{,}000$ psi. Determine the elastic-limit load P_e and the fully plastic load P_{fp}. (See Table 7.2 for K.)

8.124. A beam of span length ℓ is fixed at each end and is subjected to a uniformly distributed load w. Let the beam have a solid circular cross section of radius R and be made of a steel whose yield point is σ_e. Determine the values of the elastic-limit load w_e and the fully plastic load w_{fp} in terms of σ_e, R, and ℓ. (See Table 7.2 for K.)

8.125. A beam of span length ℓ is fixed at the left end, is simply supported at the right end, and is subjected to a concentrated load P at midspan. The beam is made of a material with a yield point σ_e. The cross section of the beam has a plane of symmetry and the load P is assumed to lie in this plane. Determine the elastic-limit load P_e in terms of c_1, ℓ, I_x, and σ_e, and the fully plastic load P_{fp} of the beam in terms of σ_e, c_1, ℓ, I_x and K, where K is a factor from Table 7.2 that depends on the shape of the cross section of the beam. Also determine the ratio of the fully plastic load to the maximum elastic load. (Assume that $c_1 > c_2$.)

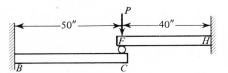

Fig. P 8.126.

8.126. Beams BC and FH in Figure P8.126 are made of the same steel which has a yield point of $\sigma_e = 36{,}000$ psi. Both beams have a rectangular cross section with the same width of 2 in.; beam BC has a depth of 4 in. and beam FH has a depth of 6 in. Determine P_{fp} for the two beams.

Torsion of Cylindrical Members

9.1. Introduction

This chapter will be concerned with the derivation of load-stress and load-deflection relations for straight members having constant cross section and subjected to torsional loads. Here, the word deflection means the angle of twist. Chapter 6 considers the most general loading on cylindrical members; one of the components of the general loading was the torsional load. The z-axis is taken as the axis through the center of twist of each cross section of the member, and each torsional load acting on the torsion member is a couple in a plane perpendicular to the z-axis.

In Figure 9.1a is shown a torsion member fixed at the left end and subjected to torsional loads T_D, T_C, and T_B. In this chapter we assume that a fixed end prevents rotation at that section but does not prevent warping of that section (see Section 9.4). At each section the torsion member is subjected to an applied twisting moment, which is the algebraic sum of the moments about the z-axis of the torsional loads that lie to one side of the section. The symbol T will be used to denote the twisting moment at any cross section. In Figure 9.1b is shown the twisting moment diagram for the torsion member. The applied twisting moment is assumed to be positive if a right-hand screw can be laid along the z-axis and the nut on the screw will advance in the positive direction along the z-axis when the nut is rotated in the direction of the applied twisting moment. Note that the applied twisting moment changes sign at points C and B along the length. Note also that the resisting twisting moment T_0, although it is shown clockwise, is positive as is the applied twisting moment from O to B.

393

As indicated in Figure 9.1b, the twisting moment T may vary over the length of the torsion member. The most stressed section of the torsion member will be that section for T is an absolute maximum, provided that the cross section is constant. We will relate this twisting moment to the shearing stress distribution over the cross section where this twisting

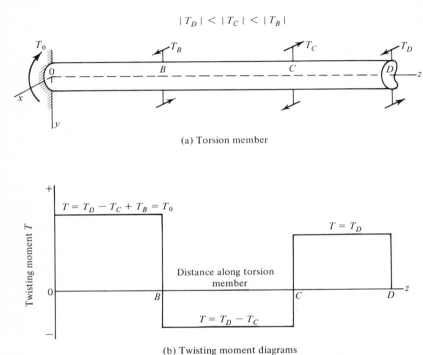

(a) Torsion member

(b) Twisting moment diagrams

Fig. 9.1.   Torsion member and twisting moment diagram.

moment is acting. It will be found that the load-stress relation will be different for each type of cross section (circle, ellipse, rectangle, and so forth). Furthermore, the load-stress relation will be different for linearly elastic and plastic behavior of the material in the torsion member.

The deflection of a torsion member at a section of the member located at distance z from the origin is the angle of twist of that section measured with respect to the section of the torsion member at the origin. Since the angle of twist depends on the magnitude and sense of the twisting moment at every section of the member between the given section and the origin, it will be necessary to derive a relation between the twisting moment and the unit angle of twist which can be assumed to be constant over an infinitesimal length dz of the torsion member.

In all the previous chapters the derivation of load-stress and load-deflection relations for members have followed the three-step procedure, called the simplified approach, presented in Section 4.3. This procedure is used in the analysis of torsion members; however, it is limited to torsion members having circular cross sections. The second procedure in Section 4.3 called the differential equation approach is followed in the treatment of torsion members having noncircular sections in Section 9.6.

Material Properties. The state of stress in torsion members is a special biaxial state of stress called pure shear (see Section 2.3). The only material properties needed for linearly elastic theories are the shearing modulus G and either the shearing yield stress τ_e for torsion members made of ductile materials and subjected to static loads, the fracture shearing stress τ_u for torsion member made of brittle materials, or the fatigue shearing strength τ_f for torsion members subjected to fatigue loading. These limiting stresses are needed to calculate failure loads in each case.

Theories of Failure. Material properties for uniaxial state of stress as obtained from tension specimens are available for most materials; however, material properties for pure shear may not be available for many materials. If material properties for pure shear are not available, they must be predicted from tension test data. The shearing modulus G is generally known (see Table 1.1) but can be obtained from Equation (4–8) if the modulus of elasticity E and Poisson's ratio v are known. Theories of failure were discussed in Section 4.6 for determining values of $\tau_e, \tau_f,$ and τ_u for pure shear from corresponding values of $\sigma_e, \sigma_f,$ and σ_u, which may be known from specimens having uniaxial state of stress. It is recommended that the octa-hedral shearing-stress theory of failure be used when failure is caused by either general yielding for static loading or by progressive fracture for fatigue loading. In the case of general yielding failure, defined by initiation of yielding, the octahedral shearing-stress theory of failure states that the magnitude of the octahedral shearing stress is the same for torsion members and the tension specimen when yielding is initiated in these members. The only nonzero stress for pure shear is τ, which is equal to τ_e at initiation of yielding. Substituting this value in Equation (4–14) gives

$$\tau_e = \frac{\sigma_e}{\sqrt{3}}, \tag{9–1}$$

where τ_e is the yield stress for pure shear and σ_e is the yield stress for a uniaxial state of stress as obtained from tension and compression specimens.

The octahedral shearing stress theory of failure is usually valid in predicting progressive fracture resulting from fatigue loading. Thus

$$\tau_f = \frac{\sigma_f}{\sqrt{3}}, \tag{9-2}$$

where τ_f is the fatigue strength for pure shear and σ_f is the fatigue strength for uniaxial state of stress.

As indicated in Section 4.6, failure of members made of brittle materials is predicted most accurately by the maximum principal stress theory of failure. The maximum principal stress at fracture for pure shear (see Section 2.3) is $\sigma_{\max} = \tau_u$. The maximum principal stress for a tension specimen of the same material at fracture is $\sigma_{\max} = \sigma_u$. Thus

$$\tau_u = \sigma_u. \tag{9-3}$$

The plastic analysis of torsion members requires that the shearing stress–shearing strain diagram for small shearing strains be known. The

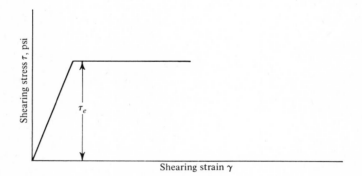

Fig. 9.2.

only plastic problems considered in this chapter will be torsion members made of materials whose shearing stress–shearing strain diagram is flat topped at the shearing yield point τ_e, as indicated in Figure 9.2; the equation of the straight line in the plastic region is (see Eq. 4–18)

$$\tau = \tau_e, \tag{9-4}$$

which indicates that the shearing stress is independent of the shearing strain after initiation of yielding.

9.2. Torsion Members Having Circular Section

The three-step simplified approach of Section 4.3 can be used in deriving load-stress and load-deflection relations for torsion members having circular cross sections. Consider the torsion member in Figure 9.3a. The origin of the x, y, z coordinate axes is shown at the left end; the z-axis passes through the centroid of each cross section. The torsion member is subjected to couples T at each end. Because each couple lies in a plane perpendicular to

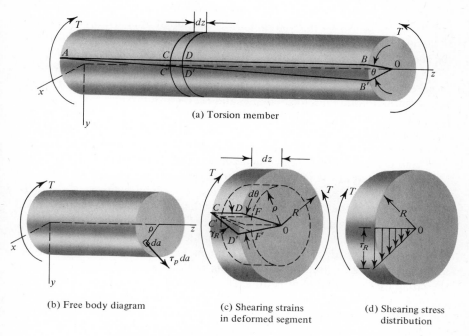

(a) Torsion member

(b) Free body diagram

(c) Shearing strains in deformed segment

(d) Shearing stress distribution

Fig. 9.3. Circular cross-section torsion member.

the z-axis, it is a torsional load. The twisting moment is constant over the length of the torsion member, is equal to T, and is positive.

The load-stress relation for a torsion member relates the twisting moment T at any cross section taken perpendicular to the z-axis and the distribution of the shearing stress on this cross section. A cutting plane perpendicular to the z-axis removes the left portion shown as a free-body diagram in Figure 9.3b; this portion is in equilibrium because the torsion member in Figure 9.3a is in equilibrium. Consider the differential area da

located at a distance ρ from the origin. The intensity of the internal force transmitted through da is a shearing stress τ_ρ. The geometrical analysis of the deformations of the torsion member in the paragraphs to follow indicates that τ_ρ is perpendicular to the line drawn from the center of the torsion member to the differential area da. The moment equilibrium equation taken with respect to the z-axis gives

$$T = \int \tau_\rho \rho \, da. \qquad (9\text{--}5)$$

The integral cannot be solved until the distribution of τ_ρ as a function of ρ is known. As indicated in Section 4.3, the simplified approach requires that the deformations of the torsion member be examined in order to determine the shearing stress distribution.

Geometry of Deformation.   Before applying the torque T to the torsion member in Figure 9.3a, scribe on the surface a longitudinal line AB and two circumferential lines located at C and D at a distance dz apart as shown. For convenience let the left end be fixed as the torque T is applied to the right end. Careful observation of these lines as T is being applied indicates that the line AB deforms into a helix which is practically a straight line for the small deformations being considered here but that circumferential lines are not distorted in the longitudinal direction. Two results are obtained by examining these deformations as follows: (1) plane sections C and D (perpendicular to the z-axis) remain plane with no distortion within the plane, and (2) the shearing strain distribution varies linearly from zero at the center to a maximum at the outside of the torsion member.

An undeformed circumferential line in Figure 9.3a remains a circle after deformation. Careful measurements indicate that different points on the circle do not move relative to each other during deformation. Physical arguments can be used to show that other points in a plane section, not on the circular boundary, also do not move relative to each other during deformation. As indicated in Section 9.5, the circular section is the only cross section for which this conclusion is valid.

Because each plane circular section of the torsion member remains plane and undistorted during loading, it can be shown that the shearing strain distribution is linear for either linearly elastic or plastic behavior of the material. Consider the length dz of the torsion member in Figure 9.3a which has been enlarged and shown in Figure 9.3c. After deformation, the length CD in Figure 9.3a can be rotated by rigid body displacements until C' coincides with C as shown in Figure 9.3c. The angle DCD' is equal to the shearing strain γ_R (see Eq. 3–2) because

$$\gamma_R = \tan(\text{angle } DCD') = \text{angle } DCD'$$

for the infinitesimal shearing strains considered here. From geometry,

$$d\theta = \frac{\gamma_R \, dz}{R},$$ (9–6)

where $d\theta$ is the angle of rotation of the section at the right end of the length dz with respect to the section at the left end. Consider another point F on radius OD at a distance ρ from 0. Since a diameter through point C remains undeformed,

$$d\theta = \frac{\gamma_\rho \, dz}{\rho}.$$ (9–7)

An examination of Equations (9–6) and (9–7) indicates that

$$\psi = \frac{\gamma_\rho}{\rho} = \frac{\gamma_R}{R} = \text{constant},$$ (9–8)

where ψ is defined as the unit angle of twist for the torsion member. Thus, the shearing strain varies linearly* from zero at the center of the circular torsion member to a maximum at the outer radius.

Load-Stress Relation for Linearly Elastic Conditions. The shearing strain distribution is known if the shearing strain is specified for any value of ρ. Because the shearing stress–shearing strain diagram for the material is assumed to be known as indicated in Figure 9.2, the shearing stress distribution can be obtained from the known shearing strain distribution and the known τ–γ diagram. The magnitude of T is then determined by using Equation (9–5). Note that the shearing strain γ_ρ in Figure 9.3c is a measure of the change in right angle formed by a longitudinal line parallel to the z-axis and a line perpendicular to the radial line OF; therefore, the shearing stress has a direction perpendicular to the radial line OF.

If the material is linearly elastic, $\tau = G\gamma$; therefore, the shearing stress distribution is also linear varying from a value of zero at the center to a maximum value at the boundary as indicated in Figure 9.3d. For the torsion member that behaves linearly elastic, Equation (9–5) becomes

$$T = \int \tau_\rho \rho \left(\frac{\rho}{\rho}\right) da = \frac{\tau_\rho}{\rho} \int \rho^2 \, da = \frac{\tau_\rho J}{\rho} \quad \text{or} \quad \tau_\rho = \frac{T\rho}{J},$$ (9–9)

in which J is the polar moment of inertia of the circular section given by the relation

$$J = \int_0^R \rho^2 \, da = \frac{\pi R^4}{2} = \frac{\pi D^4}{32},$$ (9–10)

as discussed in Appendix A.

---

* This linear variation of strain from the center to any point on the boundary of the cross section may not be true for cross sections other than a circle as will be seen later in this chapter.

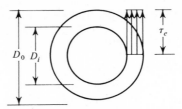

Fig. 9.4. Shearing stress distribution for fully plastic torque.

Load-Stress Relation for Fully Plastic Conditions. Consider a hollow circular cross section torsion member with inside diameter D_i and outside diameter D_0 the cross section of which is shown in Figure 9.4. Let the member be made of a material whose τ–γ diagram is flat topped at the shearing yield stress τ_e as indicated in Figure 9.2. If the torque T is increased until yielding spreads over the cross section, the shearing stress distribution is uniform at the shearing stress τ_e as indicated in Figure 9.4. Because $\tau_\rho = \tau_e$, Equation (9–5) can be integrated to give

$$T_{fp} = \tau_e \int \rho \, da = 2\pi\tau_e \int_{D_i/2}^{D_0/2} \rho^2 \, d\rho = \frac{\pi\tau_e}{12}(D_0^3 - D_i^3), \qquad (9\text{–}11)$$

where T_{fp} is the fully plastic torque.

Load-Stress Relation for Elastic–Plastic Conditions. Let the solid circular cross section torsion member in Figure 9.5 be subjected to a torque T, which causes a shearing strain equal to $K\gamma_e$ at the outer radius where $\gamma_e = \tau_e/G$ is the maximum elastic value of the shearing strain for the material and K is greater than one. Since the shearing strain distribution is linear, the radius R_e at which the shearing strain is γ_e can be obtained from geometry:

$$R_e = \frac{R}{K}. \qquad (9\text{–}12)$$

The radius R_e is the radius of the elastic-plastic boundary. For ρ less than R_e the material is elastic. For ρ greater than R_e the shearing stress is independent

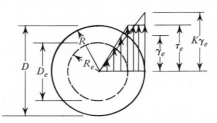

Fig. 9.5. Shearing strain and shearing stress distributions in elastic-plastic torsion member.

of ρ and is equal to τ_e. The torque T for elastic-plastic conditions can be obtained using Equation (9–9) for the elastic region and Equation (9–11) for the fully-plastic region:

$$T = \frac{2\tau_e}{D_e}\frac{\pi D_e^4}{32} + \frac{\pi\tau_e}{12}(D^3 - D_e^3) = \frac{\pi\tau_e D^3}{12}\left[1 - \frac{1}{4K^3}\right]. \tag{9–13}$$

Load-Deflection Relation. The load-deflection relation for a torsion member is the torque angle of twist relation. The angle of twist for either elastic or plastic conditions can be obtained from Equation (9–7):

$$\theta = \int_0^{\ell} \frac{\gamma_\rho}{\rho}\,dz. \tag{9–14}$$

For the special case of linearly elastic conditions, $\gamma_\rho = \tau_\rho/G$, and Equation (9–14) becomes

$$\theta = \int_0^{\ell} \frac{\tau_\rho}{G\rho}\,dz = \int_0^{\ell} \frac{T}{GJ}\,dz = \int_0^{\ell} \psi\,dz, \tag{9–15}$$

where $\psi = T/GJ$ is the unit angle of twist for elastic conditions.

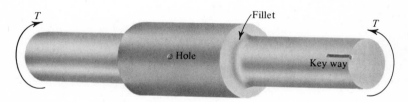

Fig. 9.6. Stress concentrations in torsion member having abrupt changes in section.

Torsion Members with Abrupt Changes in Section. Most torsion members have abrupt changes in section. Many torsion members are stepped with fillets as shown in Figure 9.6 for ease in locating gears, pulleys, bearings, and so forth. Other stress concentrations (see Section 1.7) in torsion members may be caused by holes or keyways machined in the torsion member as indicated in Figure 9.6. The maximum shearing stress in the torsion member for linearly elastic conditions is obtained by introducing a stress concentration factor k_t (see Section 1.7) in Equation (9–9) to give

$$\tau_R = k_t \frac{TR}{J}. \tag{9–16}$$

As indicated in Figure 9.7, the magnitude of k_t for a fillet depends on both

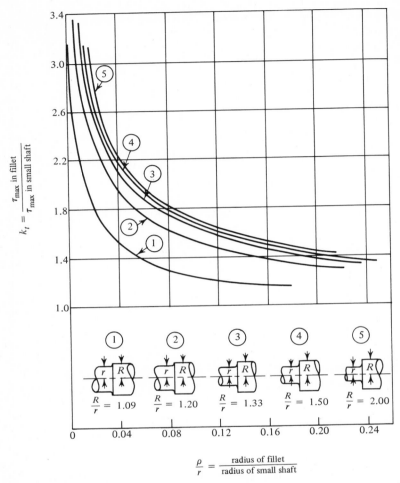

Fig. 9.7. Torsional shearing stress concentration factor at fillet in shaft of two dimensions.

the ratio of the large radius R to the small radius r for the shaft and the ratio of the radius of the fillet ρ to the small radius of the shaft.

Most of the torsion problems considered in this chapter assume that the members are made of ductile materials and subjected to static loads. In this case the effect of the stress concentration factor can be neglected as was indicated in Section 4.5. In case the torsion member either is subjected to fatigue loading or is made of a brittle material, Equation (9–16) is the load-stress relation, which must be used in design and the value of k_t will be required.

Stiffness Constant for Torsion Member. For an elastically loaded torsion member subjected to a torque T, which is constant over its length ℓ, the constant β that must be multiplied by the angle of twist θ of the member to give the torque T is called the stiffness constant for the member. Hence, by this definition,

$$T = \beta\theta. \tag{9-17}$$

For the special case in which the torsion member has a uniform cross section over the length ℓ, Equation (9–15) gives

$$T = \frac{GJ}{\ell}\theta,$$

which, when substituted in Equation (9–17), gives

$$\beta = \frac{GJ}{\ell}. \tag{9-18}$$

Illustrative Problem

9.1. The torsion member in Figure P9.1 has diameters of $D_1 = 2$ in. and $D_2 = 4$ in. and is subjected to the torsional loads shown. Neglecting the effect of stress concentrations at abrupt changes in section and assuming that the material is elastic, determine the maximum shearing stress in

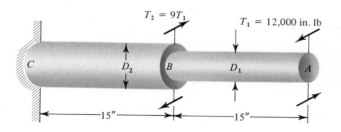

Fig. P 9.1.

the torsion member. Also determine the angle of twist of the right end of the torsion member. The torsion member is made of steel for which $G = 12,000,000$ psi.

SOLUTION. First, we must determine the twisting moment diagram for the torsion member. The twisting moment is constant from A to B and from B to C.

$$T_{AB} = T_1 = 12,000 \text{ in.-lb},$$

$$T_{BC} = T_1 - 9T_1 = -96,000 \text{ in.-lb}.$$

The maximum shearing stresses in the lengths AB and BC occur at the outer radii R_1 and R_2 and can be obtained using Equation (9–9):

$$\tau_{R_1} = \frac{T_{AB}R_1}{J_1} = \frac{T_{AB}D_1/2}{\pi D_1^4/32} = \frac{12,000(1)(32)}{\pi(2)(2)(2)(2)} = 7,640 \text{ psi},$$

$$\tau_{R_2} = \frac{T_{BC}R_2}{J_2} = \frac{T_{BC}D_2/2}{\pi D_2^4/32} = -\frac{96,000(2)(32)}{\pi(4)(4)(4)(4)} = -7,640 \text{ psi}.$$

Note that both portions of the torsion member have the same magnitude for the maximum shearing stress. An increase in the diameter of the torsion member from D_1 to D_2 increases the section modulus J/R considerably; because J increases as the fourth power of the diameter and R as the first power of the diameter, J/R increases as the cube of the diameter. As indicated by Equation (9–9), the maximum shearing stress in the two portions of the torsion member will be the same only if $T_{AB}/T_{BC} = (D_2/D_1)^3$.

The angle of twist of the right end of the torsion member can be obtained using Equation (9–15):

$$\theta = \frac{T_{AB}\ell_{AB}}{GJ_1} + \frac{T_{BC}\ell_{BC}}{GJ_2} = \frac{12,000(15)(32)}{12,000,000(\pi)(2^4)} - \frac{96,000(15)(32)}{12,000,000(\pi)(4^4)},$$

$$= 0.00954 - 0.00477,$$

$$= 0.00477 \text{ rad}.$$

The right end of the torsion member rotates through an angle of 0.00477 rad. in the counterclockwise direction.

9.2. Sometimes the strength of the outer layer of a shaft is increased by induction hardening. A 2-in. diameter shaft is made of an alloy steel, which has a shearing yield stress of $\tau_{e_1} = 30,000$ psi. Induction hardening increased the shearing yield stress of the hardened material to $\tau_{e_2} = 60,000$ psi. The thickness of the hardened material is $\frac{1}{8}$ in. The quenching treatment during the induction hardening introduces quenching stresses called residual stresses; assume that these can be neglected. Assume that the shearing stress–shearing strain diagram of each of the two materials is flat topped at the shearing yield stress. Determine the torque required to (1) initiate yielding in the untreated shaft, (2) initiate yielding in the induction hardened shaft, (3) initiate yielding in the hardened material of the induction hardened shaft, and (4) produce fully plastic conditions in the induction hardened shaft.

SOLUTION.   The twisting moment is assumed to be constant over the length of the shaft. Yielding will begin in the untreated shaft when $\tau = \tau_{e_1}$ at the outer radius R. Using Equation (9–9),

$$T_{(1)} = \frac{\tau_{e_1} J}{R} = \frac{30,000\pi R^4}{2R} = 47,100 \text{ in.-lb.}$$

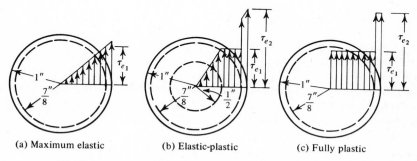

(a) Maximum elastic   (b) Elastic-plastic   (c) Fully plastic

Fig. P 9.2.   Stress distributions in induction-hardened shaft.

When yielding begins in the induction hardened shaft, the shearing stress distribution is as shown in Figure P9.2a. Yielding starts in the untreated material when $\tau = \tau_{e_1}$ at $\rho = \frac{7}{8}$ in. Note that the shearing stress at the outer radius is less than τ_{e_2}. Using Equation (9–9)

$$T_{(2)} = \frac{\tau_{e_1} J}{\rho} = \frac{30,000\pi R^4(8)}{2(7)} = 53,900 \text{ in.-lb.}$$

An elastic-plastic solution is required for part (3). In order to initiate yielding in the hardened material, $\tau = \tau_{e_2}$ at $\rho = R = 1$ in. Since the hardened material is still linearly elastic,

$$\gamma_{max} = \frac{\tau_{e2}}{G} = \frac{60,000}{12,000,000} = 0.0050.$$

This is the shearing yield strain for the hardened material. The shearing strain distribution is linear. In order to determine the elastic-plastic boundary in the untreated material, calculate the shearing yield strain for the untreated material:

$$\gamma_{e_1} = \frac{\tau_{e_1}}{G} = \frac{30,000}{12,000,000} = 0.0025.$$

From Equation (9–8) this shearing strain occurs at a radius of $\frac{1}{2}$ in. The untreated material remains elastic to a radius of $\frac{1}{2}$ in. The shearing stress distribution is shown in Figure P9.2b. The twisting moment for part (3) can be obtained using Equation (9–9) for the hardened material which remains elastic and Equation (9–13) for the untreated material. The magnitude of K is given by Equation (9–12):

$$K = \frac{7/8}{1/2} = 1.75,$$

$$T_{(3)} = \frac{\tau_{e_2}}{R}\frac{\pi}{32}[2^4 - (1.75)^4] + \frac{\pi\tau_{e_1}(1.75)^3}{12}\left[1 - \frac{1}{4(1.75)^3}\right],$$

$$= 39{,}000 + 40{,}130,$$

$$= 79{,}130 \text{ in.-lb.}$$

The fully plastic twisting moment for part (4) can be obtained using Equation (9–11) for both the hardened and untreated materials. The fully plastic stress distribution is shown in Figure P9.2c.

$$T_{(4)} = \frac{\pi\tau_{e_2}}{12}[2^3 - (1.75)^3] + \frac{\pi\tau_{e_1}}{12}(1.75)^3,$$

$$= 41{,}480 + 42{,}090,$$

$$= 83{,}570 \text{ in.-lb.}$$

Note that induction hardening increased the elastic strength of the shaft from 47,100 in.-lb to 53,900 in.-lb an increase of 14.4 per cent. The twisting moment required to initiate yielding in the hardened material is 68.0 per cent greater than that for the untreated shaft whereas the fully plastic twisting moment is 77.4 per cent greater than that for the untreated shaft.

9.3. Let the torsion member in Problem 9.2 have a length of 15 in. If the twisting moments calculated in parts (1), (2), and (3) are applied to each end of the torsion member in each case, determine the angle of twist of one end of the shaft with respect to the other in each case.

SOLUTION. It is convenient to calculate the angle of twist using Equation (9–14) in each case since the shearing strain was calculated in Problem 9.2 for particular values of ρ in each case. For part (1) yielding will be initiated in the untreated shaft when the maximum shearing strain is $\gamma_{e_1} = 0.0025$ for $\rho = R$:

$$\theta_{(1)} = \frac{\gamma_{e_1}\ell}{R} = \frac{0.0025(15)}{1} = 0.0375 \text{ rad.}$$

For part (2) yielding will be initiated in the shaft when the maximum shearing strain in the untreated material is $\gamma_{e_1} = 0.0025$ for $\rho = \frac{7}{8}$ in.

$$\theta_{(2)} = \frac{\gamma_{e_1}\ell}{\rho} = \frac{0.0025(15)}{0.875} = 0.0429 \text{ rad.}$$

For part (3) yielding will be initiated in the hardened material of the shaft when the maximum shearing strain is $\gamma_{e_2} = 0.0050$ for $\rho = R$:

$$\theta_{(3)} = \frac{\gamma_{e_2}\ell}{R} = \frac{0.0025(15)}{1} = 0.0750 \text{ rad.}$$

Problems

9.4. A twisting moment of 11,000 ft-lb is applied to a solid circular steel shaft having a diameter of 4 in. (1) Calculate the maximum shearing stress in the shaft; assume that the shearing yield stress of the steel is 24,000 psi. (2) Would the stress have the same value if the shaft were made of bronze or aluminum or any other linearly elastic material provided that it was not stressed above the proportional limit of the material?

9.5. A solid steel shaft has a diameter of 4 in. and a length of 60 in. The shaft transmits a torque of 150,000 in.-lb. If the shaft is replaced by a hollow steel shaft having an inside diameter of 3 in., determine the outside diameter if the maximum shearing stress in the hollow shaft is to be the same as that for the solid shaft when transmitting the same torque. Compare stiffnesses of the two shafts. $G = 12,000,000$ psi.

ans. By trial and error $D_2 = 4.36$ in.; hollow shaft 9.3 per cent stiffer.

9.6. How much will the elastic strength of a solid cylindrical shaft be decreased by boring a concentric longitudinal hole through the shaft, the cross-sectional area of the hole being one-half of the cross section of the solid shaft? Compare the strengths and stiffnesses of the hollow and solid shafts.

9.7. A hollow circular torsion member has a length of 9 in., an outside diameter $D_0 = 3$ in., an inside diameter $D_i = 2$ in., and is made of structural grade steel ($G = 12,000,000$ psi, $\tau_e = 24,000$ psi). Determine the magnitude of the torque required to cause yielding to spread until yielding is impending at the inner radius, that is, the shearing strain at the inner radius is $\gamma_e = \tau_e/G$. What is the angle of twist for this loading condition? Compare the torque with the maximum elastic torque T_e.

ans. $T_{fp} = 119,400$ in.-lb; $\theta = 0.018$ rad; $T_{fp}/T_e = 1.169$.

9.8. The torsion member in Figure P9.8 is made of a magnesium alloy ($G = 2,600,000$ psi). The magnitude of T_1 is 9,000 in.-lb and the magnitude of T_2 is

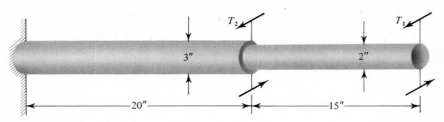

Fig. P 9.8, 9.9, 9.10.

such that the unit angle of twist is the same in the 20-in. length and in the 15-in. length. Neglecting stress concentrations, determine T_2 and the angle of twist of the free end. Assume linearly elastic conditions.

9.9. The torsion member in Figure P9.9 is made of an aluminum alloy for which $G = 4,000,000$ psi. Assuming linearly elastic behavior and neglecting the effect of stress concentrations, determine the maximum shearing stress in the torsion member if $T_1 = T_2 = 3,000\pi$ in.-lb. Also determine the angle of twist at the free end.

9.10. The torsion member in Figure P9.10 is made of a low carbon steel whose shearing stress–shearing strain diagram is flat topped at the shearing yield stress of $\tau_e = 18,000$ psi. Neglecting the effect of stress concentrations, determine the magnitude of T_1 necessary to initiate yielding in the 2-in. diameter length of the torsion member. Also determine the magnitude of T_2 if the unit angle of twist in the 3-in. diameter length of the torsion member is the same as for the 2-in. diameter length.

ans. $T_1 = 28,300$ in.-lb; $T_2 = 89,500$ in.-lb.

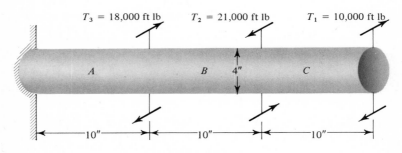

Fig. P 9.11.

9.11. The torsion member in Figure P9.11 is made of an aluminum alloy for which $G = 4,000,000$ psi. If the material in the torsion member behaves elastically, determine (1) the maximum shearing stress in the torsion member and (2) the angle of twist of the free end.

9.12. In thin wall circular torsion members, the polar moment of inertia of the cross section is closely approximated by $J = AR_m^2 = 2\pi R_m^3 t$, where R_m is the mean radius of the cross section and t is the wall thickness. Determine the ratio of the outer radius R_2 to inner radius R_1 such that the approximate value of J is in error by no more than 1 per cent.

ans. $R_2 = 1.223R_1$.

9.13. In Figure P9.13 let the tube and shaft both be made of steel and let the tube and shaft act as one body when subjected to the torques T_1 and T_2 as shown. The tube has a wall thickness of $t = \frac{1}{20}$ in. Determine the magnitudes of T_1 and T_2 such that the maximum shearing stress in the solid shaft in length AB and the average shearing stress in the tube are each equal to 10,000 psi.

ans. $T_1 = 1,970$ in.-lb and $T_2 = 2,160$ in.-lb.

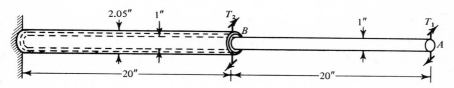

Fig. P 9.13.

9.14. If T_1 and T_2 are both equal to 2,000 in.-lb for the torsion member in Problem 9.13, determine the angle of twist of the free end.

9.15. A 1-in. diameter shaft is made of an alloy steel that has a shearing yield stress $\tau_{e_1} = 26,000$ psi. The shaft is induction hardened to a depth of $\frac{1}{8}$ in. Induction hardening increased the shearing yield stress of the hardened material to $\tau_{e_2} = 48,000$ psi. How much was the elastic strength of the shaft increased by the induction hardening?

9.16. Assume that the shearing stress–shearing strain diagrams of the untreated and hardened materials in the shaft of Problem 9.15 are flat topped at their respective shearing yield stresses. Determine both the twisting moment required to initiate yielding in the hardened material and the fully plastic torque.

9.17. The torsion member in Figure P9.17 is made of a brittle material whose ultimate strength as determined from a tension specimen is $\sigma_\mu = 25,000$ psi. The radius

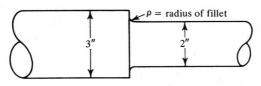

Fig. P 9.17, 9.18.

of the fillet is $\frac{1}{8}$ in. Determine the maximum twisting moment which can be applied to the torsion member based on a factor of safety of 2.5 against failure by fracture.

ans. $k_t = 1.59$; $T = 4,900$ in.-lb.

9.18. The torsion member in Figure P9.18 is made of 2024-T4 aluminum alloy. The radius of the fillet is $\frac{1}{16}$ in. The torsion member is subjected to completely reversed torsional loads. Determine the magnitude of the maximum twisting moment that can be applied to the torsion member if it is designed based on a factor of safety of 2.0 against fatigue fracture in 10^6 cycles of loading. The fatigue strength from completely reversed centrally loaded members is $\sigma_f = 27,000$ psi as indicated in Figure 1.17.

ans. $k_t = 1.93$; $\tau_f = 15,600$ psi; $T = 6,350$ in.-lb.

9.19. In Figure P9.19 a force P of 196 lb will cause a normal pressure of 15 psi on the rubbing surfaces of the friction clutch shown. If the coefficient of friction for the rubbing surfaces is 0.30 and the diameter of the shaft is 1.25 in., find the maximum shearing stress in the shaft at section AA. The shaft is made of steel which has a shearing proportional limit of 20,000 psi. Neglect effect of axial force in shaft.

ans. $\tau = 7,960$ psi.

9.20. In Figure P9.20 a disk A is keyed to a shaft B and a twisting moment $T = Pp$ is applied to the disk; the moment T is just sufficient to overcome the resisting moment offered by the machine that is driven by the shaft. Thus the disk and shaft rotate at a constant angular speed of ω rad/sec. Show that the relation among the horsepower transmitted by the shaft, the twisting moment T, and the speed n in revolutions per minute (rpm) is given by the expression

$$\text{hp} = \frac{T2\pi n}{12(33,000)} = \frac{T\pi n}{198,000},$$

in which T is expressed in inch-pounds. (1 hp = 33,000 ft-lb/min = 550 ft-lb/sec.)

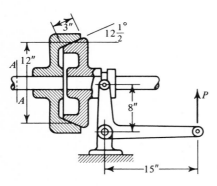

Fig. P 9.19.

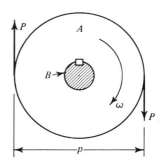

Fig. P 9.20.

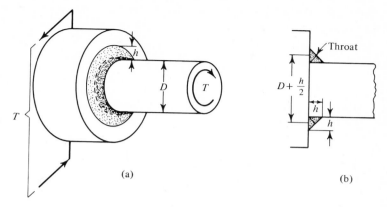

Fig. P 9.21.

9.21. A cylindrical steel shaft having a diameter D-in. is welded to a circular plate by means of a fillet weld, as shown in Figure P9.21, in which h is small compared to D. Equal and opposite twisting moments T in.-lb are applied to the ends of the member. If the shearing force on the throat section per inch of length of weld is q lb/in., show that

$$T = \frac{1}{2}\pi q\left(D + \frac{h}{2}\right)^2.$$

Is this equation dimensionally correct? Also note that the shearing stress on the throat area of the weld is

$$\tau = \frac{q}{h\cos 45°}.$$

9.22. In Figure P9.22 let it be assumed that the diameter of the bolts of the coupling are small relative to R, so that the shearing stress on the cross section of each

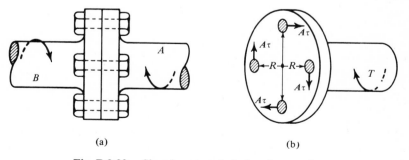

Fig. P 9.22. Shearing stress in bolts of a coupling.

bolt may be considered to be distributed uniformly. Observe from Figure P9.22b that equilibrium requires that the twisting moment T transmitted from one shaft to the other may be expressed as follows:

$$T = m\frac{\pi D^2}{4}\tau R,$$

where m is the number of bolts and D is the diameter of each bolt. If, in Figure P9.22b, $D = \frac{3}{4}$ in., $R = 3$ in., $\tau = 8,000$ psi, and the speed of the shaft is 90 rpm, what horsepower is transmitted by the shaft? (See Problem 9.20.)

9.23. A coupling (see Problem 9.22) is to be used to connect two shafts having diameters of 4 in. The maximum elastic shearing stress in the shafts is 10,000 psi, the diameter of the bolt circle is 8 in., and the elastic shearing stress in the bolts is 9,000 psi. (1) Find the number of $\frac{3}{4}$-in. bolts used. (2) Calculate the horsepower transmitted by the shaft if its speed is 100 rpm. (See Problem 9.20.)

9.24. In order to reduce the weight of a large solid shaft, a hollow shaft with a somewhat larger outside diameter may be used; this fact follows from the condition that the material near the center of the shaft is very ineffective in contributing to the strength of the shaft because the stresses near to the center are small. The solid-steel propeller shaft of a large passenger ship delivers 40,000 hp at a constant speed of 200 rpm to the propeller. (1) If the outer diameter of the solid shaft is 24 in., what is the maximum torsional shearing stress in the shaft? (See Problem 9.20.) Assume that the shaft acts elastically. (2) If a hollow shaft of the same material having an outer diameter of 26 in. is to replace the solid shaft without increasing the maximum shearing stress in the shaft, what should be the inner diameter of the hollow shaft? (3) How much weight per foot of length will be saved by use of the hollow shaft? Assume that steel weighs 0.28 lb/in.[3]

9.25. The hydraulic turbines in the Keokuk waterpower plant are rated at 10,000 hp, with an overload capacity of 13,500 hp. The vertical shaft connecting the turbine and the generator is 25 in. in diameter and rotates at 57.7 rpm. What is the maximum shearing stress in the shaft when full load is being developed, and when maximum overload is being developed? (See Problem 9.20.)

9.26. An aluminum alloy $(G_A = 3,860,000$ psi$)$ shaft, which has an outside diameter of 3 in. and an inside diameter of 2 in., is shrunk onto a solid bronze $(G_B = 6,000,000$ psi$)$ shaft having a diameter of 2 in. Assume that the two-material shaft deforms as a one-material shaft when a torque T is applied; this means that the shearing strain distribution is assumed to be linear for the two-material shaft. Show that $\tau_{A_{\max}} = 3G_A\tau_{B_{\max}}/2G_B$ where $\tau_{A_{\max}}$ is the maximum shearing stress in the aluminum alloy shaft and $\tau_{B_{\max}}$ is the maximum shearing stress in the brass shaft.

9.27. Let the two-material shaft in Problem 9.26 be subjected to a torque $T = 60,000$ in.-lb. Determine the maximum shearing stress in the aluminum alloy and in the brass.

ans. $\tau_{A_{\max}} = 10,210$ psi; $\tau_{B_{\max}} = 10,580$ psi.

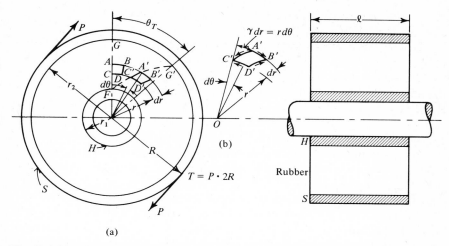

(a)

Fig. P 9.28. Shearing stress and strains in a torsional rubber spring for reducing vibrations, sometimes called a torsilastic spring.

9.28. Cylindrical rubber springs frequently are used as spring mounting of automobiles, trucks, and buses. For example, one such spring is shown in Figure P9.28 in which rubber is securely bonded on two concentric cylindrical steel shells denoted by S and H. The outer shell is attached to the frame or body of the automobile, and the inner shell is attached to the axle in such a way that the two shells twist relatively to each other when vertical relative motion between the axle and car body occurs as the car travels over rough road. The twisting moment or torque T transmitted from one shell to the other causes torsional shearing stresses and strains in the rubber. Find the shearing stress distribution and the total angle of twist of the outer shell relative to the inner shell, if it is assumed that the shearing modulus of elasticity G of the rubber is constant and that the torque is applied uniformly over the length ℓ (Fig. P9.28).

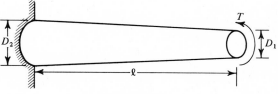

Fig. P 9.29.

9.29. Assuming that Equation (9–15) is valid for the tapered torsion member in Figure P9.29, derive the relation for the angle of twist of the free end.

9.3.   Statically Indeterminate Torsion Members

There are occasions in which a torsion member is restrained from rotating at each end. In this case equations of equilibrium are not sufficient to determine the torque at each section of the member and the torsion member is said to be statically indeterminate. The equation in addition to the equations of equilibrium needed to determine the torque at every section of the member is obtained by examining the prescribed boundary condition on the deformations of the member. If the angle of twist of one end of the torsion member with respect to the other is specified, Equation (9–15) gives an additional relation to be used along with equations of equilibrium to solve the problem.

The solution of statically indeterminate torsion members can best be obtained by following the five-step procedure outlined in Section 1.5. In these five steps, replace loads by torsional loads, elongations by angles of twist, and Equations (1–13) or (1–18) by Equation (9–15). The method of using the five steps is demonstrated in the following illustrative problem.

Illustrative Problem

9.30.   The steel circular-section torsion member in Figure P9.30a is prevented from twisting at its ends by rigid supports. Determine the maximum shearing stress in the shaft if $T_B = 40,000$ in.-lb and $T_C = 20,000$ in.-lb.

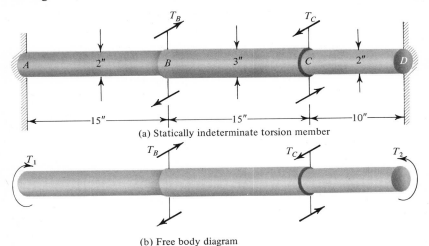

(a) Statically indeterminate torsion member

(b) Free body diagram

Fig. P 9.30.

SOLUTION. Step 1 of the five-step procedure presented in Section 1.5 is satisfied by the free-body diagram in Figure P9.30b. Using the sign convention for twisting moments given in Section 5.2, the two unknown reactions T_1 and T_2 are assumed to be positive in Figure P9.30b. It is convenient to assume all unknowns to be positive so that the reactions T_1 and T_2 will have the correct sign. Note that T_C and T_B are applied twisting moments but T_1 and T_2 are reaction twisting moments. Because there are two unknowns and only one equation of equilibrium, the order of redundancy is one (Step 2). The boundary condition for Step 3 is that the angle of twist θ of one end of the torsion member with respect to the other end is zero because the supports are rigidly fixed; thus, $\theta = 0$. In Step 4 the equilibrium moment equation about the z-axis gives

$$\sum M_z = 0 = -T_1 - T_B + T_C + T_2,$$
$$T_1 = T_C + T_2 - T_B.$$

The twisting moment in each of the three lengths AB, BC, and CD can be written in terms of T_2 as follows:

$$T_{AB} = T_1 = T_C + T_2 - T_B = T_2 - 20{,}000,$$
$$T_{BC} = T_2 + T_C = T_2 + 20{,}000, \tag{a}$$
$$T_{CD} = T_2.$$

The magnitudes of T_1 and T_2 are obtained in Step 5 using Equation (9–15), Equations (a), and the boundary condition $\theta = 0$ from Step 3:

$$\theta = \frac{T_{AB}\ell_{AB}}{GJ_{AB}} + \frac{T_{BC}\ell_{BC}}{GJ_{BC}} + \frac{T_{CD}\ell_{CD}}{GJ_{CD}} = 0,$$

$$(T_2 - 20{,}000)\ell_{AB}\frac{\pi(3)^4}{32} + (T_2 + 20{,}000)\ell_{BC}\frac{\pi(2)^4}{32} + T_2\ell_{CD}\frac{\pi(3)^4}{32} = 0,$$

$$(T_2 - 20{,}000)(15)(81) + (T_2 + 20{,}000)(15)(16) + T_2(10)(81) = 0,$$

$$T_2 = 8{,}600 \text{ in.-lb.}$$

From Equations (a)

$$T_{AB} = T_2 - 20{,}000 = -11{,}400 \text{ in.-lb,}$$
$$T_{BC} = T_2 + 20{,}000 = 28{,}600 \text{ in.-lb,}$$
$$T_{CD} = T_2 = 8{,}600 \text{ in.-lb.}$$

Substituting these values in Equation (9–9) indicates that the maximum shearing stress, neglecting stress concentrations, occurs in length AB:

$$\tau_{AB} = \frac{T_{AB}R}{J_{AB}} = \frac{11,400(1)(32)}{\pi(2)^4} = 7,260 \text{ psi.}$$

Problems

9.31. The circular cross section member in Figure P9.31 is prevented from rotating at its ends by rigid supports. A twisting moment T is applied at a distance $\ell/4$ from the left end. If the known quantities are T, ℓ, J, and G, determine the reactions at each end of the torsion member.

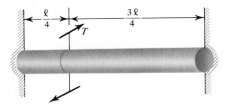

Fig. P 9.31.

9.32. Solve Problem 9.30 for the condition that $T_B = 50,000$ in.-lb and $T_C = 30,000$ in.-lb.

9.33. The steel circular cross section member in Figure P9.33 is prevented from rotating at its ends by rigid supports. Using elastic properties from Table 1.1 determine the angle of twist of the section at B.

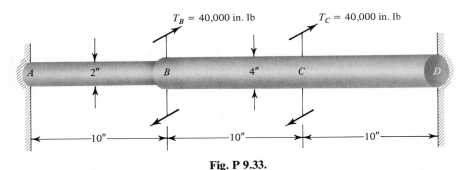

Fig. P 9.33.

9.34. The tapered shaft with circular cross section shown in Figure P9.34 is fixed at each end. If the shaft is subjected to a twisting moment T at its midsection, determine

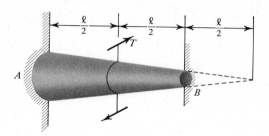

Fig. P 9.34.

the value of the reaction twisting moment at each end. Assume that Equation (9–15) is valid.

ans. $T_B = 19T/208$; $T_A = 189T/208$.

9.4. Torsion Members Having Circular Section and Linear Viscoelastic Material Behavior

The angle of twist of torsion members made of linear viscoelastic materials continues to increase with time. The only constitutive relation considered is that for the Maxwell model whose stress-strain-time relation is given by the following equation (same as Eq. 4–22):

$$\dot{\gamma} = \frac{\dot{\tau}}{G_M} + \frac{\tau}{\mu'_M} \qquad (9\text{–}19)$$

in which G_M and μ'_M are material constants and the dot designates differentiation with respect to time.

Let the torsion member in Figure 9.3a be made of a time dependent material that can be accurately approximated by a Maxwell model. Let the torsion member be loaded in such a short time that the member is elastically deformed at $t = 0$. Consider length dz in Figure 9.3c. Let line CD be scribed on the surface at zero time and let point C be held at its initial location; then line CD deforms into line $C'D'$ through angle γ_R in time dt and radius OD rotates through angle $d\theta$ in time dt. The geometry of deformation indicates that

$$\frac{\dot{\gamma}_\rho}{\rho} = \frac{\dot{\gamma}_R}{R} = \text{constant}, \qquad (9\text{–}20)$$

and

$$d\dot{\theta} = \frac{\dot{\gamma}_R \, dz}{R}. \qquad (9\text{–}21)$$

Divide Equation (9–19) by ρ and note that at the end of time dt the shearing stress τ_ρ will be $\tau'_\rho + d\tau_\rho$ where τ'_ρ is the shearing stress at zero time calculated using Equation (9–9). The resulting equation can be written in the form

$$\frac{\dot{\gamma}_\rho}{\rho} - \frac{\tau'_\rho}{\mu'_M \rho} = \frac{d\tau_\rho}{\rho}\left(\frac{1}{G_M \, dt} + \frac{1}{\mu'_M}\right). \tag{9–22}$$

The two terms on the left side of Equation (9–22) are constants since both $\dot{\gamma}_\rho$ and τ'_ρ vary linearly with ρ. For a specified increment of time dt the bracket term on the right side of Equation (9–22) is a constant; therefore, $d\tau_\rho/\rho$ is also a constant and $d\tau_\rho$ varies linearly with ρ. Obviously $d\tau_\rho = 0$ unless the torsional load on the torsion member is changed during time dt. Thus, the stress distribution in a circular section torsion member whose time-dependent material behavior is represented by a Maxwell model is linear and given by Equation (9–9).

Using Equations (9–9), (9–19), and (9–21) the following relation can be derived:

$$d\theta = \left(\frac{\dot{T}}{G_M J} + \frac{T}{\mu'_M J}\right) dz. \tag{9–23}$$

If the torque T remains constant, $\dot{T} = 0$, and Equation (9–23) can be integrated to give

$$d\theta = \left(\frac{Tt}{\mu'_M J} + C_1\right) dz. \tag{9–24}$$

The constant of integration C_1 is determined by the boundary condition $d\theta = T \, dz/G_M J$ when $t = 0$. Substituting in Equation (9–24) gives

$$\theta = \left[1 + \frac{G_M t}{\mu'_M}\right] \int \frac{T \, dz}{G_M J}. \tag{9–25}$$

At zero time note that Equation (9–25) reduces to Equation (9–15). The angle of twist θ at zero time can be calculated, and the angle of twist at any time t is then given by multiplying by the bracket term in Equation (9–25).

Illustrative Problem

9.35. A torsion member of high density polyethylene has an outside diameter of 0.50 in. and a length of 8 in. The member has an inside diameter of 0.40 in. over a length of 4 in. and is solid over the remaining 4 in. of length. It is fixed at one end and subjected to a torque of 10 in.-lb at the free end.

The material properties are $G_M = 13,000$ psi and $\mu'_M = 13,000,000$ lb-hr/in.^{2} Determine the maximum shearing stress, the angle of twist rate, and the total angle of twist in 200 hours.

SOLUTION. The polar moments of inertia for the two cross-sectional areas are

$$J_1 = \frac{\pi D^4}{32} = 0.00614 \text{ in.}^4 \quad \text{and} \quad J_2 = \frac{\pi}{32}(D^4 - D_i^4) = 0.00362 \text{ in.}^4$$

The maximum shearing stress τ_R is given by Equation (9–9).

$$\tau_R = \frac{TR}{J_2} = \frac{10(0.25)}{0.00362} = 691 \text{ psi.}$$

The angle of twist rate at the free end requires that the angle of twist θ_e for the free end for linearly elastic conditions be determined from Equation (9–15).

$$\theta_e = \frac{T\ell_1}{G_M J_1} + \frac{T\ell_2}{G_M J_2} = \frac{10(4)}{13,000(0.00614)} + \frac{10(4)}{13,000(0.00362)} = 1.35 \text{ rad.}$$

The angle of twist rate $\dot{\theta}$ for the free end of the torsion member is obtained by taking the derivative of Equation (9–25):

$$\dot{\theta} = \theta_e \frac{G_M}{\mu'_M} = \frac{1.35(13,000)}{13,000,000} = 0.00135 \text{ rad/hr.}$$

The total angle of twist is given by Equation (9–25):

$$\theta = \theta_e + \dot{\theta}t = 1.35 + 0.00135(200) = 1.62 \text{ rad.}$$

Problems

9.36. A torsion member has a length of 15 in. and is fixed at the left end. Length AB equal to 10 in. measured from the fixed end has a diameter of 1 in. In the remaining 5-in., BC has a diameter of $\frac{3}{4}$ in. The member is made of a linear viscoelastic material which can be accurately approximated by a Maxwell model. The material constants are $G_M = 60,000$ psi and $\mu'_M = 40,000,000$ lb-hr/in.^{2} A clockwise torque $T_1 = 80$ lb-in. is applied to the free end of the torsion member at C and a clockwise torque $T_2 = 120$ lb-in. is applied at B. Determine the angle of twist at the free end when $t = 0$, the angle of twist rate, and the total angle of twist at 500 hr.

9.37. Solve Problem 9.36 for the condition that $T_1 = 80$ lb-in. is clockwise and $T_2 = 300$ lb-in. is counterclockwise.

ans. $\theta_e = 0.158$ rad; $\dot{\theta} = 0.000237$ rad/hr; $\theta = 0.277$ rad at 500 hr.

9.5.   Limitations of the Simplified Approach

The solution to the torsion problem for torsion members having circular cross sections could be obtained using the simplified approach because it is possible to show that the shearing strain increases linearly from zero at the center. For linearly elastic material behavior, the shearing stress distribution is also linear with the maximum shearing stress occurring at a

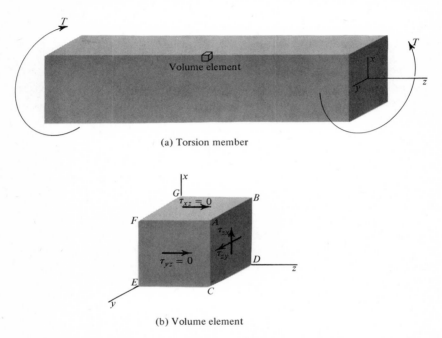

(a) Torsion member

(b) Volume element

Fig. 9.8.   Rectangular cross section torsion member.

point farthest from the center of the torsion member. Let us examine the possibility of this conclusion being valid for other cross sections. Consider the rectangular cross section member in Figure 9.8a. A volume element having two faces coinciding with the free surfaces of the torsion member has been enlarged and shown in Figure 9.8b. The shearing stress acting on the area $ABCD$ can be broken into components τ_{zx} and τ_{zy} as shown. In Chapter 2 it was found that, if τ_{zx} acts on face $ABCD$, τ_{xz} must equal τ_{zx}, and must act on face $ABFG$. Since face $ABFG$ coincides with the free surface, $\tau_{xz} = \tau_{zx} = 0$. Similarly, $\tau_{yz} = \tau_{zy} = 0$. From this it is concluded that the shearing stress is zero at each of the four corners of a rectangular cross section. Thus, the shearing stress at a point in the cross section at the greatest distance from the center of the torsion member is zero. This conclusion does not agree with that for the circular section.

The deformations of a rectangular-section torsion member subjected to large deformations is indicated in Figure 9.9. A square grid was scribed on the undeformed member. Note that the greatest distortion of the grid occurs

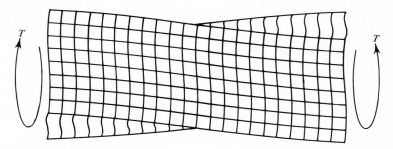

Fig. 9.9.   Large deformations of rectangular cross section torsion member.

at the center of the long side of the rectangle whereas the squares at the edges remain undeformed. Observations of the deformation of the outer surface do not give us enough information so that the shearing strain distribution can be determined. Thus, the simplified approach is not used to solve the rectangular or other noncircular cross section torsion members. Solutions for noncircular cross section torsion members are obtained from the differential-equations approach of Section 4.3.

9.6.   Torsion Members Having Noncircular Sections

Consider a solid cylindrical or prismatic bar whose length may be considered long compared to its maximum cross-sectional dimension. The usual methods of applying the torque to the ends of a torsion member do not give the same stress distribution at sections near the ends as at sections some distance from the ends. Saint Venant's principle (see Section 1.7) states that the end effects disappear rapidly with the distance from the ends. A length of the torsion member located at some distance from each end is considered here.

Choose Cartesian coordinate axes with the z-axis parallel to the longitudinal axis of the torsion member so that the xy-plane lies in an undeformed cross section at one end of the considered length, as shown in Figure 9.10a.

For convenience of discussion, let the z-axis pass through the centroid of each cross section. As indicated in Figure 9.10a, let OA and OB be line segments in the cross section which coincide with the x- and y-axes, respectively, for the undeformed torsion member.

The derivation of load-stress and load-deformation relations for the torsion member requires that the three conditions in Section 1.5 be satisfied as follows: (1) Each volume element of the torsion member is in equilibrium. (2) The geometry of deformation must satisfy the condition that each de-

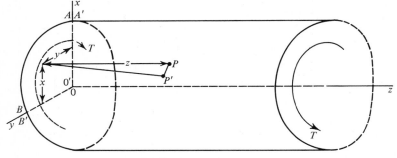

(a) Torsion member

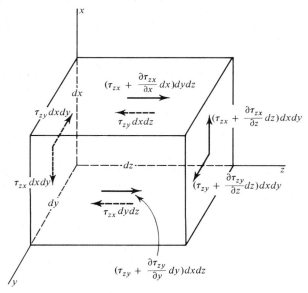

(b) Free body diagram of volume element

Fig. 9.10. Torsion member.

formed volume element of the torsion member must fit together perfectly with adjacent volume elements. (3) Stress-strain relations for the material are satisfied at every point in the member. These conditions will be satisfied using the differential-equations approach of Section 4.3. Using Saint Venant's semi-inverse method for the torsion member, it is possible by examining the deformation of the torsion member to determine the displacements of each point in the member thus satisfying geometrical conditions.*

Geometry of Deformation. Let the torsion member, a short length of which is shown in Figure 9.10a, be loaded by torques applied to each end. Let primed letters designate the location of points in the deformed torsion member. After deformation rigid body displacements can be used to locate O' at O, to align the centroidal axis along the z-axis, and to rotate the deformed torsion member until the projection of $O'A'$ on the xy-plane lies on the x-axis. In general $O'A'$ does not lie in the xy-plane because as indicated in Figure 9.9, plane sections do not remain plane; however, the warping of every section is the same, except where sections are fixed, such as fixed ends. Further examination of the deformed squares, which were scribed on the torsion member in Figure 9.9, indicates that each square is deformed by shearing strains only and that the cross-sectional dimensions of the torsion member are not changed by the deformations, at least for infinitesimal strains. Thus, $O'B'$ projects on the y-axis and γ_{xy} is zero.

Let P be a point in the undeformed torsion member with coordinates (x, y, z) as shown in Figure 9.10a. During deformation P' is displaced along the z-axis due to the warping of the cross section and has components of displacement u and v along the x- and y-axes due to a rotation of the cross section with respect to the cross section at the origin equal to ψz where ψ is the unit angle of twist. The displacements take the form.

$$u = -\psi yz$$
$$v = \psi xz \qquad (9\text{–}26)$$
$$w = w(x, y, \psi)$$

in which w is the warping function. The state of strain at a point in the torsion member is given by substituting Equations (9–26) into Equations (3–6) to obtain

$$\epsilon_x = \epsilon_y = \epsilon_z = \gamma_{xy} = 0,$$
$$\gamma_{zx} = \frac{\partial w}{\partial x} - \psi y, \qquad (9\text{–}27)$$
$$\gamma_{zy} = \frac{\partial w}{\partial y} + \psi x.$$

---

* It will not be necessary to derive the differential equations obtained from the consideration of the geometry of deformation, called compatibility conditions.

If, in Equations (9–27), γ_{zx} is differentiated partially with respect to y, γ_{zy} is differentiated partially with respect to x, and the second of these is subtracted from the first, the warping function is eliminated to give the following equation:

$$\frac{\partial \gamma_{zx}}{\partial y} - \frac{\partial \gamma_{zy}}{\partial x} = -2\psi. \qquad (9\text{–}28)$$

Equation (9–28) is a geometrical condition (compatibility condition) to be satisfied for the torsion member.

Equilibrium and Stresses at a Point. Before deriving the partial differential equations of equilibrium, it is desirable to examine the state of stress at a point in the torsion member because several stress components will be found to be zero. If the material is linearly elastic and is isotropic, it is found, by combining the first of Equations (9–27) with Hooke's stress-strain relations given by Equations (4–7), that

$$\sigma_x = \sigma_y = \sigma_z = \tau_{xy} = 0. \qquad (9\text{–}29)$$

The nonvanishing stress components are τ_{zx} and τ_{zy}. This result is valid also for the case in which the material behavior is plastic if the stress-strain diagram is single valued (no unloading permitted after plastic deformation).

An infinitesimal volume element located at point P in Figure 9.10a is enlarged and shown in Figure 9.10b. The volume element has edges parallel to the x, y, and z coordinate axes with edge lengths of dx, dy, and dz. As indicated in Equation (9–29), all of the stress components are zero except τ_{zx} and τ_{zy}. The forces shown acting on the volume element are all in the positive sense in Figure 9.10b. Note that the weight of the volume element has been neglected.

The stress components τ_{zx} and τ_{zy} in Figure 9.10b are assumed to vary in each of the three directions. The shearing stress on the negative face perpendicular to the x-axis is τ_{zx}; on the positive face this shearing stress has increased by an amount $(\partial \tau_{zx}/\partial x)\, dx$ where $\partial \tau_{zx}/\partial x$ is the rate of change of τ_{zx} in the x-direction (assumed to be a constant over the infinitesimal length dx). By applying equations of equilibrium to the forces acting on the volume element in Figure 9.10b, the differential equations of equilibrium for the volume element are found to be

$$\frac{\partial \tau_{zx}}{\partial z} = 0, \qquad (9\text{–}30)$$

$$\frac{\partial \tau_{zy}}{\partial z} = 0, \qquad (9\text{–}31)$$

$$\frac{\partial \tau_{zx}}{\partial x} + \frac{\partial \tau_{zy}}{\partial y} = 0. \qquad (9\text{–}32)$$

Equations (9–30) and (9–31) state the fact that the two stress components τ_{zx} and τ_{zy} in the torsion member are independent of z and hence do not vary along the length of the member and are therefore functions of x and y. Equation (9–32) is the differential equation of equilibrium that must be solved. It is convenient to express the two stress components τ_{zx} and τ_{zy} in Equation (9–32) in terms of a single variable by defining a stress function $\phi(x, y)$ such that

$$\tau_{zx} = \frac{\partial \phi}{\partial y},$$

$$\tau_{zy} = -\frac{\partial \phi}{\partial x}. \tag{9–33}$$

By substituting these values for τ_{zx} and τ_{zy} in Equation (9–32), it is seen that Equation (9–32) is satisfied. In fact Equation (9–32) expresses the necessary and sufficient conditions for the existence of the function $\phi(x, y)$, which is called a stress function.*

Free Surface Boundary Conditions. Boundary conditions put restrictions on the stress function ϕ. Since the lateral surface of the torsion member is free of stress, the resulting shearing stress τ at the boundary must be tangent to the boundary as indicated in Figure 9.11a. The two shearing stress components τ_{zx} and τ_{zy} acting on the triangular area bounded by dx, dy, and ds can be written in terms of τ:

$$-\tau_{zx} = \tau \sin \alpha,$$

$$\tau_{zy} = \tau \cos \alpha.$$

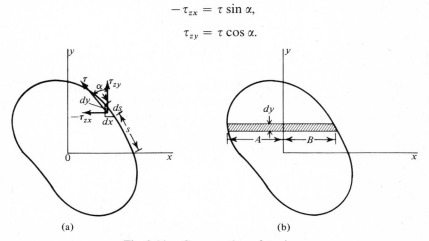

(a) (b)

Fig. 9.11. Cross section of torsion.

* St. Venant developed this solution to the torsion problem in 1853.

The distance s along the boundary is assumed to be increasing counterclockwise from the x-axis. For an increase in s in Figure 9.11a, the value of x is decreasing; therefore,

$$\sin \alpha = -\frac{dx}{ds},$$

$$\cos \alpha = \frac{dy}{ds}.$$

The component of τ normal to the boundary is zero; therefore,

$$\tau_{zy} \sin \alpha + \tau_{zx} \cos \alpha = -\tau_{zy}\frac{dx}{ds} + \tau_{zx}\frac{dy}{ds} = 0.$$

Substituting Equations (9–33) into this latter equation gives

$$\frac{\partial \phi}{\partial x}\frac{dx}{ds} + \frac{\partial \phi}{\partial y}\frac{dy}{ds} = \frac{d\phi}{ds} = 0.$$

Thus, the boundary condition is satisfied if $\phi = $ constant on the boundary. Because the shearing stresses are given by partial derivatives of ϕ (Eqs. 9–33), it is permissible to take this constant to be zero, thus

$$\phi(x, y) = 0 \text{ on the boundary.} \tag{9–34}$$

The preceding argument can be used to show that the shearing stress vector

$$\tau = \sqrt{\tau_{zx}^2 + \tau_{zy}^2} \tag{9–35}$$

at any point in the cross section is tangent to a curve $\phi = $ constant through the point.

Boundary Conditions for Each Cross Section of Torsion Member. The distribution of τ_{zx} and τ_{zy} on a given cross section must satisfy the following equilibrium equations:

$$\sum F_x = 0 = \int\int \tau_{zx}\, dx\, dy = \int\int \frac{\partial \phi}{\partial y}\, dx\, dy,$$

$$\sum F_y = 0 = \int\int \tau_{zy}\, dx\, dy = -\int\int \frac{\partial \phi}{\partial x}\, dx\, dy,$$

$$\sum M_z = T = \int\int (x\tau_{zy} - y\tau_{zx})\, dx\, dy = -\int\int \left(x\frac{\partial \phi}{\partial x} + y\frac{\partial \phi}{\partial y}\right) dx\, dy.$$

In satisfying the second of these equations, consider the strip across the cross section of thickness dy as indicated in Figure 9.11b. Since the stress function can be assumed to be independent of y for this strip, the partial derivative can be replaced by the total derivative. For the strip, the second relation becomes

$$dy \int \frac{\partial \phi}{\partial x} dx = dy \int \frac{d\phi}{dx} dx = dy \int_{\phi_A}^{\phi_B} d\phi = dy (\phi_B - \phi_A) = 0,$$

because ϕ_B and ϕ_A are each equal to zero on the boundary. The same is true for every strip so that $\sum F_y = 0$ is satisfied. In a similar manner the equation $\sum F_x = 0$ is satisfied. In the third equilibrium equation, consider the term

$$- \int \int x \frac{\partial \phi}{\partial x} dx \, dy,$$

which becomes, for the strip in Figure 9.11b,

$$- dy \int x \frac{d\phi}{dx} dx = - dy \int_{\phi_A}^{\phi_B} x \, d\phi.$$

Integrating the latter integral by parts gives

$$- dy \int_{\phi_A}^{\phi_B} x \, d\phi = - dy \left[x \int_{\phi_A}^{\phi_B} d\phi - \int \phi \, dx \right] = dy \int \phi \, dx,$$

because, as we have already seen, ϕ_A and ϕ_B are each equal to zero on the boundary. Summing up for the other strips and repeating the process using strips of thickness dx for the other term in the third equilibrium equation gives the relation

$$T = 2 \int \int \phi \, dx \, dy, \qquad (9\text{--}36)$$

which states that the torque is equal to twice the volume under the stress function.

Use of the Results to Solve Some Problems. The stress function $\phi(x, y)$ for a given cross section depends on the shape of the stress-strain diagram of the material of which the torsion member is made. Except for the fully plastic problem, consideration is limited to the linearly elastic behavior. For the torsion member, Hooke's stress-strain relations (see Eqs. 4–6 and 9–33) become

$$\tau_{zx} = \frac{\partial \phi}{\partial y} = G\gamma_{zx},$$

$$\tau_{zy} = -\frac{\partial \phi}{\partial x} = G\gamma_{zy}. \qquad (9\text{--}37)$$

The substitution of these relations in Equation (9–28) gives the following differential equation:

$$\frac{\partial^2 \phi}{\partial x^2} + \frac{\partial^2 \phi}{\partial y^2} = -2G\psi. \tag{9–38}$$

If the unit angle of twist ψ is specified, which means that the torque T is also specified, and if ϕ satisfies the boundary condition Equation (9–34), then Equation (9–38) uniquely determines the stress function $\phi(x, y)$. Once ϕ has been determined, the stresses are given by Equations (9–33), the strains are given by Equations (9–37), and the torque is given by Equation (9–36). The solution of the torsion problem for many practical cross sections requires special methods for determining the function ϕ and is beyond the scope of this book. As indicated in the following paragraphs, an indirect approach can be used to obtain solutions for some cross sections although it is not generally applicable.

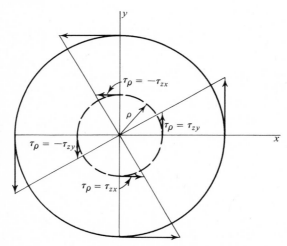

Fig. 9.12.   Circular cross section.

Circular Cross Section.   Let the circle of radius R in Figure 9.12 be the cross section of a torsion member. Consider the stress function

$$\phi = B(x^2 + y^2 - R^2) \tag{9–39}$$

where B is a constant. Because $x^2 + y^2 - R^2 = 0$ is the equation of the boundary of the circle, it is seen that Equation (9–39) satisfies the boundary condition of Equation (9–34). By substituting Equation (9–39) into Equation

(9–38), we get

$$B = -\frac{G\psi}{2},$$

which, when substituted in Equation (9–39), gives

$$\phi = -\frac{G\psi}{2}(x^2 + y^2 - R^2) \tag{9–40}$$

as the stress function for the circular section. The stress function is substituted into Equation (9–36) to obtain the torque, which is as follows:

$$T = -\frac{2G\psi}{2}[\int x^2 \, da + \int y^2 \, da - R^2 \int da]$$

$$= -G\psi(I_y + I_x - R^2 A).$$

For a circle, $I_y = I_x = J/2$ and $R^2 A = 2J$ so that the equation reduces to

$$T = G\psi J \qquad \text{or} \qquad \psi = \frac{T}{GJ}. \tag{9–41}$$

Because $\theta = \int \psi \, dz$, it is seen that Equation (9–41) is identical with Equation (9–15). Let us now examine the shearing stress distribution over the circular cross section. The two components of the shearing stress are given by Equations (9–33):

$$\tau_{zx} = -G\psi y,$$
$$\tau_{zy} = G\psi x. \tag{9–42}$$

The resultant shearing stress at any point in the cross section is given by substituting these shearing stress components in Equation (9–35) to give

$$\tau_\rho = G\psi\sqrt{x^2 + y^2} = G\psi\sqrt{\rho^2} = G\psi\rho, \tag{9–43}$$

where ρ is the radial distance from the center of the circle to the specified point. It is seen from Equation (9–43) that the shearing stress distribution is linear. The magnitude of τ_ρ is given by Equation (9–43) but the direction is given by Equations (9–42). The shearing stress distributions for four radial lines are shown in Figure 9.12. Eliminating $G\psi$ from Equations (9–41) and (9–43) gives

$$T = \frac{\tau_\rho J}{\rho}, \tag{9–44}$$

which is in agreement with Equation (9–9).

The stress function for the circular section (Eq. 9–39) was assumed to be given by a constant B multiplied by the equation of the boundary of the circle. Obviously, this stress function satisfies the boundary condition given by Equation (9–34). The stress function also has to satisfy Equation (9–38). Because the right side of Equation (9–38) is independent of x and y, the left side also has to be independent of x and y. This condition was satisfied since B was found to be a constant.

The warping function w for the solid circular cross section can now be obtained. Since the material is linearly elastic, the shearing strain components can be obtained by dividing the shearing stress components given by Equations (9–42) by the shearing modulus G. These shearing strain components are also given by Equations (9–27). Thus,

$$\gamma_{zx} = \frac{\tau_{zx}}{G} = -\psi y = \frac{\partial w}{\partial x} - \psi y,$$

$$\gamma_{zy} = \frac{\tau_{zy}}{G} = \psi x = \frac{\partial w}{\partial y} + \psi x,$$

and it is seen that the only way in which these equations can be satisfied is for the warping function w to be a constant, which is zero, since w of every point is the same and the origin of the x, y, z coordinate axes in Figure 9.10 was assumed to be located at the same point in the torsion member before and after deformation. The solid circular section and the hollow circular section with constant wall thickness are the only cross sections for which the warping function w is zero.

Other Cross Sections. The method of analysis used for the circular section can also be used for other cross sections as indicated in Table 9.1. In the case of either the ellipse, the equilateral triangle, or the rectangle cross sections shown in Table 9.1, the stress function ϕ is assumed to be equal to the product of B and the equation of the outer boundary. Therefore, Equation (9–34) is satisfied for each cross section. When substituted in Equation (9–38), B is found to be a constant for the ellipse and the equilateral triangle cross sections so that the stress functions are valid for these cross sections; however, B is found to be a function of x and y for the rectangular cross section and the resulting stress function is not valid. Special methods,[*] which are beyond the scope of this book, are required to obtain the solution for the rectangular section; however, the solution can be represented by the following equation:

$$T = \alpha b h^2 \tau_{\text{max}} = \beta b h^3 G \psi, \qquad b > h \qquad (9\text{–}45)$$

---

[*] For one method that makes use of a stress function $\phi(x, y)$ for the rectangular cross section expressed in terms of a series, see pp. 275–277 of *Theory of Elasticity* Timoshenko and Goodier, 2nd Edition 1951, McGraw-Hill.

Table 9.1

Cross Section	Stress Function	
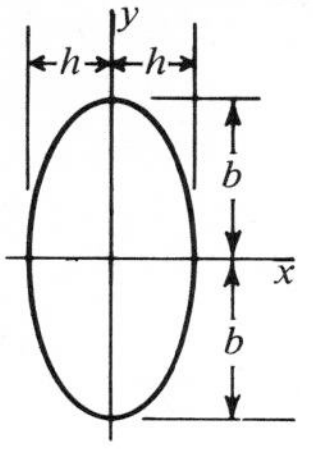 Ellipse	$\phi = B\left(\dfrac{x^2}{h^2} + \dfrac{y^2}{b^2} - 1\right)$ (valid)	$B = -\dfrac{h^2 b^2 G\psi}{h^2 + b^2}$
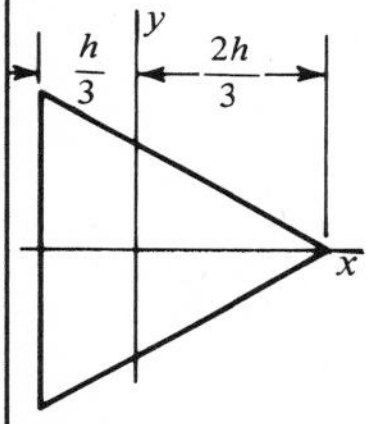 Equilateral triangle	$\phi = B\left(x - \sqrt{3}\,y - \dfrac{2h}{3}\right)$ $\left(x + \sqrt{3}\,y - \dfrac{2h}{3}\right)\left(x + \dfrac{h}{3}\right)$ (valid)	$B = \dfrac{G\psi}{2h}$
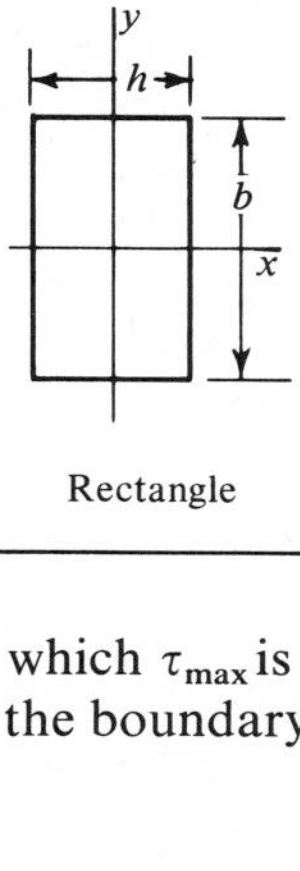 Rectangle	$\phi = B\left(x^2 - \dfrac{h^2}{4}\right)\left(y^2 - \dfrac{b^2}{4}\right)$ (not valid)	$B = \dfrac{G\psi}{\dfrac{h^2}{4} + \dfrac{b^2}{4} - x^2 - y^2}$

in which τ_{max} is the maximum shearing stress at the center of the long side at the boundary and values of α and β can be obtained from Table 9.2.

Table 9.2

b/h	1	1.5	2	2.5	3	4	6	10	∞
α	0.208	0.231	0.246	0.256	0.267	0.282	0.299	0.312	0.333
β	0.141	0.196	0.229	0.249	0.263	0.281	0.299	0.312	0.333

If an analytical solution is difficult to obtain for a given cross section, an approximate solution can be obtained experimentally using the elastic-membrane (soap-film) analogy as discussed in the next section.

In the case of each of the cross sections shown in Table 9.1, the maximum shearing stress occurs at the point on the boundary nearest the centroid of the cross section. Using Equations (9–33) and (9–36) and the stress functions shown in Table 9.1, we can derive relations between T, τ_{max}, and ψ; that is,

$$T = \frac{\pi b h^2 \tau_{max}}{2} = \frac{\pi h^3 b^3 G\psi}{h^2 + b^2} \tag{9-46}$$

for the ellipse, and

$$T = \frac{2h^3 \tau_{max}}{15\sqrt{3}} = \frac{h^4 G\psi}{15\sqrt{3}} \tag{9-47}$$

for the equilateral triangle.

Illustrative Problem

9.38. The torsion member in Figure P9.38 has a rectangular section for the first 20 in. and a square section for the remaining 10 in. It is made of an aluminum alloy ($G = 4,000,000$ psi). If the torsion member is subjected to a torque $T = 3,000$ in.-lb at its free end, determine the maximum shearing stress for the rectangular and square sections and the angle of twist of the free end. Neglect effect of stress concentrations. The support at the left end prevents rotation of this cross section but does not prevent warping of the cross section.

SOLUTION. The solution is obtained using Equation (9–45) and the appropriate values for α and β from Table 9.2. For the rectangle, $b = 2$ in. and $h = 1$ in. so that $b/h = 2$.

$$\tau_{max} = \frac{T}{\alpha b h^2} = \frac{3,000}{0.246(2)(1)(1)} = 6,100 \text{ psi.}$$

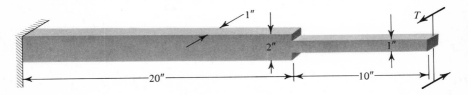

Fig. P 9.38.

For the square

$$\tau_{max} = \frac{T}{\alpha b h^2} = \frac{3,000}{0.208(1)(1)(1)} = 14,400 \text{ psi.}$$

The angle of twist of the free end is

$$\theta = \frac{T\ell_1}{\beta_1 b_1 h_1^3 G} + \frac{T\ell_2}{\beta_2 b_2 h_2^3 G},$$

$$= \frac{20(3,000)}{0.229(2)(1)(1)(1)(4,000,000)} + \frac{10(3,000)}{0.141(1)(1)(1)(1)(4,000,000)},$$

$$= 0.0328 + 0.0532,$$

$$= 0.0860 \text{ rad.}$$

Problems

9.39. For the ellipse cross section in Table 9.1, determine the shearing stress distribution along both the x- and y-axes. Also derive Equations (9–46).

9.40. Determine the shearing stress distribution along the x-axis for the equilateral triangle cross section in Table 9.1. Also derive Equations (9–47).

9.41. A square shaft is often used to transmit power from a farm tractor to other such farm implements as a combine. A 1.25-in. square shaft is made of a steel having a shearing yield stress of 32,000 psi. How much horsepower can the shaft transmit at 200 rpm if the shaft is designed using a factor of safety of 2 against initiation of yielding? (See Problem 9.20.)

ans. $T = 6,500$ in.-lb and hp = 20.6.

9.42. Three shafts (square with 2-in. sides, circle, equilateral triangle) each have the same cross-sectional area. Determine the magnitude of the torque that can be applied to each shaft to produce a maximum shearing stress of 8,000 psi.

9.43. If the three shafts of Problem 9.42 are made of the same metal, determine their relative stiffnesses.

9.7. Elastic-Membrane (Soap-Film) Analogy

Consider a torsion member whose cross-sectional shape is so complex that the stress function ϕ cannot be determined by the approach considered in Section 9.6. The elastic-membrane analogy is an experimental method by which the torque T, the unit angle of twist ψ, and the shearing stress at any point in the cross section can be related. The procedure consists in cutting a hole in a plate having the same cross section as that of the torsion member, stretching a thin membrane such as a soap film over the hole, and applying a pressure to one side of the membrane. If the slope of the membrane is everywhere small compared to one, it will be shown that the membrane and stress function have the same shape.

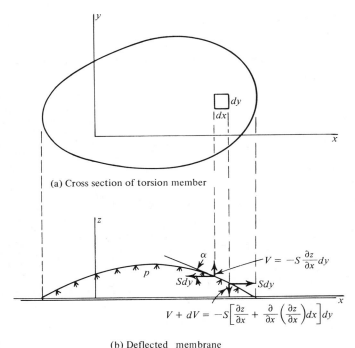

(a) Cross section of torsion member

(b) Deflected membrane

Fig. 9.13.   Cross section of torsion member with deflected membrane.

In Figure 9.13 is shown the cross section of the torsion member and the membrane deflected in the z-direction by a uniform pressure p. It will be assumed that the membrane cannot develop any bending moment or shearing stress and that, at every point in the cross section and in every direction, the force transmitted per unit length through the membrane is equal to S. Consider equilibrium of the element of area of the membrane with sides dx and dy. In Figure 9.13b are shown forces acting on edges with length dy. Forces on the other edges would be shown if one viewed the yz-plane instead of the xz-plane. The tension force in the membrane is tangent to the surface and is equal to $S\,dy$; however, horizontal and vertical components are shown in Figure 9.13b. Because the slope is assumed small, the horizontal components are each equal to $S\,dy$. The vertical component of the force V is equal to $S\,dy\sin\alpha$; but $\sin\alpha = \tan\alpha = -\partial z/\partial x$ if α is small. The magnitude of dV is equal to the product of $S\,dy$ and the rate at which $\tan\alpha = -\partial z/\partial x$ is increasing in the x-direction multiplied by the distance dx over which it is increasing; that is,

$$dV = -S\,dy\frac{\partial^2 z}{\partial x^2}\,dx$$

is the unbalanced force in the z-direction of the forces acting along the sides with length dy. Similarly, the unbalanced force in the z-direction of the forces acting along the sides with length dx can be determined. The equilibrium force equation for the z-axis gives

$$p\,dx\,dy + S\,dx\,dy\frac{\partial^2 z}{\partial x^2} + S\,dx\,dy\frac{\partial^2 z}{\partial y^2} = 0, \qquad \frac{\partial^2 z}{\partial x^2} + \frac{\partial^2 z}{\partial y^2} = -\frac{p}{S} \qquad (9\text{--}48)$$

A comparison of Equations (9–38) and (9–48) will indicate that, if $p/S = 2G\psi$ the membrane and the stress function will be identical surfaces. Thus,

$$\phi = \frac{2G\psi S}{p}z, \qquad\qquad (9\text{--}49)$$

where ϕ is the St. Venant stress function and z is the deflection of the membrane at any point (x, y) in the cross section.

Students interested in the experimental techniques should examine a recent paper*. The experimental technique requires that p/S be determined for the membrane. One procedure that can be followed is to machine a circular hole in the plate in addition to the cross section of interest. If the same membrane is used for both openings, p/S will be the same for both openings. Satisfying Equation (9–36) for the circular section of radius R and noting that Equation (9–41) is valid, we obtain

$$T = G\psi J = \frac{G\psi\pi R^4}{2} = 2\frac{2G\psi S}{p}\text{vol},$$

$$\frac{p}{S} = \frac{8\,\text{vol}}{\pi R^4}, \qquad\qquad (9\text{--}50)$$

where vol is the volume enclosed by the plane of the circular opening and the elastic membrane. With p/S known, the shearing stress at any point in

---

* "Membrane Analogy Studies Employing Visible Contour Lines", R. L. Thoms and F. D. Masch, *Developments in Theoretical and Applied Mechanics*, Vol. 2, 1965.

either cross section can be determined by measuring the maximum slope of the membrane at that point. Let the direction n be the direction of maximum slope at the specified point. Equations (9–33), (9–49), and (9–50) indicate that

$$\tau = \frac{\partial \phi}{\partial n} = \frac{\pi R^4 G \psi}{4 \, \text{vol}} \frac{\partial z}{\partial n}. \tag{9–51}$$

The magnitude of the torque is equal to twice the volume enclosed between the plane of the opening and the membrane.

Another important aspect of the elastic membrane analogy is that many valuable deductions can be made by visualizing the shape that the membrane takes without performing the experiments. For a given membrane, $G\psi$ will be identical for each cross section; therefore, the stiffness of the torsion member will be proportional to the volume under the membrane. For cross sections with the same cross sectional area, the long narrow rectangle will have the least stiffness while the circle will have the greatest stiffness.

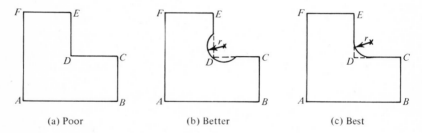

(a) Poor   (b) Better   (c) Best

Fig. 9.14.   Angle section of torsion member.

Important conclusions can also be drawn in regard to the proper design of the cross section of a torsion member to reduce the magnitude of the shearing stress. Consider the angle section shown in Figure 9.14a. At the external corners A, B, C, E, and F the membrane has zero slope and the shearing stress is zero; therefore, external corners do not constitute a design problem. However, at the re-entrant corner at D the membrane will have an infinite slope indicating an infinite shearing stress. Actually a perfect right angle is improbable and, if one could be produced, we would have to examine forces on the atomic level where stress and strain are no longer defined. In practical problems the magnitude of the shearing stress at D will be finite but will be large compared to that for other points in the cross section.

If the torsion member whose cross section is shown in Figure 9.14a is made of a ductile material and it is subjected to static loads, the material in the neighborhood of D will yield and increase the stress in the adjacent material. If, on the other hand, the material is brittle or the torsion member is subjected to fatigue loading (see Section 1.8), the shearing stress at D will limit the load carrying capacity of the member. In this case the maximum shearing stress in the torsion member can be decreased by removing some material as shown in Figure 9.14b. Preferably, the member should be re-designed to have the cross section shown in Figure 9.14c. The maximum shearing stress will be about the same for torsion members having the cross sections of Figure 9.14b and c for the same angle of twist; however, the torsion member having the cross section of Figure 9.14c will have the greater stiffness.

9.8. Long Narrow Rectangular Cross Section

The cross sections of many members the engineer uses in the design of machines and structures are made up of long narrow rectangular sections. These members are usually used to carry bending loads instead of torsion loads; however, they may be required to carry small torsional loads. The elastic membrane analogy will be used to obtain the solution for a torsion member having a long narrow rectangular section.

Consider the rectangular section shown in Figure 9.15 for which the side b is large compared to the thickness h. Sections made by the xz- and yz-planes through the membrane are shown in Figures 9.15b and c, respectively. As indicated in Figure 9.15b the elastic membrane has the cross

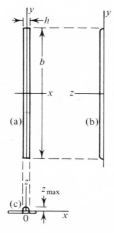

Fig. 9.15. Long narrow rectangle.

section shown in Figure 9.15c over most of its length b. The maximum shearing stress occurs along the long side of the rectangle and its magnitude can be obtained from the maximum slope of the membrane in Figure 9.15c. Because the torque is equal to twice the volume under the membrane, the error will be small if it is assumed that the cross section of the membrane shown in Figure 9.15c is independent of y. For this condition, Equation (9–48) becomes

$$\frac{d^2z}{dx^2} = -\frac{p}{S} = -2G\psi \qquad (9\text{--}52)$$

which is integrated to give

$$\frac{dz}{dx} = -2G\psi x + C_1 = -2G\psi x \qquad (9\text{--}53)$$

where the constant of integration $C_1 = 0$ (the slope of the membrane is zero at $x = 0$). Integrating Equation (9–53), and noting that $z = 0$ when $x = h/2$, gives

$$z = -G\psi x^2 + \frac{G\psi h^2}{4}. \qquad (9\text{--}54)$$

The stress function ϕ is equal to z. Substituting Equation (9–54) in Equation (9–36) gives

$$T = \frac{bh^3 G\psi}{3}, \qquad (9\text{--}55)$$

which is in agreement with Equation (9–45) and the appropriate value of β from Table 9.2. Because z is analogous to the stress function ϕ,

$$\tau_{zx} = 0 \qquad (9\text{--}56)$$
$$\tau = \tau_{zy} = -\frac{\partial \phi}{\partial x} = -\frac{dz}{dx} = 2G\psi x.$$

These shearing stress components are valid except near each end of the length b. Note that τ varies linearly across the depth h. The maximum value of τ

$$\tau_{max} = G\psi h \qquad (9\text{--}57)$$

agrees with Equation (9–45).

9.9. Thin-Walled Noncircular Torsion Members

In general the solution for a hollow torsion member is more complex than that for the solid torsion member. The complexity of the solution can be illustrated for the hollow torsion member in Figure 9.16. There are

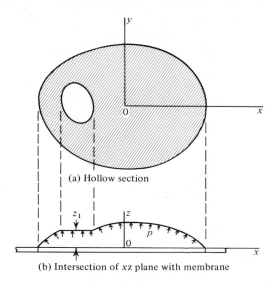

(a) Hollow section

(b) Intersection of xz plane with membrane

Fig. 9.16. Hollow torsion.

obviously no shearing stresses over the hollow region of the torsion member; this means that the stress function and the membrane must be flat topped over the hollow region. If the elastic-membrane analogy is being used, the membrane can be given a plateau over the hollow region by machining a flat plate to the dimensions of the hollow region and displacing the plate a distance z_1 as shown in Figure 9.16. One of the problems that has to be considered is that z_1 is uniquely determined by the magnitudes of p and S.

The general theory for the hollow torsion member is beyond the scope of this chapter. Except for the thin-walled torsion member, the only hollow torsion member for which solutions can be obtained are those of concentric circular torsion members. Consider the elastic membrane for the solid circular section torsion member in Figure 9.17. Because curves of $z = $ constant are concentric circles, the plateau for the hollow torsion member is indicated by the dashed line and the torque is equal to the difference between the torque for a solid torsion member with the outer radius and the torque for a solid torsion member with inner radius.

The solution for thin-walled noncircular sections is based on a simplifying assumption. Consider the thin-walled torsion member in Figure 9.18a. The plateau over the hollow area and the resulting membrane are shown in Figure 9.18b. In case the wall thickness is small compared to the other dimensions of the cross section, an element of the membrane in a plane

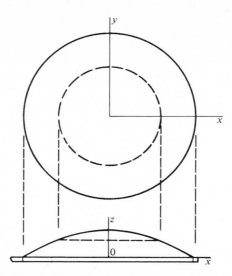

Fig. 9.17. Solid and hollow circular torsion member.

through the z-axis is approximately a straight line. The simplifying assumption is made that it is a straight line. Because the shearing stress is given by the slope of the membrane, this assumption specifies that the shearing stress is

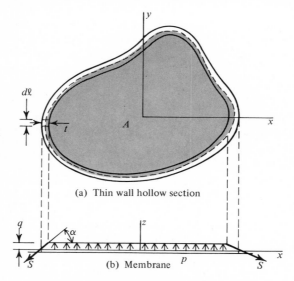

(a) Thin wall hollow section

(b) Membrane

Fig. 9.18. Thin-wall hollow torsion member.

constant through the thickness. Obviously, the shearing stress around the boundary will not be constant unless the thickness t is constant, because Figure 9.18b indicates that

$$\tau = \tan \alpha = \frac{q}{t}.$$

The quantity $q = \tau t$ has the dimensions of lb/in. and is commonly referred to in the literature as the shear flow. As indicated in Figure 9.18, the shear flow is constant around a thin-walled hollow torsion member. The torque is equal to twice the volume under the membrane,

$$T = 2Aq = 2A\tau t, \tag{9-58}$$

in which A is the area enclosed by the mean perimeter of the cross section. A relation between τ, G, ψ, and the dimensions of the cross section can be derived using the equilibrium force equation for the z direction:

$$\sum F_z = pA - \int_0^\ell S \sin \alpha \, d\ell = 0,$$

$$\frac{1}{A} \int_0^\ell \tau \, dl = \frac{p}{S} = 2G\psi, \tag{9-59}$$

where length ℓ is the length of the mean perimeter of the cross section and $\sin \alpha$ is replaced by $\tan \alpha = \tau$; S is the tensile force per unit length of the membrane.

The following illustrative problem indicates that Equations (9–58) and (9–59) predict accurate results if the wall thickness is less than one-tenth of the minimum cross-sectional dimensions.

Illustrative Problems

9.44. A hollow circular torsion member has an outside diameter of 2.20 in. and an inside diameter of 1.80 in., giving a mean diameter of $D = 2.00$ in. and $t/D = 0.10$. Let the shearing stress at the mean diameter be $\tau = 10,000$ psi. Determine T and ψ using Equations (9–58) and (9–59) and compare these values with values obtained using the exact theory. $G = 12,000,000$ psi.

SOLUTION.

$$A = \pi D^2/4 = \pi \text{ in.}^2$$

The torque is given by Equation (9–58):

$$T = 2A\tau t = 2\pi(10,000)(0.20) = 4,000\pi \text{ in.-lb.}$$

Because the wall thickness is constant, Equation (9–59) becomes

$$\psi = \frac{\tau \pi D}{2GA} = \frac{10,000(\pi)(2)}{2(12,000,000)(\pi)} = \frac{1}{1,200} = 0.000833 \text{ rad/in.}$$

Exact values of T and ψ are given by Equations (9–9) and (9–15).

$$J = \frac{\pi}{32}(2.2^4 - 1.8^4) = 0.404\pi,$$

$$T = \frac{\tau J}{\rho} = \frac{10,000(0.404)(\pi)}{1} = 4,040\pi \text{ in.-lb},$$

$$\psi = \frac{\tau}{G\rho} = \frac{10,000}{12,000,000(1)} = 0.000833 \text{ rad/in.}$$

Note that the approximate theory predicted the exact unit angle of twist and predicted a torque which was conservative by about 1 per cent. Also note that the approximate theory assumed that the shearing stress was uniformly distributed while the exact theory indicates that the maximum shearing stress is 10 per cent greater than the average value.

Problems

9.45. The shear flow in a thin-walled circular tube is 200 lb/in. when the tube is subjected to a twisting moment of 60,000 ft-lb. Calculate the mean radius of the tube. If the thickness of the tube wall is $\frac{1}{8}$ in., what is the torsional shearing stress in the tube?

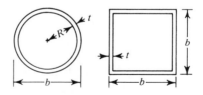

Fig. P 9.46.

9.46. If, in Figure P9.46, t and b have the same values, respectively, in the two shapes, compare the shear flows in the two shapes when the tubes are subjected to equal twisting moments.

9.47. An extruded aluminum tube has the cross section shown in Figure P9.47. If the maximum shearing stress is not to exceed 3,000 psi, determine the maximum

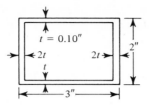

Fig. P 9.47.

torque that can be applied to the tube. What is the angle of twist over a 2-ft length? $G = 4,000,000$ psi.

ans. $T = 3,192$ in.-lb and $\theta = 0.0127$ rad.

9.10.   Fully Plastic Torque—Sand Heap Analogy

Consider a torsion member made of a material whose shearing stress–shearing strain diagram is flat topped at the yield stress τ_e. As the torque applied to the torsion member increases, yielding starts at one or more places on the boundary and spreads inward. Finally, the whole cross section becomes yielded (plastic) at the limiting torque for the cross section called the fully plastic torque. In this section we will consider the problem of computing the fully plastic torque for several cross sections.

Equations (9–33) and (9–35) are valid for both the elastic and plastic regions of each cross section of a given torsion member. At the fully plastic torque, the resultant shearing stress is $\tau = \tau_e$ at every point in the cross section. Thus Equations (9–33) and (9–35) reduce to

$$\tau_{zx}^2 + \tau_{zy}^2 = \left(\frac{\partial \phi}{\partial y}\right)^2 + \left(\frac{\partial \phi}{\partial x}\right)^2 = \tau_e^2, \tag{9–60}$$

which determines the stress function ϕ for fully plastic conditions. It will be noted that the unit angle of twist does not appear in Equation (9–60) indicating that the deformations of the torsion member are not specified at the fully-plastic torque.

Now consider the procedure by which Equation (9–60) can be used to construct the stress function surface for the fully plastic torque. Because $\phi = 0$ on the boundary and because Equation (9–60) indicates that the absolute value of the maximum slope of ϕ everywhere in the cross section is a constant equal to τ_e, the magnitude of ϕ at a point is equal to τ_e times its distance from the nearest boundary, measured along the perpendicular from the point to the nearest boundary. The contour curves of constant ϕ are perpendicular to the direction of maximum slope, and hence are parallel to the nearest boundary.

Consider the problem of constructing the stress function ϕ for a square cross section with sides $2h$ as indicated in Figure 9.19. At a given point P, the resultant shearing stress is τ_e directed along a contour curve of constant ϕ; ϕ_P is given by τ_e times its perpendicular distance to the nearest boundary. The stress function ϕ is a pyramid of height $\tau_e h$; this suggested* the sand

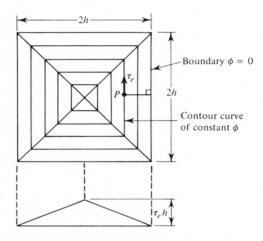

Fig. 9.19. Stress function surface for fully plastic square cross section.

heap analogy because sand poured on a flat plate having the same dimensions as the cross section of the torsion member would form a pyramid similar to that indicated in Figure 9.19.

The sand heap analogy is not needed to determine the fully plastic torque for the square section in Figure 9.19. Equation (9–36) indicates that the fully plastic torque T_{fp} is equal to twice the volume of the pyramid. Because the volume of a pyramid is equal to one-third of the area of the base times the height, the fully plastic torque for the square in Figure 9.19 is $T_{fp} = 8\tau_e h^3/3$. Using the same procedure, the fully plastic torque is easily calculated for circular sections and triangular sections. In rectangular sections the stress function is as indicated in Figure 9.20; the volume under the stress function or plastic stress surface can be broken up into a pyramid

* A. Nadai, *Theory of Flow and Fracture of Solids*, Vol. 1, McGraw-Hill Book Company, New York, 1950.

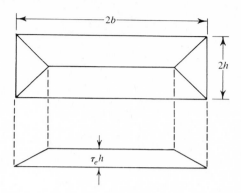

Fig. 9.20.   Stress function surface for fully plastic rectangular cross section.

with a square base plus a volume with a triangular cross section over a rectangular base:

$$T_{fp} = 2\left[\frac{4\tau_e h^3}{3} + \frac{1}{2}(2b - 2h)2h\tau_e h\right] = \frac{8\tau_e h^3}{3} + 4(b - h)\tau_e h^2.$$

In more general solid sections, the sand heap analogy can be used. If m is the angle of repose or slope of the sand heap and τ_e is the slope of the ϕ surface, the fully plastic torque may be found by an experimental determination of m and the volume of sand V by the relation

$$T_{fp} = \frac{2\tau_e V}{m}. \tag{9–61}$$

Many of the load-carrying members used by the engineer are made up of long narrow rectangles. For instance consider the angle section shown in Figure 9.21. The correct sand heap or plastic stress surface is shown in Figure 9.21a. The volume under the plastic stress surface shown in Figure 9.21b is more easily obtained; furthermore, because the volume for (b) is only slightly less than that for (a), an accurate and conservative estimate of the fully plastic torque can be obtained using the plastic stress surface shown in Figure 9.21b. For the angle section an approximate value of T_{fp} is

$$T_{fp} = 2\left[\frac{1}{3}t_2^2\frac{\tau_e t_2}{2} + \frac{1}{2}(b - t_2)t_2\frac{\tau_e t_2}{2} + \frac{1}{2}(h - t_2)t_1\frac{\tau_e t_1}{2}\right]$$

$$= \frac{\tau_e b t_2^2}{2} + \frac{\tau_e h t_1^2}{2} - \frac{\tau_e t_2^3}{6} - \frac{\tau_e t_1^2 t_2}{2}. \tag{9–62}$$

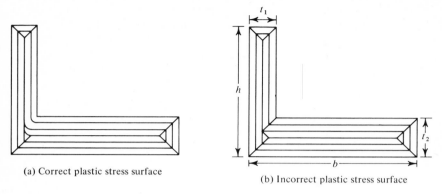

(a) Correct plastic stress surface

(b) Incorrect plastic stress surface

Fig. 9.21.   Stress function surfaces for fully plastic angle section.

The method of analysis to determine the plastic-stress surface for a hollow torsion member subjected to fully plastic torque is the same as for the elastic problem. Over the hollow region of the cross section, the stress surface must be flat topped. In order to simplify the problem we will limit our consideration to hollow torsion members having a constant wall thickness. The plastic stress surfaces for two types of hollow torsion members of constant wall thickness are shown in Figure 9.22. In either case the fully

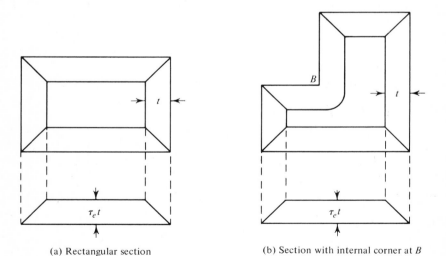

(a) Rectangular section

(b) Section with internal corner at B

Fig. 9.22.   Plastic stress surfaces for hollow torsion members having constant wall thickness.

plastic torque is equal to the fully plastic torque for a solid torsion member having the outer cross section minus the fully plastic torque for a solid torsion member having the cross section of the hollow region. The fully plastic torque can be easily calculated for the rectangular cross section in Figure 9.22a but becomes more difficult for the cross section in Figure 9.22b.

Problems

9.48. A rectangular-section torsion member has dimensions of 1-in. by 2-in. and is made of a material for which the shearing yield point stress is $\tau_e = 20,000$ psi. (1) Determine T_{fp} for this cross section. (2) Show that $T_{fp}/T_e = 1.69$ where T_e is the maximum elastic torque for the cross section.

9.49. A hollow circular torsion member has an outside diameter of 4 in. and a wall thickness of $\frac{1}{2}$ in. The shearing yield point for the material is $\tau_e = 16,000$ psi. (1) Determine the fully plastic torque for the torsion member. (2) Determine the fully plastic torque if a saw cut is made through the wall over the full length of the torsion member.

ans.   (1) $T_{fp} = 155,000$ in.-lb; and (2) $T_{fp} = 21,700$ in.-lb.

9.50. A torsion member has a cross-sectional area of 2 in.² with the shape of an equilateral triangle. Determine T_{fp} if $\tau_e = 18,000$ psi.

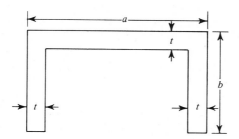

Fig. P 9.51.

9.51. A torsion member has the channel section shown in Figure P9.51. Show that $T_{fp} = \tau_e t^2(a/2 + b - 7t/6)$ if the plastic stress surface is approximated as indicated in Figure 9.21b.

CHAPTER 1

Combined Loading

10.1 Introduction

In the preceding chapters load-stress and load-deflection relations were derived for straight members of constant cross section subjected to either axial centric tensile loads (Section 1.4), bending loads (Chapters 7 and 8), or torsional loads (Chapter 9). Members of many structures and machines, however, are subjected to loads of two or more of these types. Rather than derive new theories for combined loading we wish to consider the conditions for which the state of stress at a point in the member can be determined by assuming that each load produces the same state of stress at the point that it would produce if it were the only load acting on the member. The final state of stress at the point is then given by superposition of all of these states of stress.

Superposition requires that two conditions be satisfied: (1) the material in the member must remain linearly elastic, and (2) the deflections of the member caused by one type of load must not influence the stresses at a given point caused by another of the various types of loads acting on the member. If the magnitudes of the combined loads are sufficiently large, the member will become plastically deformed, and a plastic theory has to be derived for each combination of loading. The only plastic problem considered in this book will be for combined axial centric and bending loads (see Section 10.4).

The effect of deflection resulting from one type of load on the stresses and deflections caused by another type of load is illustrated by the member in Figure 10.1 subjected to axial and bending loads. In Figure 10.1a the member is subjected to bending and tension loads. Let the bending loads be applied first. The state of stress at any point in the member as well as the deflection y

448

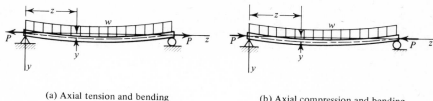

(a) Axial tension and bending   (b) Axial compression and bending

Fig. 10.1. Members subjected to axial and bending loads.

can be determined for the bending loads. Now apply the tension load. Note that the application of the axial tension load P through the centroid at each end of the member results in a bending moment $-Py$ at every section of the member. Thus, superposition is not valid unless the bending moment $-Py$ at a given section of the member is small compared to the bending moment at that section due to the bending loads.

When an axial tension load is applied to a member after bending loads have been applied (see Fig. 10.1a), the negative bending moment $-Py$ caused by the tension load decreases the magnitude of the bending moment, which is positive at every section and decreases the deflection at every section. The design of such a member using superposition will result in a conservative design since the maximum tensile stress and the maximum deflection in the actual member will be less than the calculated values based on superposition.

Let an axial compression load P be applied to the member after bending loads have been applied (Fig. 10.1b). Note that the bending moment Py at a given section is positive and thus adds to the positive bending moment due to the bending loads. The compression load increases the deflection which in turn increases the moment due to P. If the magnitude of P is sufficiently large, the member becomes unstable and fails because of buckling. Instability and buckling problems are considered in Chapter 11. The member in Figure 10.1b is called a beam column; the analysis* of beam columns is not considered in this book.

10.2. Combined Axial-Centric and Bending Loads

In Figure 10.2 is shown a member subjected to axial-centric tension and bending loads. All of the loads lie in the yz-plane and the y-axis is an axis of symmetry for the cross section. The x- and y-axes are principal axes

* See *Theory of Stability*, S. P. Timoshenko and J. M. Gere, 2nd Ed., McGraw-Hill, 1961 (Chapter 1).

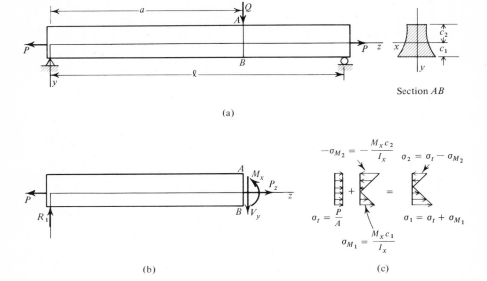

Fig. 10.2. Member subjected to axial tension and bending loads and stress distribution.

of inertia for the cross section; therefore, bending occurs only about the x-axis. The shear center lies on the y-axis; its location does not have to be determined because the plane of the loads passes through every point on the y-axis and must therefore pass through the shear center. The action line of the axial load P is parallel to the z-axis and passes through the centroid of the section at each end of the member. The bending moment $-Py$ at any section where y is the deflection of that section of the member is assumed to be so small that it can be neglected.

Let it be required to determine the maximum tensile stress in the member in Figure 10.2, which is subjected to combined axial-centric tension and bending loads. The tensile stress on planes perpendicular to the z-axis due to the axial-centric load P is the same for every point in the member. The maximum tensile stress caused by bending occurs at the section of the member with maximum moment, which is located at the section where load Q is applied. Section AB was passed through the member just to the left of load Q; a free-body diagram of the left portion is shown in Figure 10.2b. The internal forces being transmitted through section AB can be broken up into components made up of the axial-centric load P_z, the transverse shear V_y, and the bending moment M_x, all of which lie in the yz-plane which is the plane of the loads. Note that P_z, V_y, and M_x are all positive quantities.

In calculating the state of stress at any point in section AB, we treat each component of load separately and then use superposition to obtain the actual state of stress at that point for the given loading. The axial-centric load $P_z = P$ gives a uniform normal stress distribution $\sigma_t = \sigma_z = P/A$ (see Eq. 1–10) as shown in Figure 10.2c. Another normal stress distribution results from the bending moment M_x is given by the relation $\sigma_M = \sigma_z = M_x y / I_x$ (see Eq. 7–11) and is shown in Figure 10.2c. The algebraic addition of these two normal stress distributions is given by the relation

$$\sigma = \frac{P}{A} + \frac{M_x y}{I_x}. \tag{10–1}$$

The normal stress distribution given by Equation (10–1) is shown in Figure 10.2c. The maximum tensile stress occurs when $y = c_1$, whereas the maximum compressive stress occurs when $y = -c_2$.

In addition to the normal stress distribution on section AB in Figure 10.2c, there is a transverse shearing stress distribution resulting from the transverse shear V_y as discussed in Section 7.10. The transverse shearing stress is zero at the bottom and top of the beam where Equation (10–1) indicates the tension and compression stresses have their maximum values. In general, we do not have to consider the transverse shear in the design of members subjected to combined loading. The exceptions are the members considered in Sections 7.11 and 7.12.

Illustrative Problem

10.1. The member in Figure P10.1 has the triangular cross section shown and is made of 7075-T6 aluminum alloy with yield stress $\sigma_e = 72{,}000$ psi, which may be assumed to be the same for tension and compression. Neglecting stress concentrations, determine the maximum tensile and compressive stresses in the member. What was the factor of safety used in the design of the member?

SOLUTION. The centroidal x- and y-axes for the cross section are shown in Figure P10.1a. Because the centroid of a triangular cross section is located at a distance from base b of one-third of height h, $c_2 = 2$ in., and $c_1 = 4$ in. Using the theory presented in the Appendix A, the moment of inertia of the triangle about the x-axis is

$$I_x = \frac{bh^3}{36} = \frac{4(6)(6)(6)}{36} = 24 \text{ in.}^4$$

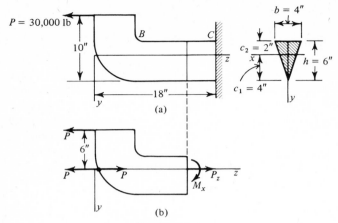

Fig. P 10.1.

If the deflections of the member and stress concentrations are neglected, the normal stress distribution is the same for every section between B and C. Pass a section perpendicular to the z-axis to give the free-body diagram in Figure P10.1b. The internal forces being transmitted through the cut section can be broken up into components made up of the axial-centric load $P_z = P$ and bending moment $-M_x = -6P$. The maximum tensile and compressive stresses are given by Equation (10–1) and occurs when $y = -c_2$ and $y = c_1$, respectively:

$$\sigma_2 = \frac{P}{A} + \frac{(-M_x)(-c_2)}{I_x} = \frac{30,000}{12} + \frac{6(30,000)(2)}{24}$$

$$= 2,500 + 15,000 = 17,500 \text{ psi,}$$

$$\sigma_1 = \frac{P}{A} + \frac{(-M_x)(c_1)}{I_x} = \frac{30,000}{12} - \frac{6(30,000)(4)}{24}$$

$$= 2,500 - 30,000 = -27,500 \text{ psi.}$$

It is seen that the maximum absolute magnitude of the normal stress is the compressive stress that occurs at the bottom of the member.

The load-stress relation for the member is linear; therefore, the factor of safety can be applied either to loads or stresses. Because the yield stresses for tension and compression are equal and since the state of stress is uniaxial, the factor of safety N against initiation of yielding in the member is

$$N = \frac{\sigma_e}{\sigma_1} = \frac{72,000}{27,500} = 2.62.$$

The magnitude of N is independent of the theory of failure used because material properties are obtained from specimens having uniaxial state of stress and the state of stress in the member to be designed is also uniaxial.

Problems

10.2. The magnitude of P is sufficiently small so that the material in the member in Figure P10.2 remains linearly elastic. Known quantities are P, b, and h. The load P lies in the yz-plane of symmetry. The member is sufficiently short so that the deflections can be neglected. Determine the maximum value of d so that there will not be any tensile stresses in the member.

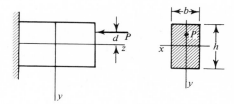

Fig. P 10.2.

10.3. The member in Figure P10.3 is built up by nailing four 1-in. by 3-in. boards together to produce the cross section shown. Neglecting stress concentrations, determine the maximum tensile and compressive stresses on the cross section at the wall.

ans. $\sigma_t = 1{,}328$ psi (tension); $\sigma_c = 1{,}168$ psi (compression).

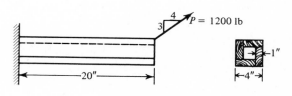

Fig. P 10.3.

10.4. The rectangular section member shown in Figure P10.4 has the stress distribution shown. If the deflections of the member can be neglected, determine the magnitude and location of the load P necessary to produce the stress distribution. The load P lies in the yz-plane of symmetry. Locate P from the bottom of the member.

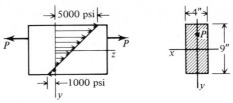

Fig. P 10.4.

10.5. The member in Figure P10.5 has a T-section for which $I_x = 33.33$ in.[4] The member is made of a material with yield point in tension and compression of σ_e. Derive expressions for the load P as a function of Y if yielding is impending at section AB. Neglect effect of deformations.

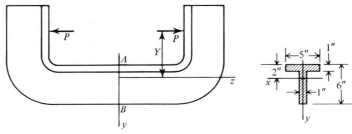

Fig. P 10.5.

ans.   Yielding occurs at both A and B when $Y = 3.333$ in.

$$P = \frac{33.33\sigma_e}{2Y + 3.333} \text{ for } Y \leq 3.333 \text{ in.}; P = \frac{33.33\sigma_e}{4Y - 3.333} \text{ for } Y \geq 3.333 \text{ in.}$$

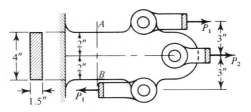

Fig. P 10.6.

10.6. In Figure P10.6 is shown a machine member having a rectangular cross section 1.5-in. by 4-in. It is acted on by a force $P_2 = 90,000$ lb and two equal forces P_1, the action lines of which are shown in the figure. Find the value of P_1 if the maximum elastic tensile stress in the member (at section AB) is 20,000 psi.

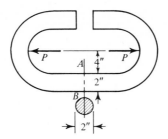

Fig. P 10.7.

10.7. The open-chain link shown in Figure P10.7 is made of a steel bar having a diameter of 2 in. The yield point of the material is $\sigma_e = 40,000$ psi. If the value of P is 2,390 lb, calculate the maximum values for the tensile and compressive stresses at section AB. What was the factor of safety used in design of the open chain-link?

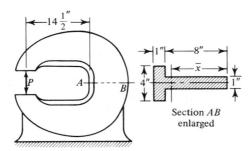

Fig. P 10.8.

10.8. The frame shown in Figure P10.8 is used for small riveting, punching, and stamping machines. Find the elastic stress developed at A and B when the load P is 4,000 lb.

ans. $\sigma_A = 2,930$ psi; $\sigma_B = -3,750$ psi.

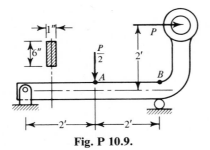

Fig. P 10.9.

10.9. Determine the value of P in Figure P10.9 that will cause the maximum tensile stress to be equal to the yield point of the material. The tensile yield point of the material is $\sigma_e = 36,000$ psi.

ans. $P = 8,650$ lb

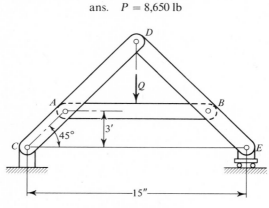

Fig. P 10.10.

10.10. The cross bar AB in the pin-connected frame shown in Figure P10.10 is subjected at its midpoint to a load $Q = 4,000$ lb. The cross bar is a 7-in., 15.3-lb I-beam. (See Appendix B.) The yield point of the material is $\sigma_e = 40,000$ psi. Determine the maximum tensile stress in the cross bar and determine the factor of safety used in the design of the cross bar.

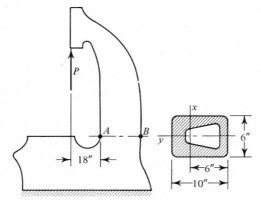

Fig. P 10.11.

10.11. A cast-iron machine frame shown in Figure P10.11 is subjected to load P of 8,000 lb. The area of the cross section at AB is 40 in.^{2}, and the centroidal x-axis is 6 in.

from the outer edge of the section. The moment of inertia of the area with respect to the centroidal axis is 400 in.[4] Find the maximum elastic tensile and compressive stresses on the section AB.

ans. $\sigma_A = 1,960$ psi; and $\sigma_B = -2,440$ psi.

10.3. Combined Axial-Centric, Bending, and Torsional Loads

Let a given member be subjected to combined axial-centric, bending, and torsional loads. We treat each load as if it were acting alone on the member. The load-stress relation for each type of load acting alone give either a normal or shearing stress distribution on a plane perpendicular to the longitudinal axis (z-axis) of the member.

As indicated in Section 1.4, axial-centric loads produce a uniform normal stress distribution, $\sigma_z = P/A$ (Eq. 1–10), on a given cross section of the member; the state of stress is uniaxial.

If the bending loads are couples, the member is subjected to pure bending, and only normal stresses, $\sigma_z = M_x y/I_x$ (Eq. 7–11), act on a given cross section of the member (see Chapter 7). The state of stress in a beam subjected to pure bending is uniaxial. Most beams are subjected to transverse shear loads. A transverse shear load on a given cross section of the member produces a shearing-stress distribution on the cross section and the resulting state of stress is biaxial except at the top and bottom of the member where the transverse shearing stresses are zero. In general, the transverse shearing stresses do not have to be considered because they are usually zero for the point in the cross section where we have the maximum and minimum principal stresses and the maximum shearing stress. It may be necessary to consider transverse shearing stresses in short beams built up of thin wall sections such as short I-beams.

Members subjected to torsional loads only are considered in Chapter 9. Torsional loads produce a shearing-stress distribution on the cross section of the member; the state of stress is a special case of biaxial state of stress called pure shear. Most of the practical members subjected to combined loading are shafts that have a circular cross section for which the shearing stress distribution is given by the relation $\tau_\rho = T\rho/J$ (Eq. 9–9).

The state of stress at any specified point in the member can be determined for any component of load acting alone. The state of stress at the specified point in the member subjected to combined axial-centric, bending, and torsional loads is obtained by superposition of the several states of stress. The point of interest in the design of the member is the point located where the combination of stresses gives the most serious chance of damage to the material in the member. This point of interest may depend for its location on the type of material of which the member is made, because the failure of the member depends on the type of material. Theories of failure are discussed in Section 4.6. In members made of brittle materials, failure is caused by fracture and is governed by the maximum principal stress; here, we must locate the point in the member where the principal tensile stress is maximum. In members made of ductile materials and subjected either to static loading or to fatigue loading, failure is caused by general yielding or fatigue fracture, respectively, and is governed by the maximum octahedral shearing stress theory of failure; in this case, we must locate the point in the member where the octahedral shearing is maximum and this location may not be the point where the principal tensile stress is maximum.

Illustrative Problems

10.12. The circular section shaft in Figure P10.12a has a diameter of 3 in. and has a short length so that buckling due to the compressive load is not a problem. The shaft is made of a so-called brittle material (gray cast iron), which has a tensile ultimate strength of $\sigma_{ut} = 21,000$ psi, and a compressive ultimate strength $\sigma_{uc} = 65,000$ psi. Assume that the material is linearly elastic up to fracture. Also, assume that the radius of the fillet at the wall is sufficiently large so that the stress concentration factor is approximately 1. If $P_c = 80,000$ lb and $T = 60,000$ in.-lb, determine the maximum and minimum principal stresses in the shaft. What was the factor of safety used in the design of the shaft? Would the factor of safety be increased or decreased if T remained unchanged and P_c is decreased to zero?

SOLUTION. If the load P_c is assumed to act alone, it produces a uniform normal stress distribution (see Section 1.4 and Eq. 1–10) on every cross section perpendicular to the axis of the shaft.

$$\sigma_z = -\frac{P_c}{A} = -\frac{80,000(4)}{\pi(3)^2} = -11,320 \text{ psi}.$$

The torque T, if acting alone, produces a linear shearing stress distribution, with zero value at the center of the shaft, on every cross section perpendicular to the axis of the shaft with a maximum value at the outer radius:

$$\tau_r = \frac{Tr}{J} = \frac{60,000(1.5)(32)}{\pi(3)^4} = 11,320 \text{ psi}.$$

The normal stress σ_z and maximum torsional shearing stress τ_r are shown acting on the infinitesimal volume element in Figure P10.12b. The volume

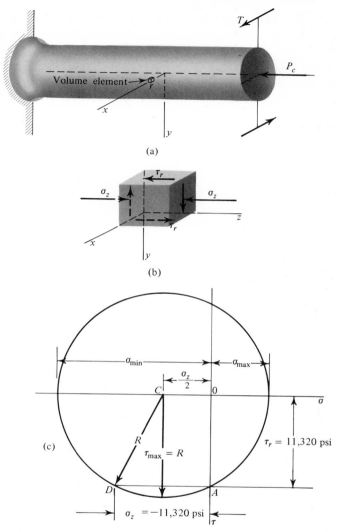

Fig. P 10.12. Shaft subjected to combined compression and torsion loads.

element is oriented in the shaft on the x-axis so that the face adjacent to the positive end of the x-axis is part of the stress free surface of the shaft and σ_z is normal to a face which is part of a plane perpendicular to the axis of the shaft. All of the stress components lie in a plane parallel to a plane tangent to the free surface of the shaft; for convenience, this plane is taken to be the

yz-plane. We use Mohr's circle of stress to determine the maximum and minimum principal stresses in the shaft. Choose σ and τ coordinate axes as indicated in Figure P10.12c. The distance OC to the center of Mohr's circle of stress is (see Eq. 2–6):

$$OC = \frac{\sigma_z}{2} = -5{,}660 \text{ psi.}$$

The coordinates σ_z and τ_r locate point D on Mohr's circle. The radius R of the circle is equal to distance CD (see Eq. 2–7):

$$R = CD = \sqrt{\left(\frac{\sigma_z}{2}\right)^2 + \tau_r^2} = \sqrt{(-5{,}660)^2 + (11{,}320)^2} = 12{,}660 \text{ psi}$$

The maximum and minimum principal stresses are (see Eqs. 2–8 and 2–9)

$$\sigma_{max} = OC + R = -5{,}660 + 12{,}660 = 7{,}000 \text{ psi,}$$

$$\sigma_{min} = OC - R = -5{,}660 - 12{,}660 = -18{,}320 \text{ psi.}$$

The material is brittle; therefore, we assume that the maximum principal stress theory of failure (see Section 4.6) was used in the design of the shaft. The load-stress relations for the shaft are linear so that the factor of safety can be applied to the stresses as well as to the loads. If fracture is assumed to occur in tension

$$N_T = \frac{\sigma_{ut}}{\sigma_{max}} = \frac{21{,}000}{7{,}000} = 3.00.$$

Although there may be a question as to the theory of failure for fracture of brittle materials in compression, we will assume that fracture in compression in the shaft will occur when the maximum compressive stress in the shaft is 65,000 psi.

$$N_C = \frac{\sigma_{uc}}{\sigma_{min}} = \frac{-65{,}000}{-18{,}320} = 3.55.$$

Thus,

$$N = N_T = 3.00.$$

If the torque T remains unchanged and the axial compressive load P_c becomes zero, the state of stress in the shaft is pure shear, and

$$\sigma_{max} = -\sigma_{min} = \tau_r = 11{,}320 \text{ psi,}$$

and the factor of safety becomes

$$N = \frac{\sigma_{ut}}{\sigma_{max}} = \frac{21{,}000}{11{,}320} = 1.86.$$

Note that the compressive load actually strengthens the shaft. This conclusion is valid only if the shaft is made of a brittle material because in general brittle materials are much stronger in compression than in tension.

10.13. The 2-in. diameter shaft in Figure P10.13*a* is supported in flexible bearings at *A* and *D*, and two gears *B* and *C* are keyed to the shaft at

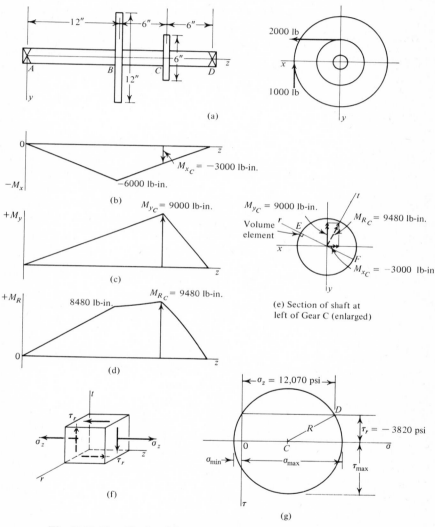

Fig. P 10.13. Shaft subjected to combined bending and torsion.

locations shown. The gears are acted on by tangential forces as shown by the end view. Determine values of the maximum principal stress and of the maximum shearing stress in the shaft. The shaft is made of a ductile steel that has a yield stress of $\sigma_e = 42{,}000$ psi. Assume that the loads shown acting on the gears are peak loads that are applied only a relatively few times so that the mode of failure of the shaft is assumed to be general yielding and not fatigue fracture. Thus we neglect the stress concentrations. Determine the factor of safety used in the design of the shaft.

SOLUTION. The shaft is subjected to a constant twisting moment between the two gears B and C of $(1{,}000)(6)$ or $(2{,}000)(3)$, which is 6,000 lb-in. This portion of the shaft is also subjected to bending moments in both the xz- and yz-planes. Moment diagrams for M_x and M_y are shown in Figure P10.13b and c, respectively. The resultant bending moment M_R at any given cross section is given by the relation

$$M_R = \sqrt{M_x^2 + M_y^2}.$$

A plot of M_R along the shaft is shown in Figure P10.13d; it should be noted that the plane of the bending moment M_R is not the same at every section of the shaft.

At a cross section of the shaft just to the left of gear C, the shaft is subjected to a bending moment of 9,480 lb-in. that lies in the longitudinal plane denoted by EF in Figure P10.13e and to a torque of 6,000 lb-in. The maximum tensile stress (or compressive stress) in the cross section caused by bending is

$$\sigma_z = \frac{M_{R(\max)}c}{I} = \frac{9{,}480(1)(64)}{\pi(2)^4} = 12{,}070 \text{ psi,}$$

and is located at the point E (or F) on the boundary of the cross section just to the left of the gear C. The maximum shearing stress due to torsion occurs at all points on the boundary of the cross section and is

$$\tau_r = \frac{Tc}{J} = \frac{6{,}000(1)(32)}{\pi(2)^4} = 3{,}820 \text{ psi.}$$

The state of stress due to superposition of the two states of stress is indicated on the volume element in Figure P10.13f. The volume element is taken from the shaft at the point E in Figure P10.13e. The stress components lie in a longitudinal plane parallel to a plane tangent to the free surface of the shaft at the point E in Figure P10.13e. Let the tz-plane be the plane of the stress components. Mohr's circle of stress is shown in Figure P10.13g. The distance to the center of the circle is OC (see Eq. 2–6):

$$OC = \frac{\sigma_z}{2} = 6{,}040 \text{ psi.}$$

The coordinates of point D are $\sigma_z = 12,070$ psi and $\tau_r = -3,820$ psi. The radius R of Mohr's circle of stress is equal to distance CD and is given by the relation (see Eq. 2–7):

$$R = CD = \sqrt{\left(\frac{\sigma_z}{2}\right)^2 + \tau_r^2} = \sqrt{(6,040)^2 + (3,820)^2} = 7,150 \text{ psi}.$$

The maximum and minimum principal stresses and the maximum shearing stress are

$$\sigma_{\max} = OC + R = 13,190 \text{ psi} = \sigma_1,$$

$$\sigma_{\min} = OC - R = -1,110 \text{ psi} = \sigma_2,$$

$$\tau_{\max} = \frac{\sigma_{\max} - \sigma_{\min}}{2} = 7,150 \text{ psi}.$$

Maximum Shearing-Stress Theory. As indicated in Section 4.6, two theories of failure are commonly used in the design of members such as this if failure is assumed to be general yielding; they are the maximum shearing stress and maximum octahedral shearing-stress theories of failure. Because the load-stress relations for the member are linear, the factor of safety N can be applied to stress as well as load. The tension test is used to obtain material properties. The maximum shearing stress theory of failure states that yielding will begin in the member to be designed and in the tension specimen at the same magnitude of the maximum shearing stress. Thus, from Equation (4–13),

$$N\tau_{\max} = \frac{N(\sigma_{\max} - \sigma_{\min})}{2} = \frac{\sigma_e}{2},$$

$$N = \frac{42,000}{2(7,150)} = 2.94.$$

Maximum Octahedral Shearing Stress Theory. The octahedral shearing-stress theory of failure states that yielding will begin in the member and in the tension specimen at the same magnitude of the octahedral shearing stress. The third principal stress σ_3 is the normal stress at the free surface of the shaft in the direction of the r-axis (see Fig. P10.13e and f) and is zero. Because the three principal stresses have been determined, τ_G for the member can be calculated using either Equation (2–31) or (4–14). Using the former we have

$$\frac{1}{3}\sqrt{(N\sigma_1 - N\sigma_2)^2 + (N\sigma_2 - N\sigma_3)^2 + (N\sigma_3 - N\sigma_1)^2}$$

$$= \frac{1}{3}\sqrt{(\sigma_e - 0)^2 + (0 - 0)^2 + (0 - \sigma_e)^2}$$

where the left side shows the principal stresses in the shaft at failure and the right shows the principal stresses in the tensile specimen at failure. The substitution of the values of σ_1, σ_2, and σ_3 in the shaft at the point E (Fig. P10.13e) gives the following results:

$$N\sqrt{(14,300)^2 + (13,190)^2 + (1,110)^2} = \sqrt{2}\sigma_e,$$

$$N = 3.05.$$

Note that the maximum shearing-stress theory of failure is more conservative because it states that yielding will be initiated when the working loads are increased by a factor of 2.94 whereas the octahedral shearing-stress theory of failure states that they can be increased by a factor of 3.05 before initiation of yielding.

Problems

10.14. A load $P = 10,000$ lb on the crankpin of the steel crankshaft shown in Figure P10.14 is required to turn the shaft at constant speed when the shaft is subjected to a constant resisting torque Qq. If the diameter D of the shaft is 4 in., find the maximum

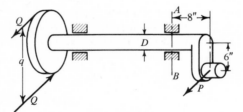

Fig. P 10.14.

and minimum principal stresses and the maximum shearing stress at section AB. The direction of P is perpendicular to the axis of the crankpin and the crank. Neglect stress concentration caused by the bearing and assume that the material in the crankshaft remains linearly elastic.

10.15. A steel bar shown in Figure P10.15 is held fixed at one end and has a wrench, indicated by AB, attached at the other end; a force P is applied as shown to the handle of the wrench. Assume the following values: $P = 150$ lb, $p = 20$ in., $\ell = 24$ in., $D = 2$ in. The bar is made of a ductile steel that has a yield stress $\sigma_e = 30,000$ psi. Calculate the maximum and minimum principal stresses and the maximum shearing stress in the bar, neglecting the stress concentration caused by the gripping of the bar at the fixed end. State where in the bar the maximum tensile principal stress occurs.

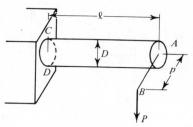

Fig. P 10.15.

What is the magnitude of the load P necessary to initiate yielding in the bar based on octahedral shearing stress theory of failure?

ans.   At C, $\sigma_{max} = 5,270$ psi and $\tau_{max} = 2,980$ psi; $P_{max} = 796$ lb.

10.16. A solid circular-steel ship propeller shaft 6 in. in diameter transmits 400 hp at a speed of 120 rpm. If the thrust (compressive axial load) of the propeller is 80,000 lb, calculate the maximum and minimum principal stresses and the maximum shearing stress in the shaft; assume that bending of the shaft is prevented, that stress concentrations are negligible, and that the shaft acts elastically. (See Prob. 9.20.)

ans. $\sigma_{max} = 3,735$ psi; $\sigma_{min} = -6,565$ psi; $\tau_{max} = 5,150$ psi.

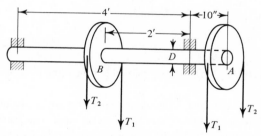

Fig. P 10.17.   Shaft subjected to combined torsional and bending loads.

10.17. Two pulleys A and B are mounted on a shaft as shown in Figure P10.17. The driving pulley A transmits 15 hp to the shaft and the driven pulley B. It turns the shaft at 120 rpm. The smaller belt tension T_2 is 250 lb. The diameter D of the shaft is 2.5 in., and the diameter of each pulley is 2 ft. Find the maximum normal and shearing stresses in the shaft. (See Prob. 9.20.)

ans. $\sigma_{max} = 8,330$ psi; $\tau_{max} = 4,560$ psi.

10.18. Solve Problem 10.17 if the two belt tensions on pulley B are horizontal instead of vertical, that is they have directions perpendicular to those on pulley A.

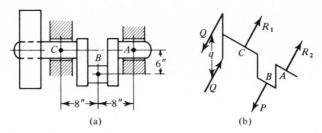

(a)   (b)

Fig. P 10.19.   Crankshaft subjected to combined torsional and bending loads.

10.19.   The crankpin load P (Fig. P10.19) in a direction perpendicular to the crank is 2,000 lb when the shaft is turned against a constant resisting moment Qq. The diameter of the shaft at A, B, and C is 2 in. Find the reactions R_1 and R_2 of the bearings and also the maximum normal and shearing stresses in the cross section of the shaft at B.

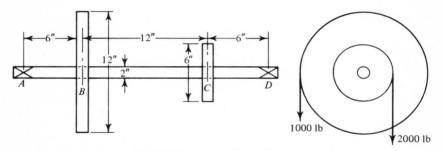

Fig. P 10.20.   Combined torsional and bending loads on shaft.

10.20.   In Figure P10.20 a shaft 2 in. in diameter is supported in flexible bearings at A and D, and two gears B and C are keyed to the shaft. The gears are acted on by tangential forces, as shown by the end view in Figure P10.20. Calculate the maximum and minimum principal stresses and the maximum shearing stress, and show in a sketch approximately where in the shaft they occur. Neglect stress concentrations, and assume that the shaft acts elastically.

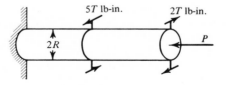

Fig. P 10.21.

10.21. The bar in Figure P10.21 is assumed to remain straight when the axial-centric load P is applied. If we neglect the effect of stress concentrations, derive relations for the maximum and minimum principal stresses and the maximum shearing stress in terms of the known quantities P, T, and R.

10.22. A steel shaft 4 in. in diameter is subjected to an axial end thrust of 9 tons and also a bending moment of 6,000 lb-ft and a twisting moment of 10,000 lb-ft. Calculate the maximum and minimum principal stresses and the maximum shearing stress in the shaft. If the shaft is made of a ductile steel having a yield stress of $\sigma_e = 36{,}000$ psi, determine the factor of safety used in the design.

10.23. A piece of chalk of diameter D is subjected to an axial-centric tensile load P and to a torque T. The axial-centric load $P = \sigma_u(\pi D^2/8)$, where σ_u is the ultimate tensile strength of the chalk. Assume that the chalk remains linearly elastic up to the ultimate strength σ_u. Determine the magnitude of the torque T to initiate fracture in terms of the known quantities σ_u and D. Determine the angle at which the fracture will intersect a longitudinal line drawn on the chalk.

$$\text{ans.} \quad T = \pi\sigma_u D^3/(16\sqrt{2}); \theta = 54.7°.$$

10.24. The 4-in. diameter bar shown in Figure P10.24 is made of a steel that has a yield stress of $\sigma_e = 35{,}000$ psi. The free end of the bar is subjected to a static load $P = 10{,}000$ lb, making equal angles with the positive directions of the three coordinate

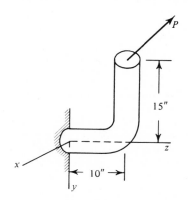

Fig. P 10.24.

axes. Determine the maximum and minimum principal stresses, the maximum shearing stress, and the factor of safety used in the design, neglecting the stress concentration factors and neglecting transverse shearing stresses, which are small quantities.

$$\text{ans.} \quad \sigma_{max} = 14{,}100 \text{ psi}; \sigma_{min} = -3{,}380 \text{ psi}; \tau_{max} = 8{,}740 \text{ psi}; N = 2.18.$$

10.4. Combined Axial-Centric and Bending Loads for Plastic Conditions

Combined axial-centric and bending loads were considered in Section 10.2 for the condition that the loads were sufficiently small so that the material in the member remained linearly elastic. Two conditions were assumed to be valid in Section 10.2 as follows: (1) the member was assumed to have a plane of symmetry and the loads were assumed to lie in this plane; (2) the deflections of the member were assumed to be so small that the moment Py, where P is the axial load and y is the deflection, is negligibly small. These conditions are also assumed to be valid in this section.

We make the simplifying assumption that the material in the member subjected to combined axial-centric and bending loads has a yield point and that the stress-strain diagram for both tension and compression has the

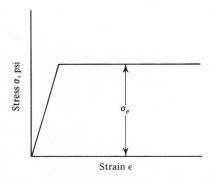

Fig. 10.3.   Tension and compression stress-strain diagram.

shape indicated in Figure 10.3. Consider the member in Figure 10.4, which is the same member shown in Figure 10.2. The maximum values of the loads P and Q for linearly elastic conditions can be determined as discussed in Section 10.2.

As the magnitudes of the loads P and Q in Figure 10.4a are increased, yielding will spread across the depth of the member. The loads will reach their maximum or fully plastic values when yielding spreads completely through the depth of the member. We will limit our consideration to these limiting or fully plastic loads.

The practical engineering problem is to determine the magnitudes of the fully plastic loads P and Q for the member in Figure 10.4 when the ratio of P to Q is specified. The critical section of the member is section AB.

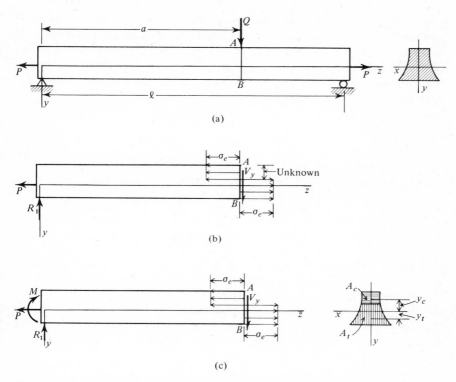

Fig. 10.4. Fully plastic stress distribution for member subjected to axial tension and bending loads.

We pass a section through AB to give the free-body diagram of the left portion as shown in Figure 10.4b. Because yielding has spread across the depth of the member at section AB, the normal stress distribution will have a uniform tensile stress equal to σ_e over the region that has yielded in tension and a uniform compressive stress equal to σ_e over the region that has yielded in compression. The resisting transverse shear V_y is found to have little influence on the normal stress distribution as long as the average transverse shearing stress is less than $0.1\tau_e$ where τ_e is the yield stress for pure shear.

The magnitudes of the fully plastic values of the loads P and Q in Figure 10.4b are easily calculated if the location of the neutral axis is known. A trial-and-error solution is required when the ratio of P to Q is specified since the location of the neutral axis is not known. An inverse method is used in the solution of the problem. We assume that the location of the neutral axis is known as indicated in Figure 10.4c and that the axial load P

and bending moment M are unknown. The neutral axis divides the cross section into areas A_t and A_c shown in Figure 10.4c. A tensile force $A_t\sigma_e$ acts through the centroid of area A_t; the distance from the neutral axis to the centroid of A_t is y_t as indicated in Figure 10.4c. Similarly the action line of the compressive force $A_c\sigma_e$ is located at the centroid of A_c at a distance y_c from the neutral axis. Using equations of equilibrium

$$P = \sigma_e(A_t - A_c), \tag{10-2}$$

$$M = \sigma_e(A_t y_t + A_c y_c). \tag{10-3}$$

By choosing different locations of the neutral axis and using Equations (10–2) and (10–3), the fully plastic magnitudes of P and Q in Figure 10.4a can be determined for any given ratio of P to Q.

Illustrative Problem

10.25. The eccentrically loaded T-section tension member in Figure P10.25a is made of structural grade steel that has a yield point of 30,000 psi. Determine the magnitude of the fully plastic load P_{fp}.

SOLUTION.   The location of the centroid of the T-section is 2.6-in. below the top of the member. Our problem is to determine the location of the neutral axis so that Equations (10–2) and (10–3) satisfy the conditions

$$P = P_{fp},$$

$$M = 3.60P_{fp}$$

where 3.60 in. is the centroidal distance to the load P_{fp}.

Every section of the member has the same stress distribution if deflections are assumed to be negligibly small. The portion of the member to the left of section AB is shown in Figure P10.25b. For the first trial, the neutral axis is assumed to be located at a distance of 4.4 in. from the top of the member. The stress distribution shown will determine values of P and M. It is convenient to represent the resultant of the stress distribution in the flange by the force $4\sigma_e$ and the resultant of the tension and compression stress distributions in the web by the forces $3.4\sigma_e$ and $2.6\sigma_e$, respectively (Fig. P10.25c). Equations (10–2) and (1–3) give

$$P = 4\sigma_e + 3.4\sigma_e - 2.6\sigma_e = 4.8\sigma_e,$$

$$M = 4\sigma_e(2.1) + 3.4\sigma_e(-0.10) + 2.6\sigma_e(3.1) = 16.12\sigma_e = 3.36P.$$

The ratio of M to P is 3.36. Because this value is not 3.60, other trials are required. A second trial with the neutral axis located 4.2 in. below the top of the member gave the results

$$P = 4.4\sigma_e,$$

$$M = 16.8\sigma_e = 3.82P.$$

The correct location of the neutral axis lies between 4.2 in. and 4.4 in. below the top of the member. A linear interpolation using the results of the

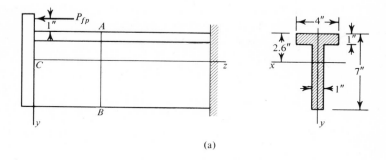

(a)

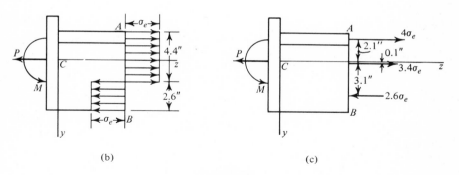

(b) (c)

Fig. P 10.25.

first two trials gives a reasonably accurate result. The correct location of the neutral axis is 4.292-in. below the top of the member.

$$P = 4\sigma_e + 3.292\sigma_e - 2.708\sigma_e = 4.584\sigma_e = 137,500\,\mathrm{lb} = P_{fp},$$

$$M = 4\sigma_e(2.1) + 3.292\sigma_e(-0.046) + 2.708\sigma_e(3.046)$$

$$= 16.50\sigma_e = 3.60P = 3.60P_{fp}.$$

The fully plastic load is $P_{fp} = 137,500\,\mathrm{lb}$.

Problems

10.26. Let the neutral axis for the T-section member in Problem 10.25 be located 1 in. below the top of the member. Determine the magnitude and sense of the fully plastic load P_{fp} and locate its action line with respect to the top of the member.

ans. $P_{fp} = -60,000$ lb (compression);
the location of P_{fp} is 11.0 in. below the top of the member.

10.27. Determine the load P_1 in Problem 10.6 that will cause the fully plastic condition in the member if the yield point of the material is 36,000 psi.

10.28. Determine the fully plastic load P_{fp} for the member in Problem 10.9.

ans. $P_{fp} = 13,500$ lb.

Buckling Load—Instability—Columns

11.1. Introduction

Most readers are familiar with the common yardstick made of wood; the cross-sectional dimensions may be $\frac{1}{6}$-in. by $1\frac{1}{8}$-in. If the yardstick is subjected to an axial-centric tension load, the theory presented in Section 1.4 indicates that it will carry a load of 500 lb and the stress will be well within the yield strength of the wood (see Table 1.1). Suppose the axial-centric load is compression rather than tension. Most of us have had experience with long slender compression members and know that the yardstick will safely carry in compression only a very small fraction of the load that it can carry in tension. Because of the instability resulting from the compression load, the yardstick buckles due to column action and fails at a very small load. The theory developed in this chapter indicates that the buckling load for the yardstick is only 6 lb if E for the wood is 1,800,000 psi (see Table 1.1 for yellow pine).

Most of the emphasis in this chapter will be devoted to deriving relations for predicting the buckling load for initially straight axially loaded compression members. Such a member is only one of several types of load-carrying members that can fail by buckling. Buckling may be a problem in any load-carrying member where compressive stresses are approximately uniformly distributed through the thickness of the member if the thickness dimension is small compared to other cross-sectional dimensions of the member. Failure due to buckling may occur in thin-walled cylinders and spheres subjected to external pressures (the hull of a submarine, for instance), in thin-walled hollow torsion members, in the compression flanges of beams built up of thin plates, and in the thin web of built up beams if the

473

shear load becomes excessive. In some of these members buckling may be restricted to a localized portion of the member, especially in thin-walled cylinders under compression or in the compression flanges of beams, and so forth. These topics are usually found in more advanced treatments of the subject.

11.2.   Critical Buckling Load

The load-deflection relations for each of the members considered in previous chapters have been linear as long as the material in the member remained linearly elastic. A characteristic of members that buckle such as the axially loaded straight bar in compression is that the load-deflection relation is indeterminate. Below a given load called the critical buckling load, the lateral deflection in the direction perpendicular to the action line of the

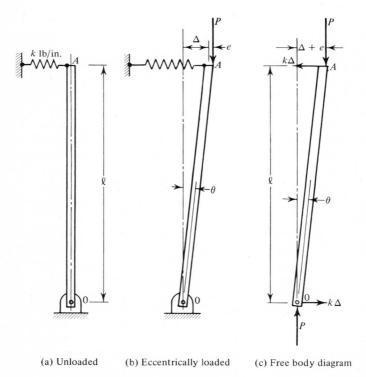

(a) Unloaded   (b) Eccentrically loaded   (c) Free body diagram

Fig. 11.1.   Eccentrically loaded structure.

load is zero for equilibrium conditions. At the critical buckling load the deflection is zero unless a slight disturbance results in a lateral deflection; the member is in equilibrium for either zero deflection or any small deflection. Above the critical buckling load the lateral deflection is zero unless a slight disturbance results in a lateral deflection; when this happens the member becomes unstable for any deflection no matter how small and failure occurs as the result of excessive lateral deflection.

In order to better interpret the buckling phenomenon, it is convenient to consider the structure in Figure 11.1a made up of a straight rigid bar OA pivoted on a frictionless pin at O and supported by an elastic spring with spring constant k at the upper end. The bar OA is vertical when the structure is unloaded. If the vertical load P is an axial-centric load applied so that its action line passes through the centroid of each cross section of the bar and through the center of the pin at O, the load-deflection relation for the structure is indeterminate. To solve the problem, the possible geometric changes must be introduced into the equilibrium equations. To do this let us apply the load P parallel to the axis through a point in the upper end of the bar at an eccentricity e measured from the centroid of the section. Such a load is called an eccentric load. The resulting load-deflection curve for the structure is determinate. The effect of the eccentricity e on the load-deflection curve as e approaches zero will be considered.

Let the horizontal (or lateral) deflection Δ of the upper end of the bar OA in Figure 11.1b be small compared to the length ℓ of the bar so that $\cos \theta = 1$ and $\sin \theta = \tan \theta = \theta$. In this case the stretch in the spring is equal to Δ and the force in the spring is equal to $k\Delta$. The free-body diagram of the bar is shown in Figure 11.1c. The moment equilibrium equation about O gives

$$\ell k\Delta - P(e + \Delta) = 0. \tag{11–1}$$

If $e = 0$ is set in Equation (11–1), the load $P = k\ell$. This load is called the critical buckling load $P_{cr} = k\ell$. By dividing each term in the Equation (11–1) by ℓ, the deflection in dimensionless form can be obtained as follows:

$$\frac{\Delta}{\ell} = \frac{(P/k\ell)(e/\ell)}{1 - (P/k\ell)} = \frac{(P/P_{cr})(e/\ell)}{1 - (P/P_{cr})}. \tag{11–2}$$

Dimensionless load-deflection curves given by Equation (11–2) are shown in Figure 11.2 for values of e/ℓ equal to 0.01, 0.001, and 0.0001. Note that the load-deflection curve approaches the two straight lines OB and BC as e approaches zero and the maximum load approaches the value P_{cr}, which is the critical buckling load for the structure. The critical buckling load can be obtained from Equation (11–1) by setting $e = 0$ and is the load,

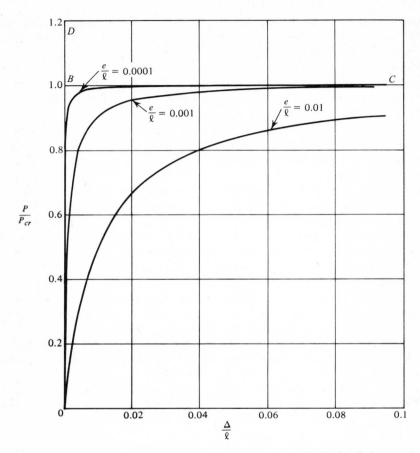

Fig. 11.2.   Dimensionless load-deflection curves for eccentrically loaded structure.

for this case, required to hold the structure in equilibrium for the deflected configuration, where Δ is any small deflection one wishes to give to the end A of the bar.

A question arises. Will the load-deflection curve follow the two straight lines OB and BC in Figure 11.2 if $e = 0$? Actually it is possible for the load-deflection curve to follow the straight line OBD; however, an infinitesimal horizontal force acting on the bar, or if the value of e is not exactly equal to zero when the load is equal to $P_{cr} = OB$, will cause the load-deflection curve to follow path OBC. At point B there are two different paths that can be followed; either BC or BD. The branching point at B is called the *bifurcation point.* The load at the bifurcation point is called the critical buckling load for the structure. In this chapter we use the bifurcation theory to obtain the critical buckling loads for columns and structures. If the lateral deflection of a column or structure remains zero as the load is increased, the critical buckling load is the load at which the column or structure will be held in equilibrium in a laterally deflected configuration (the deflections are assumed to be small).

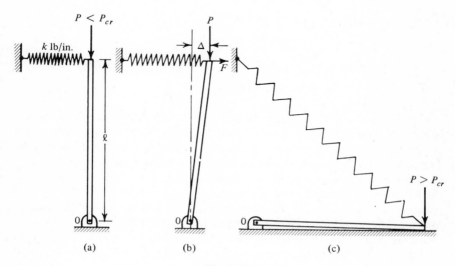

Fig. 11.3.

Instability. Below the critical buckling load a column or structure is stable whereas above this load the column or structure becomes unstable. Let us examine the problem of stability for the structure in Figure 11.1 for the case when $e = 0$. Give the bar a deflection Δ as shown in Figure 11.3b and apply a force F to hold the bar in equilibrium in the deflected configuration. The moment equilibrium equation about the pin at 0 gives

$$\ell k\Delta - P\Delta - F\ell = 0.$$

Because $k\ell = P_{cr}$, this equation becomes

$$F = (P_{cr} - P)\frac{\Delta}{\ell}. \qquad (11\text{--}3)$$

For $P < P_{cr}$, Equation (11–3) indicates that F in Figure 11.3b is positive and acts to the right. If F is reduced to zero while $P < P_{cr}$, the structure springs back to its undeformed configuration shown in Figure 11.3a. Thus the stable behavior of the structure for load P less than P_{cr} corresponds to the stable behavior of a ball in a spherical bowl as indicated in Figure 11.4a. A force Q is required to hold the ball at a position above the bottom of the bowl; however, the ball returns to the equilibrium position at the bottom of the bowl when Q is released.

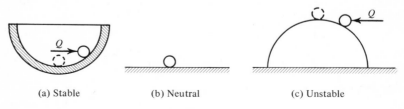

(a) Stable   (b) Neutral   (c) Unstable

Fig. 11.4.

For $P = P_{cr}$, Equation (11–3) indicates that F is zero for all values of Δ (assumed small). The structure is said to be in neutral equilibrium and corresponds to the ball on a flat horizontal surface as shown in Figure 11.4b. The ball is in equilibrium at every point on the horizontal surface.

For $P > P_{cr}$, Equation (11–3) indicates that F is negative and acts to the left to prevent deflection from becoming larger. When $P > P_{cr}$ and F is reduced in magnitude, the structure is unstable, it is no longer possible to find a stable equilibrium configuration for small deflection, and the bar rotates until it strikes the frame as indicated in Figure 11.3c. This corresponds to the ball on a hemisphere as shown in Figure 11.4c. A force Q is required to hold the ball in equilibrium if the ball is displaced from its unstable equilibrium position at the top of the hemisphere. When the force Q is released, the ball rolls downward and seeks a new equilibrium position (on the flat plane).

The foregoing discussion indicates that the critical buckling load represents the transition between loads (loads less than P_{cr}) for which the column or structure is stable and loads (loads greater than P_{cr}) for which the column or structure is unstable.

Problems

11.1 Through 11.4. Determine the value of the critical buckling load for each of the structures shown in Figures P11.1 through P11.4. All bars are rigid and weightless and all pins are frictionless. The rotational springs produce a resisting bending moment $M = \beta\theta$, where θ is the rotation in radians at the frictionless pin, and the helical springs produce a resisting force equal to $k\Delta$, where Δ is the deflection of the spring.

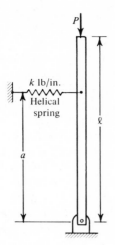

Fig. P 11.1.

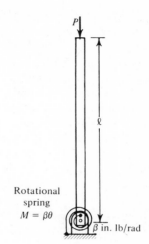

Fig. P 11.2.

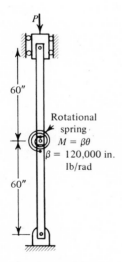

Fig. P 11.3.

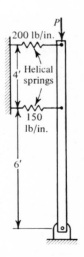

Fig. P 11.4.

ans.   Problem 11.3 $P_{cr} = 4\beta/\ell = 4{,}000$ lb.

11.3. Euler's Buckling Load for Axially Loaded Elastic Columns

Consider an ideally straight long slender compression member with constant cross section. Let the action lines of the compression loads P, which are applied to each end of the member which rests on a semispherical bearing supports, be collinear and pass through the centroid of each cross section of the member. As long as the column remains straight, it is subjected to axial-centric loading. This member is called an axially loaded pivot-ended column because the flat side of the semispherical bearings is arranged to fit against the flat end of the column as shown in Figure 11.5. Theoretically this member will remain straight for all magnitudes of the loads P. However, based on our consideration of the structure in Figure 11.1 in Section 11.2, when a certain critical buckling load P_{cr} is applied to the axially loaded column, it will hold the column in equilibrium for the deflected configuration shown in Figure 11.5 where the maximum deflection Δ is assumed to be small compared to the length ℓ of the column. Euler's formula for this critical buckling load is

$$P_{cr} = \frac{\pi^2 E I_x}{\ell^2} \tag{11–4}$$

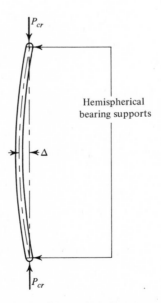

Fig. 11.5. Buckling of ideal Euler column.

where E is the modulus of elasticity of the material and I_x is the minimum value for the second moment of the area (commonly called moment of inertia of the cross section). Dividing both sides of Equation (11–4) by the cross-sectional area A of the column gives

$$\frac{P_{cr}}{A} = \frac{\pi^2 E}{(\ell/r)^2} \tag{11–5}$$

where r is the radius of gyration of the cross section ($r = \sqrt{I_x/A}$) and the ratio ℓ/r is called the slenderness ratio for the column.

Instead of deriving Euler's formula (Eq. 11–4), directly, it is convenient to derive the load-deflection relation for an eccentrically loaded column (see Fig. 11.6) and then show that this solution approaches Equation (11–4)

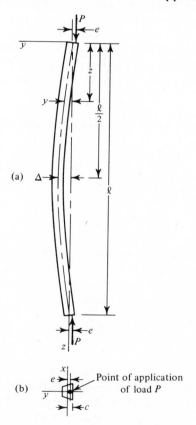

Fig. 11.6.   Eccentrically loaded column.

as a limiting case when the eccentricity e approaches zero. It is assumed in Figure 11.6 that the action lines of the compression loads P are collinear and pass through a point in the cross section at each end of the column at the same eccentricity e. As e approaches zero, it approaches the loading of an ideal column. An eccentrically loaded column is realistic because it is practically impossible to make the column perfectly straight so that the axial load passes through the centroid of every cross section; furthermore, the solution for eccentrically loaded columns will indicate the range of e for which Equations (11–4) and (11–5) are applicable.

The principal axes of inertia for the column cross section are shown in Figure 11.6b as the x- and y-axes. As the eccentricity e approaches zero, the column bends about the axis having the minimum moment of inertia; for this reason the eccentricity e is taken in the yz-plane and the cross section is assumed to have the minimum moment of inertia about the x-axis.

In deriving the load-deflection relation for the eccentrically loaded column in Figure 11.6a, it is assumed that the maximum deflection Δ of the column is small compared to ℓ. The bending moment M_x at any distance z from the origin is positive and is given by the relation

$$M_x = P(e + y).$$

Substituting this value of M_x in the elastic curve equation (Eq. 8–10) gives

$$\frac{d^2y}{dz^2} = -\frac{P}{EI_x}(e + y).$$

This equation can be rewritten as

$$\frac{d^2y}{dz^2} + \frac{P}{EI_x}y = -\frac{P}{EI_x}e. \qquad (11-6)$$

The solution of this linear differential equation is given in any elementary text on differential equations as the sum of the general solution of the differential equation when $e = 0$ and the particular solution which satisfies Equation (11–6). The resulting solution is

$$y = C_1 \sin z\sqrt{\frac{P}{EI_x}} + C_2 \cos z\sqrt{\frac{P}{EI_x}} - e$$

where C_1 and C_2 are constants of integration that must be obtained from the boundary conditions. Whether or not Equation (11–4) gives the buckling load for a pivot ended column, it does have the dimensions of a load; therefore, there is a quantity K such that $P = P_{cr}/K^2 = \pi^2 EI_x/K^2\ell^2$. When the latter value of P is substituted into the foregoing solution of Equation

(11–6), the following equation results:

$$y = C_1 \sin \frac{\pi z}{K\ell} + C_2 \cos \frac{\pi z}{K\ell} - e. \tag{11–7}$$

As indicated in Figure 11.6a, the deflection y of the eccentrically loaded column is zero when $z = 0$ and when $z = \ell$. Substituting the first boundary condition in Equation (11–7) gives

$$0 = 0 + C_2 - e,$$

$$C_2 = e.$$

The second boundary condition gives

$$0 = C_1 \sin \frac{\pi}{K} + e \cos \frac{\pi}{K} - e,$$

$$C_1 = e \frac{1 - \cos(\pi/K)}{\sin(\pi/K)} = e \frac{\sin(\pi/2K)}{\cos(\pi/2K)}.$$

The elastic curve equation for the eccentrically loaded column now becomes

$$y = e \left[\frac{\sin(\pi/2K)}{\cos(\pi/2K)} \sin \frac{\pi z}{K\ell} + \cos \frac{\pi z}{K\ell} - 1 \right]. \tag{11–8}$$

The maximum deflection of the eccentrically loaded column in Figure 11.6a is $y_{max} = \Delta$ and occurs when $z = \ell/2$. Substituting these values for y and z in Equation (11–8) gives, after simplification,

$$\Delta = e \left(\sec \frac{\pi}{2K} - 1 \right).$$

In order to further interpret the significance of the foregoing equation it is convenient to introduce dimensionless quantities. The most characteristic dimension of the column cross section is the minimum radius of gyration $r = \sqrt{I_x/A}$ where I_x is the minimum value of the moment of inertia of the cross section and A is the cross-sectional area. Dividing both sides of the foregoing equation by r gives

$$\frac{\Delta}{r} = \frac{e}{r} \left(\sec \frac{\pi}{2K} - 1 \right) = \frac{e}{r} \left(\sec \frac{\pi}{2} \sqrt{\frac{P}{P_{cr}}} - 1 \right), \tag{11–9}$$

where Δ/r, e/r, and $K = \sqrt{P_{cr}/P}$ are all dimensionless quantities.

Equation (11–9) was used to construct the curves in Figure 11.7 where dimensionless load-deflection curves are shown as solid lines for values of the dimensionless eccentricity e/r equal to 1.0, 0.1, 0.01, and 0.001. It will be

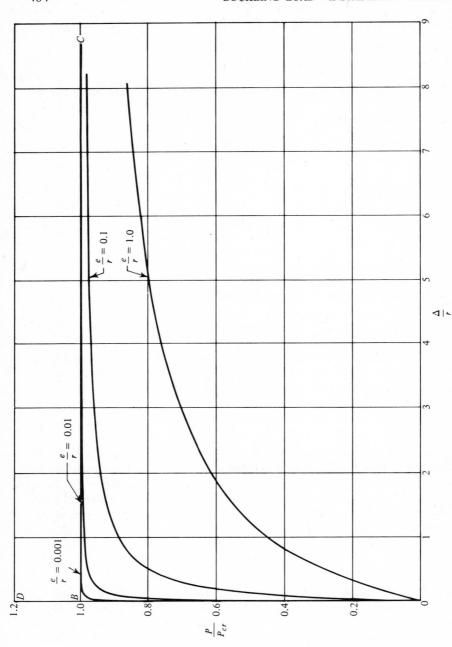

Fig. 11.7.   Dimensionless load-deflection curves for eccentrically loaded columns.

noted that all curves are asymptotic to the line BC corresponding to the critical buckling load P_{cr} given by Equation (11–4). As e approaches zero, note that the load-deflection curve approaches the two straight lines OB and BC and the deflection Δ becomes indeterminate. The critical buckling load given by Equation (11–4) for the axially loaded pivot ended column ($e = 0$) is the load which will hold the column in equilibrium when it is given a small deflection Δ. The deflected shape of a pivot ended column is given by Equation (11–7) ($K = 1$ and $C_2 = e = 0$), which simplifies to

$$y = C_1 \sin \frac{\pi z}{\ell} = \Delta \sin \frac{\pi z}{\ell}, \tag{11–10}$$

where $C_1 = \Delta$ is given by the boundary condition that $y = \Delta$ when $z = \ell/2$.

The curves in Figure 11.7 are valid for all eccentrically loaded columns made of linearly elastic materials*. For specified values of Δ/r, e/r, and P_{cr}, the load P can be obtained either from Equation (11–9) or from Figure 11.7. The only material property that influences the magnitude of P is the modulus of elasticity E because this is the only material property required to determine P_{cr} (see Eq. 11–4). The range of applicability of the curves in Figure 11.7 is limited by the proportional limit of the material. Another limitation that should be noted is that the curves are valid only for small deflections; the largest value Δ/r can have, and still be considered small, must be determined. Both of these limitations will be considered in the paragraphs that follow.

Maximum Compressive Stress in Eccentrically Loaded Columns.   It is convenient to change the sign convention for normal stress when studying columns and let compressive stresses be positive. The maximum compressive stress in an eccentrically loaded column is the sum of the compressive stress due to the axial-centric compressive load and the compressive stress due to bending. Thus,

$$\sigma_{max} = \frac{P}{A} + \frac{M_{max}c}{I_x}.$$

But $M_{max} = P(e + \Delta)$; therefore,

$$\sigma_{max} = \frac{P}{A} + \frac{P(e + \Delta)c}{I_x},$$

where c is the distance $y = c$ from the neutral axis of the cross section to the location of the maximum compressive stress (see Fig. 11.6b) and I_x is the

---

* Exceptions would be columns whose cross sections are made with thin elements such as I-sections with very thin flanges and webs in which local buckling could occur in the thin wall at loads below the critical buckling load for the columns. For a treatment of this topic see Chapter 20, *Advanced Mechanics of Materials*, Seely and Smith, 2nd Ed., 1952, John Wiley and Sons.

moment of inertia of the cross sectional area with respect to the neutral axis about which the bending moment M_{max} acts. Multiplying and dividing the last term in the equation by the cross-sectional area A and using the definition $r^2 = I_x/A$, we obtain

$$\sigma_{max} = \frac{P}{A}\left[1 + \left(\frac{e}{r} + \frac{\Delta}{r}\right)\frac{c}{r}\right].$$

By substituting the expression for Δ/r from Equation (11–9) into the foregoing equation, the following equation is obtained:

$$\sigma_{max} = \frac{P}{A} + \frac{P}{A}\frac{ec}{r^2}\sec\frac{\pi}{2}\sqrt{\frac{P}{P_{cr}}} \qquad (11\text{–}11a)$$

The substitution of P_{cr} from Equation (11–5) into Equation (11–11a) gives

$$\sigma_{max} = \frac{P}{A}\left[1 + \frac{ec}{r^2}\sec\frac{\ell}{r}\sqrt{\frac{P}{4AE}}\right]. \qquad (11\text{–}11b)$$

Equation (11–11b) is known as the secant formula for columns.

In Equations (11–11) the terms e, c, r, and A are obtained from the given dimensions. The term P_{cr} is computed from Equation (11–4). Because the derivation of Equations (11–11) depends on the flexure formula ($\sigma_z = Mc/I_x$), the value of σ_{max} computed by these equations must be limited to values of stress at or below the proportional limit of the material. Experience has shown that for most practical eccentrically loaded columns Equations (11–11) gives a significant relationship between σ_{max} and the load P when the load P is substituted into Equations (11–11) and gives a value of σ_{max} equal to the proportional limit of the material; this value of the load P is equal to or less than the ultimate or collapse load. Such a computed value of the load P is considered to be most useful because, for values of eccentricity e small compared to the radius of gyration r, the load is only slightly less than the ultimate or collapse load.

Limitations of Small Deformations. The theoretical analysis of large deflections of columns ($e = 0$) is beyond the scope of this book; however, the result of the large deflection theory is required if we are to determine the limiting magnitude of Δ/r in Figure 11.7 for small deflections. The large deflection theory for columns* indicates that the load-deflection curve in Figure 11.7 curves upward above the critical buckling load for large deflections if the material in the columns remains linearly elastic. The theory

---

* S. P. Timoshenko and J. M. Gere, *Theory of Stability*, 2nd Ed., McGraw-Hill Book, 1961, pp. 76–81.

indicates that $\Delta/r = 0.055 \, \ell/r$ when the load P is 0.1 per cent greater that P_{cr} and that $\Delta/r = 0.170 \, \ell/r$ when the load P is 1.0 per cent greater than P_{cr}.

The load-deflection curve in Figure 11.7 is very nearly horizontal, as shown by line BC, for practical values of Δ/r. The upper limit for the slenderness ratio of most engineering columns is 200. In order for a column with ℓ/r of 200 to remain elastic for $P/P_{cr} = 1.01$, Equations (11–11) indicates that the proportional limit of the material must be greater than $0.09E$; the proportional limit of most engineering materials is only a fraction of this. Even greater values are required for the proportional limit if the slenderness ratio is less than 200 and the material in the column is linearly elastic for $P/P_{cr} = 1.01$.

Illustrative Problem

11.5. A T-section column is made by nailing two 12-ft lengths of 2-in. by 6-in. oak boards together as indicated by the cross section in Figure P11.5a. The material properties for the oak are $E = 1,800,000$ psi and $\sigma_{PL} = 3,750$ psi. (1) Determine the critical buckling load for the column loaded as a pivot ended column ($e = 0$). (2) Determine the maximum elastic load that can be applied to the column if the column is eccentrically loaded and $e = \frac{1}{2}$ in. as shown in Figure P11.5a. (3) Compute the maximum deflection of the eccentrically loaded column in part (2).

SOLUTION.—PART (1).   The centroidal axes for the cross section are indicated by the x- and y-axes in Figure P11.5a. By inspection it is seen that I_y will be the minimum moment of inertia for the cross section because more of the area is concentrated near this axis than is the case for the x-axis.

$$I_y = \frac{2(6)^3}{12} + \frac{6(2)^3}{12} = 40.0 \text{ in.}^4$$

Show that $I_x = 136$ in.^{4} The radius of gyration is

$$r = \sqrt{\frac{I_y}{A}} = \sqrt{\frac{40}{24}} = 1.29 \text{ in.}$$

The slenderness ratio can now be computed:

$$\frac{\ell}{r} = \frac{12(12)}{1.29} = 111.6.$$

The average stress in the column when it buckles is given by Equation (11–5):

$$\sigma_{\text{ave}} = \frac{P_{cr}}{A} = \frac{\pi^2 E}{(\ell/r)^2} = \frac{9.87(1,800,000)}{111.6(111.6)} = 1,427 \text{ psi.}$$

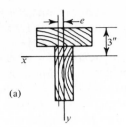

(a)

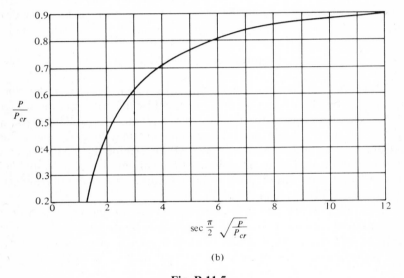

$$\sec \frac{\pi}{2} \sqrt{\frac{P}{P_{cr}}}$$

(b)

Fig. P 11.5.

This is a valid solution because σ_{ave} is less than σ_{PL}. The buckling load is

$$P_{cr} = 24(1{,}427) = 34{,}200 \text{ lb.}$$

PART (2). An eccentricity $e = \frac{1}{2}$ in. means that the action line of the load P is located on an axis parallel to the z-axis at a distance $e = \frac{1}{2}$ in. as indicated in Figure P11.5a. The solution to part (2) is a trial-and-error solution of Equation (11–11). The value of ec/r^2 is computed:

$$\frac{ec}{r^2} = \frac{0.5(3.00)}{1.29(1.29)} = 0.902.$$

Equation (11–11) is solved by trial and error for the load P. The values of $A = 24$ in.^{2}, $\sigma_{max} = \sigma_{PL} = 3{,}750$ psi, $P_{cr} = 34{,}200$ lb, and $ec/r^2 = 0.902$ are given. The right side of Equation (11–11) is divided and multiplied by P_{cr} so that it takes the following form:

$$\sigma_{max} = \frac{P_{cr}}{A} \frac{P}{P_{cr}} \left[1 + \frac{ec}{r^2} \sec \frac{\pi}{2} \sqrt{\frac{P}{P_{cr}}} \right]. \tag{a}$$

The given values of σ_{max}, ec/r^2, A, and P_{cr} are now substituted into Equation (a) except that the ratio P/P_{cr} is left as the variable. Thus, Equation (a) becomes as follows:

$$3{,}750 = 1{,}427 \frac{P}{P_{cr}} \left[1 + 0.902 \sec \frac{\pi}{2} \sqrt{\frac{P}{P_{cr}}} \right]. \tag{b}$$

Now a graph of values of P/P_{cr} versus $\sec \pi/2 \sqrt{P/P_{cr}}$ is constructed as shown in Figure P11.5b. Let a value of $P/P_{cr} = 0.6$ be chosen. From Figure P11.5b the $\sec \pi/2 \sqrt{0.6} = 2.88$. Putting this value in Equation (b) gives

$$3{,}750 = 1{,}427(0.6)[1 + 0.902(2.88)] = 3{,}080,$$

which shows that a new value of $P/P_{cr} = 0.7$ should be tried. The $\sec \pi/2 \sqrt{0.7} = 3.92$ from Figure P11.5b. Putting these values in Equation (b) gives

$$3{,}750 = 1{,}427(0.7)[1 + 0.902(3.92)] = 4{,}540.$$

A linear interpolation of the values so far calculated suggests a trial of $P/P_{cr} = 0.65$. The $\sec \pi/2 \sqrt{0.65} = 3.35$. Then Equation (b) becomes

$$3{,}750 = 1{,}425(0.65)[1 + 0.902(3.35)] = 3{,}740.$$

This solution of Equation (b) is close enough. Therefore,

$$\frac{P}{P_{cr}} = 0.65 \quad \text{and} \quad P = 0.65(34{,}200) = 22{,}200 \text{ lb.}$$

The eccentrically loaded column ($e = \frac{1}{2}$ in.) will carry, for maximum elastic conditions, only 65 per cent of the critical buckling load for pivot end conditions. Do not conclude that this load is the maximum load that can be applied to the column before collapse. The column will collapse at a higher load after considerable plastic strain has occurred; however, the calculation of the actual collapse load for eccentrically loaded columns is beyond the scope of this book*.

---

* *Inelastic Behavior of Load-Carrying Members*, J. O. Smith and O. M. Sidebottom, John Wiley and Sons, New York, 1965, pp. 177–193.

PART (3).   The deflection of the eccentrically loaded column ($e = \frac{1}{2}$ in.), when the maximum elastic load $P = 22,200$ lb is applied, is given by Equation (11–9):

$$\Delta = e\left(\sec\frac{\pi}{2}\sqrt{\frac{P}{P_{cr}}} - 1\right),$$

$$= 0.5(3.35 - 1),$$

$$= 1.18 \text{ in.}$$

Problems

11.6.   A pivot-ended column has a circular cross section with a diameter of 2 in. The column is made of low carbon structural steel which has a proportional limit of 36,000 psi. What maximum length may the column have if the critical buckling load must not exceed 30,000 lb?

ans. $\ell = 88.0$ in.

11.7.   Determine the dimensions of the square cross section of a pivot-ended oak timber column 24-ft long to resist a safe axial load of 18,000 lb. Use a factor of safety of 8, which means that the critical buckling load is to be 8 times the given load. The material properties for the oak are given in Table 1.1; assume that the proportional limit for the oak is 0.9 of the yield strength. Justify the use of Euler's formula by showing that P_{cr}/A is less than the proportional limit of the oak.

11.8.   A rectangular section column has cross sectional dimensions of 3-in. by 4-in. and has a length of 60 in. The column is made of an aluminum alloy for which the modulus of elasticity is 10,800,000 psi and the proportional limit is 34,000 psi. The column is eccentrically loaded with $e/r = 0.1$ where r is the radius of gyration with respect to a centroidal axis parallel to the 4-in. dimension. Using the method of solution of Problem 11.5, determine the magnitude of P at which yielding would be initiated in the column.

ans. $P_{cr}/A = 22,200$ psi; $P = 0.786$; $P_{cr} = 209,000$ lb.

11.9.   A 4-ft long column with rectangular cross section is made of a high strength steel. The column has pivot ends and buckles elastically when an axial load causes an average compressive stress in the column of 30,000 psi. If one side of the cross section is 3 in., determine the length of the other side, and the critical buckling load.

11.10.   Three axially loaded pivot ended columns have the same cross-sectional areas of 2 in.^{2}, have the same length of 30 in., and are made of 7075-T5 aluminum alloy ($E = 10,400,000$ psi and $\sigma_{PL} = 65,000$ psi). Determine the critical buckling load for each of the columns if their cross sections are either solid square, solid circular, or hollow circular with inside diameter of $\frac{1}{2}$ in.

11.11. It is necessary to design a pivot-ended structural steel column that has a length of 87 in. and must carry a load of 14,500 lb, with a factor of safety of 2.5. Determine the dimensions of a rolled-steel equal-leg angle section from the appropriate table in Appendix B that will satisfy the design conditions. Justify the use of Euler's formula by showing that P_{cr}/A is less than the proportional limit of the steel.

ans.   Use 3-in. by 3-in. by $\frac{1}{2}$-in. angle. $P_{cr}/A = 13,180$ psi.

11.12. A spruce airplane compression member is 66-in. long and has an elliptical cross section with major and minor diameters of $b = 4$ in. and $a = 1.5$ in., respectively. Calculate the slenderness ratio of the column. If Euler's formula is applicable, calculate the safe axial load that this column will stand as a pivot-ended column using a factor of safety of 3.0. Assume that $E = 1,600,000$ psi. The moment of inertia about the major diameter b is $\pi b a^3/64 = 0.663$ in.^{4} and $A = \pi a b/4 = 4.71$ in.^{2}

ans. $\ell/r = 176; P_w = 800$ lb.

11.13. Select a structural steel I-section (see Appendix B) to serve as a column 20-ft long to resist an axial load of 60,000 lb. Use a factor of safety of 4, and assume the column to have pivot ends. Justify the use of Euler's formula by showing that P_{cr}/A is less than the proportional limit of the material.

11.14. An extruded T-section pivot ended column is made of 2024-T4 aluminum alloy. It has a length of 40 in., has a flange width of 2 in., has a depth of 2.25 in., and has flange and web thicknesses of 0.25 in. Material properties are $E = 10,000,000$ psi and $\sigma_{PL} = 34,000$ psi. Determine the slenderness ratio for the column and the critical buckling load.

11.15. Two 5-in. by 3.50-in. by 0.50-in. structural steel angles (see Appendix B) are welded together to form a box section pivot ended column having external dimensions of 5-in. by 4-in. The column length is 20 ft. Assume that the cross-sectional area of the welded material is negligible. Determine the slenderness ratio for the column and the critical buckling load. Justify the use of Euler's formula.

ans. $\ell/r = 162; P_{cr} = 89,900$ lb; $P_{cr}/A = 11,240$ psi.

11.4.   Columns with General End Conditions

The most general end conditions for a column are indicated in Figure 11.8a where the bending moment M_B has been assumed to have a greater magnitude than M_A, for convenience in the following discussion. The deformations of the column have been exaggerated in order that they may be observed. The inflection points, points of zero moment, for the column are indicated by points C and D. The column has been redrawn in Figure

492

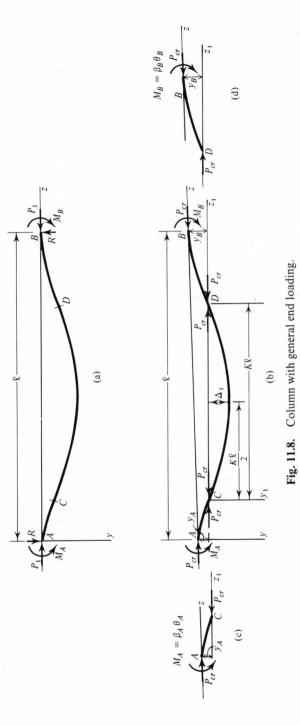

Fig. 11.8. Column with general end loading.

11.8b where the z_1-axis is located through points C and D with origin at C. Because the bending moment is zero at points C and D, the compression loads being transmitted through the column at points C and D must have their lines of action collinear with the z_1-axis as indicated in Figure 11.8b and have the same magnitude. The reaction R in Figure 11.8a is of sufficient magnitude so that the resultant of forces P_1 and R at either A or B is the force P_{cr} whose action line is parallel to the z_1-axis as indicated in Figure 11.8b. In most column problems, M_A and M_B are small quantities so that R is small compared to P_1, and P_1 is assumed to be equal to P_{cr}. It is seen from Figures 11.8c and d that

$$M_A = P_{cr}y_A,$$
$$M_B = P_{cr}y_B.$$

The remaining elastically restrained column problems considered in this book will be those for which moments M_A and M_B in Figure 11.8 are caused by rotational springs at the ends of the column with spring constants β_A and β_B having dimensions of inch-pounds per radian; that is, $M_A = \beta_A\theta_A$ where θ_A is the angle change at the end of the column measured with respect to the z-axis.

The problem here is to determine the critical buckling load for the column in Figure 11.8 assuming that it is elastically restrained. The portion of the column from C to D is an axially loaded column with pivot ends; the load $P_1 = P_{cr}$ necessary to hold this portion of the column in equilibrium with center deflection Δ_1 is given by Equation (11–4) if length ℓ in Equation (11–4) is replaced by length $K\ell*$:

$$P_{cr} = \frac{\pi^2 EI_x}{(K\ell)^2} \qquad \frac{P_{cr}}{A} = \frac{\pi^2 E}{(K\ell/r)^2}. \qquad (11\text{–}12)$$

Length $K\ell$ is called the *effective length* of the column.

The lateral deflection Δ of the center of a pivot ended column was found to be indeterminate. In other words the collapse load given by Euler's formula (Eqs. 11–4 or 11–5) is valid for all values of Δ as long as Δ is small compared to the length ℓ of the column. If Equation (11–12) gives the critical buckling load for the elastically restrained column, the magnitude of P_{cr} given by Equation (11–12) must be independent of Δ_1. This is shown to be true in the following paragraph.

---

* Later in this section it is demonstrated that $K(K^2 = P_{cr}/P)$ in Equation (11–9) can be interpreted as the ratio of the length $K\ell$ of a pivot ended column to the actual length ℓ of the eccentrically loaded column such that P_{cr} for the pivot-ended column is equal to P for the eccentrically loaded column.

The deflected shape of length CD of the elastically restrained column in Figure 11.8b is given by Equation (11–10):

$$y_1 = \Delta_1 \sin \frac{\pi z_1}{K\ell}. \tag{11–13}$$

Note that the loading on the portion of the column to the left of inflection point C is identical to that to the right of point C and that the loading on the portion of the column to the right of inflection point D is identical to that to the left of point D; therefore, Equation (11–13) is valid from A to B. The assumption—that points C and D are fixed points along the column (K = constant)—satisfies the boundary conditions and indicates that these boundary conditions are independent of Δ_1. As long as Δ_1 is small, the angle change θ_A at A is equal to the slope dy/dz at A. But y_A, y_B, and θ_B are directly proportional to Δ_1 because K is a constant. Free-body diagrams of lengths AC and BD of the elastically restrained column are shown in Figures 11.8c and d, respectively. Equilibrium of these free-body diagrams requires that $P_{cr}y_A = \beta_A\theta_A$ and $P_{cr}y_B = \beta_B\theta_B$. Because both of these relations are independent of Δ_1, K is a constant and the critical buckling load is given by Equation (11–12).

We can show that Equation (11–13) is valid also for the eccentrically loaded column in Figure 11.9a, although in this case K is not independent of Δ_1. Let the z_1-axis coincide with the action line of the loads P. Extend the

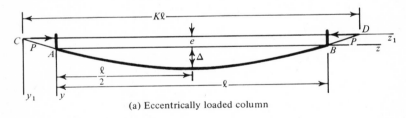

(a) Eccentrically loaded column

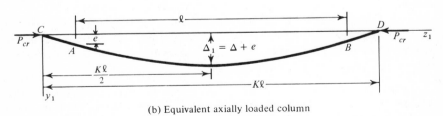

(b) Equivalent axially loaded column

Fig. 11.9.   Eccentrically loaded column and equivalent axially loaded column.

sine curve until it intersects the z_1-axis at inflection points C and D at a distance $K\ell$ apart. The load P necessary to produce a center deflection Δ of the eccentrically loaded column in Figure 11.9a is equal to P_{cr} given by Equation (11–12) for the pivot ended column in Figure 11.9b for deflection $\Delta_1 = e + \Delta$. It is seen that, because points A and B are fixed points along the column and e is a constant, the length $K\ell$ will depend on the magnitude of Δ_1. It is possible to derive Equation (11–9), starting with Equation (11–13). It is found that K in Equation (11–13) is the same as K in Equation (11–9).

Other than the eccentrically loaded column (equal eccentricities at each end) considered in Section 11.3, for which the deflection of the column is determinate, the only additional end conditions considered in this chapter are those illustrated in Figure 11.10 for which the deflection of the column is indeterminate. The critical buckling load P_{cr} is applied to each column to hold it in equilibrium for the deflected configuration. The problem in each case is to determine the magnitude of K to substitute in Equations (11–12).

(1) Figure 11.10a represents the axially loaded pivot-ended column for which $K = 1$.

(2) Figure 11.10b represents a fixed-ended column; the ends are restrained so that the tangents to the elastic curve at the ends are parallel to the original axis (z-axis) of the column. The points of inflection, C and D, are at a distance $\ell/4$ from each end; therefore, for the fixed ended column $K = \frac{1}{2}$.

(3) Figure 11.10c represents a column with one end fixed and the other end free from all restraints. One inflection point for the column is at A so that points A and C coincide. The other point D is at a distance 2ℓ from C so that $K = 2$.

(4) Figure 11.10d represents a column with one end fixed and one end pivot-ended. One inflection point for the column is at A so that points A and C coincide. The other inflection point D is at a distance 0.7ℓ from C so that $K = 0.7$. This value for K can be derived using Equation (11–13). The deflection y_B with respect to the z_1-axis is given by Equation (11–13) when $z_1 = \ell$:

$$y_B = \Delta_1 \sin \frac{\pi}{K}.$$

The slope of the column at B with respect to the z_1-axis is obtained by the differentiation of Equation (11–13) with respect to z_1, which gives

$$\left.\frac{dy_1}{dz_1}\right|_{z_1=\ell} = \frac{\Delta_1 \pi}{K\ell} \cos \frac{\pi}{K}.$$

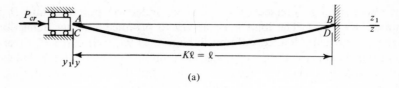

(a)

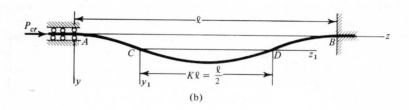

(b)

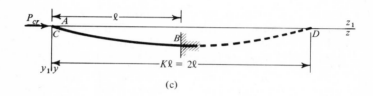

(c)

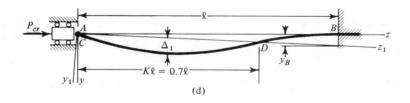

(d)

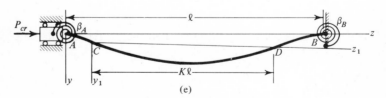

(e)

Fig. 11.10.   Columns with various end conditions.

Because the column is tangent to the z-axis at B,

$$\frac{\Delta_1 \pi}{K\ell} \cos \frac{\pi}{K} = \frac{y_B}{\ell} = \frac{\Delta_1}{\ell} \sin \frac{\pi}{K},$$

which reduces to

$$\tan \frac{\pi}{K} = \frac{\pi}{K} = 4.493$$

and

$$K = 0.699,$$

which is approximately equal to 0.7.

(5) Figure 11.10e represents the most general end loading for which the deflection of the column is indeterminate. When general loading is considered in the problems to follow, the magnitude of K will be given. Methods of determining K when $\beta_A = \beta_B$ or when $\beta_A = 0$ ($\beta_B \neq 0$) are considered in Section 11.7.

Problems

11.16. A solid circular steel column has fixed ends, has a length of 100 in., and must support a compression load of 9,000 lb. Determine the minimum required diameter using a factor of safety of 2.0. What is the minimum value of the proportional limit for the steel in order for the column to buckle at a stress P_{cr}/A less than the proportional limit?

11.17. Four yellow pine boards 1-in. by 5-in. (see Table 1.1 for properties) are nailed together to form a 6-in. by 6-in. column which is fixed at one end and pivot-ended at the other end. If the column is 25-ft long, determine the critical buckling load. What is the minimum value of the proportional limit for the yellow pine in order for the column to buckle at a stress P_{cr}/A less than the proportional limit?

ans. $K\ell/r = 101$; $P_{cr} = 34{,}900$ lb; $\sigma_{PL} \geq P_{cr}/A = 1{,}740$ psi.

11.18. In Figure P11.18 a rigid weightless bar AB is pivoted at A. When $Q = 0$, bar AB is horizontal and the two columns C and D are of such lengths as to fit exactly in the space between AB and the supporting base. Both columns are made of aluminum ($E = 10{,}000{,}000$ psi) and have the same circular cross section with diameter of 4 in. Column C has pivot ends while column D is fixed at the bottom and has a pivot end at the top. Determine the least magnitude of Q to cause one of the columns to buckle.

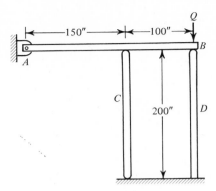

Fig. P 11.18.

11.19. A pivot ended rectangular section column 6-ft long has the cross-sectional dimensions shown in Figure P11.19. The column is braced at midlength in the direction of the least dimension; the brace prevents deflection in the x-direction but does not offer any resistance either to deflection in the y-direction or to rotation of the column

Fig. P 11.19.

about the y-axis. The modulus of elasticity and the proportional limit for the material for which the column is made are 10,000,000 psi and 40,000 psi, respectively. Determine the critical buckling load using Euler's formula. Justify the use of this equation. (*Hint:* the deflected configuration of the column is two lobes of a sine curve if it deflects in the x-direction but is only one lobe of a sine curve if it deflects in the y-direction.)

ans. $P_{cr} = 85,700$ lb; $P_{cr}/A = 14,300$ psi.

11.20. A timber column has a length of 20 ft and rectangular cross section with dimensions of 4-in. by 6-in. The modulus of elasticity and proportional limit for the wood are 1,200,000 psi and 3,000 psi, respectively. The column has pivot ends if the column deflects in a direction parallel to the 6-in. dimension and is partially restrained such that $K = 0.6$ if the column deflects in a direction parallel to the 4-in. dimension. Determine the maximum allowable load for the column based on a factor of safety of 3.0.

11.21. A column has a length of 200 in. and the cross section shown in Figure P11.21. The column is made of an aluminum alloy for which $E = 10,000,000$ psi. The column has pivot ends for bending about the x-axis but is partially restrained for

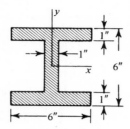

Fig. P 11.21.

bending about the y-axis so that $K = 0.75$. Determine the Euler buckling load for the column.

ans. $P_{cr} = 159,000$ lb.

11.22. A water tank is located at the top of a hollow steel pipe which has an outside diameter of 12 in. and an inside diameter of 10 in. The proportional limit of the steel is 40,000 psi. The center of gravity of the filled tank is 25 ft above the base of the pipe where it is fixed. Neglecting the weight of the pipe and assuming elastic conditions, determine the maximum allowable weight W of the tank plus water based on a factor of safety of 2.5. Is the assumption that Euler's formula is applicable a valid assumption?

ans. $W = 173,000$ lb; $P_{cr}/A = 12,500$ psi.

11.23. In order to increase the elevation of the water tank in Problem 11.22, guy wires are attached to the water tank to prevent any horizontal deflection of the tank. If the component of the load in the guy wires along the pipe is negligible, determine the distance between the base of the tank and the center of gravity of the filled tank if $W = 173,000$ lb and the factor of safety is 2.5.

11.24. The rigid plate in Figure P11.24 weighs 4,000 lb and is supported by four square steel columns 2 in. on a side. The columns are fixed to the plate and are fixed at their lower ends. The four steel guy wires prevent the plate from deflecting horizontally when the plate is loaded. Before loading the plate, the stress in each wire is 30,000 psi. The cross-sectional area of each guy wire is 0.40 in.² Determine the magnitude of load Q which, when applied to the center of the plate, causes the four columns to buckle. What is the stress σ in each guy wire at the buckling load?

ans. $P_{cr}/A = 12,200$ psi; $\sigma = 26,300$ psi; $Q = 166,000$ lb.

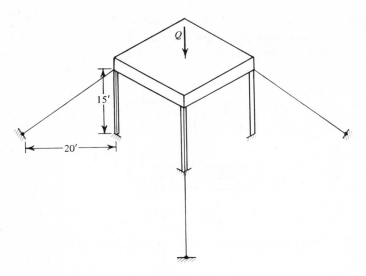

Fig. P 11.24.

11.5.   Plastic Buckling—Tangent Modulus Buckling Load

The only material property required to determine the critical buckling load for a column made of a linearly elastic material is the modulus of elasticity E. Euler's formula as indicated by Equations (11–12) was used to construct curve GBC in Figure 11.11 for columns made of 2024-T4 aluminum alloy for which $E = 10,800,000$ psi; the stress-strain diagram of this material is shown in Figure 11.12 and indicates that the proportional limit of the material is 27,000 psi, also occurring at point B in Figure 11.11. Hence, when $K\ell/r$ is sufficiently small (less than 60 in Fig. 11.11, say) the average stress in the column will be greater than the proportional limit of the material before the critical buckling load is reached. Because point B in Figure 11.11 corresponds to an average of 27,000 psi, the portion BC of the curve is dashed and hence this portion of the curve is not applicable for columns made of 2024-T4 aluminum alloy. Our problem in this section is to derive a theory for determining the critical buckling load P_{cr} for columns having small values of $K\ell/r$. This theory, given later in this section, called the tangent modulus formula, $P_T/A = \pi^2 E_T/(K\ell/r)^2$, was used to obtain the values of P_{cr}/A as given by the ordinates to curve BD in Figure 11.11.

The tangent modulus at any point on the compressive stress-strain curve, such as point F in Figure 11.12, is the slope $E_T = \Delta\sigma/\Delta\epsilon$ of a line

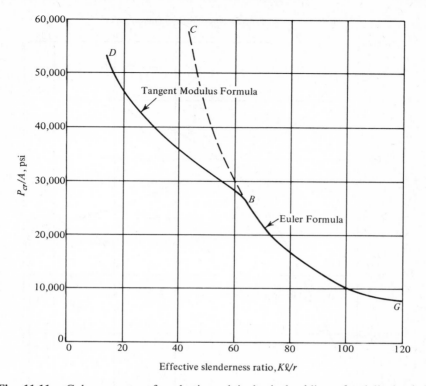

Fig. 11.11. Column curves for elastic and inelastic buckling of axially loaded columns made of 2024-T4 aluminum alloy.

drawn tangent to the curve at F. The horizontal scale at the top of Figure 11.12 represents E_T and the curve $O'G'B'F'D'$ represents the values of E_T for all levels of the stress. The shape of curve $B'F'D'$ in Figure 11.12 is greatly influenced by the accuracy of the values of E_T that are obtained from the slope of the compressive stress-strain diagram for small inelastic strains such as the points in the neighborhood of F in Figure 11.12. Great care must be exercised in determining the compressive stress-strain diagram of the material if accurate determination of the values of E_T, and hence of the inelastic buckling loads of columns made of the material are required.

The critical buckling load for inelastically deformed columns is defined by the bifurcation point in the load-deflection diagram as indicated by point B in Figure 11.7. An ideally straight column would load along OBD; however, at point B even an infinitesimal side force would cause the load-deflection diagram to be horizontal at B and tangent to BC. The column is

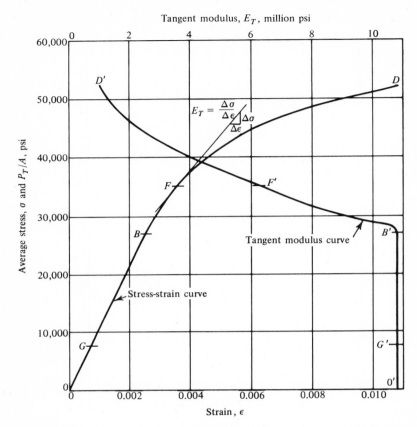

Fig. 11.12. Compression stress-strain diagram and tangent modulus for 2024-T4 aluminum alloy.

in neutral equilibrium for small deflections (i.e., for a short distance along *BC* in Fig. 11.7) at the critical buckling load and then becomes unstable due to the fact that the stiffness of the material as indicated by the slope of the stress-strain diagram in Figure 11.12 continues to decrease with an increase in the inelastic strain.

The actual load-deflection diagram for a real column that was loaded axially is indicated in Figure 11.13 for a fixed-ended column having a rectangular section and made of 2024-T4 aluminum alloy whose stress-strain diagram is shown in Figure 11.12; the average stress in the column is plotted versus Δ/r where Δ is the maximum lateral deflection at the center of the column and r is the minimum radius of gyration. The column was tested as a

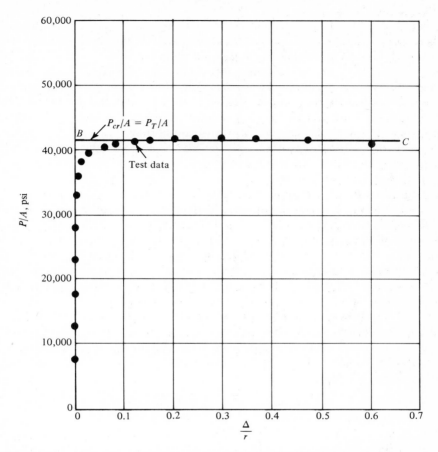

Fig. 11.13. Comparison between tangent modulus buckling load and test data for fixed-ended column made of 2024-T4 aluminum alloy ($K\ell/r = 28.7$).

fixed-ended column. The magnitude of $K\ell/r$ was only 28.7, which is much smaller than $K\ell/r = 65$ at the point B in Figure 11.11 where the transition from elastic buckling to inelastic buckling occurs. Using the tangent modulus theory developed later in this section, the bifurcation point for the column is at point B in Figure 11.13. The actual load-deflection data did not follow path OBC but followed a curve similar to one of the curves in Figure 11.7 for an eccentrically loaded column for which the eccentricity is small. It is possible to derive load-deflection curves for eccentricity loaded inelastically deformed columns; however, the theory is beyond the scope of this book*. The load-deflection curve in Figure 11.13 indicates stable or neutral equilibrium until $\Delta/r = 0.4$. For larger deflections the load-deflection diagram falls off indicating unstable equilibrium.

In deriving the tangent modulus theory, we assume that the load-deflection curve for all real inelastically deformed columns follow curves similar to the one indicated in Figure 11.13. Consider the axially loaded column in Figure 11.14a. Let the maximum deflection Δ have its smallest value such that the column is in neutral equilibrium. We assume that the deflection has been increasing with the load P and that the stress on the concave side of the column has not decreased in magnitude when $P_{cr} = P_T$ is reached. The stress distribution in the column at the critical buckling load is shown in Figure 11.14a with the stress at the centroid given by σ_C. A tangent to the stress-strain diagram at point C in Figure 11.14b has a slope called the tangent modulus and designated as E_T. The straight line with slope E_T represents the stress-strain relation for the material at every point in the column as long as Δ is sufficiently small so that the maximum and minimum stresses in the column fall within the range of tangency between the line with slope E_T and the actual stress-strain diagram. For sufficiently small values of Δ, the stress-strain relation for the material in the inelastically deformed column is linear as it was for Euler's elastic solution. The critical buckling load for a pivot-ended inelastically deformed column is given by Equation (11–4) if E is replaced by E_T. For more general end conditions the critical buckling load $P_{cr} = P_T$ is given by Equations (11–12) if E is replaced by E_T. Thus,

$$P_T = \frac{\pi^2 E_T I_x}{(K\ell)^2} \qquad \text{or} \qquad \frac{P_T}{A} = \frac{\pi^2 E_T}{[K(\ell/r)]^2}. \qquad (11\text{–}14)$$

The tangent modulus load given by Equations (11–14) is the lower bound to the actual critical buckling load and is therefore conservative. The error in most cases is insignificant as indicated for the fixed-ended column in Figure 11.13.

An upper bound to the critical buckling load for inelastically deformed columns is obtained if we assume that the column remains straight up to the critical buckling load at point B in Figure 11.7. All of the material in the column has yielded at this load. Now give the column a small lateral deflection. The critical buckling load will hold the column in neutral equilibrium for the deflected configuration. On the concave side of the column the strains increase and the resulting stress-strain relation is given by the tangent

* See pp. 177–193 *Inelastic Behavior of Load-Carrying Members*, J. O. Smith and O. M. Sidebottom, 1965, John Wiley and Sons, New York.

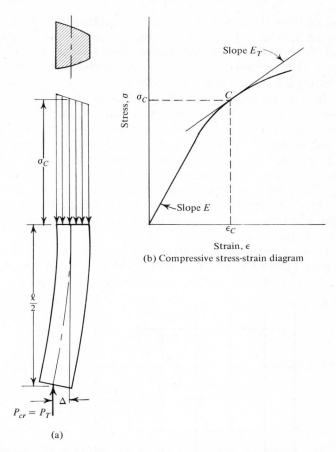

Fig. 11.14.   Stress distribution for tangent modulus buckling load.

modulus E_T. On the convex side of the column the strains decrease and the resulting stress-strain relation is given by the modulus of elasticity E because the material is assumed to unload elastically. The critical buckling load depends on the magnitudes of both E and E_T and the theory is called the double modulus theory. Because the double modulus theory is nonconservative, it is little used and its derivation will not be given here*.

   Trial-and-Error Solution.   The use of Equations (11–14) to obtain the tangent modulus buckling load for a column with given $K\ell/r$ and made of

* See pp. 599–602 *Advanced Mechanics of Materials*, F. B. Seely and J. O. Smith, 2nd Ed., 1952, John Wiley and Sons, New York.

a given material requires a trial-and-error solution for the reasons that E_T cannot be selected until P_T/A is known. Equations (11–14) can best be satisfied for a given compressive stress-strain diagram such as that shown in Figure 11.12 by determining the tangent modulus at several stress levels and plotting a curve of tangent modulus versus stress as indicated in Figure 11.12. By reading off corresponding values of stress (P_T/A) and tangent modulus (E_T) from the curve in Figure 11.12 to substitute in Equations (11–14) a curve of P_T/A versus $K\ell/r$ can be constructed as shown by the curve BD in Figure 11.11. This curve can be used in the design of axially loaded columns having any cross section (assuming that no local buckling occurs) and made of this particular material. Note that every bar of 2024-T4 will not have the same compressive stress-strain diagram as that given in Figure 11.12. A curve similar to that shown in Figure 11.11 must be constructed when the stress-strain diagram has a shape different from that shown in Figure 11.12.

One of our most common structural metals is low carbon or structural grade steel. Euler's formula (Eqs. 11–14) with $E = 30,000,000$ psi determines curve GBFC in Figure 11.15a; corresponding points on the stress-strain

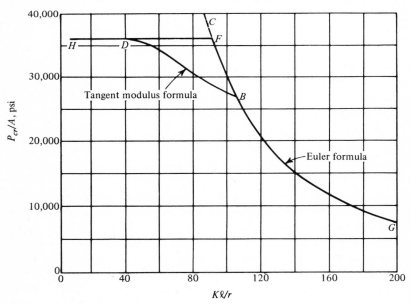

(a) Dimensionless critical buckling load curves

Fig. 11.15a.

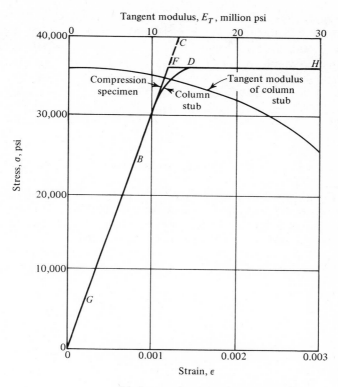

(b) Compressive stress-strain diagram

Fig. 11.15b.

diagram are labeled G, B, F, and C in Figure 11.15b. If the stress-strain diagram for this steel is a straight line up to the lower yield point of 36,000 psi at which stress the steel yields as shown by the curve $OGBFDH$ in Figure 11.15b, the tangent modulus is zero when yielding is initiated as shown by the horizontal line FDH in Figure 11.15b, and the relation between P_{cr}/A and $K\ell/r$ in Figure 11.15a is given by the curve $GBFDH$ and is flat topped from F to H at $P_{cr}/A = 36,000$ psi. Many low carbon steel columns have been hot rolled into angle sections, I-sections, and H-sections. The hot forming and quenching processes introduce into the member locked in residual stresses. These residual stresses are both tensile and compressive because the resultant force transmitted through a section of the member when the member is unloaded must be zero. If a short stub is cut off one end of the column and is tested as a compression specimen, the load stresses add to the compressive residual stresses to initiate yielding when the load stress is appreciably below the lower yield point. The resulting stress-strain diagram is indicated in Figure 11.15b by curve $OGBDH$. Substituting corresponding values of $\sigma = P_T/A$ and E_T in Equations (11–14) gives the curve BDH in Figure 11.15a. Note that the tangent modulus curve BDH in Figure 11.15a for the low carbon steel is more nearly horizontal than was the case for the 2024-T4 aluminum alloy as shown by the curve BD in Figure 11.11.

Illustrative Problem

11.25. The column in Figure P11.25 has a length of 45 in., has a rectangular cross section 2-in. by 3-in., is made of 2024-T4 aluminum alloy, and is loaded through frictionless pins. Calculate the maximum load that the column can withstand if the factor of safety is 2.0.

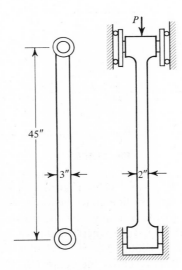

Fig. P 11.25.

SOLUTION. It is necessary first to determine the direction the column will deflect when it buckles. The column buckles in a direction perpendicular to the axis for which $K\ell/r$ is a maximum because the larger value gives the least buckling load. The column has pivot ends with $K = 1$ if it deflects in the direction of the 3-in. dimension:

$$r = \sqrt{\frac{I}{A}} = \sqrt{\frac{bh^3}{12bh}} = \frac{h}{2\sqrt{3}} = \frac{\sqrt{3}}{2}$$

$$\frac{K\ell}{r} = \frac{45(2)}{\sqrt{3}} = 52.0.$$

The column has fixed ends with $K = \frac{1}{2}$ if it deflects in the direction of the 2-in. dimension:

$$r = \frac{h}{2\sqrt{3}} = \frac{1}{\sqrt{3}}$$

$$\frac{K\ell}{r} = \frac{45\sqrt{3}}{2} = 39.0.$$

Thus, the column buckles as a pivot ended column with $K\ell/r = 52.0$. Entering Figure 11.11 with $K\ell/r = 52.0$, we read

$$\frac{P_{cr}}{A} = 31,500 \text{ psi},$$

$$P_{cr} = 189,000 \text{ lb}.$$

The working load is

$$P = \frac{P_{cr}}{N} = 94,500 \text{ lb}.$$

Problems

11.26. The fixed-ended 2024-T4 aluminum alloy axially loaded column whose load-deflection data are shown in Figure 11.13 has cross-sectional dimensions of 0.475-in. by 0.494-in. If $P_{cr}/A = 41,000$ psi for this column, determine the length of the column.

ans. $\ell = 7.87$ in.

11.27. A 8-in. by 8-in., 34.4 lb/ft H-section made of structural steel is used as a pivot-ended column in a building. A steel handbook gives the following properties for the cross section; $A = 10.09$ in.^{2}, $I_{max} = 115.4$ in.^{4}, and $I_{min} = 35.1$ in.^{4} If the length of the column is 15 ft, it has pivot ends, and the stress-strain curve for a stub cut off the end of the column is as shown by the curve $OGBDH$ in Figure 11.15b, what is the buckling load for the column?

ans. $K\ell/r = 96.5$; $P_{cr} = 282,000$ lb.

11.28.   Determine the buckling load for the *H*-section column in Problem 11.27 if the column has pivot ends for bending about the axis with maximum moment of inertia and is partially restrained with $K = 0.65$ for bending about the axis with minimum moment of inertia.

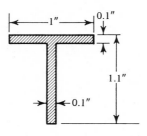

Fig. P 11.29.

11.29.   A T-section fixed ended axially loaded column of 2024-T4 aluminum alloy has the cross-sectional dimensions shown in Figure P11.29. If the column has a length of 15 in., determine the maximum load that can be applied to the column based on a factor of safety of 2.0.

ans. $K\ell/r = 36.6$; $P = 3,770$ lb.

11.30.   It is found that the compressive stress-strain diagram of a given material can be approximated by the equation $\sigma = 10^5 \sqrt{\epsilon}$ over a range of stress that is of interest in designing columns made of this material. Determine the buckling load of an axially loaded pivot-ended column 80-in. long which has a solid square cross section 2 in. on a side.

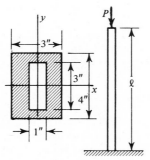

Fig. P 11.31.

11.31.   An axially loaded column has the cross section shown in Figure P11.31, and is made of a material whose compressive stress-strain diagram can be assumed to be given by the relation $\sigma = 10^5 \epsilon^{1/3}$ in the stress range of interest. The column is fixed at the bottom; however, the upper end is free to deflect in any direction. Determine the maximum length that the column can have if the buckling load is $P_{cr} = 90,000$ lb.

ans. $E_T = 3,333,000$ psi; $\ell = 28.3$ in.

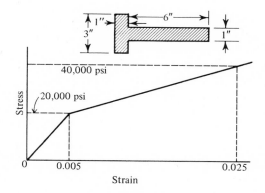

Stress — Strain

40,000 psi

20,000 psi

0   0.005   0.025

Fig. P 11.32.

11.32. A fixed-ended column has a length of 18 in. The T-shaped cross section of the column and the compressive stress-strain diagram of the material are shown in Figure P11.32. Calculate the maximum compressive load the column can withstand with a factor of safety of 2.5.

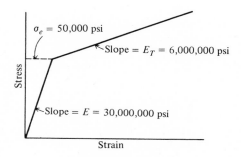

$\sigma_e = 50,000$ psi

Slope $= E_T = 6,000,000$ psi

Slope $= E = 30,000,000$ psi

Stress — Strain

Fig. P 11.33.

11.33. A pivot-ended column has a circular cross section with a diameter of 2 in. The column is made of a steel whose compressive stress-strain diagram is shown in Figure P11.33. Note that the proportional limit of the material is 50,000 psi. The average stress in the column is approximately 50,000 psi when it buckles. The length ℓ of the column is unknown and the problem is to find the length ℓ. Consider two cases and determine ℓ for each case. (1) The average stress is slightly higher than 50,000 psi. (2) The average stress is slightly lower than 50,000 psi.

11.6. Empirical Column Formulas

Most axially loaded columns of practical importance will fail by buckling only after inelastic behavior of the material has occurred. An analytical theory for the design of these columns was derived in Section 11.5 as the tangent modulus theory. Because of the trial-and-error solution required to obtain the tangent modulus buckling load, the design of columns using the tangent modulus theory is most easily accomplished by constructing a P_{cr}/A versus $K\ell/r$ curve (e.g., see Figs. 11.11 and 11.15) for each compressive stress-strain diagram. Each design engineer must be supplied with the particular P_{cr}/A versus $K\ell/r$ curve that is valid for the material used in manufacturing the columns he is asked to design.

Instead of using a P_{cr}/A versus $K\ell/r$ curve in the design of columns, many engineers prefer to approximate the portion of the curve of interest to them by a simple equation and use the equation in the design of columns. The resulting equation is an empirical formula since it approximates either the actual test data or the tangent modulus formula and perhaps part of the Euler formula for the given material.

Three different empirical column formulas are generally used as follows:

$$\frac{P_{cr}}{A} = \sigma_0 - C\left(\frac{K\ell}{r}\right) \qquad \text{(straight line)} \qquad (11\text{--}15)$$

$$\frac{P_{cr}}{A} = \frac{\sigma_0}{1 + C(K\ell/r)^2} \qquad \text{(Gordon–Rankine)} \qquad (11\text{--}16)$$

$$\frac{P_{cr}}{A} = \sigma_0 - C\left(\frac{K\ell}{r}\right)^2 \qquad \text{(parabolic)} \qquad (11\text{--}17)$$

These equations are known by the names shown in parentheses after each equation. The magnitudes of σ_0 and C in each equation depend on both the equation used (Eqs. 11–15, 11–16, or 11–17) and the shape of the compressive stress-strain diagram.

The empirical constants σ_0 and C in Equations (11–15), (11–16), and (11–17) are obtained by fitting the given equation to axially loaded column test data. As an example, consider curve GBDH in Figure 11.15a for rolled

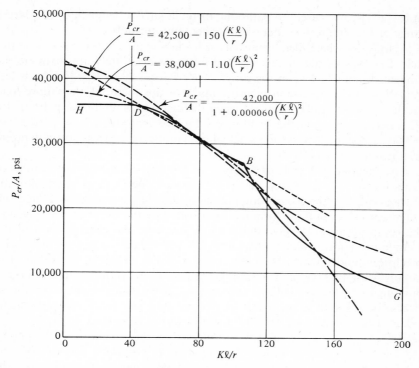

Fig. 11.16. Comparison of the Euler-tangent modulus column formulas and empirical column formulas for structural steel rolled sections.

sections of structural steel. Curve *GBDH* is a plot of the Euler and the tangent modulus formulas; however, axially loaded column test data will be found to be accurately approximated by this curve. The curve is redrawn in Figure 11.16 and is indicated by the solid curve.

The straight-line column formula (Eq. 11–15) is indicated in Figure 11.16 by the dotted curve where $\sigma_0 = 42,500$ psi and $C = 150$ psi. Note that this formula is limited to the range of $K\ell/r$ from 40 to 105.

The Gordon–Rankine column formula (Eq. 11–16) is shown in Figure 11.16 by the dashed curve where $\sigma_0 = 42,000$ psi and $C = 0.000060$. Although the Gordon–Rankine column formula has the same general shape as curve *GBD*, good fit can generally be accomplished only over a limited range of $K\ell/r$.

The parabolic column formula given by Equation (11–17) is shown in Figure 11.16 by the dash-dot curve where $\sigma_0 = 38,000$ psi and $C = 1.10$ psi.

In this particular case, the parabolic formula gave a better fit over a larger range of $K\ell/r$ than the other empirical column formulas.

Note that the Euler formula is valid in Figure 11.16 for $K\ell/r$ greater than 105. Any of the three empirical formulas accurately approximate the tangent modulus curve in the range of $K\ell/r$ from 40 to 105. If $K\ell/r$ is less than 40 for a compression member made of this material, the failure load for the member can be obtained using the load-stress relation (see Eq. 1–10) $P = \sigma_e A$ where σ_e is the yield stress for the material which is equal to 36,000 psi for the low carbon steel whose compressive stress-strain diagram is shown in Figure 11.15b.

Application of Factor of Safety. In the empirical column formulas of Equations (11–15), (11–16), and (11–17), the value of P_{cr}/A represents the average stress on the cross section of the column at the critical buckling load. Often both sides of these formulas are divided by the factor of safety N, and the resulting formulas give the average stress on the cross section of the column for working loads. The value of N will depend largely on the service conditions under which the column is used. For example, the value of N usually is about 2.00 for structural grade (low carbon) steel columns used in building or bridges, and it is usually about 1.5 for aluminum alloy or stainless steel columns used in the structure of some type of aircraft. Working loads can also be obtained by dividing the critical buckling load by the factor of safety. This will be the procedure followed in the problems at the end of this section. In each problem the appropriate empirical column formula will be specified (i.e., straight line, Gordon–Rankine, or parabolic) and the values of σ_0 and C valid for the given material will be given.

Illustrative Problem

11.34. Let a pivot-ended steel column be subjected to a load parallel to the longitudinal axis with a small eccentricity e such that the value of $ec/r^2 = 0.250$ (this value has been recommended by an ASCE Special Committee on Steel Column Research as an allowance for initial column crookedness and unintentional eccentricity). Let the steel have a compressive yield point of 36,000 psi. The maximum or ultimate load P for this column can be determined by making use of the secant formula (Eq. 11–11b), which gives the load that initiates yielding in the column and which, with the given data, is stated as follows:

$$36,000 = \frac{P}{A}\left[1 + 0.25 \sec \frac{K\ell}{r} \sqrt{\frac{P}{4AE}}\right]. \tag{a}$$

This equation is quite inconvenient to use in designing columns. (1) Make a graph of values of P/A versus $K\ell/r$ to represent Equation (a) if $E = 30 \times 10^6$ psi. (2) Choose the constants σ_0 and C in the parabolic formula

$$\frac{P}{A} = \sigma_0 - C\left(\frac{K\ell}{r}\right)^2 \qquad\qquad (b)$$

so that Equation (b) can be used instead of Equation (a) for computing values of P/A for values of $K\ell/r$ between 0 and 120. (3) Choose the constants σ_0 and C in the Gordon–Rankine formula

$$\frac{P}{A} = \frac{\sigma_0}{1 + C(K\ell/r)^2} \qquad\qquad (c)$$

to make it fit Equation (a) for values of $K\ell/r > 120$. (4) Apply a factor of safety of 1.8 to Equations (b) and (c) to obtain working load formulas for columns made of this material.

SOLUTION. PART (1). Equation (a) is used to calculate values of P/A when $K\ell/r$ is equal to 0, 120, and 200. These are found to be $P/A = 28,800$ psi when $K\ell/r = 0$, $P/A = 15,800$ psi when $K\ell/r = 120$, and $P/A = 6,800$ psi when $K\ell/r = 200$.

PART (2). Two sets of values of P/A and $K\ell/r$ are needed to determine the constants σ_0 and C in Equation (b). Points chosen were $P/A = 28,800$ psi for $K\ell/r = 0$ and $P/A = 15,800$ psi for $K\ell/r = 120$. The substitution of these two sets of values of P/A and $K\ell/r$ into Equation (b) gives two equations that are solved for $C = 0.903$ and $\sigma_0 = 28,800$ psi. Hence Equation (b) is as follows:

$$\frac{P}{A} = 28,800 - 0.903\left(\frac{K\ell}{r}\right)^2. \qquad\qquad (d)$$

The error in P/A computed from Equation (d) for values of $K\ell/r$ between 0 and 120 is not more than about 1 per cent when compared with the correct value from Equation (a).

PART (3). Two sets of values of P/A and $K\ell/r$ are chosen as before in Part (2). These were $P/A = 15,800$ psi for $K\ell/r = 120$ and $P/A = 6,800$ psi for $K\ell/r = 200$. The substitution of these two sets of values into Equation (c) gives two equations for obtaining the constants σ_0 and C, which are found to be $\sigma_0 = 61,800$ psi and $C = 0.000202$. Hence Equation (c) becomes

$$\frac{P}{A} = \frac{61,800}{1 + 0.000202(K\ell/r)^2}. \qquad\qquad (e)$$

The error in P/A computed from Equation (e) for values of $K\ell/r$ between 120 and 200 is not more than about 2 per cent when compared with the correct value found from Equation (a).

PART (4).   Working loads. The right sides of each of Equations (d) and (e) are divided by 1.8 and the equations that follow are obtained:

$$\frac{P_w}{A} = \frac{28,800}{1.8} - \frac{0.902}{1.8}\left(\frac{K\ell}{r}\right)^2 = 16,000 - 0.501\left(\frac{K\ell}{r}\right)^2 \qquad 0 \le \frac{K\ell}{r} \le 120 \tag{f}$$

and

$$\frac{P_w}{A} = \frac{34,300}{1 + 0.000202(K\ell/r)^2} \qquad\qquad 120 \le \frac{K\ell}{r} \le 200 \tag{g}$$

Problems

11.35.   A 2014-T6 aluminum alloy I-section 8-in. deep and weighing 8.81 lb/ft is used as a column having a length of 8 ft. The column has fixed ends. Use the straight-line column formula (Eq. 11–15) with $\sigma_0 = 64,700$ psi and $C = 543$. The structural aluminum handbook gives the following data for the I-section: $A = 7.49$ in.^{2}, $I_{max} = 68.73$ in.^{4}, $I_{min} = 4.66$ in.^{4}, $r_{max} = 3.03$ in., and $r_{min} = 0.79$ in. Calculate the allowable load for the column using a factor of safety of 2.0.

ans. $P_w = 118,700$ lb.

11.36.   A standard 12-in. 27.9-lb structural steel I-beam 9-ft long is used as an axially loaded column with pivot ends. Use the parabolic column formula (Eq. 11–17) with $\sigma_0 = 34,000$ psi and $C = 0.970$ psi. What is the allowable load for the column based on a factor of safety of 2.0? (See Appendix B.)

11.37.   A 6061-T6 aluminum alloy round tube 6-in. outside diameter and $\frac{1}{4}$-in. thick weighing 5.31 lb/ft is used as a column having a length of 12 ft. Let it be assumed that the ends of the column are partly fixed so that the value of $K = 0.75$. Use the straight-line column formula (Eq. 11–15) with $\sigma_0 = 38,300$ psi and $C = 202$ psi. The structural aluminum handbook gives the following data for the tube: $A = 4.52$ in.^{2}, $I = 18.7$ in.^{4}, and $r = 2.035$ in. Determine the allowable load for the column using a factor of safety of 1.5.

11.38.   A structural steel column assumed to have pivot ends has a length of 20 ft and is made up of 12-in. by $\frac{1}{2}$-in. plate to which are riveted four 5-in. by $3\frac{1}{2}$-in. by $\frac{1}{2}$-in. angles as shown in Figure P11.38. Use the parabolic column formula (Eq. 11–17) with $\sigma_0 = 34,000$ psi and $C = 0.970$ psi. What is the allowable load for the column based on a factor of safety of 2.0? (See Appendix B.)

ans. $P = 237,000$ lb.

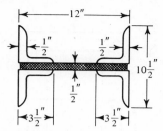

Fig. P 11.38. Structural-steel-column cross section.

11.39. The member *BC* of the truss shown in Figure P11.39 consists of an angle section having equal legs. Select the proper size of angle (use Appendix B) assuming that the column has pivot ends and is axially loaded. Use the straight-line column formula (Eq. 11–15) with $\sigma_0 = 42,500$ psi and $C = 150$ psi. Assume that the factor of safety is 2.2.

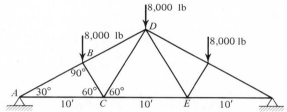

Fig. P 11.39. Truss in which some members act as columns.

11.40. A pivot-ended structural steel column 20-ft long has the cross section shown in Figure P11.40. It is subjected to an axial load. Calculate the allowable load for the column by using Equation (11–17) with $\sigma_0 = 34,000$ psi and $C = 0.970$ psi and a factor of safety of 1.8.

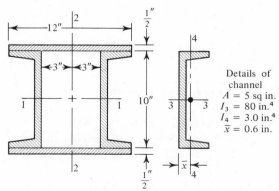

Fig. P 11.40. Cross section of eccentrically loaded steel compression member.

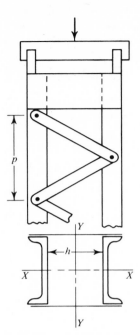

Fig. P 11.41.   Latticed column.

11.41. A latticed partially restrained structural steel column is made of two 10-in. 15.3-lb channels (see Fig. P11.41). The distance h between backs is such that the moments of inertia about the x- and y-axes are equal. The column is 20-ft long. The column is subjected to an axial load P_w. Calculate the slenderness ratio and the working load for the column. The effective length of the column is $7\ell/8$; that is $K = \frac{7}{8}$. Use Equation (11–17) with $\sigma_0 = 34{,}000$ psi and $C = 0.970$ psi and a factor of safety of $N = 2.0$. (See Appendix B.)

$$\text{ans.} \quad P = 139{,}000 \text{ lb.}$$

11.7.   Elastically Restrained Columns

The most general elastically restrained column is shown in Figure 11.10e. In this section the problem is to determine the effective length $K\ell$ for the column in Figure 11.10e for the restricted conditions that either $\beta_A = 0$ or $\beta_A = \beta_B$.

The column in Figure 11.17 is elastically restrained at B at one end and is pivot ended at the other end A (i.e., $\beta_A = 0$). The column of length AB

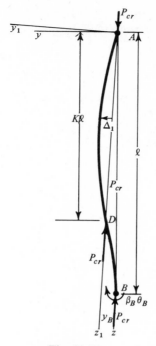

Fig. 11.17.

has inflection points at A and D. Because the bending moment at point D is zero, the moment equilibrium equation of length BD gives

$$P_{cr}y_B = \beta_B\theta_B. \qquad (11\text{--}18)$$

The magnitude of y_B is given by Equation (11–13) when $z_1 = \ell$:

$$y_B = \Delta_1 \sin\frac{\pi}{K}. \qquad (11\text{--}19)$$

The angle change θ_B is small and is equal to the slope of the column at B if the slope of the column is measured with respect to the z-axis.

$$\theta_B = \frac{dy}{dz}\bigg|_{z=\ell} = \frac{dy_1}{dz_1}\bigg|_{z_1=\ell} - \frac{y_B}{\ell}.$$

Using Equations (11–13) and (11–19)

$$\theta_B = \frac{\Delta_1\pi}{K\ell}\cos\frac{\pi}{K} - \frac{\Delta_1}{\ell}\sin\frac{\pi}{K}. \qquad (11\text{--}20)$$

After substitution of Equations (11–14), (11–19), and (11–20) in Equation (11–18), the relation can be simplified to give

$$\frac{\beta_B \ell}{E_T I_x} = \frac{\pi^2 \tan(\pi/K)}{K\pi - K^2 \tan(\pi/K)}. \tag{11–21}$$

If the column buckles elastically, replace the tangent modulus E_T in Equation (11–21) by E. Equation (11–21) was used to construct the curve designated $\beta_A = 0$ in Figure 11.19. As β_B approaches infinity, the curve becomes asymptotic to the line $K = 0.7$ as indicated in Figure 11.10d for the axially loaded column fixed at one end and pivoted at the other end.

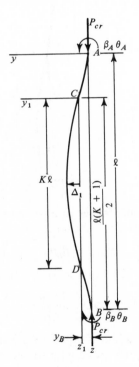

Fig. 11.18.

The axially loaded elastically restrained column in Figure 11.18 has the same elastic restraint at each end (i.e., $\beta_A = \beta_B$). The inflection points for the column are located at points C and D. Because the bending moment at point D is zero, Equation (11–18) is valid for length BD. The magnitude of y_B is given by Equation (11–13); that is, $y_1 = \Delta_1 \sin \pi z_1/K\ell$ with $z_1 = \ell(K + 1)/2$:

$$y_B = \Delta_1 \sin \frac{\pi(K + 1)}{2K}. \qquad (11\text{–}22)$$

The angle change θ_B is small and is equal to the slope of the column at B with respect to the z-axis:

$$\theta_B = \frac{dy}{dz}\bigg|_{z=\ell} = \frac{dy_1}{dz_1}\bigg|_{z_1=\ell(K+1)/2} = \frac{\Delta_1 \pi}{K\ell} \cos \frac{\pi(K + 1)}{2K}. \qquad (11\text{–}23)$$

After the substitution of Equations (11–14), (11–22), and (11–23) in Equation (11–18), the relation can be simplified to give

$$\frac{\beta_B \ell}{E_T I_x} = \frac{\pi}{K} \tan \frac{\pi(K + 1)}{2K}. \qquad (11\text{–}24)$$

If the column buckles elastically, replace the tangent modulus E_T in Equation (11–24) by E. The curve designated $\beta_A = \beta_B$ in Figure 11.19 was constructed by using Equation (11–24). As $\beta_A = \beta_B$ approaches infinity, the curve becomes asymptotic to the line $K = 0.50$ as indicated in Figure 11.10b for the fixed-ended column.

The curves in Figure 11.19 can be used to determine easily the effective length $K\ell$ of any column of length ℓ and moment of inertia I_x if β_B and E are known for the elastic column or if β_B and E_T are known for the plastic column. The column is assumed to be supported so that it will buckle in the plane for which the moment of inertia I_x is taken. If the column buckles plastically, E_T is generally not known. In this case a trial-and-error solution is required. From a plot of average stress σ versus E_T (see Fig. 11.12 for 2024-T4 aluminum alloy or Fig. 11.15b for structural steel rolled sections), choose a value of E_T corresponding to a given σ. Determine K using Figure 11.19. Calculate $P_T/A = \sigma$ using Equation (11–14). If this calculated value of σ is not equal to the value that corresponds to E_T, choose another value of E_T and repeat the calculations.

It is of interest to note in Figure 11.19 that a relatively small end restraint (i.e., at small values of the abscissa) causes the effective length of the column to be greatly reduced. Also note that the moment $\beta_B \theta_B$ applied to the end of the column by the end restraint is extremely small and is less than or at most equal to $P_{cr}\Delta_1$; the moment applied by the end restraint will be equal to $P_{cr}\Delta_1$ only for the fixed-ended columns when $\beta_A = \beta_B$ are infinite. Any end condition (restraint) that applies a small moment to one or both ends of a column has an appreciable effect on changing the value of the buckling load for the column. If the moment has the same sense as the angle of rotation

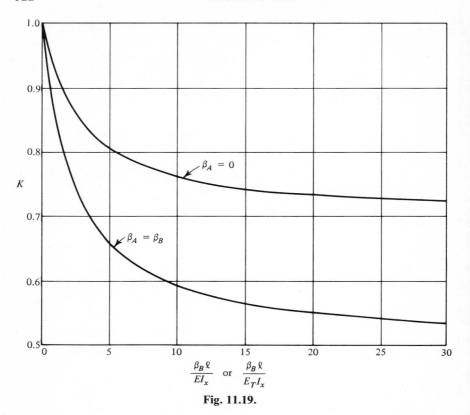

Fig. 11.19.

θ of the end, the moment greatly reduces the buckling load. If the moment has a sense opposite to θ (i.e., it restrains rotation), the moment greatly increases the buckling load as indicated in Figure 11.19.

Illustrative Problem

11.42. Column AB in Figure P11.42 is made of 2024-T4 aluminum alloy and has a 2-in. by 2-in. square cross section. Beams AC and BD have a circular cross section with a diameter of 3 in., are made of the same material, and are welded to the column at points A and B. The stress-strain diagram and tangent modulus curve for the material are given in Figure 11.12. (1) Determine P_{cr} for the column based on the assumption that the material in the column remains linearly elastic. (2) Determine the correct value of P_{cr} based on the actual material properties given in Figure 11.11.

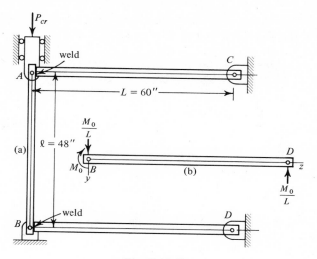

Fig. P 11.42.

SOLUTION.   The first step is to determine the rotational spring constant β for either beam. The magnitude of β is the same for either elastic or plastic behavior of the column. A free-body diagram of beam BD is shown in Figure P11.42b where

$$M_0 = \beta_B \theta_B = \beta_B \frac{dy}{dz}\bigg|_{z=0}. \tag{a}$$

The elastic curve equation (Eq. 8–10) becomes

$$-E_{BD}I_{BD}\frac{d^2y}{dz^2} = M_x = M_0 - \frac{M_0}{L}z,$$

which is integrated to give

$$-E_{BD}I_{BD}\frac{dy}{dz} = M_0 z - \frac{M_0}{2L}z^2 + C_1$$

$$-E_{BD}I_{BD}y = \frac{1}{2}M_0 z^2 - \frac{M_0}{6L}z^3 + C_1 z + C_2. \tag{b}$$

The first boundary condition $y = 0$ when $z = 0$ gives $C_2 = 0$. The second boundary condition $y = 0$ when $z = L$ determines C_1:

$$C_1 = -\frac{M_0 L}{3}.$$

This value of C_1 can be substituted in Equation (b) to determine the slope of the beam. But the slope of the beam at $z = 0$ is equal to the slope of the column at B. Equations (a) and (b) give

$$\theta_B = \frac{dy}{dz}\bigg|_{z=0} = \frac{M_0 L}{3 E_{BD} I_{BD}} = \frac{M_0}{\beta_B}$$

$$\beta_B = \frac{3 E_{BD} I_{BD}}{L} = \frac{3(10,800,000)\pi(3)^4}{60(64)} = 2,147,000 \text{ in.-lb/rad.}$$

The abscissa in Figure 11.19 can now be calculated:

$$\frac{\beta_B \ell}{E I_x} = \frac{2,147,000(48)}{10,800,000(1.333)} = 7.16.$$

Figure 11.19 indicates from the curve marked $\beta_A = \beta_B$ that $K = 0.623$ for this abscissa; the effective column length is $K\ell = 29.9$ in. The critical buckling load is given by Equation (11–12) if the material in the column is assumed to remain linearly elastic:

$$P_{cr} = \frac{\pi^2 E I_x}{(K\ell)^2} = \frac{9.87(10,800,000)(1.333)}{29.9(29.9)} = 159,000 \text{ lb}$$

and

$$\frac{P_{cr}}{A} = 39,800 \text{ psi.}$$

The stress-strain diagram of the material in Figure 11.12 indicates that the average stress for the elastic solution is greater than the proportional limit of the material. A trial-and-error solution is required for the plastic solution. After several trials, a value of $E_T = 7,900,000$ psi corresponds to an average stress $P_{cr}/A = 31,800$ psi was read from the tangent modulus curve in Figure 11.11. The abscissa in Figure 11.19 can be calculated:

$$\frac{\beta_B \ell}{E_T I_x} = \frac{2,147,000(48)}{7,900,000(1.333)} = 9.79.$$

Figure 11.19 indicates that $K = 0.595$; the effective column length is $K\ell = 28.6$ in. The critical buckling load is given by Equation (11–14):

$$P_{cr} = \frac{\pi^2 E_T I_x}{(K\ell)^2} = \frac{9.87(7,900,000)(1.333)}{28.6(28.6)} = 127,000 \text{ lb}$$

and

$$\frac{P_{cr}}{A} = 31,800 \text{ psi.}$$

This is the correct solution because this value of average stress agrees with the value corresponding to the value of $E_T = 7,900,000$ psi.

Suppose an engineer is asked to build the structure in Figure P11.42 and determine experimentally the critical buckling load for the column. Should one expect good agreement between theory and experiment? Good agreement will not be found between theory and experiment unless extreme care is exercised in determining the material properties and in the design of the test set-up. First, the compressive stress-strain diagram in Figure 11.12 should be obtained by testing several compression specimens cut off the ends from the same bar from which the column was cut; it is impossible for the theory to be exact unless the required material properties are known. Second, the center lines of the pins at A and B must pass through the centroid of the column cross section: an eccentricity in the action line of the load will lower the buckling load. Third, the bearings at pins A and B have to be frictionless; a small frictional moment will increase the buckling load. Fourth, beams AC and BD have to be perpendicular to the column so that the initial moments at A and B are equal to zero when P equals zero; an initial moment at either A or B will lower the buckling load.

Problems

11.43. The two beams and the column in Problem 11.42 are made of extruded tubing of 7075-T6 aluminum alloy ($E = 10,400,000$ psi and $\sigma_{PL} = 76,000$ psi). The tubing has an outside diameter of 2 in. and an inside diameter of 1.8 in. Determine the critical buckling load for the elastically restrained column.

11.44. Let the upper beam in Problem 11.43 be removed so that the column is restrained only at the bottom. Determine the critical buckling load.

ans. $P_{cr} = 16,100$ lb.

11.45. In Figure P11.42 member AB has a length $\ell = 30$ ft and is an 8-in. by 8-in. 34.4 lb/ft H-section steel column for which $A = 10.09$ in.^{2}, $I_{max} = 115.4$ in.^{4}, and $I_{min} = 35.1$ in.^{4} Beams CA and BD are 8-in. 18.4 lb/ft I-section beams (see Appendix B) and each has a length of 19 ft. The column is supported so that it cannot deflect out of the plane of the structure; therefore, it buckles about the axis having I_{max}. Determine K, E_T, and P_{cr} assuming that the curves in Figure 11.15 are valid.

ans. $K = 0.686$, $E_T = 17,200,000$ psi, $P_{cr} = 320,000$ lb.

Dynamic Loads

12.1. Introduction

Static Loads. In the preceding chapters, it was assumed that the loads acting on a member were applied gradually (without impact) and that the member was in stable equilibrium (not accelerated) at each instant or stage of the loading. Actually, some part of the member will be accelerated as the loads on the member are increasing. We assume that, for static loading, the rate of applying the loads is so small that the acceleration of each part of the member will be so small that the effect of the acceleration can be neglected. In general, material properties are obtained from tests of specimens for which the rate of loading is sufficiently small so that the specimen can be considered in stable equilibrium at all times.

Dynamic Loads—High Velocity Impact. A member is subjected to dynamic loads when the loads cause any part of the member to be accelerated and the magnitude of the maximum acceleration cannot be considered to be small. High-velocity impact loads would include those dynamic loads caused by high velocity collision of another body with the given member thus causing accelerations of great magnitude in the member. The derivation of load-stress and load-deflection relations for a member subjected to high velocity impact is beyond the scope of this book for two reasons as follows:

(1) In general high velocity impact causes plastic deformation particularly at the point of impact. For this reason the magnitude of the impact load is difficult to determine. Even if the magnitude of the impact load is known, it is difficult to relate this load to the state of stress at any point in the member because the impact load produces strain waves in the material; the stresses and strains at any point in the member depend on the velocity of propagation of these strain waves.

526

(2) If any of the material is plastically deformed, it is necessary that the stress-strain relation for the material be known. The material properties of most materials are influenced by the rate of loading and may be appreciably different during high velocity impact than during static loading. In general the required material properties for high velocity impact are not known for most materials.

Dynamic Loads—Low Velocity Impact.   During low velocity impact the rate of applying the loads is sufficiently small so that the magnitude of the strain waves developed in the member are small enough to be neglected and the material in the member exhibits substantially the same properties as are involved in response to so-called static (gradually applied) loads. Under these conditions, the impact effect of the loads may be considered to be equivalent to an additional static load, as is discussed in Sections 12.2 and 12.4. It is difficult to define precisely the conditions as to when a given impact may be considered to be low velocity impact. The magnitude of the relative velocity of two bodies (load-carrying member being hit by another body) for low velocity impact depends on the relative masses of the two bodies (Section 12.5), on the connections of the member with other members in the structure, and the properties of the material in the bodies.

Vibrational Effect of Dynamic Loading.   The dynamic load applied by the moving body will cause a vibration of the member. In this chapter it is assumed that the dynamic load is applied only once. We are interested in the maximum deflection that occurs during the first cycle of vibration; the deflection decreases with number of cycles due to damping in the system. In many applications the dynamic load may be applied at a constant frequency. If the frequency of the impulses of the dynamic load is nearly the same as the natural frequency of vibration of the load carrying member, a condition, called resonance, is established, which causes excessive deflection, and which usually soon leads to complete failure or destruction of the member. Several suspension bridges under the influence of wind pressure (aerodynamic loading) have been destroyed in this fashion. Many machine parts and airplane parts also are likely to be subjected to resonant vibration if special care is not exercised to avoid such conditions.

12.2.   Equivalent Static-Load Method

As previously noted, members of engineering structures and machines are often required to resist dynamic loads in the form of low-velocity impact. The usual method of determining the stresses and deformations caused by such loads is first to estimate the maximum pressure or force exerted by the moving body on the member; this load is then considered to be a static load (a so-called equivalent static load) and is used in the equations developed in the preceding chapters.

The method of determining the maximum load exerted by a moving body when it comes in contact with the load-carrying member may be different for the problems considered in this book than for many of the practical engineering problems found in practice. In this chapter we will determine the so-called equivalent static load by equating the energy imparted to the load-carrying member by the moving body and the work done by the equivalent static load that causes the same deflection of the member as that caused by the moving body. In engineering practice the equivalent static load caused by a moving load is obtained by multiplying the moving load by an impact factor (Section 12.3).

Examples of low velocity impact would include the load caused by a moving train on a bridge, by a moving crowd of people in a stadium, by the blast pressure of a bomb explosion on a building, by the pressure of the earth on the wheels of an airplane as it lands on the runway, by an earthquake force on buildings, by pressure on gear teeth in gear-driven machinery, by wind pressure on buildings, and so forth. The total equivalent static load in each case may consist of the weight of the member or structure (called dead load), such as the weight of a bridge, plus the live load, such as the weight of a train moving on the bridge, plus the product of an impact factor and the live load.

12.3. Impact Factors

As already noted, if the body that applies a load to a member or structure is in motion when it comes in contact with the load-carrying member, the stresses caused in the member are larger than would be produced by the same load at rest. The increase in the static load required to cause the same stress that the dynamic load produces is called the impact effect or merely the impact load. It is usually found by multiplying the moving (live) load by an impact factor.

The impact factor is different for each different type of dynamic loading, and the value for the factor never can be considered to be more than a rough approximation to the actual dynamic effect of the moving load. For, in spite of much experimental work in this field on actual structures, as well as on laboratory models, it is difficult to predict the behavior of the structure accurately; the conditions influencing the action of the member or structure under dynamic loading are always numerous and uncertain.

Values for impact factors have been proposed in codes for certain service conditions by various technical societies and government agencies, such as the American Railway Engineering Association (AREA); the subcommittee on Air Force-Navy-Civil Aircraft Design Criteria of the Munitions Board, Aircraft Committee, Designated as ANC-5 Bulletin on Strength of Metal Aircraft Elements; American Society of Civil Engineers (ASCE), American Society of Mechanical Engineers (ASME); City Government Building Codes, and so forth.

12.4. Low Velocity Impact Problem—Elastic Condition

The low velocity impact problem can be divided into two parts. The first part of the problem is to determine the effective energy applied to the load-carrying member. The effective energy is that portion of the total energy given up by the moving body which produces the maximum deflection of the load-carrying member. For the problems considered in this chapter, the reader is assumed to know how to calculate the energy given up by the moving body; this energy is equal to the sum of the change in kinetic energy and of the change in potential energy of the moving body. Some of this energy may be absorbed by the supports of the load-carrying member, some may be absorbed by local plastic deformation of the body and member and dissipated as heat, and some small amount may be absorbed in developing sound waves. The remaining energy is the effective energy that causes the deflection of the member.

The most difficult part of the impact problem is to determine what percentage of the energy given up by the moving body is the effective energy. Unless stated otherwise we will assume that the effective energy is equal to the energy given up by the moving body.

If the effective energy for low velocity impact is applied at one point to a member, the deflected shape of the load-carrying member for maximum deflection is identical to the deflected shape for the member when subjected to an equivalent static load applied at the same point. At the instant the member experiences its maximum deflection, every point in the member is at rest and the strain energy U of the member is equal to the effective energy. Because the member is at rest at that instant, the strain energy is the same for the member subjected to the energy load and the same member subjected to the equivalent static load. Thus the deflection of the member can be determined using the relation

$$\text{effective energy} = U = \text{work done by equivalent static load.} \quad (12\text{--}1)$$

In the preceding chapters of this book, load-stress and load-deflection relations were derived for several different types of members. For each of these members it is possible to determine the strain energy U using either the known state of stress at each point in the member caused by the equivalent static load or by setting it equal to the work done by the equivalent static load as indicated by Equation 12–1. Both procedures are considered.

Strain Energy Based on Stresses. One procedure by which the strain energy U absorbed by a given member can be determined is to derive a relation for the strain energy per unit volume called the strain energy density, U_0 (see Section 1.3 for derivation of U_0 for uniaxial state of stress). If load-stress relations for the member are known so that the state of stress at every point in the member can be determined, the strain energy U for the member is obtained by integrating U_0 over the volume of the member.

In members having uniaxial state of stress (axially loaded members and beams) in which the only nonzero stress component is σ_z, the magnitude of U_0 is given by Equation (1–4) as

$$U_0 = \frac{\sigma_z^2}{2E}, \tag{12–2}$$

Consider axial-centric loading of a tension member of length ℓ and cross-sectional area A for which the stress concentrations can be considered negligible. For this member the magnitude of U_0 is the same for every point in the member, and the strain energy is

$$U = U_0 A\ell = \frac{\sigma^2 A\ell}{2E} = \frac{P}{2}\frac{P\ell}{AE} = \tfrac{1}{2}Pe \tag{12–3}$$

where $P = \sigma_z A$ is the axial-centric load and e is the elongation of the tension member.

Equations (12–2) and (12–3) demonstrate the importance of the elastic properties of the material in the design of members to carry low velocity impact loads and also may be used to show the advantage in the design of a member having the maximum stress distributed uniformly over a large volume of the member. When σ_z in Equation (12–2) is equal to the proportional limit, the specific strain energy for uniaxial state of stress is defined as the modulus of resilience of the material. The strain energy U that can be carried by a given member for elastic conditions is directly proportional to the modulus of resilience of the material. An ideal material to be used for resisting energy loads is one for which the proportional limit is large and the modulus of elasticity is small. For uniaxial state of stress, Equation (12–2) indicates that a volume element with stress $\sigma_z/2$ will absorb only 25 per cent as much energy as an equivalent volume element with stress σ_z.

Recommended Procedure for Determining Strain Energy of Member. The recommended procedure for determining the strain energy U for a given member is to set U equal to the work done by an equivalent static load as indicated by Equation (12–1). The strain energy for axial-centric loading of a tension member is

$$U = \text{work} = \tfrac{1}{2}Pe, \qquad (12\text{–}4)$$

where P is the equivalent static load and e is the elongation (deflection) of the tension member, which is assumed to deform with P linearly related to e; for a torsion member is

$$U = \text{work} = \tfrac{1}{2}T\theta, \qquad (12\text{–}5)$$

where T is the equivalent static torque and θ is the angle of twist (deflection) of the torsion member which is assumed to twist with T linearly related to θ; and for a beam

$$U = \text{work} = \tfrac{1}{2}Py_P, \qquad (12\text{–}6)$$

where P is the equivalent static load (assumed to be a concentrated load applied at the location of impact) and y_P is the deflection of the beam under load P, which is assumed to be linearly related to y_P.

Most members have stress concentrations. It is necessary to know the effect of these stress concentrations on the ability of a member to carry energy loads. We found in Section 4.5 that stress concentrations do not effect the load-deflection diagram for members if the material in the member has sufficient ductility. Therefore, stress concentrations do not need to be considered in low velocity impact problems if the material in the member has sufficient ductility. The question of whether a material has sufficient ductility is not easy to answer. The ductility of most materials decreases with an increase in rate of loading and with a decrease in temperature. It is recommended that impact tests (such as the Charpy Test or the Izod Test) be made of the material at the lowest temperature at which the member is to be used in order to determine the suitability of the material to be used in the design of the member to carry low velocity impact loads.

Illustrative Problems

12.1 Tension members B and C in Figure P12.1a are circular cylinders made of a ductile steel for which the proportional limit is equal to $\sigma_e = 48{,}000$ psi. (1) Construct the load-elongation diagrams for the two tension members for loads up to the maximum elastic load. Determine the strain energy U for maximum elastic conditions for each tension member

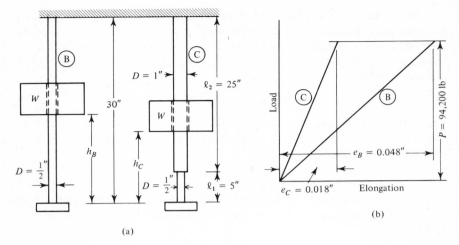

Fig. P 12.1.

neglecting the effect of stress concentrations. (2) What is the maximum height h above the end of each member that weight $W = 300$ lb can be dropped for maximum elastic conditions if the effective energy is 88 per cent of the change in potential energy of W?

SOLUTION—PART (1). Because the minimum cross section of each tension member is the same, the maximum elastic load for each tension member in Figure P12.1a is the same:

$$P = \sigma_e A = \frac{48,000\pi}{2(2)(4)} = 94,200 \text{ lb.}$$

However the elongation given by Equation (1–13) will not be the same for the two members:

$$e_B = \frac{P\ell}{AE} = \frac{\sigma_e \ell}{E} = \frac{48,000(30)}{30,000,000} = 0.048 \text{ in.}$$

$$e_C = \frac{P\ell_1}{A_1 E} + \frac{P\ell_2}{A_2 E} = \frac{48,000(5)}{30,000,000} + \frac{12,000(25)}{30,000,000} = 0.008 + 0.010 = 0.018 \text{ in.}$$

The load-elongation diagrams are linear up to the maximum elastic load and are shown in Figure P12.1b. The strain energy for each tension member for maximum elastic conditions is indicated by the area under each load-elongation diagram:

$$U_B = \tfrac{1}{2}Pe_B = 2,260.8 \text{ in.-lb,}$$

$$U_C = \tfrac{1}{2}Pe_C = 847.8 \text{ in.-lb.}$$

Note that although the volume of material in tension member C is 3.25 times greater than member B, member C will absorb only 37.5 per cent as much energy as member B. This result points out the importance in the design of a tension member to carry low velocity energy loads to have as much of the volume of the member as possible at constant stress which, except for stress concentrations, is the maximum stress in the member.

PART (2).   The effective energy is equal to 88 per cent of the change in potential energy of weight W. The magnitude of h for member B is given by Equation (12–1):

$$0.88W(h_B + e_B) = U_B,$$

$$h_B = \frac{2{,}260.8}{0.88(300)} - 0.048 = 8.51 \text{ in.}$$

The magnitude of h for member C is

$$0.88W(h_C + e_C) = U_C,$$

$$h_C = \frac{847.8}{0.88(300)} - 0.018 = 3.19 \text{ in.}$$

12.2.   The aluminum ($E = 10{,}800{,}000$ psi) beam in Figure P12.2 has a rectangular section with a width of 4 in. and a depth of 3 in., is simply

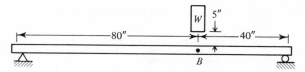

Fig. P 12.2.

supported at each end, and is subjected to a low velocity impact load when weight $W = 400$ lb is dropped and impacts the beam at a distance $2\ell/3$ from the left end. If the effective energy for the beam is equal to the change in potential energy of weight W, determine the equivalent concentrated load P_B, the deflection y_B of the beam at the point of impact, and the maximum bending stress in the beam.

SOLUTION.   The first step is to determine the relation between the equivalent concentrated load P_B and the deflection y_B. This relation was derived in Illustrative Problem 8.11 and is given by the relation

$$y_B = \frac{4P_B\ell^3}{243EI_x} = \frac{4(120)(120)(120)P_B}{243(10{,}800{,}000)(9)} = 0.000293P_B. \tag{a}$$

Equation (12–1) takes the form

$$W(5 + y_B) = \tfrac{1}{2}P_B y_B.$$ (b)

Equations (a) and (b) simplify to

$$P_B^2 - 800P_B - 13,652,000 = 0,$$

$$P_B = 400 \pm \sqrt{160,000 + 13,652,000},$$

$$= 4,117 \text{ lb or } -3,317 \text{ lb}.$$

The positive root is the value of the equivalent concentrated load P_B. Substituting this value of P_B in Equation (a) gives

$$y_B = 1.206 \text{ in.}$$

When the equivalent concentrated load $P_B = 4,117$ lb is applied at point B, the reactions are $R_1 = 1,372$ lb at the left end and $R_2 = 2,745$ lb at the right end. The maximum bending moment occurs at the section at B:

$$\sigma_{\max} = \frac{M_x c}{I_x} = \frac{1,372(80)(1.5)}{9} = 18,300 \text{ psi.}$$

12.3.   The structure in Figure P12.3 is made up of a tension member connected by a pin to the free end of a cantilever beam. (1) Derive an expression for the strain energy U for the structure if the equivalent concentrated load P is applied to the free end of the tension member. (2) The beam

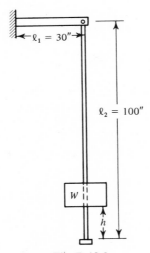

$$\ell_1 = 30''$$

$$\ell_2 = 100''$$

$$W$$

$$h$$

Fig. P 12.3.

has a diameter of 3 in. and a length of 30 in. The tension member has a cross sectional area of 0.10 in.^{2} and a length of 100 in. Both members are made of steel ($E = 30,000,000$ psi). Determine the maximum height h that weight $W = 50$ lb can be dropped such that the maximum allowable stress in either member is 16,000 psi (neglect stress concentrations).

SOLUTION—PART (1). The deflection Δ of the free end of the tension member when load P is applied is equal to the sum of the deflection of the beam and the elongation of the tension member:

$$\Delta = \frac{P\ell_1^3}{3E_1 I_1} + \frac{P\ell_2}{A_2 E_2}. \tag{a}$$

The strain energy U is given by the relation

$$U = \frac{1}{2}P\Delta = \frac{P^2\ell_1^3}{6E_1 I_1} + \frac{P^2\ell_2}{2A_2 E_2}. \tag{b}$$

PART (2). The maximum allowable value for the equivalent concentrated load P can be determined because the maximum stress is given:

$$P_1 = \sigma A_2 = 16,000(0.10) = 1,600 \text{ lb,}$$

$$P_2 = \frac{\sigma I_x}{c\ell_1} = \frac{16,000\pi(3)(3)(3)(3)}{64(1.5)(30)} = 1,414 \text{ lb.}$$

Thus, $P = P_2 = 1,414$ lb. Using Equation (a)

$$\Delta = \frac{1,414(30)(30)(30)(64)}{(3)30,000,000\pi(3)(3)(3)(3)} + \frac{1,414(100)}{0.10(30,000,000)} = 0.154 \text{ in.}$$

The magnitude of h is given by Equation (12–1):

$$W(h + \Delta) = \tfrac{1}{2}P\Delta,$$

$$h = \frac{P\Delta}{2W} - \Delta = \frac{1,414(0.154)}{100} - 0.154,$$

$$= 2.02 \text{ in.}$$

Problems

12.4. A structural-steel bar and an oak bar used as direct tension members are required to absorb the energy of a falling weight. The cross-sectional area of the steel and oak bars are 1 and 3 sq. in., respectively; the lengths are 3 ft for the steel bar and 7 ft for the oak. The modulus of elasticity of the oak is $\frac{1}{15}$ of that of steel. The proportional limit of the oak is $\frac{1}{10}$ of that of steel. Which bar can resist the greater energy load without causing inelastic action in the bar?

12.5. The piston rods of the forging hammers in a certain steel plant frequently broke, and, when they were finally replaced by a higher carbon steel, the trouble ceased. If the proportional limit of the low carbon steel was 36,000 psi and that of the higher carbon steel was 60,000 psi, how much more energy could the higher carbon steel rod absorb without being stressed above the proportional limit?

ans.   The higher carbon steel rod will absorb 2.78 times as much elastic
energy as the lower carbon steel rod.

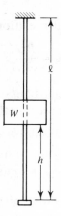

Fig. P 12.6.

12.6. A body W (Fig. P12.6) having a weight of 15 lb falls a height h of 5 ft when it comes in contact with the end of a rod having a length ℓ of 8 ft. If the rod is made of steel having a proportional limit of 60,000 psi, what cross-sectional area should the rod have in order to prevent the stress from exceeding the proportional limit?

ans.   0.157 in.^{2}

12.7. A steel bar having a length of 15 in. and a cross sectional area of 1.0 in^2 has a low-velocity axial load applied to it. The work done on and energy absorbed by the bar when the body is brought to rest is 9 ft-lb. Find the maximum stress developed in the bar.

12.8. A low carbon steel bar 20-in. long and an aluminum-alloy bar, each $\frac{1}{2}$ in. in diameter, are each subjected to equal low velocity impact loads causing axial stress. If it is specified that the energy absorbed by each bar per unit volume is one third of the modulus of resilience of the material, what should be the length of the aluminum-alloy bar? (Consult Table 1.1 and assume that the proportional limit of each material is equal to the yield stress.)

12.9. A $\frac{1}{2}$-in. diameter 7075-T6 aluminum alloy bar ($\sigma_e = 75,000$ psi and $E = 10,400,000$ psi) with a length of 20 in. is connected to the end of a $\frac{3}{4}$-in. diameter steel bar of 30-in. length ($\sigma_e = 36,000$ psi and $E = 30,000,000$ psi) making a rod with a total length of 50 in. Determine the axially applied energy load U for maximum elastic conditions that can be carried by the 50-in. bar. Note that the connection of dissimilar metals without insulation is not good engineering practice because contact between them may cause corrosion.

ans. $U = 1,307$ in.-lb.

12.10. Often the energy absorption of a machine or structural part can be increased by the removal of material so that a higher percentage of the remaining volume of the member is subjected to the maximum stress. Consider the two designs of a tension link in Figure P12.10 that has a cross section of 1-in. by $\frac{1}{8}$-in., a hole diameter or slot width of $\frac{1}{2}$ in., and a length between center lines of the holes of 6 in. The link is made of steel that has a proportional limit stress of $\sigma_e = 36,000$ psi. Neglecting the effect of stress concentrations, determine the maximum elastic strain energy U for each of the two links. The maximum elastic equivalent concentrated static load P is the same for the two links.

ans. $U_{(a)} = 4.05$ in.-lb and $U_{(b)} = 8.10$ in.-lb.

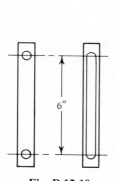

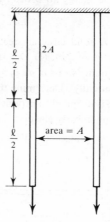

Fig. P 12.10. **Fig. P 12.11.**

12.11. Determine the ratio of the energy loads that can be carried by the two tension members in Figure P12.11 to produce the same maximum stress neglecting–stress concentration effects at the change in cross section and at the fixed end. Assume linearly elastic condition.

12.12. A 2-in. diameter shaft of length ℓ connects a power driven machine to its power source. When the clutch is engaged at the power source, it is found that an energy load of 800 in.-lb has to be absorbed by the shaft before the end of the shaft at the machine begins to rotate. Design criteria require that the maximum shearing stress in the shaft shall not exceed $\tau_e/2$ where τ_e is the shearing proportional limit of the material in the shaft. Determine the minimum length ℓ for the shaft for each of the following available materials: (1) medium carbon steel for which $\tau_e = 30,000$ psi and $G = 11,600,000$ psi; (2) heat-treated alloy steel for which $\tau_e = 120,000$ psi and $G = 11,600,000$ psi; (3) 7075-T6 aluminum alloy for which $\tau_e = 40,000$ psi and $G = 3,900,000$ psi. Assume that all of the energy load is absorbed as elastic strain energy by the shaft.

and. $\ell_{(1)} = 52.6$ in.; $\ell_{(2)} = 3.28$ in.; $\ell_{(3)} = 9.93$ in.

12.13. Let each of the two steel members in Problem 12.1 be subjected to torsional energy loads applied at the free (lower) end. Assuming linearly elastic behavior and neglecting stress concentrations, determine the energy that can be absorbed by each of the two members if the maximum shearing stress developed in each member is $\tau = 10,000$ psi.

12.14. A solid circular shaft has a diameter D and length ℓ. Another circular shaft of the same material is hollow and has the same outside diameter and same length but has only 50 per cent of the weight. For the same maximum shearing stress determine the ratio of the energy absorbed by the two shafts.

ans. $U_{\text{hollow}} = 0.75 U_{\text{solid}}$.

12.15. A solid circular steel horizontal cantilever beam has a length of 50 in. and a diameter of 2 in. (1) Determine the magnitude of weight W that produces a maximum bending stress of $\sigma_z = 5,000$ psi in the beam when W is applied at the free end statically (gradually). Determine the height h above the free end of the beam at which the weight W is dropped to produce (2) a maximum stress $2\sigma_z$ and (3) a maximum stress of $4\sigma_z$. Assume linearly elastic behavior.

ans.   (1) $W = 78.5$ lb; (2) $h = 0$; (3) $h = 0.555$ in.

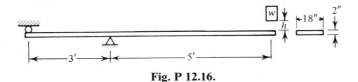

Fig. P 12.16.

12.16. The beam in Figure P12.16 is a hickory board for which $E = 1,800,000$ psi. If $W = 150$ lb, determine the height h that W can be dropped such that the maximum stress in the board is 4,000 psi. What is the maximum deflection?

12.17. The two beams in Figure P12.17 each have a width of 2 in. and are made of oak for which $E = 1,800,000$ psi. Determine the height h from which $W = 100$ lb can be dropped if the maximum stress in either beam is to be 2,000 psi.

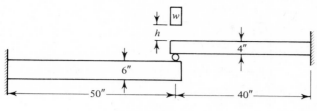

Fig. P 12.17.

12.18. An energy load causes an equivalent concentrated load P to act at the end of the cantilever beams shown in Figure P12.18. The beams are made of a ductile metal which has a proportional limit equal to the yield stress σ_e. (1) Determine the maximum elastic value for the strain energy U for the beam in Figure P12.18a that has constant cross section. (2) The beam in Figure P12.18b is tapered and contains only half as much material as the beam in Figure 12.18a. Determine the maximum elastic value of the strain energy U for the tapered beam to show that the removal of material increased its energy absorption capacity.

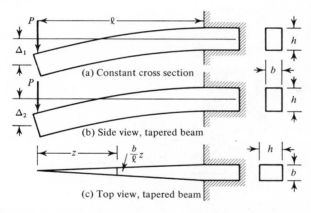

Fig. P 12.18. Effect of shape of member on energy absorbed by member.

12.19. Three steel beams, A, B, and C, all of the same dimensions are arranged as shown in Figure P12.19 similar to one type of draft gear. Each beam is 3-in. square and has a span of 12 in. (1) What static load applied at the midspan will cause a maximum elastic stress of 20,000 psi? (2) Will all the beams when arranged as shown in Figure P12.19 resist a greater static load than any one of the beams alone? (3) What is the weight of a body which when allowed to fall a height h of 8 in. will cause a stress of 20,000 psi? (4) Assume that all of the energy of the falling body is absorbed equally by the resisting

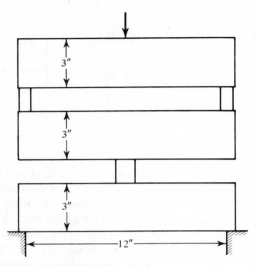

Fig. P 12.19. Method of increasing energy absorption by adding material.

beams. What stress would the weight in (3) cause if it were resisted by only one of the three beams?

ans.   (1) 30,000 lb; (2) no; (3) 29.9 lb; (4) 34,500 psi.

12.20. A tapered cantilever beam (Fig. P12.20) has a width $k_1 z$ and a depth $k_2 z$ where z is the distance from the free end, and k_1 and k_2 are constants. Show that if the

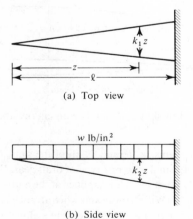

(a) Top view

(b) Side view

Fig. P 12.20. Method of increasing energy absorption by variable cross section.

beam is subjected to a uniformly distributed load w psi as shown in the figure, the maximum bending stress on all sections is constant; hence show that the energy absorption per unit volume is constant at all points on the top and bottom surface. Note that many aircraft wings have approximately a double taper such as in Figure P12.20.

12.5. Energy Absorbed by Local Plastic Deformation Due to Inertia of Load-Carrying Member

It was stated previously that the strain energy U is the energy actually absorbed by the member and that one of the ways in which the energy of the moving body is dissipated is in causing local yielding of the moving body and the load-carrying member. The energy dissipated in this way may be relatively large if the weight W_1 of the member is large compared to the weight W of the moving body. Often a third body of weight W_2 is attached to the member and this causes even more of the energy of the moving body to be dissipated as heat resulting from the local yielding.

This principle is recognized in the design of structures and machines by decreasing the magnitude of the impact factor (see Section 12.3) as the ratios W_1/W and W_2/W increase. In accordance with this principle, a heavy floor on a suspension bridge decreases the stress from impact in the vertical rods that connect the floor to the cables; for the same reason, the specifications for the drop test for steel rails specify, in addition to the height of drop, not only the weight of the striking tup but also that of the spring-supported anvil block to which the rail supports are attached.

By using the principle of conservation of momentum for the condition of plastic impact, an expression for U may be found in terms of W_1/W, W_2/W, and E_k where E_k is the energy given up by the moving body as it comes in contact with the load-carrying member; the expression is $U = nE_k$ in which n has the following values:

(1) For an axial low velocity impact load on a tension member;

$$n = \frac{1 + q_1 + q/3}{(1 + q_1 + q/2)^2} \quad \text{where} \quad q_1 = \frac{W_2}{W} \quad \text{and} \quad q = \frac{W_1}{W}. \quad (12\text{--}7)$$

(2) For an impact load applied at the center of a simple beam with W_2 attached at the center of the span,

$$n = \frac{1 + q_1 + 17q/35}{(1 + q_1 + 5q/8)^2} \quad \text{where} \quad q_1 = \frac{W_2}{W} \quad \text{and} \quad q = \frac{W_1}{W}. \quad (12\text{--}8)$$

The values of n given by Equations (12–7) and (12–8) should be regarded as relative rather than absolute values because of some of the assumptions made in the derivations. Waves of stress or vibrations caused by impact are here neglected.

12.6.   Low Velocity Impact Problem—Plastic Condition

One of the great advantages of designing members using ductile material is that these members will absorb an energy load many times larger than the design load before the member fractures. For instance a train wreck on a railroad bridge may cause many of the members in the bridge to become plastically deformed; however, the bridge will probably remain standing and can be repaired by replacing several of the damaged members. If the bridge had been made of brittle materials, the wreck probably would have caused fracture of the bridge and the train and bridge would have fallen into the river.

In order to determine the strain energy U for a plastically deformed load-carrying member, it is necessary that we know the load-deflection diagram for the member. In previous sections, localized yielding at point of impact was not considered in determining the magnitude of U. Equation (12–1) is valid for the plastic problem and the work done by the equivalent static load is equal to the area under the load-deflection diagram. We will limit our consideration to tension members and beams.

Axial-Centric Loading of Tension Members.   The load-deflection diagram for axial centric loading of tension members having constant cross section has the same shape as the engineering stress-strain diagram (Section 1.3). The area under the stress-strain diagram is equal to the strain energy density U_{0f} and is defined as the toughness of the material. A sufficiently accurate value of the toughness U_{0f} is given by Equation (1–5).

$$U_{0f} = \frac{\sigma_e + \sigma_u}{2} \epsilon_u, \tag{12–9}$$

where σ_e is the yield stress, σ_u is the ultimate stress, and ϵ_u is the fracture strain.

Stress-strain diagrams of three different steels and 7075-T6 aluminum alloy are shown in Figure 12.1. The toughness of each of these metals is considered to be large. Using Equation (12–9) and values of σ_e, σ_u, and ϵ_u from the curves in Figure 12.1, the toughness is found to be $U_{0f} = 13,400$ in. lb/in.^{3} for structural grade steel and is found to be

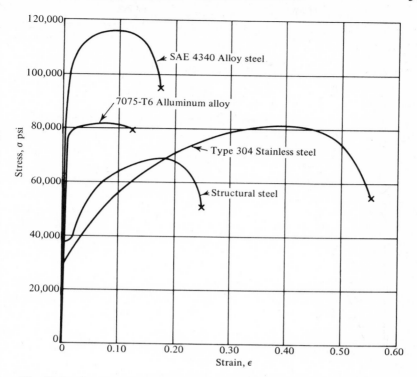

Fig. 12.1. Typical stress-strain diagrams of metals with great toughness.

$U_{0f} = 9,610$ in. lb/in.^{3} for 7075-T6 aluminum alloy. Do not confuse ductility and toughness because structural grade steel is considered to be one of our most ductile metals whereas 7075-T6 aluminum alloy is a metal with limited ductility. A metal is ductile if we can disregard stress concentrations when this metal is used in the design of load-carrying members for static loads (see Section 4.5). In addition to toughness a ductile metal has a large ratio of fracture strain ϵ_u to yield strain ϵ_e. The data in Figure 12.1 indicate that $\epsilon_u = 197 \, \epsilon_e$ for structural grade steel whereas $\epsilon_u = 16 \, \epsilon_e$ for 7075-T6 aluminum alloy.

Beams. The derivation of load-deflection diagrams for plastically deformed beams is beyond the scope of this book; however, the diagram can be approximated with reasonable accuracy over the range of the fully plastic load if the stress-strain diagram of the material in the beam is flat topped at the yield point. A dimensionless load-deflection curve for either a cantilever beam or a simple beam made of structural grade steel is shown in Figure 12.2

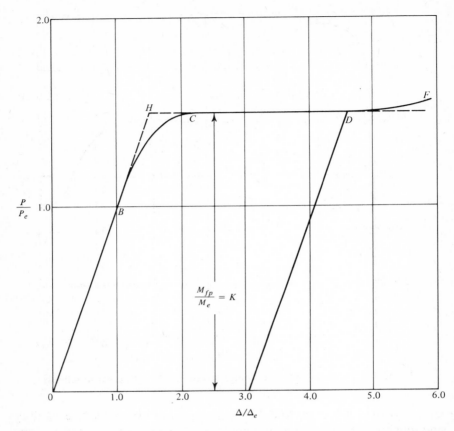

Fig. 12.2. Typical dimensionless load-deflection curve for cantilever beam (loaded by concentrated load at free end) or simple beam (loaded by concentrated load at midspan) made of structural steel.

by curve $OBCDF$. The flat topped curve begins to rise at D for a deflection of approximately $4.5\Delta_e$ when the material in the outer fibers of the beam begin to strain harden. The dimensionless load-deflection curve can be approximated with reasonable accuracy by the two straight lines OH and HD for Δ/Δ_e as large as 5.0. Unloading the beam from any point such as D, the dimensionless load-deflection curve for unloading is approximately a straight line parallel tó OH. The magnitudes of $K = M_{fp}/M_e$ for several beam cross sections are listed in Table 7.2.

Illustrative Problem

12.21. A cantilever beam has a circular cross section with a diameter of 1 in., a length of 20 in., and is made of structural grade steel for which the yield point is $\sigma_e = 36,000$ psi. (1) Determine the strain energy U of the beam for maximum elastic conditions and also when $\Delta = 4\Delta_e$. (2) What is the maximum value of W that can be dropped from a height of 10 in. above the end of the beam for each of the two conditions under (1)? (3) What is the permanent set in the beam when unloaded from the load that produces $\Delta = 4\Delta_e$ (see Fig. 12.2)? Assume that none of the energy is dissipated by local plastic deformation at the point of impact.

SOLUTION—PART (1). The equivalent concentrated load P_e and resultant deflection Δ_e for maximum elastic conditions are easily determined.

$$M_e = 20P_e = \frac{\sigma_e I_x}{c},$$

$$P_e = \frac{36,000(\pi)(1)^3}{20(64)(0.5)} = 176.7 \text{ lb},$$

$$\Delta_e = \frac{P_e \ell^3}{3EI_x} = \frac{176.7(20)(20)(20)(64)}{3(30,000,000)(\pi)} = 0.320 \text{ in.}$$

The strain energy U_e for maximum elastic conditions is

$$U_e = \tfrac{1}{2}P_e\Delta_e = \frac{176.7(0.320)}{2} = 28.27 \text{ in.-lb.}$$

For fully plastic conditions the magnitude of K can be obtained from Table 7.2 as 1.7 for the circular section. The fully plastic load is

$$P_{fp} = KP_e = 1.7(176.7) = 300.4 \text{ lb.}$$

The strain energy U for the inelastically deformed beam is (see Fig. 12.2)

$$U = \tfrac{1}{2}P_{fp}K\Delta_e + P_{fp}(4\Delta_e - K\Delta_e),$$

$$= \frac{300.4(1.7)(0.320)}{2} + 300.4(4 - 1.7)(0.320),$$

$$= 302.8 \text{ in.-lb.}$$

Note that this value of strain energy is 10.7 times greater than U_e.

PART (2).   Solutions to this part are obtained using Equation (12–1). For maximum elastic conditions,

$$W_e(10.0 + \Delta_e) = U_e$$

$$W_e = \frac{28.27}{10.32} = 2.74 \text{ lb.}$$

For inelastic conditions

$$W(10.0 + 4\Delta_e) = U$$

$$W = \frac{302.8}{11.28} = 26.8 \text{ lb.}$$

PART (3).   The permanent set Δ_{set} is given by the relation

$$\Delta_{set} = 4\Delta_e - K\Delta_e = (4 - 1.7)(0.320) = 0.736 \text{ in.}$$

Problems

12.22.   The two circular section tension members B and C in Problem 12.1 are made of the structural grade steel for which $\sigma_e = 38,000$ psi, $\sigma_u = 69,000$ psi, and $E = 30,000,000$ psi. (1) Determine the strain energy in each of the tension members just before fracture. (2) Determine the minimum value of weight W required to fracture each tension member if the weight is dropped a distance $h = 10$ in. above the end of the member $\epsilon_u = 0.280$.

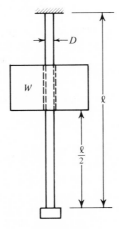

Fig. P 12.23.

12.23. The rod shown in Figure P12.23 has a circular cross section with a diameter $\frac{1}{2}$ in., has a length $\ell = 20$ in., and is made of 7075-T6 aluminum alloy. A static tension test of this material indicates that the stress-strain diagram is approximately flat topped at a stress of 75,000 psi until fracture at a strain of 10 per cent. If $E = 10,400,000$ psi, determine the amount of energy that can be absorbed by a cubic inch of the material in the tension specimen before fracture. Assuming that a unit volume of the rod in Figure P12.23 will absorb the same amount of energy under impact as the static tension specimen, determine the minimum weight W necessary to fracture the rod.

ans. $U_{0f} = 7,229$ in. lb/in.^{3}; $U = 28,380$ lb.in.; $W = 2,365$ lb.

12.24. The stress-strain diagram of structural grade steel is flat topped for strains as large as $10\epsilon_e$ to $20\epsilon_e$ where $\epsilon_e = \sigma_e/E$. A structural grade steel ($\sigma_e = 36,000$ psi) tension member has a length of 25 in. and a cross-sectional area of 0.30 in.^{2} Determine the strain energy required to produce a permanent set of $e_{set} = 0.150$ in.

12.25. A rectangular section beam has a length of 100in., a depth of 6 in., a width of 2 in., and is made of structural grade steel that has a yield point $\sigma_e = 33,000$ psi. The beam is loaded as a simple beam and is subjected to a low velocity impact load at the center of the beam. What was the magnitude of the energy load if the permanent set in the beam after the beam is unloaded is 0.60 in.? Assume that the material in the beam did not strain harden.

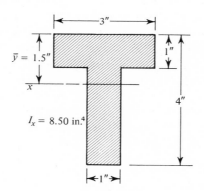

Fig. P 12.26.

12.26. A cantilever beam of length 50 in. has the T-section indicated in Figure P12.26. The beam is made of a structural grade steel having a yield point $\sigma_e = 30,000$ psi. Determine the magnitude of a low velocity impact energy load applied at the free end of the beam to cause a deflection $\Delta = 4.0\Delta_e$.

ans. $M_{fp}/M_e = 1.765$; $U = 3,740$ in.-lb.

Connections and Fasteners

13.1. Introduction

In the development of the subject of mechanics of deformable bodies, major emphasis has been placed on the elements of a machine or structure (called members) that resist loads. Looking at the whole machine or structure one may see an assemblage of members. In such an assemblage the members must somehow be connected or fastened to each other. Such connections are sometimes referred to as joints. Typical joints are made by welding, riveting, or bolting the members together. If the two members must move relative to each other, such as a connecting rod and piston, the joint is effected by a single pin and such a joint is said to be a pinned joint.

The procedure to be used in making a rational analysis of connections and fasteners is illustrated in this chapter by presenting the analyses of riveted joints, bolted joints, and welded joints. In each case the rational procedure described in Section 4.4 is followed.

13.2. Riveted or Bolted Joints

It is convenient to divide riveted or bolted joints into three general groups: (1) structural joints used in connecting members in bridges, buildings, cranes, and other so-called heavy structures, usually made of steel; (2) boiler, tank, or pipe joints used in connecting plates in various types of pressure vessels; and (3) structural joints used in connecting relatively thin sheets and plates of aluminum alloys, magnesium alloys, or stainless steel such as used in aircraft structures and railway-car construction. In structural joints,

548

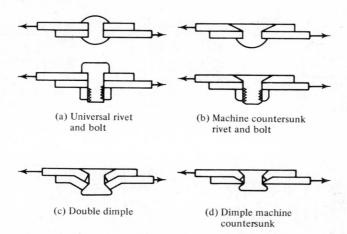

(a) Universal rivet and bolt

(b) Machine countersunk rivet and bolt

(c) Double dimple

(d) Dimple machine countersunk

Fig. 13.1. Single-riveted and bolted lap joint with different types of riveting and bolting for aircraft structures.

strength is the main requirement, whereas in boiler and pipe joints, tightness in addition to strength must be considered. In the first two types of joints, rivets or bolts of the type shown in Figure 13.1a are commonly used. However, if one end of the rivet or bolt must be flush with the surface, as in the outer surface of aircraft structure, one of the arrangements of Figure 13.1b, c, or d may be used. Rivets of the dimpled type (Fig. 13.1c or d) when properly assembled will produce a joint that resists permanent set (often called slip in connection with riveted joints) between the fastened plates and thus improve the tightness of the joint.

Riveted or bolted joints may also be classified as to arrangement of the plates and rivet or bolt patterns. Two widely used types are lap joints and butt joints (see Fig. 13.2), and both lap and butt joints may be single, double, or triple riveted or bolted, and so forth, according to whether one, two, or three rows pierce each of the two plates that are connected. Furthermore, a butt joint may have two cover plates (or straps) or only one cover plate, and both lap and butt joints may have the rivets or bolts arranged in the form of chain (Fig. 13.2b) or in the form of staggered riveting or bolting (Fig. 13.2d and e).

Definitions. The following terms are used in subsequent paragraphs.

The *pitch* of a row of rivets or bolts is the distance between the centers of any two adjacent rivets or bolts in the row. The pitch is not necessarily the same for all rows. Thus, in Figure 13.2e the pitch for the inner rows is denoted by p and for the outer row by p_1, in which p_1 equals $2p$.

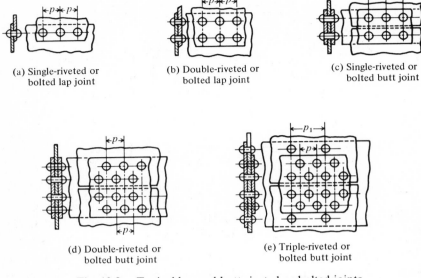

(a) Single-riveted or bolted lap joint

(b) Double-riveted or bolted lap joint

(c) Single-riveted or bolted butt joint

(d) Double-riveted or bolted butt joint

(e) Triple-riveted or bolted butt joint

Fig. 13.2. Typical lap and butt riveted or bolted joints.

A *gusset plate* or *splice plate* is a plate used in structural joints to form part of the joint connecting two or more members of a structure (see Fig. P13.2c). It corresponds to a cover plate or strap in a boiler or pipe butt joint.

The term *efficiency* of a riveted or bolted joint is the ratio of the ultimate (fracture) strength of the joint to the ultimate tensile strength of the solid (unpunched, or unwelded) plate.

13.3. Ultimate Load Analysis for Riveted or Bolted Joints Subjected to Static Loads

The first step is to determine the mode or modes of failure. A riveted or bolted joint is usually considered to fulfill its function satisfactorily in a load-carrying structure until the ultimate or breaking load of the joint is reached, especially when the strength (rather than tightness) of the joint is the main factor considered. Three values of the ultimate load, however, must be obtained because the ultimate load for the joint may be limited by ' the stresses on any one of three areas—namely, the shearing stress on the cross section of the rivet or bolt as in Figure 13.3a, the tensile stress on the cross section of the plate through the holes as in Figure 13.3b, and the

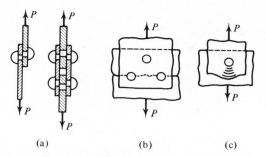

Fig. 13.3. Modes of failure of structural riveted or bolted joint.

bearing (compressive) stress of the rivet or bolt on the plate indicated in Figure 13.3c. It is assumed that other modes of failure will not occur if the usual joint dimensions are specified.

The second step in the procedure is to determine the relationship between the three ultimate loads mentioned in step 1 and the stress that is associated with each of these loads. For this purpose let the single riveted or bolted joint (shown in Fig. 13.4a and b) be chosen. The analysis of this joint will serve to illustrate the solution of this problem for more complicated joints.

Tensile Ultimate Static Load, P_{ut}. Let the joint be cut by a plane section through one plate, severing the plate through the center of the hole (Fig. 13.4c), and let the ultimate load be P_{ut}, which will cause a uniformly distributed stress on the section to be equal to the ultimate tensile strength σ_{ut}. The tensile-stress distribution on the cut section is as shown in Figure 13.4c. From the free-body diagram of Figure 13.4c and the condition of equilibrium, the ultimate load in tension may be written:

$$P_{ut} = t(p - d)\sigma_{ut} \qquad \text{or} \qquad \sigma_{ut} = \frac{P_{ut}}{t(p - d)}. \qquad (13\text{--}1)$$

Shearing Ultimate Static Load, P_{us}. Let the joint be cut by a plane section passing between the two plates and cutting the rivet or bolt in half. Figure 13.4d shows the cross section of the rivet or bolt and Figure 13.4e shows the uniform distribution of the ultimate shearing stress τ_u over the rivet or bolt cross section. The total resisting shearing force is $A_s\tau_u$ where A_s is the cross-sectional area of the rivet or bolt. By making use of the equilibrium condition of the free-body diagram of Figure 13.4e, the shearing ultimate load P_{us} is expressed by the following equation:

$$P_{us} = A_s\tau_u \qquad \text{or} \qquad \tau_u = \frac{P_{us}}{A_s}. \qquad (13\text{--}2)$$

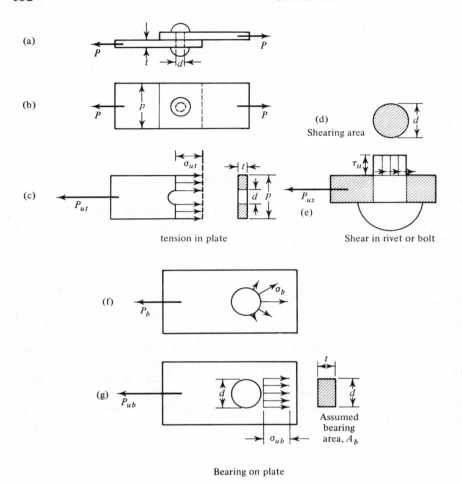

Fig. 13.4. Ultimate load on riveted or bolted joint.

Bearing Ultimate Static Load, P_{ub}. Let the joint be cut so that we obtain Figure 13.4f, and let the bearing (compressive) stresses exerted on the inside of the hole in the plate be as indicated by the radial arrows to the curve around the right side of the hole. The exact shape of this curve is not known. However, as was true in tension of the plate and in shear of the rivet, the first plastic deformation due to the maximum bearing stress as shown in Figure 13.4f usually does not damage the plate. Moreover, it may be assumed that plastic deformation in bearing of the plate will not be excessive until the ultimate compressive stress σ_{ub} is uniformly distributed over an assumed bearing area of dimensions of t by d, where t is the plate thickness and d is the hole diameter. Thus the ultimate load P_{ub} in bearing may be written

$$P_{ub} = A_b\sigma_{ub} = td\sigma_{ub} \qquad \text{or} \qquad \sigma_{ub} = \frac{P_{ub}}{td}. \tag{13-3}$$

The least of the three ultimate loads as given by Equations (13–1), (13–2), and (13–3) is the ultimate load for the joint.

Values of Ultimate Stresses.   The third step in the rational procedure for the ultimate load analysis of a riveted or bolted joint is to determine the values of the ultimate stresses σ_{ut}, σ_{ub}, and τ_u. The tensile ultimate stress σ_{ut} is obtained from a tensile test of a specimen cut from the plate used in the joint. Often the plate material is purchased under standard specifications for such materials and the minimum value of σ_{ut} is guaranteed by the manufacturer. The same is true of the ultimate shearing stress of the rivet material. The ultimate bearing strength to be used in Equation (13–3) is usually taken to be approximately 1.6 times the value of σ_{ut}.

Safety Factor.   The fourth step in the rational procedure for the design of a riveted or bolted joint is to apply a factor of safety to the value of the ultimate load as determined by the least load, P_{ult}, found from the Equations (13–1), (13–2), or (13–3). Let N be the factor of safety and let P_w be the working load for the riveted or bolted joint. Then

$$P_w = \frac{P_{ult}}{N}. \tag{13-4}$$

Equation (13–4) can be written also in terms of working stresses if the value of P_{ult} from the appropriate one of Equations (13–1), (13–2), or (13–3) is substituted in Equation (13–4). For example, let P_{ult} be given by Equation (13–1) and this is substituted into Equation (13–4), which then becomes

$$P_w = \frac{t(p - d)\sigma_{ut}}{N} = t(p - d)\sigma_{wt}, \tag{13-5}$$

where $\sigma_{wt} = \sigma_{ut}/N$ is called the working value of the tensile stress. Similar transformations can be made for P_{ult} taken from Equations (13–2) and (13–3).

Joint with More Than One Rivet or Bolt.   Equations similar to (13–1), (13–2), and (13–3) can be derived for a joint with more than one rivet or bolt. An assumption is usually made when the loads are centrally located on the joint that each cross section of each rivet or bolt resists the same shearing stress. Such an assumption will be true if the least of the ultimate loads is P_{us} the ultimate load in shear. Similarly, an assumption is made that each bearing area between a rivet or bolt and the plate carries the same bearing stress. Such an assumption will be true if the joint fails by bearing.

The illustrative problem that follows will show how the rational procedure is applied.

Illustrative Problem

13.1. The diameter of the rivets or bolts in the butt joint shown in Figure P13.1 is $\frac{7}{8}$ in., the thickness of the main plates is $\frac{3}{4}$ in., the thickness of the cover plates is $\frac{1}{2}$ in. The plates are of an alloy steel for which the ultimate strengths in tension and bearing are $\sigma_{ut} = 75{,}000$ psi, and $\sigma_{ub} = 1.6(75{,}000) = 120{,}000$ psi. The value of the ultimate shearing strength of the rivets or bolts is $\tau_u = 60{,}000$ psi. Compute the working value of the static load P_w for a factor of safety of $N = 5$.

SOLUTION. In accordance with the preceding discussion we compute the ultimate load P_{us} for failure by fracture of the rivets or bolts in shear, P_{ub} for failure of the main plate in bearing, and P_{ut} for failure of the main plate by tensile fracture or failure of the cover plates by tensile fracture.

Because each rivet or bolt has two cross sections subjected to shear (called double shear) the ultimate load P in shear is P_{us} computed as follows:

$$P = P_{us} = 2(5)\frac{\pi(7/8)^2}{4}(60{,}000) = 10(0.601)(60{,}000) = 360{,}600 \text{ lb}.$$

Similarly the ultimate load P in bearing is

$$P = P_{ub} = 5(7/8)(3/4)(120{,}000) = 393{,}600 \text{ lb}.$$

The ultimate load $P = P_{ut}$ for tensile fracture of the plate must be computed for two different cross sections AA and BB of the main plate (Fig. P13.1c and d) and for cross section CC of the cover plates (Fig. P13.1e). The load P is transmitted across the section AA (Fig. P13.1c). The ultimate load in tension for cross section AA is, therefore,

$$P = P_{ut} = \tfrac{3}{4}(8 - 2 \times \tfrac{7}{8})(75{,}000) = 351{,}500 \text{ lb}.$$

The load resisted by, or transmitted across, cross section BB (Fig. P13.1d) is $3P/5$ because $2P/5$ is resisted by the two upper rivets or bolts. Therefore, the ultimate load based on the ultimate tensile stress on cross section BB is

$$\tfrac{3}{5}P = P_{ut} = \tfrac{3}{4}(8 - 3 \times \tfrac{7}{8})(75{,}000) = 302{,}400 \text{ lb},$$

$$P = \tfrac{5}{3}302{,}400 = 504{,}000 \text{ lb}.$$

The load P is transmitted across the section CC of the cover plates in Figure

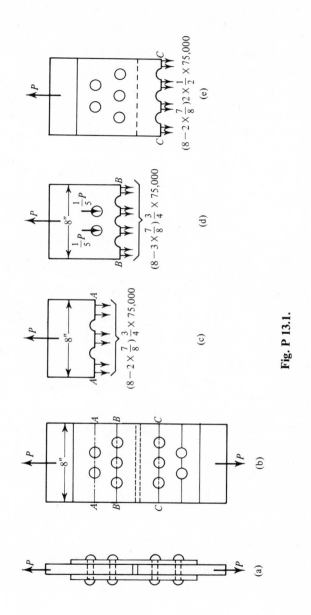

Fig. P 13.1.

P13.1*e*. The ultimate load in tension for cross section CC is, therefore,

$$P = P_{ut} = 2\tfrac{1}{2}(8 - 3 \times \tfrac{7}{8})(75,000) = 403,100 \text{ lb}.$$

The ultimate load P_{ult} for the joint is the minimum of the five values of P that were computed. Therefore

$$P_{ult} = 351,500 \text{ lb}.$$

This load is divided by the factor of safety of $N = 5$, which gives an allowable or working load P_w. Thus,

$$P_w = \frac{P_{ult}}{5} = \frac{351,500}{5} = 70,300 \text{ lb}.$$

Problems

13.2. The members of the Fink truss shown in Figure P13.2*a* are connected by riveted joints. The arrangement of the joint at C is shown in Figure P13.2*b*. Show that the forces in members BC and DC are 13,000 lb compression and 13,000 lb tension, respectively. The rivets are $\tfrac{3}{4}$ in. in diameter. The working or allowable stresses are

$$\sigma_{wt} = 20,000 \text{ psi}, \qquad \tau_w = 15,000 \text{ psi}$$

and

$$\sigma_{wb} = 32,000 \text{ psi (when rivets are in single shear)}.$$

Determine the shearing stress in the rivets connecting the members BC and DC to the gusset plate and in the rivets connecting the gusset plate to the lower chord $ACEG$. Also find the bearing stress of the members BC and DC on the rivets and the tensile stress in CD. Are the computed values less than the corresponding working values?

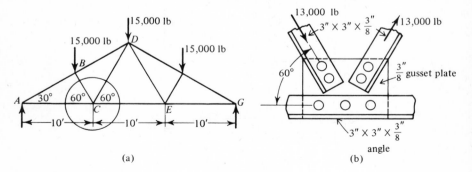

(a)   (b)

Fig. P 13.2.

[*Note.* It will be found that all of these stresses, except the shearing stress in the rivets in *BC* and *DC*, are considerably less than the allowable values. This result is not unusual in a truss such as this, because the force in a compression member such as *BC* is limited to lower values by its buckling strength as discussed in Chapter 11.]

ans. $\tau = 14{,}700$ psi in rivets connecting *BC* and *DC*; $\tau = 9{,}800$ psi in rivets connecting gusset plate to lower chord; $\sigma_b = 23{,}000$ psi for *BC* and *DC*; $\sigma_t = 7{,}100$ psi.

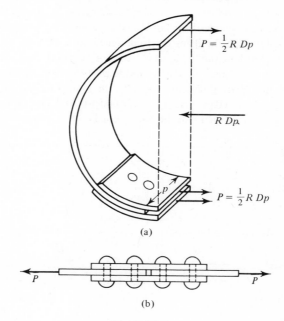

(a)

(b)

Fig. P 13.3.

13.3. A boiler having a diameter D of 68 in. is designed to resist a working internal steam pressure R of 120 psi. The longitudinal joint is a double-riveted butt joint shown in Figure P13.3. The thickness t of the plates is $\frac{7}{16}$ in., the diameter d of the rivets is $\frac{3}{4}$ in., and the pitch is 3.5 in. Assume that, for the material in the rivets and plate, $\tau_u = 40{,}000$ psi, $\sigma_{ut} = 60{,}000$ psi, and $\sigma_{ub} = 90{,}000$ psi. Determine whether this boiler is safe for use at the given pressure by a factor of safety of 5 based on the ultimate strength of the joint. Also determine the efficiency of the joint.

13.4. In an ideal joint the ultimate loads in shear, bearing, and tension are equal. (1) By equating the ultimate shearing load to the ultimate bearing load, show that the diameter of the rivets or bolts in a lap joint is 2.55 times the thickness of the plate ($d = 2.55t$), if the value of $\tau_u = 60{,}000$ psi and $\sigma_{ub} = 120{,}000$ psi are used. (2) Similarly, show that in an ideal butt joint having two cover plates, $d = 1.27t$. Which of these two types of joints is better suited for boilers, pipes, and so forth, having thick plates? *Hint*: If *n* represents the number of rivets or bolts, we have for (1)

$$n\frac{\pi d^2}{4}\tau_u = nt\,d\sigma_{ub} \qquad \text{or} \qquad d = \frac{4}{\pi}\frac{\sigma_{ub}}{\tau_u}t.$$

13.5. By equating the ultimate tensile load to the ultimate bearing load, show that the pitch in an ideal double-riveted or bolted lap joint is four times the diameter of the rivets or bolts ($p = 4d$), if $\sigma_{ut} = 80{,}000$ psi and $\sigma_{ub} = 120{,}000$ psi. Also, show that the efficiency of an ideal double-riveted or bolted lap joint of this material is 75 per cent.

13.6. A boiler 60 in. in diameter is designed to withstand an internal fluid pressure of 80 psi. The longitudinal joint is a single-riveted lap joint; the rivets have a pitch of 2.5 in.; the plates are $\frac{3}{8}$-in. thick, and the rivets are $\frac{7}{8}$-in. in diameter. Find the shearing, tensile, and bearing ultimate loads for the joint using the following values: $\tau_u = 60{,}000$ psi, $\sigma_{ut} = 75{,}000$ psi, and $\sigma_{ub} = 120{,}000$ psi. Also find the efficiency of the joint. What is the factor of safety for the boiler based on the ultimate load?

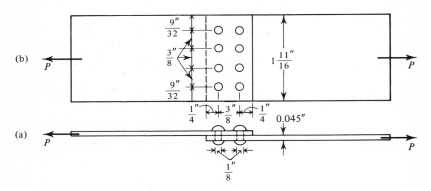

Fig. P 13.7.

13.7. In Figure P13.7 is shown a riveted lap joint connecting two aluminum alloy sheets of Alclad 24S-T3 fastened by rivets of aluminum alloy 24S-T31. Compute the ultimate load for the joint. The ultimate shearing strengths of the sheet and rivets, as given in Strength of Metal Aircraft Elements (ANC-5 Bulletin) are as follows: In shearing of the rivets $\tau_u = 41{,}000$ psi, in tension of the sheet $\sigma_{ut} = 60{,}000$ psi, in bearing of the sheet $\sigma_{ub} = 114{,}000$ psi. *Note*: The value of σ_{ub} specified is less than the value given here when the ratio d/t of the rivet diameter to the sheet thickness is greater than 3 for rivets in single shear and is greater than 1.5 for rivets in double shear. The factors for use in reducing σ_{ub} are given in Table 3.6111(a) of ANC-5 Bulletin. The reason for the reduction in compressive strength is that thin sheet tends to buckle around the rivet hole, owing to the high compressive stresses where the plate is in contact with the rivet.

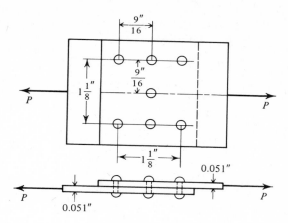

Fig. P 13.8.

13.8. In Figure P13.8 is shown a joint in an aircraft structure that consists of two aluminum alloy sheets of Alclad 24S-T3 fastened by seven $\frac{5}{32}$-in. diameter A17S-T3 aluminum alloy rivets. In ANC-5, June 1951, the following data are given for these metals: for the sheets $\sigma_{ut} = 60,000$ psi and $\sigma_{ub} = 114,000$ psi; for the rivets $\tau_u = 30,000$ psi. By making use of a factor of safety of 1.5 based on the ultimate load and a stress-concentration factor of $k_t = 1.2$, determine the working load for the joint. All marginal distances are $\frac{9}{25}$ in.

ans. $P_w = 2,240$ lb.

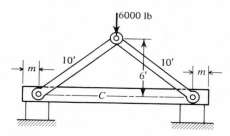

Fig. P 13.9.

13.9. In Figure P13.9, the joints are steel pins 1 in. in diameter, and C is a yellow-pine timber member having a square cross section 6 in. on a side. The ultimate shearing strength of the timber parallel to the grain is 800 psi. In Figure P13.9 assume that the grain is horizontal and that the member does not fail until the ultimate shearing strength of the material on the two shearing areas $2A_s = 12m$ is reached. Use a factor of safety of 6 and calculate the minimum value for the dimension m.

13.4. Ultimate Load Analysis for Riveted or Bolted Joint Subjected to Repeated Loads

Riveted or bolted joints of the types shown in Figure 13.2 that are subjected to repeatedly applied loads usually fail by fracture of the plate. The fracture occurs in a cross-sectional area through the line of rivet or bolt holes in the plate where the maximum value σ_{max} of the average tensile stress, based on the net cross-sectional area, occurs in the plate. The value of σ_{max} associated with fatigue fracture of the plate occurs when the maximum load P_{max} on the joint is applied; however, the value of this stress σ_{max} also depends on the average normal stress σ_{min} on the net cross section through the same holes that occurs when the minimum load P_{min} is applied to the joint. Furthermore, σ_{max} depends on the number of cycles N of application of the loads.

Let A_n be the net area of the cross section through the holes, P_{max} the maximum load, and P_{min} the minimum load. Then

$$\sigma_{max} = \frac{P_{max}}{A_n} \quad \text{and} \quad \sigma_{min} = \frac{P_{min}}{A_n}. \qquad (13\text{–}6)$$

Modified Goodman Diagram for Failure of Bolted Joints.   Figure 13.5a shows a typical bolted lap joint of ASTM A-7 steel with A325 high-strength steel bolts. Fatigue tests of many joints of this type were made* and the results are presented in Figure 13.5b in a modified Goodman diagram (see Section 1.9) as shown by the ordinates σ_{max} to the line AD and the ordinates σ_{min} to the line BD for fatigue fracture at two million cycles of loading. The values of σ_{max} and σ_{min} were computed from the maximum and minimum repeated loads given by the test data by making use of Equations (13–6), in which the area A_n was the net cross-sectional area in Figure 13.5a through the main plate (center) at the bolt line marked nn when the thickness of the main plate was less than the total thickness of the two outer plates; A_n was the net cross-sectional area through the two outer plates at the bolt line marked mm when the total thickness of the outer plates was less than the thickness of the main (center) plate.

The modified Goodman diagram (Fig. 13.5b) for the bolted joint is interpreted as follows: for completely reversed load cycles the stress $\sigma_{max} = 20,000$ psi and $\sigma_{min} = -20,000$ psi, as represented by the ordinates to A and B, respectively; for loads that vary from $P_{min} = 0$ to P_{max}, $\sigma_{min} = 0$ and $\sigma_{max} = 30,000$ psi as represented by the ordinate OC; and the ordinate to

---

* E. Chesson, Jr., and W. H. Munse, "Studies of the Behavior of High Strength Bolts and Bolted Joints," University of Illinois Engineering Experiment Station, Bulletin 469, 1965.

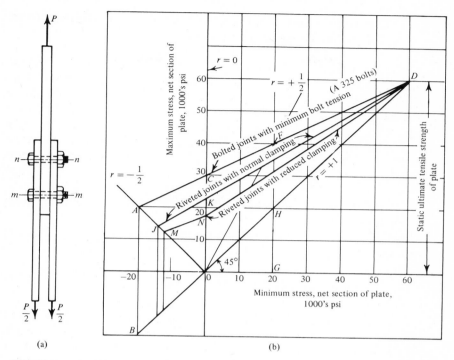

Fig. 13.5. Modified Goodman diagram of bolted or riveted joint of ASTM A7 steel plates. Values of normal stress on the net area of cross section are average stress on the section computed from the maximum and minimum loads. Failure is based on 2,000,000 cycles of load.

the point D represents the static load ultimate tensile strength of the plate, $\sigma_u = 60,000$ psi. One further example will help. Let the load P_{min} be equal to $P_{max}/2$; this fact means that $r = \sigma_{min}/\sigma_{max} = P_{min}/P_{max} = \frac{1}{2}$. The line OF in Figure 13.5b represents the condition that $r = \sigma_{min}/\sigma_{max} = \frac{1}{2}$. OF intersects line AD at $\sigma_{max} = 40,000$ psi and the ordinate to F intersects line BD to give the ordinate $GH = \sigma_{min} = 20,000$ psi.

Modified Goodman Diagram for Failure of Riveted Joint. In Figure 13.5b the ordinate to the lines JKD and BD represents the values of σ_{max} and σ_{min}, respectively, for riveted joints of the type shown in Figure 13.5a (where rivets are used instead of bolts). These data were determined the same way* as for the bolted joint tests of the same grade of steel (ASTM A-7), which

---

* F. Baron and E. W. Larson, Jr., "Results of Static and Fatigue Tests of Riveted and Bolted Joints Having Different Lengths of Grip," *Proceedings of ASTM*, Vol. 53, 1953, pp. 805–823.

were just discussed. These results are interpreted as follows: for completely reversed load cycles the stress $\sigma_{max} = 14,200$ psi and $\sigma_{min} = -14,200$ psi; for loads that vary from $P_{min} = 0$ to P_{max}, $\sigma_{max} = 22,000$ psi and $\sigma_{min} = 0$ as represented by the ordinate OK; and the ordinate to the point D represents the static load ultimate tensile strength of the plate, which is, as before, $\sigma_u = 60,000$ psi, because there is no difference in the static ultimate strength of a riveted and bolted joint of the same dimensions if failure occurs by static load tensile fracture of the plate.

Reason for Difference in Fatigue Strength of Bolted and Riveted Joint. The high-strength bolts used in bolted joints are tightened so that the very high tensile forces in the bolts create a much larger (than the rivets) pressure between the plates. The pressure is accompanied by friction forces between the plates, which always oppose the applied loads. This fact means that the stress σ_{max} on the net cross-sectional area of the plate through the holes is reduced by whatever resistance is offered by the friction forces between the plates. Therefore, the repeated maximum load P_{max} which will cause fatigue fracture failure of the plates in two million cycles in a bolted joint, will be higher than that for the same joint fastened with rivets. When this higher load P_{max} sustained by the bolted joint is divided by the net area A_n, the stress $\sigma_{max} = P_{max}/A_n$ appears to be higher than the corresponding value in the tests of the riveted joint.

Further evidence to support the idea that the friction between the plates influences the results of the tests on the value of σ_{max} is given by the ordinates to the line MND, which gives the values of σ_{max} obtained from tests of riveted joints in which the clamping forces between the plates was reduced by reducing the tensile forces in the rivets. Note that the ordinates to line MND are significantly less than those to line JKD where the results are shown for rivets having the normal or usual tensile forces. Furthermore, the ordinates to the line ACD are significantly increased above those to line JKD when high-strength bolts were used to obtain still higher clamping tensile forces between the plates.

Illustrative Problem

13.10.   A double-lap joint as shown in Figure 13.5a is made of plates of ASTM A-7 steel and fastened with high strength A325 steel bolts, which are tightened as follows: The nut is tightened by the full effort of a man with an ordinary spud wrench; in general this will mean that the nut is turned one-half turn (180°) after it has been tightened to the snug position by hand. This procedure will give the minimum bolt tension necessary for the curves in Figure 13.5b to be applicable. The joint is required to resist a dead load P_d

at all times and an additional load P_L called a live load is applied and released two million times. Let N_d be the factor of safety for the dead load and let N_L be the factor of safety for the live load. Let A_n be the smallest net cross-sectional area of the plates (main plate or the two outer plates, whichever is smaller). (1) By making use of Equations (13–6) and Figure 13.5b derive the relationship needed to determine the dimensions of the joint for a given set of values of P_d, P_L, N_d, and N_L. (2) Let $P_L = P_d$, $N_d = 1.8$, $N_L = 2.2$, $A_n = 3.00$ in.^{2} and determine the values of σ_{max}, σ_{min}, P_d, and P_L from Figure 13.5b and the equation found in the solution of part 1.

SOLUTION—PART (1).   The loads P_d and P_L are each multiplied by the appropriate factor of safety to obtain loads $N_d P_d$ that will be used in computing failure values of σ_{min} and σ_{max} from Equations (13–6):

$$\sigma_{min} = \frac{N_d P_d}{A_n} \tag{a}$$

and

$$\sigma_{max} = \frac{N_d P_d + N_L P_L}{A_n}. \tag{b}$$

The ratio r of the stresses is obtained by dividing Equation (a) by Equation (b) as follows:

$$r = \frac{\sigma_{min}}{\sigma_{max}} = \frac{(N_d P_d / A_n)}{(N_d P_d + N_L P_L)/A_n} = \frac{1}{1 + (N_L P_L / N_d P_d)}. \tag{c}$$

A radial line through point O in Figure 13.5b is drawn with the value of r from Equation (c). The use of Equations (a), (b), and (c) is illustrated in the solution of part 2.

PART (2).   The substitution of the values of $N_L = 2.2$, $N_d = 1.8$ and $P_L = P_d$ into Equation (c) gives

$$r = \frac{1}{1 + (2.2 P_d / 1.8 P_d)} = \frac{1}{2.22}.$$

When a radial line through point O in Figure 13.5b is drawn with this slope (value of r), the intersection with the line ACD gives a value of $\sigma_{max} = 38,700$ psi. Using this value for σ_{max} and Equations (a), (b), and (c), the following values are calculated: $\sigma_{min} = 17,400$ psi; $P_d = 29,000$ lb; $P_L = 29,000$ lb.

Problems

13.11 Through 13.14.   A lap joint is arranged and loaded as shown in Figure 13.5a and is made of plates of ASTM A-7 steel fastened together with high-strength A 325 steel bolts, which are tightened as described in Problem 13.10. There is a dead load P_d on the joint continuously with an additional live load P_L, which may be applied and released two million times. The safety factor for the dead load is N_d and for the live load N_L. Let it be assumed that there are a sufficient number of bolts to resist shearing and bearing stresses and that the failure of the joint, when it occurs, will be due to fatigue fracture across the plate cross section on the area A_n where the average values of the tensile stress is maximum.

13.11. Let $P_d = 50,000$ lb, $P_L = 40,000$ lb, $N_d = 1.8$, $N_L = 2.3$; by making use of the data in Figure 13.5b determine the required value of the cross-sectional area A_n of the plate.

ans. $A_n = 4.55$ in.^{2}

13.12. Let $P_L = 30,000$ lb, $N_d = 1.8$, $N_L = 2.2$, $A_n = 4.00$ in.^{2}; by using the data in Figure 13.5b determine the maximum value of the dead load P_d that can be allowed.

ans. $P_d = 62,000$ lb.

13.13. Let $P_d = 30,000$ lb, $N_d = 1.8$, $N_L = 2.2$, $A_n = 4.00$ in.^{2}; by using the data in Figure 13.5b determine the maximum value of the live load P_L that can be repeatedly applied for 2,000,000 cycles.

ans. $P_L = 42,300$ lb.

13.14. Let the live (repeated) load $P_L = 1.3P_d$, and $N_d = 1.8$, $N_L = 2.2$, and $A_n = 4.00$ in.^{2} Use the data in Figure 13.5b to determine the values of P_L and P_d that can be applied to the joint.

ans. $P_d = 32,200$ lb; $P_L = 41,900$ lb.

13.5. Eccentric Shear Load on Riveted Joint

Let Figure 13.6a represent a gusset plate B, which is fastened by rivets to the flange of column A. The loads P and M will be held in equilibrium by the rivets in which are developed the resisting forces F_1, F_2, F_3, and F_4 as shown in the free-body diagram of Figure 13.6b.

The magnitude and direction of the resisting forces F_1, F_2, F_3, and F_4 for the four rivets in Figure 13.6b must be determined in terms of the magnitude, direction, and location d of load P, the magnitude and sense of moment M, the cross-sectional areas of the rivets, and the location of the rivets. The usual assumption that the gusset plate is a rigid body greatly simplifies the solution of the problem. There is one point (point O to the left of the rivets) that will not be displaced by the action of the loads P and M

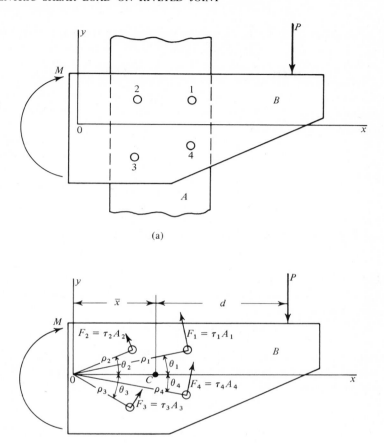

(a)

(b)

Fig. 13.6. Riveted joint subjected to eccentric shear load.

on the gusset plate. This point O is the center about which the gusset plate will rotate (a very small amount). If the gusset plate is assumed to be rigid, the displacement at each rivet will be in a circular path whose center is at O, and hence the displacement of each rivet will be proportional to its distance ρ from the point O to the centroid of the rivet. This also means that each of the resisting forces can be assumed to be perpendicular to the corresponding radius ρ from the point O, as shown in Figure 13.6b.

Let the radii ρ_1, ρ_2, ρ_3, and ρ_4 perpendicular to the corresponding forces F_1, F_2, F_3, and F_4 make angles θ_1, θ_2, θ_3, and θ_4, respectively, with the x-axis, which is taken through the point O and is perpendicular to the action line of the load P. Also, let the point O be at the distance $\bar{x}$ from the centroid C of the four rivet areas and let the load P be located a distance d from the centroid C.

The forces F_1, F_2, F_3, and F_4 may be set equal to $\tau_1 A_1, \tau_2 A_2, \tau_3 A_3$, and $\tau_4 A_4$ where τ_1, τ_2, τ_3, and τ_4 are each equal to the average shearing stress on the rivet cross-sectional areas A_1, A_2, A_3, and A_4, respectively. The equations of equilibrium of the forces on the free-body diagram of Figure 13.6b are as follows:

$$\sum F_x = 0 = \sum_{i=1}^{n} \tau_i A_i \sin \theta_i \tag{13-7}$$

$$\sum F_y = 0 = P - \sum_{i=1}^{n} \tau_i A_i \cos \theta_i \tag{13-8}$$

$$\sum M_0 = 0 = M + P(d + \bar{x}) - \sum_{i=1}^{n} \tau_i A_i \rho_i \tag{13-9}$$

in which n is the number of rivets, $n = 4$, for the riveted joint in Figure 13.6. Equations (13–7) through (13–9) are valid for any riveted joint having any number n of rivets and can be used to determine the average shearing stress τ in each of the rivets when the loads P and M are specified.

Elastic Strain Behavior. Assume that the rivets are made of an elastic material and that the loads P and M are limited to values for which the rivets behave elastically. It has been shown in the foregoing discussion that the displacement of each rivet is directly proportional to the distance ρ from the center of rotation O. Therefore, the shearing strain γ in a given rivet is also directly proportional to the radius ρ of that rivet from O. For elastic behavior of the rivet the shearing stress $\tau = G\gamma$, where G is the shearing modulus of elasticity. Thus, if k is the proportionality constant, the following law of distribution of shearing stress among the rivets is stated:

$$\frac{\tau_1}{\rho_1} = \frac{\tau_2}{\rho_2} = \frac{\tau_3}{\rho_3} = \frac{\tau_4}{\rho_4} = \frac{\tau_i}{\rho_i} = k. \tag{13-10}$$

From Equations (13–10) the relationship $\tau_i = k\rho_i$ is substituted into Equations (13–7) through (13–9), which then are as follows:

$$k \sum_{i=1}^{n} A_i \rho_i \sin \theta_i = 0 \tag{13-11}$$

$$P - k \sum_{i=1}^{n} A_i \rho_i \cos \theta_i = 0 \tag{13-12}$$

$$M + P(d + \bar{x}) - k \sum_{i=1}^{n} A_i \rho_i^2 = 0 \tag{13-13}$$

in which n is the number of rivets equal to 4 for the riveted joint in Figure 13.6. In equation (13–11) the expression $\sum_{i=1}^{n} A_i \rho_i \sin \theta_i$ is equal to the first moment of the rivet cross-sectional areas with respect to the x-axis. Because this first moment is equal to zero, the x-axis must pass through the centroid C of the rivet cross-sectional areas. (Note: x-axis is perpendicular to P.)

In Equation (13–12) the expression $\sum_{i=1}^{n} A_i \rho_i \cos \theta_i$ represents the first moment of the rivet cross-sectional areas with respect to the y-axis. Let A_T be the sum of the rivet cross-sectional areas. Then, the first moment with respect to the y-axis is $A_T \bar{x}$. Hence

$$k \sum_{i=1}^{n} A_i \rho_i \cos \theta_i = k A_T \bar{x},$$

which can be substituted into Equation (13–12) to give

$$\bar{x} = \frac{P}{k A_T}. \tag{13–14}$$

In Equation (13–13) the term $\sum_{i=1}^{n} A_i \rho_i^2$ represents the second moment or polar moment of inertia J_O of the rivet cross-sectional areas with respect to the point O, that is,

$$\sum_{i=1}^{n} A_i \rho_i^2 = J_O. \tag{13–15}$$

Using the parallel-axis theorem (Section A.3 of Appendix A) and setting the polar moment J_C with respect to the centroid of the rivet area, we have

$$J_O = J_C + A_T \bar{x}^2. \tag{13–16}$$

The substitution of Equations (13–14), (13–15), and (13–16) into Equation (13–13) gives the following value of k:

$$k = \frac{M + Pd.}{J_C}. \tag{13–17}$$

The substitution of this expression for k into Equation (13–14) gives

$$\bar{x} = \frac{P}{M + Pd} \frac{J_C}{A_T}. \tag{13–18}$$

The value of $\bar{x}$ determines the location of the center of rotation O; therefore, the values of the radii ρ_i from the center of rotation O to the centers of the rivets can be determined. Finally, the substitution of k from Equation (13–17) into (13–10) gives the magnitude of the shearing stress τ_i in the ith rivet as follows:

$$\tau_i = \rho_i \frac{M + Pd}{J_C}. \tag{13–19}$$

Special Case $M = 0$ **and** $d = 0$. In this case the load P passes through the centroid C. For this special case the value of k given by Equation (13–17) is

$$k = \frac{0 + P(0)}{J_C} = 0.$$

The value of $\bar{x}$ given by Equation (13–18) is

$$\bar{x} = \frac{P}{0 + 0} \frac{J_C}{A_T} = \infty.$$

Because $\bar{x}$ becomes infinite, the value of ρ becomes infinite for each rivet. This fact indicates that the displacement of the gusset plate consists of a translation with no rotation. Thus, the rivets share the load P in such a way that the shearing strain is the same in all rivets. The shearing stress is the same in each rivet and is given by the relation

$$\tau = \frac{P}{A_T}, \tag{13–20}$$

where $A_T = \sum_{i=1}^{n} A_i$ is the sum of the cross-sectional areas of the rivets.

Special Case $P = 0$. For this special case Equation (13–17) gives the value of k as

$$k = \frac{M + 0}{J_C} = \frac{M}{J_C}, \tag{13–21}$$

and Equation (13–18) gives

$$\bar{x} = \frac{0}{M + 0} \frac{J_C}{A_T} = 0. \tag{13–22}$$

Equation (13–22) shows that for the special case in which $P = 0$ the center of rotation O coincides with the centroid C of the rivet cross-sectional areas. Thus the shearing stress τ_i in a given rivet is given by Equation (13–10)

$$\tau_i = \rho_i k = \rho_i \frac{M}{J_C}, \tag{13–23}$$

in which ρ_i is the radial distance from the centroid C to the rivet.

Illustrative Problem

13.15. Solve for the shearing stress in each of the rivets in the gusset plate in Figure P13.15. The rivet diameter of each rivet is $\frac{3}{4}$ in.

FIRST SOLUTION. Because of symmetry the centroid C of the rivet areas is easily located as indicated in Figure P13.15a. The polar moment of

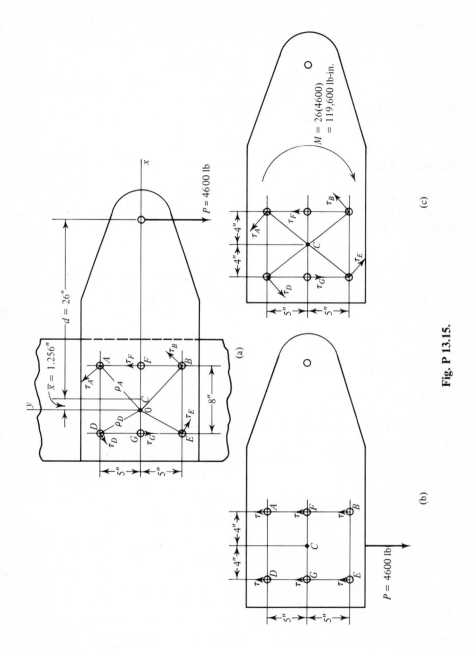

Fig. P 13.15.

inertia J_C of the six rivet cross-sectional areas in Figure P13.15a with respect to the centroid C is

$$J_C = 6\bar{J} + \sum_{i=1}^{6} A_i\bar{\rho}_i^2 = \sum_{i=1}^{6} A_i\bar{\rho}_i^2, \tag{a}$$

in which $\bar{J}$ is the polar moment of inertia of the cross-sectional area of a single rivet about its own centroid, is neglected as being a small quantity. In Equation (a) A_i is the cross-sectional area of the ith rivet and $\bar{\rho}_i$ is the radial distance from the centroid C to the centroid of the ith rivet. From the dimensions given in Figure 13.15a the magnitudes of $\bar{\rho}_i$ can be determined as follows:

$$\bar{\rho}_A = \bar{\rho}_B = \bar{\rho}_D = \bar{\rho}_E = \sqrt{4^2 + 5^2} = 6.40 \text{ in.}; \qquad \rho_F = \rho_G = 4.00 \text{ in.} \tag{b}$$

Equations (a) and (b) give

$$J_C = 4(6.40)^2 A + 2(4.00)^2 A = \frac{196.00\pi(0.75)^2}{4} = 86.6 \text{ in.}^4$$

The sum A_T of the cross-sectional areas of the 6 rivets is as follows:

$$A_T = \frac{6\pi(0.75)^2}{4} = 2.651 \text{ in.}^2$$

From Equation (13–18)

$$\bar{x} = \frac{P}{0 + Pd} \frac{J_C}{A_T} = \frac{4{,}600(86.6)}{4{,}600(26)(2.651)} = 1.256 \text{ in.}$$

Thus, the point 0 is located a distance $\bar{x} = 1.256$ in. to the left of C in Figure P13.15a. The average shearing stress in each rivet is given by Equation (13–19). The various values of ρ_i can be computed as follows:

$$\rho_A = \rho_B = \sqrt{5.256^2 + 5^2} = 7.25 \text{ in.}; \; \rho_D = \rho_E = \sqrt{2.744^2 + 5^2} = 5.70 \text{ in.};$$

$$\rho_F = 5.256 \text{ in.}; \; \rho_G = 2.744 \text{ in.}$$

The substitution of each of these values of ρ_i in Equation (13–19) gives the average shearing stresses in the rivets:

$$\tau_A = \tau_B = \rho_A \frac{Pd}{J_C} = 7.25\frac{4{,}600(26)}{86.6} = 7.25(1{,}380) = 10{,}000 \text{ psi,}$$

$$\tau_D = \tau_E = 5.70(1{,}380) = 7{,}870 \text{ psi,}$$

$$\tau_F = 5.256(1{,}380) = 7{,}250 \text{ psi,}$$

$$\tau_G = 2.744(1{,}380) = 3{,}790 \text{ psi.}$$

In each rivet the shearing stress is perpendicular to the radial distance ρ.

SECOND SOLUTION—METHOD OF SUPERPOSITION. Figure P13.15b shows the central load $P = 4{,}600$ lb passing through the centroid C; Figure P13.15c shows the moment $M = 4{,}600(26) = 119{,}600$ lb-in. The superposition of these two loads gives the equivalent load shown in Figure P13.15a.

In Figure P13.15b we use Equation (13–20) to obtain the shearing stress on each rivet caused by the central load P acting alone as follows:

$$\tau = \frac{P}{A_T} = \frac{4{,}600}{2.651} = 1{,}740 \text{ psi.}$$

In Figure P13.15c we use Equation (13–23) in which $\rho_i = \bar{\rho}_i$ are given by Equations (b) to obtain the shearing stresses in the rivets caused by the moment $M = 119{,}600$ lb-in. Thus,

$$\tau_A = \tau_B = \tau_D = \tau_E = \bar{\rho}_A \frac{M}{J_C} = \frac{6.40(119{,}600)}{86.6} = 8{,}830 \text{ psi,}$$

$$\tau_G = \tau_F = \bar{\rho}_G \frac{M}{J_C} = \frac{4.00(119{,}600)}{86.6} = 5{,}520 \text{ psi.}$$

All the shearing stresses are perpendicular to the radial line from the centroid C to the respective rivet, as indicated in Figure P13.15c.

The resultant shearing stress on the rivet at A, for example, is obtained by determining the vector sum of $\tau_A = 1{,}740$ psi (Fig. P13.15b) and $\tau_A = 8{,}830$ psi (Fig. P13.15c) as shown in Figure P13.15a. The result is $\tau_A = 10{,}000$ psi, which confirms the result found in the first solution.

Problems

13.16. A metal gusset plate is fastened to a wide flange metal column by six metal rivets each $\frac{3}{4}$ in. in diameter. One arrangement of the rivets is shown in Figure

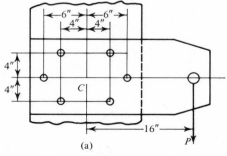

(a)

Fig. P 13.16a.

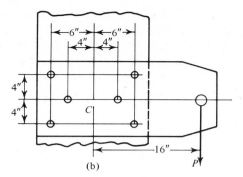

Fig. P 13.16b.

P13.16a and a second arrangement in Figure P13.16b. The distance from the load P to the centroid of the rivet cross-sectional areas is 16 in. in each figure. If the maximum shearing stress in a rivet must not be greater than 11,000 psi, which arrangement of rivets will resist the greater load? What is the maximum value of P?

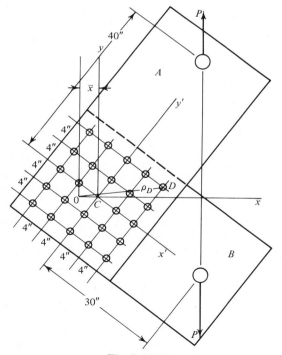

Fig. P 13.17.

13.17. Two rectangular metal plates A and B are fastened together by 24 metal rivets, each $\frac{3}{4}$ in. in diameter, arranged as shown in Figure P13.17. A load $P = 23,000$ lb is transmitted from plate B to plate A through the rivets. Compute the maximum shearing stress in the rivets and show that it occurs in the rivet at D.

Hint: $J_C = I_x + I_y = I_{x'} + I_{y'}$, and the radial distance

$$\rho_D = \sqrt{(x'_D - x'_0)^2 + (y'_D - y'_0)^2}.$$

ans. $\tau_D = 11,000$ psi.

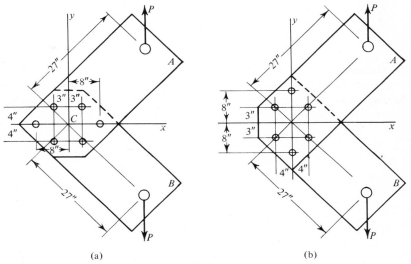

(a)   (b)

Fig. P 13.18.

13.18. Two rectangular metal plates, A and B, have small triangles cut off one corner. The ends with the corner cut off are fastened together by six metal rivets, each 1 in. in diameter. Two different arrangements of the plates and rivets are shown in Figures P13.18a and b. The geometrical arrangement of rivets is the same in both cases, except that in Figure P13.18b it is rotated 90° from that in Figure P13.18a. If a maximum shearing stress of 11,000 psi is allowed in the most highly stressed rivet, which arrangement gives the greater load P? What is the maximum value of P?

13.6. Welded Joints

Welding consists primarily of the joining of two or more pieces of metal (called base metal) by the application of heat, causing localized consolidation

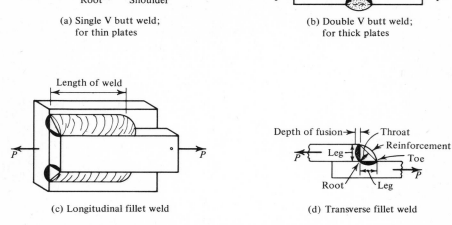

(a) Single V butt weld;
for thin plates

(b) Double V butt weld;
for thick plates

(c) Longitudinal fillet weld

(d) Transverse fillet weld

Fig. 13.7. Common types of welded joints.

of the metal of the pieces. The most common method of welding load-carrying members involves fusion (melting) of the metal—the heat being supplied in several different ways. In fusion welding, pressure between the pieces is not applied. Arc welding, gas welding, and Thermit welding are classified as fusion welding. The most widely used method of fusion welding is metal arc welding, which is a localized progressive melting and flowing together of adjacent edges of the base-metal parts caused by high temperatures produced by an electric arc between a metal electrode or rod and the base metal. The welding material in the form of a welding rod or electrode, together with the adjacent base metals, melts; upon cooling, it solidifies and thereby joins the two or more pieces by continuous material.

The two main classes of welds are fillet welds and butt welds. These two types of welds with the names of the various parts of the welds are shown in Figure 13.7. Attention should be called to the fact, however, that the sketches in Figure 13.7 are rather misleading in indicating lines of demarcation between the base metal and the deposited weld metal because, as already noted, in a satisfactory welded joint the weld consists of nearly uniform metal from the base metal of one member to the base metal of another member. The dark areas indicate the depth of fusion of the weld material with the base metal.

Two other types of welded joints may be used to join members; these are joints formed by plug welding and by spot welding (Fig. 13.8). Plug

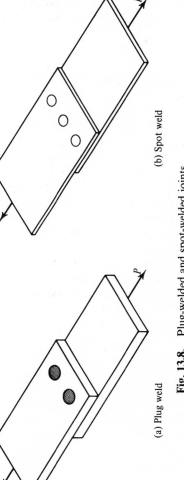

(a) Plug weld

(b) Spot weld

Fig. 13.8. Plug-welded and spot-welded joints.

welding (Fig. 13.8*a*) requires that holes be cut in one of the two plates to be joined. The two plates are made to overlap and the holes are filled with weld metal. Spot welding (Fig. 13.8*b*) is used when relatively thin plates are to be welded together. The plates are made to overlap, two electrodes are pressed against the plates from either side, and an electric arc causes the base metal of the two plates to melt and fuse together. No weld metal is deposited in spot welding.

13.7. Ultimate Load Analysis for Welded Joints Subjected to Static Loads

The first step is to determine the mode of failure. Note that, unlike riveted or bolted joints, welded joints can be made so that the static strength is as strong or stronger than that of either of the members being joined. The discussion that follows assumes that the welded joint is weaker than either of the members being joined and is the location where failure will occur if the loads on the structure are increased. The failure load for a welded joint is assumed to be the ultimate or fracture load. The mode of failure of most welded joints is easily determined because failure occurs on planes of maximum shearing stress through the weld.

The second step in the procedure is to determine the relationship between the ultimate load and the stress associated with this load. Each of the welded joints in Figures 13.7 and 13.8 will be considered.

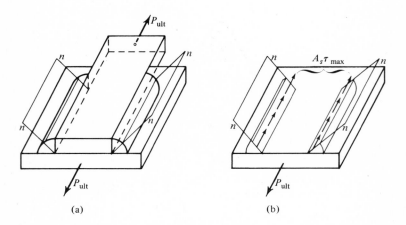

(a)   (b)

Fig. 13.9.   Ultimate load for longitudinal fillet-welded joint.

Ultimate Load for Butt-Welded Joint. Two types of butt-welded joints are shown in Figure 13.7a and b. The design of these joints for static loads does not introduce any problem because the welded joint is as strong as the plates being joined.

Ultimate Load for Longitudinal Fillet-Welded Joint. Let the two ductile metal plates in Figure 13.9a that are joined by the two longitudinal fillet welds be loaded as shown by the static load P. It is required that the ultimate load $P = P_{ult}$ for this joint be determined. The minimum shearing area for the welded joint is through the throat of the weld as indicated by the cutting planes nn in Figure 13.9a. The load P is transmitted through the throat section by the resisting shearing forces as shown in Figure 13.9b. When $P = P_{ult}$, the shearing stress distribution over the shearing areas A_s is assumed to be uniform and equal to the ultimate shearing strength τ_u. From the conditions of equilibrium

$$P = P_{ult} = A_s \tau_u \qquad \text{or} \qquad \tau_u = \frac{P_{ult}}{A_s} \qquad (13\text{--}24)$$

If the two fillet welds have a total length ℓ and have equal legs of length h and the thickness of the reinforcement is negligible (Fig. 13.7d), the shearing area $A_s = \ell h/\sqrt{2} = 0.707\ell h$.

Ultimate Load for Transverse Fillet-Welded Joint. Let the two ductile metal plates in Figure 13.10a that are joined by the transverse fillet weld be loaded as shown by the ultimate static load $P = P_{ult}$. Because the shearing ultimate strength τ_u of the weld metal is less than the tensile ultimate strength σ_u of the weld metal and because the two legs of the weld are assumed to be equal, fracture occurs on the area cut by a cutting plane passed between the two plates to remove the free-body diagram shown in Figure 13.10b. When $P = P_{ult}$, the shearing stress distribution over the shearing area A_s is assumed

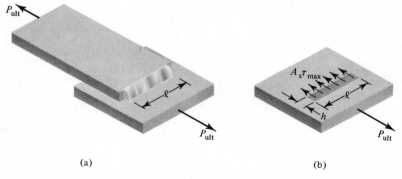

(a) (b)

Fig. 13.10. Ultimate load for transverse fillet-welded joint.

to be uniform and equal to the ultimate shearing strength τ_u. It is seen that Equation (13–24) is valid for this weld and that $A_s = \ell h$, where ℓ is the length of the transverse fillet weld and h is the length of the leg of the weld.

Note: In comparing a transverse fillet weld and a longitudinal fillet weld having the same total length ℓ with the same leg length h, the shearing area A_s for the transverse fillet weld is 41.4 per cent greater than that for the longitudinal fillet weld. It would be expected that the transverse fillet weld would have a strength 41.4 per cent greater than that for the longitudinal fillet weld; however, test data indicate that the difference in strength is only approximately 30 per cent. The usual design procedure is to assume that Equation (13–24) is valid for the transverse fillet weld with A_s equal to the throat area of the weld. Thus, the shearing area A_s to be substituted in Equation (13–24) for a given welded joint is given by the relation

$$A_s = 0.707\ell h, \tag{13–25}$$

where ℓ is the total length of both the longitudinal and the transverse welds and h is the length of each leg of the weld. Equation (13–25) is assumed to be valid in the remainder of this section and Section 13.8.

Ultimate Load for Plug-Welded and Spot-Welded Joints. Equation (13–24) is also valid for the plug welded and spot welded joints in Figure 13.8a and b, respectively. The shearing areas A_s in each case is obtained by determining the cross-sectional area of a single plug weld or spot weld and multiplying by the number of plug welds or spot welds for the joint.

Values of Ultimate Shearing Stress. The third step in the rational procedure for the ultimate load analysis of a welded joint is to determine the value of the ultimate shearing strength τ_u for the material in each welded joint. Except for the spot weld, the material for which τ_u is to be determined is the weld metal deposited in the weld. It should be expected that the deposited weld metal will have a different ultimate shearing strength than the original weld rod. An accurate value of τ_u for the deposited weld metal can be obtained only by making a welded joint and loading it to fracture. In most welded joints, the weld metal has a higher strength than the base metal. In this case a conservative estimate of τ_u for the weld metal is to determine the ultimate strength σ_u of the base metal from tensile tests and assume that $\tau_u = 2\sigma_u/3$.

Safety Factor. The fourth step in the rational procedure for the design of a welded joint is to apply a factor of safety to the value of the ultimate load P_{ult}, as determined from Equation (13–24). Let N_f be the factor of safety and let P_w be the working load for the welded joint. Then

$$P_w = \frac{P_{ult}}{N_f}. \tag{13–26}$$

If the value of P_{ult} given by Equation (13–24) is substituted into Equation (13–26), the working load P_w is given in terms of the working shearing stress as follows:

$$P_w = \frac{A_s \tau_u}{N_f} = A_s \tau_w, \tag{13–27}$$

where $\tau_w = \tau_u/N_f$ is called the working value of the shearing stress.

Illustrative Problem

13.19. A 5-in. by 3.5-in. by $\frac{1}{2}$-in. steel angle section has a cross-sectional area of 4.00 in.^{2} and is welded to a flat plate by the transverse fillet weld and two longitudinal welds each having equal legs of $\frac{1}{2}$ in. as shown in Figure P13.19a. The angle section is subjected to a tension load of $P = 50,000$ lb whose line of action is located as shown. The transverse fillet weld has a length of 5 in. Determine the length of each of the two longitudinal fillet welds in order for the shearing stress to be uniformly distributed in the throat of the weld. The ultimate shearing strength of the weld metal is $\tau_u = 42,000$ psi and the factor of safety is $N_f = 3.00$.

SOLUTION. The working shearing stress for the weld metal is

$$\tau_w = \frac{\tau_u}{N_f} = \frac{42,000}{3.00} = 14,000 \text{ psi.}$$

The shearing area A_s is given by Equation (13–27) as follows:

$$A_s = \frac{P_w}{\tau_w} = \frac{50,000}{14,000} = 3.57 \text{ in.}^2$$

Each unit length of the weld is assumed to carry the same portion q of the load; the total length ℓ of the weld is given by Equation (13–25).

$$\ell = \frac{A_s}{0.707h} = \frac{3.57}{0.707(\frac{1}{2})} = 10.10 \text{ in.}$$

The magnitude of q is given by the relation

$$q = \frac{P}{\ell} = \frac{50,000}{10.10} = 4,950 \text{ lb/in.}$$

The lengths of the two longitudinal welds ℓ_1 and ℓ_2 are obtained by considering the free-body diagram in Figure P13.21b. Equations of

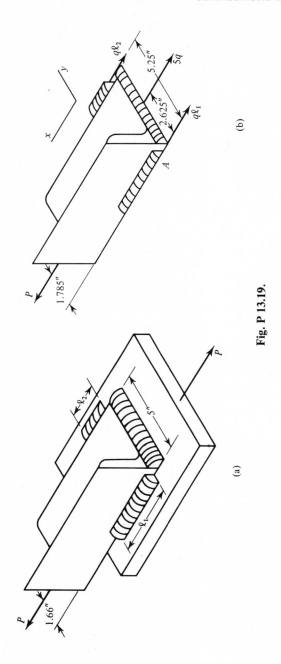

Fig. P 13.19.

equilibrium give

$$\sum F_x = 0 = P - (5.00 + \ell_1 + \ell_2)q$$

$$\sum M_A = 0 = 1.785P - 5.00q(2.625) - \ell_2 q(5.25)$$

from which, when the value of $q = 4,950$ lb/in. is substituted, we get

$$\ell_1 = 4.166 \text{ in.}$$

$$\ell_2 = 0.934 \text{ in.}$$

Problems

13.20. A steel bar 3.5-in. wide, $\frac{1}{2}$-in. thick, and 20-ft long is connected by a fillet-welded joint at one end to a plate as shown in Figure 13.9. The two longitudinal welds have equal legs with a length of $\frac{1}{2}$ in. The ultimate shearing strength of the weld is $\tau_u = 45,000$ psi and the yield strength of the steel bar is $\sigma_e = 45,000$ psi. Determine the magnitude of the load P carried by the joint if the factor of safety against yielding in the bar is 2.00. What is the length of each of the two longitudinal fillet welds if the factor of safety against fracture of the welds is 3.00?

ans. $P = 39,400$ lb; each weld is 3.72-in. long.

13.21. Let the angle section in Problem 13.19 be subjected to a load $P = 25,000$ lb whose line of action is located 1.66 in. along the 5-in. leg from the corner at the junction of the two legs of the angle section. Two longitudinal welds with $\frac{1}{2}$-in. legs are located along the two edges of the 5-in. width. Determine the lengths of each of the two welds if each weld is assumed to have a uniform shearing stress of $\tau_w = 15,800$ psi.

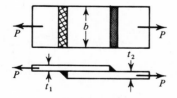

Fig. P 13.22.

13.22. In Figure P13.22, $t_1 = t_2 = \frac{1}{2}$ in. and $b = 6$ in. It may be assumed that each weld transmits one half the load and that $\tau_u = 35,000$ psi for the weld material. Calculate the ultimate load P for the joint based on the usual assumption that the shearing stress in the throat of the weld is equal to the load divided by the area of the throat of the weld.

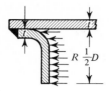

Fig. P 13.23.

13.23. In Figure P13.23, $t = \frac{3}{8}$ in. and the diameter D of the pressure vessel is 5 ft. If the steam pressure R in the pressure vessel is 100 psi, calculate the average shearing stress on the section through the throat of the weld. What is the factor of safety based on the ultimate strength of the weld if $\tau_u = 42{,}000$ psi?

13.24. Figure P13.24 shows a fixture in an aircraft structure in which a gusset plate of thickness $t = 0.050$ in. is welded into the corner of two intersecting tubes, each of which has a wall thickness of 0.058 in. The gusset plate transmits a diagonal (45°)

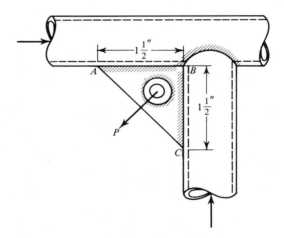

Fig. P 13.24.

load P to the tubes. The gusset plate and the tubes are made of an alloy steel, and the ultimate shearing strength on the throat area of the fillet weld connecting the gusset plate and tubes is $\tau_u = 43{,}000$ psi. Find the working load for this fixture using a factor of safety of 1.5. Assume that each leg of the weld is $h = 0.040$ in. The fillet weld is on both sides of the plate.

13.8. Ultimate Load Analysis for Butt Welds, Longitudinal Fillet Welds, and Transverse Fillet Welds Subjected to Repeated Loads

Welded joints that are subjected to repeatedly applied loads fail by fracture of either the weld or base metal depending on the type of weld and the relative dimensions of the weld and the two members being joined. Fatigue data for welded joints are usually presented in the form of a modified Goodman diagram. Some of the available data* for welded joints of ASTM A-7 steel using either E6010, E6012, or E7016 electrodes are presented in the paragraphs that follow.

Modified Goodman Diagram for Failure of Butt-Welded Joints. Figure 13.7a and b show typical butt-welded joints. The two plates being joined are assumed to have the same cross-sectional dimensions to eliminate the stress concentration due to changes in geometry at the welded joint. Note that the weld reinforcement (see Fig. 13.7) causes a small change in geometry; the removal of the reinforcement may increase the fatigue strength of the joint 10 to 20 per cent. A modified Goodman diagram for fatigue failure at two million cycles of loading for the butt-welded joints of ASTM A-7 steel with reinforcement on are shown in Figure 13.13 by line AD for $\sigma_{max} = P_{max}/A$ and by line BD for $\sigma_{min} = P_{min}/A$ where A is the cross-sectional area of the plates being joined.

The modified Goodman diagram (Fig. 13.13) for the butt-welded joint is interpreted as follows: for completely reversed load cycles $\sigma_{max} = 14,000$ psi and $\sigma_{min} = -14,000$ psi, as represented by the ordinates to A and B, respectively; for loads that vary from $P_{min} = 0$ to P_{max}, $\sigma_{min} = 0$ and $\sigma_{max} = 24,000$ psi as represented by the ordinate $0C$; and the ordinate to the point D represents the static load ultimate tensile strength of the plate, $\sigma_u = 60,000$ psi.

Modified Goodman Diagram for Failure of Longitudinal Fillet-Welded Joints. A typical longitudinal welded joint is shown in Figure 13.11. Fatigue failure of these welded joints occurs either through the throat of the weld or through the base metal of the side plates at the stress concentration located at the front of the longitudinal weld (as indicated in Fig. 13.11), depending on the length of the longitudinal welds. Assuming that the longitudinal weld is sufficiently short so that fatigue failure occurs through the throat of the weld, the modified Goodman diagram for fatigue failure at two million cycles of loading is indicated in Figure 13.13 by line GD for $\tau_{max} = P_{max}/A_s$ and by line HD for $\tau_{min} = P_{min}/A_s$, where A_s is the total throat area. If the fatigue failure occurs through the base metal, the modified

* Prepared by W. H. Munse and edited by La Motte Grover, "Fatigue of Welded Steel Structures," Welding Research Council, 1964.

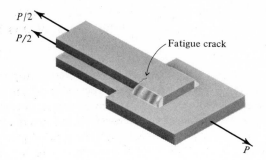

Fig. 13.11.   Longitudinal fillet-welded joint subjected to fatigue loading.

Goodman diagram for fatigue failure at two million cycles of loading is indicated in Figure 13.13 by line JD for $\sigma_{max} = P_{max}/A$ and by line KD for $\sigma_{min} = P_{min}/A$, where A is the cross-sectional area of the two side plates. The fatigue strength of the plate without a stress concentration is about 4.5 times greater than the same plate with a longitudinal fillet weld.

Modified Goodman Diagram for Failure of Transverse Fillet-Welded Joints.   A typical transverse fillet-welded joint is shown in Figure 13.12.

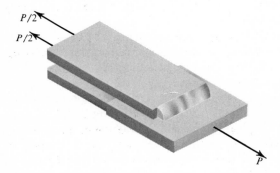

Fig. 13.12.   Transverse fillet-welded joint subjected to fatigue loading.

Fatigue failure of these joints always occurs either in the weld or in the weld effected zone of the base metal. In either case the modified Goodman diagram for fatigue failure at two million cycles of loading is indicated by line GD for $\tau_{max} = P_{max}/A_s$ and by line HD for $\tau_{min} = P_{min}/A_s$, where A_s is the throat area. Thus, the fatigue strengths of longitudinal fillet-welded joints and transverse fillet-welded joints are assumed to be the same as shown by GD; test data indicate that the difference is slight.

Illustrative Problem

13.25. The side plates for the welded joint in Figure 13.11 have cross-sectional dimensions of 6 in. by $\frac{3}{4}$ in. The joint is subjected to a dead load of $P_D = 30,000$ lb and to 2,000,000 cycles of live load that varies from zero to P_L. Determine P_L and the length L of each of the four longitudinal fillet welds based on the following conditions: the fatigue failure is assumed to occur simultaneously in the plate and in the throat of the welds; the factor of safety for P_D is $N_D = 1.50$; the factor of safety for P_L is $N_L = 2.00$.

SOLUTION. The minimum load P_{min} at failure is given by the relation

$$P_{min} = N_D P_D = 1.5(30,000) = 45,000 \text{ lb.}$$

Assume that fatigue failure will occur in tension in the side plates. The tensile cross-sectional area of the side plates is $A = 2(6)(\frac{3}{4}) = 9.00$ in.^{2} and σ_{min} is given by the relation

$$\sigma_{min} = \frac{P_{min}}{A} = \frac{45,000}{9} = 5,000 \text{ psi.}$$

The magnitude of σ_{max} is given by the ordinate to curve JD in Figure 13.13 when the abscissa is $\sigma_{min} = 5,000$ psi. This ordinate is found to be

$$\sigma_{max} = 12,000 \text{ psi} \qquad \text{and} \qquad P_{max} = \sigma_{max}A = 12,000(9) = 108,000 \text{ lb.}$$

But

$$P_{max} = P_{min} + N_L P_L \qquad \text{and} \qquad 108,000 = 45,000 + 2.00 P_L$$

$$P_L = 31,500 \text{ lb.}$$

The length L of each of the four longitudinal fillet welds is now determined. The shearing area through the throat of the welds is given by Equation (13–25).

$$A_s = 0.707 \ell h = 0.707(4L)h = 0.707(4L)\tfrac{3}{4} = 2.121L.$$

The maximum and minimum values of the average shearing stress in the throat of the welds are given by the relations

$$\tau_{max} = \frac{P_{max}}{A_s} = \frac{108,000}{2.121L} = \frac{50,900}{L} \qquad \text{or} \qquad L = \frac{50,900}{\tau_{max}}, \tag{a}$$

$$\tau_{min} = \frac{P_{min}}{A_s} = \frac{45,000}{2.121L} = \frac{21,200}{L} \qquad \text{or} \qquad L = \frac{21,200}{\tau_{min}}.$$

The magnitude of L is obtained using a trial-and-error solution along with curve GD in Figure 13.13. Assume $\tau_{min} = 15,000$ psi and read from the curve

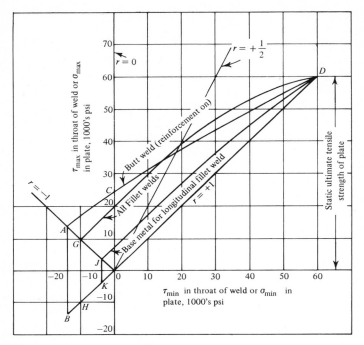

Fig. 13.13. Modified Goodman diagrams of welded joints of ASTM A7 steel using either E6010, E6020, or E7016 electrodes. Failure is based on 2,000,000 cycles of load. From W. H. Munse.

$\tau_{max} = 34,000$ psi. The calculated values of L using Equations (a) are

$$L = \frac{50,900}{34,000} = 1.46 \text{ in.} \quad \text{and} \quad L = \frac{21,200}{15,000} = 1.41 \text{ in.}$$

For a second trial, assume $\tau_{min} = 14,000$ psi and read from curve GD $\tau_{max} = 33,600$ psi. The calculated values of L using Equations (a) are

$$L = \frac{50,900}{33,600} = 1.51 \text{ in.} \quad \text{and} \quad L = \frac{21,200}{14,000} = 1.51 \text{ in.}$$

Thus, the length of each of the four longitudinal fillet welds is 1.51 in.

Problems

13.26. The side plates for the transverse fillet-welded joint in Figure 13.12 have cross-sectional dimensions of 6 in. by $\frac{1}{2}$ in. The length of each of the two welds is 6 in.

and each leg of the welds is $\frac{1}{2}$ in. The joint is subjected to a dead load $P_D = 20,000$ lb and to 2,000,000 cycles of live load that varies from zero to P_L. Determine the magnitude of P_L based on the following factors of safety: $N_D = 1.80$ and $N_L = 2.20$.

ans. $P_L = 37,600$ lb.

13.27. The side plates for the longitudinal fillet-welded joint in Figure 13.11 have cross-sectional dimensions of 12-in. by 1-in. Each of the four welds have a length of 2 in. The joint is subjected to 2,000,000 cycles of load that varies from zero to P_{max}. Determine the magnitude of P_{max} to cause fatigue failure of the joint.

13.28. The pressure vessel in Problem 13.23 is made by shaping a plate into the 5 ft diameter circle and joining the edges by a butt weld parallel to the axis of the pressure vessel. The pressure in the pressure vessel is cycled from zero to 100 psi two million times. What is the factor of safety for the pressure vessel (1) based on the strength of the butt weld, and (2) based on the fillet welds that are used to attach the ends of the pressure vessel as shown in Figure P13.23.

Second Moment or Moment of Inertia of an Area

A.1. Moment of Inertia of an Area Defined

In deriving load-stress relations for torsion members and for beams we find it necessary to find solutions for the following integrals:

$$I_x = \int y^2 \, da, \qquad\qquad (A-1)$$

$$I_y = \int x^2 \, da, \qquad\qquad (A-2)$$

$$J = \int \rho^2 \, da. \qquad\qquad (A-3)$$

In these integrals the element of area da is an infinitesimal part of the cross-sectional area A of a shaft or beam. Before deriving load-stress relations for torsion members and beams, we find it convenient to define these integrals and to consider methods of obtaining solutions to these integrals.

Consider an area A lying in the xy-plane as shown in Figure (A.1). This area is the cross-sectional area of a shaft or beam having general cross section. The element of area da is located at a distance x from the y-axis, at a distance y from the x-axis, and at a distance ρ from the z-axis. The integral in Equation (A–1) has the term $y^2 \, da$ where the distance y is the moment arm for the element of area da about the x-axis; therefore, the term $y^2 \, da$ is the second moment of the element of area da about the x-axis. The solution of this integral gives the sum of all of the terms $y^2 \, da$ for all of the other elements of area for the cross section. Thus, the integral in Equation

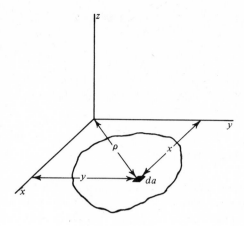

Fig. A.1.

(A–1) is the second moment of the area A about the x-axis. The integrals in Equations (A–1), (A–2), and (A–3) are commonly called moment of inertia of the area on account of the fact that the expression is of the same form as an expression defined as the moment of inertia of a body in the field of dynamics. Obviously, the area A does not have an inertia so that moment of inertia of an area is a misnomer.

The second moment of an area is given the symbol I if the axis lies in the plane of the area (see Eqs. A–1 and A–2). When the axis is perpendicular to the area (see Eq. A–3), the second moment of the area is called the *polar moment of inertia* and is given the symbol J.

Units and Sign. The units of I_x, I_y, and J can be obtained by considering the units of the terms under the integrals in Equations (A–1), (A–2), and (A–3). The element of area da has units of an area (in.^{2}) while x, y, and ρ are all lengths having dimensions of inches because cross-sectional dimensions are usually expressed in inches. Thus, I_x, I_y, and J each have dimensions of inches to the fourth power (in.^{4}). Because da is always positive and a length squared is always positive regardless of whether the length is positive or negative, the integrals given by Equations (A–1), (A–2), and (A–3) are always positive.

A.2. Radius of Gyration

The solution of the integral in either Equation (A–1), (A–2), or (A–3) gives a magnitude with dimensions of in.^{4} This magnitude obviously is equal to the product of the area A and the square of a distance r. Thus,

$$I_x = \int y^2 \, da = Ar_x^2: \qquad I_y = \int x^2 \, da = Ar_y^2; \qquad J = \int \rho^2 \, da = Ar_z^2. \tag{A-4}$$

The distance r is called the *radius of gyration* of the area with respect to the given axis; the subscript denotes the axis with respect to which the moment of inertia is taken.

A.3. Parallel Axis Theorem

If the moment of inertia of an area with respect to a centroidal axis in the plane of the area is known, the moment of inertia with respect to any axis in the plane parallel to the given axis may be determined, without integrating,

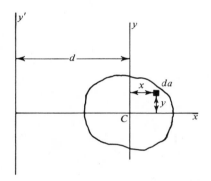

Fig. A.2.

by means of a proposition established as follows: In Figure A.2, let the y-axis be any axis through the centroid C of an area, and let the y'-axis be any axis parallel to the y-axis and at a distance d therefrom. Furthermore, let the moment of inertia of the area with respect to the y-axis be denoted by $\bar{I}_y$ and the moment of inertia with respect to the y'-axis be denoted by I'_y. By definition then,

$$I'_y = \int (x + d)^2 \, da = \int x^2 \, da + 2d \int x \, da + d^2 \int da.$$

Therefore,

$$I'_y = \bar{I}_y + Ad^2 \qquad \text{because} \qquad \int x \, da = A\bar{x} = 0. \tag{A-5}$$

The following proposition may be stated:

> *The moment of an area with respect to either any axis in the plane of the area or any axis perpendicular to the plane of the area is equal to the moment of inertia of the area with respect to a parallel centroidal axis plus the product of the area and the square of the distance between the two axes. This proposition is called the parallel axis theorem.*

A corresponding relation exists between the radii of gyration of the area with respect to two parallel axes, one of which passes through the centroid of the area. For, by replacing I'_y by Ar_y^2 and $\bar{I}_y$ by $A\bar{r}_y^2$, Equation (A–5) becomes

$$Ar_y^2 = A\bar{r}_y^2 + Ad^2.$$

Therefore,

$$r_y^2 = \bar{r}_y^2 + d^2, \qquad\qquad \text{(A–6)}$$

where r_y denotes the radius of gyration of the area with respect to the y'-axis and $\bar{r}_y$ denotes the radius of gyration of the area with respect to the parallel centroidal y-axis.

Illustrative Problems

A.1.   Determine the moment of inertia of a rectangle in terms of its base b and height h, with respect to (1) a centroidal axis parallel to the base; (2) an axis coinciding with the base.

SOLUTION TO PART (1)—CENTROIDAL AXIS: The element of area da is selected so that all of da is at the same distance y from the centroidal x-axis as indicated in Figure PA.1. The moment of inertia of the rectangle with

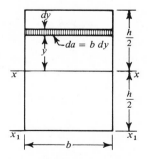

Fig. P A.1.

respect to the x-axis is given by Equation (A–1):

$$I_x = \int y^2 \, da = \int_{-h/2}^{+h/2} y^2 b \, dy = \tfrac{1}{12}bh^3. \tag{a}$$

The value of $\bar{I}_x = bh^3/12$ given by Equation (a) for the rectangular area is widely used and should be remembered.

SOLUTION TO PART (2)—AXIS COINCIDING WITH THE BASE. The moment of inertia for the rectangle for the x'-axis through the base in Figure PA.1 can be obtained using either Equation (A–1) or Equations (a) and (A–5). Using Equations (A–5) and (a),

$$I'_x = \bar{I}_x + A\left(\frac{h}{2}\right)^2 = \frac{1}{12}bh^3 + bh\frac{h^2}{4} = \frac{1}{3}bh^3$$

A.2. Locate the x-axis through the centroid of the T-section shown in Figure PA.2 and find the moment of inertia of the area with respect to this centroidal axis.

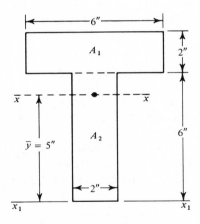

Fig. P A.2.

SOLUTION. The distance $\bar{y}$ of the x-axis from the x_1-axis may be found from the equation

$$A\bar{y} = A_1\bar{y}_1 + A_2\bar{y}_2.$$

Thus,

$$\bar{y} = \frac{12(7) + 12(3)}{12 + 12} = 5.00 \text{ in.}$$

The moment of inertia with respect to the x-axis is obtained using the parallel axis theorem (Eq. A–5) on the two areas A_1 and A_2:

$$\bar{I}_x = \bar{I}_1 + A_1\bar{y}_1^2 + \bar{I}_2 + A_2\bar{y}_2^2 = \frac{6(2)^3}{12} + 12(2)^2 + \frac{2(6)^3}{12} + 12(2)^2 = 136 \text{ in.}^4$$

Problems

A.3. Determine the moment of inertia of a triangle, in terms of its base b and height h, with respect to a centroidal axis parallel to the base.

$$\text{ans.} \quad \bar{I} = bh^3/36.$$

A.4. Determine the polar moment of inertia of the area of a circle of radius R and diameter D with respect to a centroidal axis.

$$\text{ans.} \quad \bar{J} = \pi R^4/2 = \pi D^4/32.$$

A.5. Show that $J = I_x + I_y$ for all cross sections. Consider a circular cross section with radius R and diameter D and let the x- and y-axes pass through the centroid. Show that $\bar{I}_y = \bar{J}/2$. Determine $\bar{I}_x$ for the area of a circle.

A.6. Show that $\bar{J} = 2\bar{I} = \pi(R_1^4 - R_2^4)/2$ for a hollow circular area with outer radius R_1 and inner radius R_2.

A.7. Determine the moments of inertia of the area of an ellipse, the principal axes of which are $2b$ and $2h$, with respect to the principal axes.

$$\text{ans.} \quad \bar{I}_b = \pi bh^3/4; \quad \bar{I}_h = \pi hb^3/4.$$

A.8. Determine, by use of Equation A–3, the polar moment of inertia of the area of a rectangle of base b and altitude h with respect to the centroidal axis.

$$\text{ans.} \quad \bar{J} = \tfrac{1}{12}bh(b^2 + h^2).$$

A.9. The base of a triangle is 8 in., its altitude is 10 in. Find the moment of inertia and radius of gyration of the area of the triangle with respect to the base.

A.10. Find the polar moment of inertia, with respect to a centroidal axis, of the area of an isosceles triangle having a base b and altitude h.

$$\text{ans.} \quad \bar{J} = \tfrac{1}{12}bh(\tfrac{1}{4}b^2 + \tfrac{1}{3}h^2).$$

A.11. A wooden member is built up by nailing four 2-in. by 8-in. planks together to form a member whose cross section is a hollow rectangle having external dimensions of 8 in. by 12 in. Let the x-axis be parallel to the 8-in. dimension and pass through the centroid. Determine $\bar{I}_x$.

A.12. Two 5-in. by 1-in. steel plates are welded together to form a T-section member. Locate the x-axis through the centroid of the T-section parallel to the flange and find the moment of inertia of the cross section with respect to this centroidal axis.

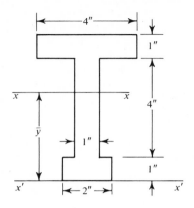

Fig. P A.13.

A.13. Locate the x-axis through the centroid of the I-section shown in Figure PA.13 and find the moment of inertia of the area with respect to this centroidal axis.

ans. $\bar{y} = 3.50$ in.; $\bar{I}_x = 40.83$ in.^{4}

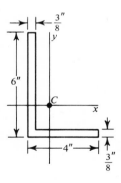

Fig. P A.14.

A.14. Find the moment of inertia of the angle section (Fig. PA.14) with respect to each of the centroidal axes parallel to the two legs of the angle.

A.4. Approximate Method

It is sometimes necessary to determine the moment of inertia of an area that has a boundary curve that cannot be defined by a mathematical equation. An approximate value of the moment of inertia of such an area may be found by the following method. For convenience, however, a simple area will be selected so that the approximate value of the moment of inertia as determined by this method may be compared with the exact value. Thus, let the moment of inertia of the area of a rectangle, with respect to an axis coinciding with its base, be found. The area may be divided into any convenient number of equal narrow strips parallel to the base, as shown in Figure A.3; the narrower the strips, the more closely will the result agree

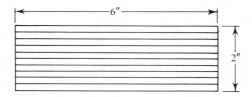

Fig. A.3.

with the exact result. Let the area be divided into ten such strips each 0.2 in. in thickness. The moment of inertia of the rectangle is equal to the sum of the moments of inertia of the strips. The moment of inertia of any particular strip with respect to the base of the rectangle is

$$\frac{1}{12}(6)(0.2)^3 + 6(0.2)y^2,$$

where y is the distance of the center of the particular strip from the base. The first term is small and may be omitted without serious error. The moment of inertia of each strip then is approximately equal to the product of the area of the strip and the square of the distance of its center from the base. Hence, the moment of inertia of the rectangle is

$$I = \tfrac{6}{5}(0.1^2 + 0.3^2 + 0.5^2 + 0.7^2 + 0.9^2 + 1.1^2 + 1.3^2 + 1.5^2 + 1.7^2 + 1.9^2)$$

$$= 15.96 \text{ in.}^4$$

According to Problem A.1, the exact value is

$$I = \tfrac{1}{3}bh^3 = \tfrac{1}{3}(6)(2)^3 = 16 \text{ in.}^4$$

A.5. Product of Inertia Defined

If the moments of inertia of an area with respect to any two rectangular axes are known, the moment of inertia with respect to any other axis passing through the point of intersection of the two axes frequently may be obtained most easily in terms of the moments of inertia of the area with respect to the two rectangular axes and an expression of the form $\int xy \, da$, in which da is an element of the given area and x and y are the coordinates of the element with respect to the two rectangular axes. This expression is called the *product of inertia* of the area with respect to the axes and is denoted by I_{xy}. Hence, the product of inertia of an area with respect to any two rectangular axes may be defined as the sum of the products obtained by multiplying each element of area by the product of the two coordinates of the element with respect to the two rectangular axes. That is,

$$I_{xy} = \int xy \, da. \tag{A-7}$$

The product of inertia of an area, like the moment of inertia of an area, is of four dimensions of length and therefore is expressed as inches (or feet, and so forth) to the fourth power (in.^{4}, ft^4, and so forth). Unlike the moment of inertia, however, the product of inertia of an area is not always positive, but may be negative or may be zero, because either x or y may be negative and hence their product may be negative, and the sum of the products may be equal to zero.

Axes of Symmetry. The product of inertia of an area with respect to two rectangular axes is zero if either one of the axes is an axis of symmetry. This follows from the fact that, for each product $xy \, da$ for an element on one side of the axis of symmetry, there is an equal product of opposite sign for the corresponding element on the other side of the axis, and hence the expression $\int xy \, da$ equals zero.

Illustrative Problems

A.15. Find the product of inertia of the area of the triangle, shown in Figure PA.15, with respect to the x- and y-axes. Reader should solve part b.

SOLUTION. For Figure PA.15a, the equation of the diagonal of the triangle is $y = h/3 - hx/b$. Hence,

$$\bar{I}_{xy} = \int xy \, da = \int_{-b/3}^{2b/3} \int_{-h/3}^{h(b-3x)/3b} xy \, dx \, dy$$

$$= \frac{h^2}{6b^2} \int_{-b/3}^{2b/3} (3x^3 - 2bx^2) \, dx = -\frac{b^2 h^2}{72}.$$

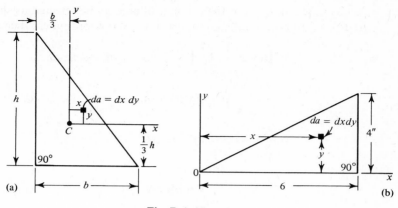

Fig. P A.15.

A.16. Find the product of inertia of the area of the quadrant of a circular area (Fig. PA.16) with respect to the x- and y-axes, in terms of its radius R.

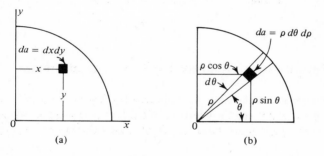

Fig. P A.16.

SOLUTION—FIRST METHOD. Let the element of area da be selected as shown in Figure PA.16a and expressed in terms of rectangular coordinates; then,

$$I_{xy} = \int_0^R \int_0^{\sqrt{R^2 - x^2}} xy \, dx \, dy = \int_0^R x \left[\frac{y^2}{2} \right]_0^{\sqrt{R^2 - x^2}} dx$$

$$= \int_0^R x \frac{R^2 - x^2}{2} dx = \frac{1}{8} R^4$$

SECOND METHOD.   Let the element of area da be selected as shown in Figure PA.16b and be expressed in terms of polar coordinates; then,

$$I_{xy} = \int xy\, da = \int_0^R \int_0^{\pi/2} \rho \cos \theta\, \rho \sin \theta\, \rho\, d\rho\, d\theta,$$

$$= \int_0^R \int_0^{\pi/2} \rho^3 \frac{1}{2} \sin 2\theta\, d\theta\, d\rho = \frac{R^4}{8} \int_0^{\pi/2} \sin 2\theta\, d\theta,$$

$$= \frac{R^4}{8}(-\tfrac{1}{2}\cos 2\theta)_0^{\pi/2} = \tfrac{1}{8} R^4.$$

Problems

A.17.   Find, by use of Equation (A–7), the product of inertia of the area of a rectangle having a base b and height h, with respect to two adjacent sides.

ans. $b^2 h^2/4$.

A.18.   Find the product of inertia, with respect to the coordinate axes, of the area bounded by the parabola $y^2 = hx$, the line $x = b$, and the x-axis.

ans. $\tfrac{1}{6} hb^3$.

A.6.   Parallel Axis Theorem for Products of Inertia

When the product of inertia of an area is known for any pair of rectangular axes passing through the centroid of the area, the product of inertia of the area with respect to any parallel set of axes may be determined without

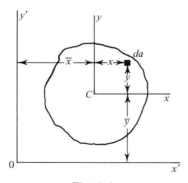

Fig. A.4.

integrating. Thus, in Figure A.4, x and y are axes through the centroid C of the area; x' and y' are parallel axes passing through the point O. The coordinates of C with respect to x' and y' are denoted by $\bar{x}$ and $\bar{y}$. If the product of inertia of the area with respect to x' and y' is denoted by $I_{x'y'}$ and the product of inertia with respect to x and y is denoted by $\bar{I}_{xy}$, then, by definition,

$$I_{x'y'} = \int (x + \bar{x})(y + \bar{y}) \, da$$

$$= \int xy \, da + \bar{x}\bar{y} \int da + \bar{y} \int x \, da + \bar{x} \int y \, da.$$

Because each of the last two integrals is the first moment of the area with respect to a centroidal axis, each integral is equal to zero. The equation then becomes

$$I_{x'y'} = \bar{I}_{xy} + A\bar{x}\bar{y}, \qquad (A-8)$$

which is called the parallel axis theorem for products of inertia of areas.

That is, the product of inertia of any area with respect to any pair of rectangular axes in its plane is equal to the product of inertia of the area with respect to a pair of parallel centroidal axes plus the product of the area and the coordinates of the centroid of the area with respect to the given pair of axes.

Illustrative Problem

A.19. Determine the values of I_x, I_y, and I_{xy} for the Z-bar in Figure PA.19 by using the parallel axis theorem.

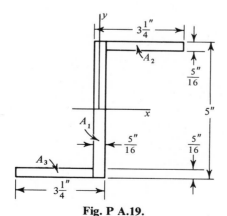

Fig. P A.19.

SOLUTION. The area is divided into three parts A_1 (web), A_2, and A_3 (flanges) as shown. The table that follows has been prepared for the calculation of the terms necessary for the use of Equations (A–4) and (A–8).

Properties of Cross Section of Z-bar (Fig. PA.19)

Col. No.	1	2	3	4	5	6	7	8	9
Part	Area A	$\bar{x}$	$\bar{y}$	$\bar{I}_x$	$A\bar{y}^2$	I_y	$A\bar{x}^2$	$\bar{I}_{xy}$	$A\bar{x}\bar{y}$
A_1	1.56	0	0	3.25	0	0.0127	0	0	0
A_2	0.918	1.625	2.344	0.0074	5.044	0.658	2.43	0	3.5
A_3	0.918	−1.625	−2.344	0.0074	5.044	0.658	2.43	0	3.5

By using the parallel axis theorem (Eqs. A-4 and A-8) and the results given in the table, we obtain the following:

$$I_x = \sum (\bar{I}_x + A\bar{y}^2) = 13.35 \text{ in.}^4,$$

where I_x is the sum of columns 4 and 5.

$$I_y = \sum (\bar{I}_y + A\bar{x}^2) = 6.19 \text{ in.}^4,$$

where I_y is the sum of columns 6 and 7.

$$I_{xy} = \sum (\bar{I}_{xy} + A\bar{x}\bar{y}) = 7.00 \text{ in.}^4,$$

where I_{xy} is the sum of columns 8 and 9.

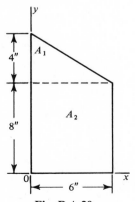

Fig. P A.20.

Problems

A.20. Find the product of inertia of the area $A = A_1 + A_2$, shown in Figure PA.20 with respect to the x- and y-axes.

$$\text{ans.} \quad I_{xy} = 792 \text{ in.}^4$$

A.21. Locate the centroid C of the angle section in Problem A.14 and determine the product of inertia with respect to centroidal axes parallel to the two legs of the angle.

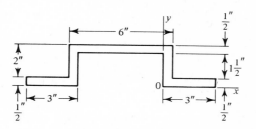

Fig. P A.22.

A.22. Calculate the product of inertia of the area shown in Figure PA.22 with respect to the axes indicated.

A.7. Relation Between Moments of Inertia and Products of Inertia with Respect to Two Sets of Rectangular Axes Through the Same Point in the Area

Let I_x, I_y, I_{xy} denote the moments of inertia and product of inertia of the area in Figure A.5 with respect to the axes Ox and Oy. Let it be required to find the moments of inertia I_{x_1} and I_{y_1} and the product of inertia $I_{x_1y_1}$, with respect to the axes Ox_1 and Oy_1, which are inclined at an angle θ with the axes Ox and Oy. The moment of inertia of the area in Figure A.5 with respect to the axis Ox_1 is expressed by the equation

$$I_{x_1} = \int y_1^2 \, da = \int (y \cos\theta - x \sin\theta)^2 \, da,$$

$$= \cos^2\theta \int y^2 \, da + \sin^2\theta \int x^2 \, da - 2\sin\theta\cos\theta \int xy \, da,$$

$$= I_x \cos^2\theta + I_y \sin^2\theta - 2I_{xy} \sin\theta \cos\theta, \tag{A-9}$$

$$= \tfrac{1}{2}(I_x + I_y) + \tfrac{1}{2}(I_x - I_y)\cos 2\theta - I_{xy} \sin 2\theta. \tag{A-10}$$

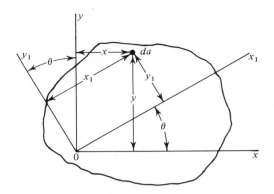

Fig. A.5.

Similarly,

$$I_{x_1y_1} = \int x_1 y_1 \, da = \int (x \cos \theta + y \sin \theta)(y \cos \theta - x \sin \theta) \, da,$$

$$= (\cos^2 \theta - \sin^2 \theta) \int xy \, da + (\cos \theta \sin \theta) \int (y^2 - x^2) \, da,$$

$$= I_{xy} \cos 2\theta + \tfrac{1}{2}(I_x - I_y) \sin 2\theta \tag{A--11}$$

Thus, from Equations (A–9) through (A–11), the moments of inertia and product of inertia of an area with respect to any set of rectangular axes may be found, without integrating, in terms of the moments of inertia and product of inertia with respect to a given set of rectangular axes passing through the same origin.

Axes for Which the Product of Inertia Is Zero. It may be shown that, through any point in an area, one set of rectangular axes may be drawn for which the product of inertia is zero. Thus, in Equation (A–11), if $I_{x_1y_1}$ is made equal to zero, we obtain

$$\tan 2\theta = -\frac{I_{xy}}{\tfrac{1}{2}(I_x - I_y)}, \tag{A--12}$$

and hence when θ (Fig. A.5) has a value given by this equation, the product of inertia with respect to the Ox_1 and Oy_1 axes is zero; in the next section it is shown that the axes for which the product of inertia is zero are principal axes.

A.8.   Mohr's Circle for Moment and Product of Inertia of Areas

A graphical solution of Equations (A–10) and (A–11) is obtained by Mohr's circle in exactly the same way as for Equations (2–3) and (2–4) in Chapter 2 for plane state of stress and as for Equations (3–10) and (3–11) in Chapter 3 for a plane problem of strain. Equations (A–10) and (A–11) are rewritten as follows:

$$I_{x_1} - \tfrac{1}{2}(I_x + I_y) = \tfrac{1}{2}(I_x - I_y)\cos 2\theta - I_{xy}\sin 2\theta, \qquad \text{(A–13)}$$

$$I_{x_1y_1} = I_{xy}\cos 2\theta + \tfrac{1}{2}(I_x - I_y)\sin 2\theta. \qquad \text{(A–14)}$$

In comparing the transformation equations for moments of inertia (Eqs. A–13 and A–14) with the transformation equations of stress (Eqs. 2–3 and 2–4) note that the equations have the same form except that the sign for terms involving I_{xy} and $I_{x_1y_1}$ in Equations (A–13) and (A–14) is opposite the sign for terms involving τ_{xy} and $\tau_{x_1y_1}$ in Equations (2–3) and (2–4). Therefore, in order to insure that the sense of rotation of the angle θ is the same for the xy-plane of the cross-sectional area in Figure A.5 and for Mohr's circle for moments of inertia in Figure A.6, it is necessary to choose the

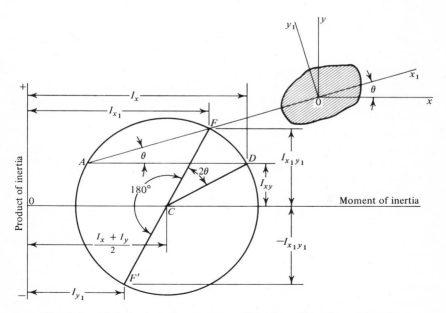

Fig. A.6.   Mohr's circle for moment of inertia and product of inertia.

positive sense for the product of inertia upward as shown in Figure A.6 (the positive sense for the shearing stress was downward for Mohr's circle of stress). Equations (A–13) and (A–14), taken together, represent a circle. To show this fact note that Equations (A–13) and (A–14) can be squared and added to each other to eliminate the angle 2θ as shown by the following equation:

$$[I_{x_1} - \tfrac{1}{2}(I_x + I_y)]^2 + I_{x_1y_1}^2 = \tfrac{1}{4}(I_x - I_y)^2 + I_{xy}^2. \tag{A–15}$$

Equation A–15 represents a circle whose center is located on the I_{x_1}-axis in Figure A.6 by the abscissa

$$OC = \frac{I_x + I_y}{2}, \tag{A–16}$$

and the radius R of the circle is

$$R = \sqrt{\tfrac{1}{4}(I_x - I_y)^2 + I_{xy}^2}. \tag{A–17}$$

The construction of the circle, as shown in Figure A.6, can be made with the data in Equations (A–16) and (A–17), but it can also be done by noting that the point D, whose coordinates are (I_x, I_{xy}), is a point on the circle. Then with C as center and CD as radius the circle can be constructed as shown in Figure A.6.

Construction of I_{x_1} and $I_{x_1y_1}$.   In Figure A.6 the objective is to determine the values of I_{x_1} and $I_{x_1y_1}$ for the axes x_1 and y_1 at the counterclockwise angle θ from the given axes x and y. We now obtain I_{x_1} and $I_{x_1y_1}$ graphically by constructing the radius CF in Figure A.6 so that the angle between CF and CD is the counterclockwise angle 2θ. The abscissa of F is I_{x_1} and the ordinate of F is $I_{x_1y_1}$. Note that the direction of the x_1-axis is indicated by chord AF.

Construction of I_{y_1}.   In Figure A.6 we construct the radius CF' at a counterclockwise angle $2\theta + 180°$ from CD. The abscissa of F' is I_{y_1} and the ordinate of F' is $-I_{x_1y_1}$. These results are obtained from Equations (A–10) and (A–11) if the angle 2θ is replaced with the angle $2\theta + 180°$.

Principal Axes.   In the analysis of many engineering problems, the moment of inertia of an area must be found with respect to a certain axis called a principal axis. A principal axis of inertia of an area, for a given point in the area, is an axis about which the moment of inertia of the area is either greater or less than for any other axis passing through the given point. It will be proved in this section that, through any point in an area, two rectangular axes can be drawn for which the moments of inertia of the area are greater and less, respectively, than for any other axes passing through the point. There are then two principal axes of inertia of an area for any point in

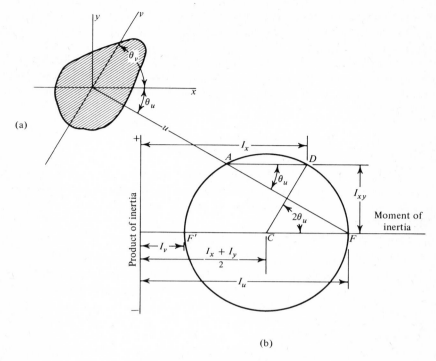

(a)

(b)

Fig. A.7.   Principal axes of inertia.

the area. Furthermore, it will be shown that axes for which the product of inertia is zero are principal axes. And, because the product of inertia of an area is zero for axes of symmetry, it follows that axes of symmetry are principal axes. The foregoing statements may be demonstrated as follows:

Let Figure A.7a be any area and let I_x, I_y, and I_{xy} be the moments of inertia and product of inertia, respectively, for any set of rectangular axes x, y through a point in the area. Let Figure A.7b be Mohr's circle for moments and products of inertia. The points F and F' at the ends of a horizontal diameter of the circle represent the largest moment of inertia I_u and the smallest moment of inertia I_v, respectively, for the area. In order to locate the axis uu in Figure A.7a that corresponds to the maximum moment of inertia I_u we rotate clockwise from the positive end of the x-axis through the angle θ_u, which is one-half the angle $FCD = 2\theta_u$ in Figure A.7b. Note that the direction of the u-axis is indicated by chord AF. Likewise, for the axis vv corresponding to the minimum moment of inertia I_v we rotate counterclockwise from the positive end of the x-axis through the angle θ_v, which is one half the angle $F'CD = 2\theta_v$ in Figure A.7b.

Note in Figure A.7b that the ordinate of F and F' is zero for both points. This means that for the principal axes the product of inertia is zero. Note that the value of angle θ_u can be computed from Equation A–12 and that $\theta_v = 90 - \theta_u$.

Illustrative Problem

Problem A.23. Find the moments of inertia of the angle section shown in Figure PA.23a with respect to principal axes passing through the centroid. Check the values of the moments of inertia and their location by using Mohr's circle.

SOLUTION.   The steps in the solution will be made as follows:

(1) The centroid of the area will be located; that is, $\bar{x}$ and $\bar{y}$ will be found.

(2) The moments of inertia and the product of inertia ($\bar{I}_x$ and $\bar{I}_y$, and $\bar{I}_{xy}$) with respect to the centroidal x- and y-axes then will be found by the methods discussed in Sections A.3 and A.6.

(3) The directions of the principal axes then will be found by use of the equations of Section A.7.

(4) The moment of inertia with respect to each of the principal axes, u and v, then will be found by means of Equation (A–10).

(5) Mohr's circle will be used to check results in 3 and 4.

Centroid:

$$\bar{x} = \frac{4(\frac{3}{8})(2) + 5\frac{5}{8}(\frac{3}{8})(\frac{3}{16})}{4(\frac{3}{8}) + 5\frac{5}{8}(\frac{3}{8})} = \frac{3.396}{3.61} = 0.94 \text{ in.,}$$

$$\bar{y} = \frac{4(\frac{3}{8})(\frac{3}{16}) + 5\frac{5}{8}(\frac{3}{8})(3\frac{3}{16})}{4(\frac{3}{8}) + 5\frac{5}{8}(\frac{3}{8})} = \frac{7.01}{3.61} = 1.94 \text{ in.}$$

Moments of Inertia:

$$\bar{I}_x = \tfrac{1}{12}(\tfrac{3}{8})(5\tfrac{5}{8})^3 + 5\tfrac{5}{8}(\tfrac{3}{8})(1\tfrac{1}{4})^2 + \tfrac{1}{12}(4)(\tfrac{3}{8})^3 + 4(\tfrac{3}{8})(1\tfrac{3}{4})^2,$$

$$= 5.57 + 3.30 + 0.02 + 4.59 = 13.48 \text{ in.}^4,$$

$$\bar{I}_y = \tfrac{1}{12}(5\tfrac{5}{8})(\tfrac{3}{8})^3 + 5\tfrac{5}{8}(\tfrac{3}{8})(\tfrac{3}{4})^2 + \tfrac{1}{12}(\tfrac{3}{8})(4)^3 + 4(\tfrac{3}{8})(1\tfrac{1}{16})^2,$$

$$= 0.02 + 1.19 + 2.00 + 1.69 = 4.90 \text{ in.}^4$$

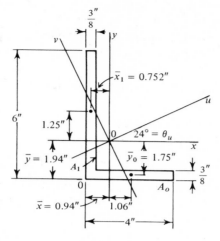

(a) Angle section

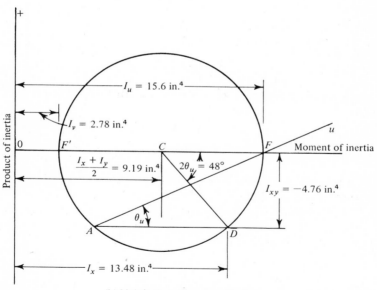

(b) Mohr's circle for moments of
inertia about principal axes

Fig. P A.23.

The value of $\bar{I}_{xy}$ may be found by means of Equation (A–8). Thus,

$$\bar{I}_{xy} = \bar{I}_{Oxy} + A_0 \bar{x}_0 \bar{y}_0 + \bar{I}_{1xy} + A_1 \bar{x}_1 \bar{y}_1,$$

$$= 4(\tfrac{3}{8})(1.06)(-1.75) + 5.62(\tfrac{3}{8})(1.25)(-0.752),$$

$$= -4.76 \text{ in.}^4$$

Principal Axes: The directions of the principal axes are found from Equation (A–12). Thus,

$$\tan 2\theta = \frac{2(-4.76)}{4.90 - 13.48} = 1.11,$$

$$2\theta = 48° \text{ or } 228°, \quad \theta = 24° \text{ or } 114°.$$

Principal Axis Moments of Inertia: From Equation (A–10) the moment of inertia with respect to the axis making an angle of 24° with Ox (denoted by Ou) is

$$I_u = 13.48 \cos^2 24° + 4.90 \sin^2 24° - 2(-4.76) \sin 24° \cos 24°,$$

$$= 11.23 + 0.81 + 3.53 = 15.59 \text{ in.}^4$$

Using $\theta = 114°$ and denoting the corresponding axis by Ov, we have

$$I_v = 13.48 \cos^2 114° + 4.90 \sin^2 114° - 2(-4.76) \sin 114° \cos 114°,$$

$$= 2.23 + 4.08 - 3.53 = 2.78 \text{ in.}^4$$

Construction of Mohr's Circle.   This construction is shown in Figure PA.23b.

Problems

A.24.   Consider a standard 10-in. 25-lb steel I-beam for which $\bar{I}_x = 122.1$ in.^{4}, $\bar{I}_y = 6.89$ in.^{4}, and $A = 7.38$ in.^{2} Let the x-axis be a centroidal axis parallel to the flanges. Find the moment of inertia and radius of gyration of the section with respect to a line through the centroid, making an angle of 30° with the x-axis. Check results by making use of Mohr's circle.

ans. $\bar{I} = 93.3$ in^4.

A.25.   Show, by use of Equation (A–10), that the moment of inertia of the area of a square is constant for all axes in the plane of the area that pass through the centroid C, and hence that every such axis is a principal axis. Show that Mohr's circle for the moments of inertia is a point circle with radius of zero.

A.26. For the Z-section shown in Problem A.19, $\bar{I}_x = 13.35$ in.^{4}, $\bar{I}_y = 6.19$ in.^{4}, and $\bar{I}_{xy} = 7.00$ in.^{4} Find the principal moments of inertia. Check the results by using Mohr's circle.

A.27. In the angle section 8 in. by 8 in. by 0.75 in., $A = 11.44$ in.^{2}, $\bar{x} = \bar{y} = 2.28$ in., $\bar{I}_x = \bar{I}_y = 69.7$ in.^{4}, $\bar{I}_{xy} = -41.5$ in.^{4}. Locate the principal axes of inertia, and calculate the principal moments of inertia. Also determine the minimum radius of gyration. Check the results by using Mohr's circle. The x- and y-axes are parallel to the legs of the angle.

ans. $I_u = 111.0$ in.^{4}, $I_v = 28.4$ in.^{4}, $r_v = 1.57$ in.

Properties of Rolled-Steel Sections

Note. The tables given here are not complete. They are intended to illustrate the type of material that may be found in handbooks and are included in this book for convenience in solving problems. Similar tables for aluminum-alloy structural sections are found in *Structural Handbook of Aluminum Company of America,*

Table B.1

Properties
of
Channels

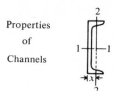

DEPTH OF CHAN- NEL	WEIGHT PER FOOT	AREA OF SECTION	WIDTH OF FLANGE	THICK- NESS OF WEB	AXIS 1–1			AXIS 2–2			
					I	r	I/c	I	r	I/c	x
in.	lb.	in.^{2}	in.	in.	in.^{4}	in.	in.^{3}	in.^{4}	in.	in.^{3}	in.
15	55.0	16.11	3.814	0.814	429.0	5.16	57.2	12.1	0.87	4.1	0.82
15	45.0	13.17	3.618	0.618	373.9	5.33	49.8	10.3	0.88	3.6	0.79
15	33.9	9.90	3.400	0.400	312.6	5.62	41.7	8.2	0.91	3.2	0.79
12	40.0	11.73	3.415	0.755	196.5	4.09	32.8	6.6	0.75	2.5	0.72
12	20.7	6.03	2.940	0.280	128.1	4.61	21.4	3.9	0.81	1.7	0.70
10	35.0	10.27	3.180	0.820	115.2	3.34	23.0	4.6	0.67	1.9	0.69
10	15.3	4.47	2.600	0.240	66.9	3.87	13.4	2.3	0.72	1.2	0.64
9	25.0	7.33	2.812	0.612	70.5	3.10	15.7	3.0	0.64	1.4	0.61
9	13.4	3.89	2.430	0.230	47.3	3.49	10.5	1.8	0.67	0.97	0.61
8	21.25	6.23	2.619	0.579	47.6	2.77	11.9	2.2	0.60	1.1	0.59
8	11.5	3.36	2.260	0.220	32.3	3.10	8.1	1.3	0.63	0.79	0.58
7	19.75	5.79	2.509	0.629	33.1	2.39	9.4	1.8	0.56	0.96	0.58
7	9.8	2.85	2.090	0.210	21.1	2.72	6.0	0.98	0.59	0.63	0.55
6	15.5	4.54	2.279	0.559	19.5	2.07	6.5	1.3	0.53	0.73	0.55
6	8.2	2.39	1.920	0.200	13.0	2.34	4.3	0.70	0.54	0.50	0.52
5	11.5	3.36	2.032	0.472	10.4	1.76	4.1	0.82	0.49	0.54	0.51
5	6.7	1.95	1.750	0.190	7.4	1.95	3.0	0.48	0.50	0.38	0.49
4	7.25	2.12	1.720	0.320	4.5	1.47	2.3	0.44	0.46	0.35	0.46
4	5.4	1.56	1.580	0.180	3.8	1.56	1.9	0.32	0.45	0.29	0.46
3	6.0	1.75	1.596	0.356	2.1	1.08	1.4	0.31	0.42	0.27	0.46
3	4.1	1.19	1.410	0.170	1.6	1.17	1.1	0.20	0.41	0.21	0.44

Table B.2

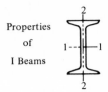

Properties
of
I Beams

DEPTH OF BEAM	WEIGHT PER FOOT	AREA OF SECTION	WIDTH OF FLANGE	THICK- NESS OF WEB	AXIS 1–1			AXIS 2–2		
					I	r	I/c	I	r	I/c
in.	lb.	in.^{2}	in.	in.	in.^{4}	in.	in.^{3}	in.^{4}	in.	in.^{3}
27	90.0	26.34	9.000	0.524	2958.3	10.60	219.1	75.3	1.69	16.7
24	120.0	35.13	8.048	0.798	3010.8	9.26	250.9	84.9	1.56	21.1
24	79.9	23.33	7.000	0.500	2087.2	9.46	173.9	42.9	1.36	12.2
24	74.2	21.70	9.000	0.476	1950.1	9.48	162.5	61.2	1.68	13.6
21	60.4	17.68	8.250	0.428	1235.5	8.36	117.7	43.5	1.57	10.6
20	100·0	29.20	7.273	0.873	1648.3	7.51	164.8	52.4	1.34	14.4
20	65.4	19.08	6.250	0.500	1169.5	7.83	116.9	27.9	1.21	8.9
18	90.0	26.29	7.236	0.796	1256.5	6.91	139.6	51.9	1.40	14.3
18	54.7	15.94	6.000	0.460	795.5	7.07	88.4	21.2	1.15	7.1
18	48.2	14.09	7.500	0.380	737.1	7.23	81.9	30.0	1.46	8.0
15	75.0	21.85	6.278	0.868	687.2	5.61	91.6	30.6	1.18	9.8
15	42.9	12.49	5.500	0.410	441.8	5.95	58.9	14.6	1.08	5.3
15	37.3	10.91	6.750	0.332	405.5	6.10	54.1	19.9	1.35	5.9
12	55.0	16.04	5.600	0.810	319.3	4.46	53.2	17.3	1.04	6.2
12	40.8	11.84	5.250	0.460	268.9	4.77	44.8	13.8	1.08	5.3
12	31.8	9.26	5.000	0.350	215.8	4.83	36.0	9.5	1.01	3.8
12	27.9	8.15	6.000	0.284	199.4	4.95	33.2	12.6	1.24	4.2
10	40.0	11.69	5.091	0.741	158.0	3.68	31.6	9.4	0.90	3.7
10	30.0	8.75	4.797	0.447	133.5	3.91	26.7	7.6	0.93	3.2
10	25.4	7.38	4.660	0.310	122.1	4.07	24.4	6.9	0.97	3.0
10	22.4	6.54	5.500	0.252	113.6	4.17	22.7	9.0	1.17	3.3
9	35.0	10.22	4.764	0.724	111.3	3.30	24.7	7.3	0.84	3.0
9	30.0	8.70	4.601	0.561	101.4	3.40	22.5	6.4	0.85	2.8
9	21.8	6.32	4.330	0.290	84.9	3.67	18.9	5.2	0.90	2.4
8	25.5	7.43	4.262	0.532	68.1	3.03	17.0	4.7	0.80	2.2
8	18.4	5.34	4.000	0.270	56.9	3.26	14.2	3.8	0.84	1.9
7	20.0	5.83	3.860	0.450	41.9	2.68	12.0	3.1	0.74	1.6
7	15.3	4.43	3.660	0.250	36.2	2.86	10	2.7	0.78	1.5
6	17.25	5.02	3.565	0.465	26.0	2.28	8.7	2.3	0.68	1.3
6	12.5	3.61	3.330	0.230	21.8	2.46	7.3	1.8	0.72	1.1
5	10.0	2.87	3.000	0.210	12.1	2.05	4.8	1.2	0.65	0.82
4	10.5	3.05	2.870	0.400	7.1	1.52	3.5	1.0	0.57	0.70
3	7.5	2.17	2.509	0.349	2.9	1.15	1.9	0.59	0.52	0.47
3	5.7	1.64	2.330	0.170	2.5	1.23	1.7	0.46	0.53	0.40

612

Table B.3

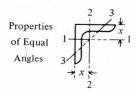

Properties of Equal Angles

SIZE	WEIGHT PER FOOT	AREA OF SECTION	AXIS 1–1 AND AXIS 2–2				AXIS 3–3*
			I	r	I/c	x	r
inches	lb.	in.^{2}	in.^{4}	in.	in.^{3}	in.	in.
$8 \times 8 \times 1\frac{1}{8}$	56.9	16.73	98.0	2.42	17.5	2.41	1.55
$8 \times 8 \times \frac{1}{2}$	26.4	7.75	48.6	2.51	8.4	2.19	1.58
$6 \times 6 \times 1$	37.4	11.00	35.5	1.80	8.6	1.86	1.16
$6 \times 6 \times \frac{3}{8}$	14.9	4.36	15.4	1.88	3.5	1.64	1.19
$5 \times 5 \times 1$	30.6	9.00	19.6	1.48	5.8	1.61	0.96
$5 \times 5 \times \frac{3}{8}$	12.3	3.61	8.7	1.56	2.4	1.39	0.99
$4 \times 4 \times \frac{13}{16}$	19.9	5.84	8.1	1.18	3.0	1.29	0.77
$4 \times 4 \times \frac{1}{4}$	6.6	1.94	3.0	1.25	1.0	1.09	0.79
$3\frac{1}{2} \times 3\frac{1}{2} \times \frac{13}{16}$	17.1	5.03	5.3	1.02	2.3	1.17	0.67
$3\frac{1}{2} \times 3\frac{1}{2} \times \frac{1}{4}$	5.8	1.69	2.0	1.09	0.79	0.97	0.69
$3 \times 3 \times \frac{5}{8}$	11.5	3.36	2.6	0.88	1.3	0.98	0.57
$3 \times 3 \times \frac{1}{2}$	9.4	2.75	2.2	0.90	1.1	0.93	0.58
$3 \times 3 \times \frac{3}{8}$	7.2	2.11	1.8	0.91	0.83	0.89	0.58
$3 \times 3 \times \frac{1}{4}$	4.9	1.44	1.2	0.93	0.58	0.84	0.59
$2\frac{1}{2} \times 2\frac{1}{2} \times \frac{1}{2}$	7.7	2.25	1.2	0.74	0.73	0.81	0.47
$2\frac{1}{2} \times 2\frac{1}{2} \times \frac{1}{8}$	2.08	0.61	0.38	0.79	0.20	0.67	0.50
$2 \times 2 \times \frac{7}{16}$	5.3	1.56	0.54	0.59	0.40	0.66	0.39
$2 \times 2 \times \frac{1}{8}$	1.65	0.48	0.19	0.63	0.13	0.55	0.40
$1\frac{1}{2} \times 1\frac{1}{2} \times \frac{3}{8}$	3.35	0.98	0.19	0.44	0.19	0.51	0.29
$1\frac{1}{2} \times 1\frac{1}{2} \times \frac{1}{8}$	1.23	0.36	0.08	0.46	0.07	0.42	0.30
$1 \times 1 \times \frac{1}{4}$	1.49	0.44	0.04	0.29	0.06	0.34	0.19
$1 \times 1 \times \frac{1}{8}$	0.80	0.23	0.02	0.31	0.03	0.30	0.19

* Axis 3–3 is the principal axis about which the radius of gyration is least.

Table B.4

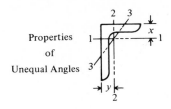

Properties
of
Unequal Angles

SIZE	WEIGHT PER FOOT	AREA OF SEC- TION	AXIS 1–1				AXIS 2–2				AXIS 3–3*
			I	r	I/c	x	I	r	I/c	y	r
inches	lb.	in.^{2}	in.^{4}	in.	in.^{3}	in.	in.^{4}	in.	in.^{3}	in.	in.
$8 \times 6 \times 1$	44.2	13.00	80.8	2.49	15.1	2.65	38.8	1.73	8.9	1.65	1.28
$8 \times 6 \times \frac{7}{16}$	20.2	5.93	39.2	2.57	7.1	2.45	19.3	1.80	4.2	1.45	1.30
$8 \times 3\frac{1}{2} \times 1$	35.7	10.50	66.2	2.51	13.7	3.17	7.8	0.86	3.0	0.92	0.73
$8 \times 3\frac{1}{2} \times \frac{7}{16}$	16.5	4.84	32.5	2.59	6.4	2.95	4.1	0.92	1.5	0.70	0.74
$7 \times 3\frac{1}{2} \times 1$	32.3	9.50	45.4	2.19	10.6	2.70	7.5	0.89	3.0	0.96	0.74
$7 \times 3\frac{1}{2} \times \frac{3}{8}$	13.0	3.80	19.6	2.27	4.3	2.48	3.5	0.96	1.3	0.73	0.76
$6 \times 4 \times 1$	30.6	9.00	30.8	1.85	8.0	2.17	10.8	1.09	3.8	1.17	0.85
$6 \times 4 \times \frac{3}{8}$	12.3	3.61	13.5	1.93	3.3	1.94	4.9	1.17	1.6	0.94	0.88
$6 \times 3\frac{1}{2} \times 1$	28.9	8.50	29.2	1.85	7.8	2.26	7.2	0.92	2.9	1.01	0.74
$6 \times 3\frac{1}{2} \times \frac{5}{16}$	9.8	2.87	10.9	1.95	2.7	2.01	2.9	1.00	1.0	0.76	0.77
$5 \times 4 \times \frac{7}{8}$	24.2	7.11	16.4	1.52	5.0	1.71	9.2	1.14	3.3	1.21	0.84
$5 \times 4 \times \frac{3}{8}$	11.0	3.23	8.1	1.59	2.3	1.53	4.7	1.20	1.6	1.03	0.86
$5 \times 3\frac{1}{2} \times \frac{7}{8}$	22.7	6.67	15.7	1.53	4.9	1.79	6.2	0.96	2.5	1.04	0.75
$5 \times 3\frac{1}{2} \times \frac{5}{16}$	8.7	2.56	6.6	1.61	1.9	1.59	2.7	1.03	1.0	0.84	0.76
$5 \times 3\frac{1}{2} \times \frac{1}{2}$	13.6	4.00	10.0	1.58	3.0	1.66	4.0	1.01	1.6	0.91	0.75
$5 \times 3 \times \frac{13}{16}$	19.9	5.84	14.0	1.55	4.5	1.86	3.7	0.80	1.7	0.86	0.64
$5 \times 3 \times \frac{5}{16}$	8.2	2.40	6.3	1.61	1.9	1.68	1.8	0.85	0.75	0.68	0.66
$4\frac{1}{2} \times 3 \times \frac{13}{16}$	18.5	5.43	10.3	1.38	3.6	1.65	3.6	0.81	1.7	0.90	0.64
$4\frac{1}{2} \times 3 \times \frac{5}{16}$	7.7	2.25	4.7	1.44	1.5	1.47	1.7	0.87	0.75	0.72	0.66
$4 \times 3\frac{1}{2} \times \frac{13}{16}$	18.5	5.43	7.8	1.19	2.9	1.36	5.5	1.01	2.3	1.11	0.72
$4 \times 3\frac{1}{2} \times \frac{5}{16}$	7.7	2.25	3.6	1.26	1.3	1.18	2.6	1.07	1.0	0.93	0.73
$4 \times 3 \times \frac{13}{16}$	17.1	5.03	7.3	1.21	2.9	1.44	3.5	0.83	1.7	0.94	0.64
$4 \times 3 \times \frac{1}{4}$	5.8	1.69	2.8	1.28	1.0	1.24	1.4	0.89	0.60	0.74	0.65
$3\frac{1}{2} \times 3 \times \frac{13}{16}$	15.8	4.62	5.0	1.04	2.2	1.23	3.3	0.85	1.7	0.98	0.62
$3\frac{1}{2} \times 3 \times \frac{1}{4}$	5.4	1.56	1.9	1.11	0.78	1.04	1.3	0.91	0.58	0.79	0.63
$3 \times 2\frac{1}{2} \times \frac{9}{16}$	9.5	2.78	2.3	0.91	1.2	1.02	1.4	0.72	0.82	0.77	0.52
$3 \times 2\frac{1}{2} \times \frac{1}{4}$	4.5	1.31	1.2	0.95	0.56	0.91	0.74	0.75	0.40	0.66	0.53
$3 \times 2 \times \frac{1}{2}$	7.7	2.25	1.9	0.92	1.0	1.08	0.67	0.55	0.47	0.58	0.43
$3 \times 2 \times \frac{1}{4}$	4.1	1.19	1.1	0.95	0.54	0.99	0.39	0.57	0.25	0.49	0.43
$2\frac{1}{2} \times 2 \times \frac{1}{2}$	6.8	2.00	1.1	0.75	0.70	0.88	0.64	0.56	0.46	0.63	0.42
$2\frac{1}{2} \times 2 \times \frac{1}{8}$	1.86	0.55	0.35	0.80	0.20	0.74	0.20	0.61	0.13	0.49	0.43
$2 \times 1\frac{1}{2} \times \frac{3}{8}$	3.99	1.17	0.43	0.61	0.34	0.71	0.21	0.42	0.20	0.46	0.32
$2 \times 1\frac{1}{2} \times \frac{1}{8}$	1.44	0.42	0.17	0.64	0.13	0.62	0.09	0.45	0.08	0.37	0.33

* Axis 3–3 is the principal axis about which the radius or gyration is least.

Index

DATE DUE

OCT 1 3		
NOV 0 8		
AUG 2 5		
OCT 0 9		
MAY 5		
APR - 1 A.M.		
SEP 1 9		
SEP 1 9		